Lippincott®
Illustrated Reviews:
Anatomy

Lippincott®
Illustrated Reviews:
Anatomy

Kelly M. Harrell, PhD, MPT

Assistant Professor
Department of Anatomy and Cell Biology
Brody School of Medicine at East Carolina University
Greenville, North Carolina

Ronald Dudek, PhD

Professor Emeritus
Department of Anatomy & Cell Biology
Brody School of Medicine at East Carolina University
Greenville, North Carolina

. Wolters Kluwer

Philadelphia • Baltimore • New York • London
Buenos Aires • Hong Kong • Sydney • Tokyo

Acquisitions Editor: Crystal Taylor
Product Development Editor: Kelly Horvath/Andrea Vosburgh
Editorial Coordinator: Jeremiah Kiely
Editorial Assistant: Brooks Phelps
Marketing Manager: Phyllis Hitner
Production Project Manager: Marian Bellus
Design Coordinator: Steve Druding
Manufacturing Coordinator: Margie Orzech
Prepress Vendor: S4Carlisle Publishing Services

Library of Congress Cataloging-in-Publication Data

Names: Harrell, Kelly, author. | Dudek, Ronald W., 1950- author.
Title: Anatomy / Kelly Harrell, Ronald Dudek.
Other titles: Lippincott's illustrated reviews.
Description: Philadelphia: Wolters Kluwer, [2019] | Series: Lippincott
    illustrated reviews | Includes bibliographical references.
Identifiers: LCCN 2018042670 | ISBN 9781496317902
Subjects: | MESH: Anatomy | Outlines
Classification: LCC QP34.5 | NLM QS 18.2 | DDC 612—dc23 LC record available at
    https://lccn.loc.gov/2018042670

shop.lww.com

CCS1018

Dedication

To my Fox and Flower—Knox and Lily,
who inspire me every day to be the best version of myself.
I am forever grateful for the love and laughter you bring to my life.
— Kelly M. Harrell

Acknowledgments

When opportunity comes knocking, you open the door and let it in.

Over 4 years ago, I was asked to come on board to what would be one of the richest learning experiences of my professional life. At the time, the LIR series was missing a vital component—anatomic sciences—that needed to be filled to complete the set. The LIR team reached out to veteran author Ron Dudek to spearhead the task of putting together an integrated embryology, gross anatomy, and histology text. A few days later, I, a lowly assistant professor of anatomy, opened an email from Dr. Dudek that invited me to join as a coauthor. This gracious offer was quickly met with excitement as I formulated my response. With little thought of the time and energy it may require, I said "yes," eager to put my stamp on something of significance in anatomy education.

During the early planning phases, I quickly learned that I would need to rely on my colleagues and students for contributions, whether in the form of radiologic images, consulting, or time spent assisting in dissection. We were assembling a team, and without that team, *LIR Anatomy* would not exist in such a well-rounded, aesthetically pleasing form.

First and foremost, Ron and I would like to acknowledge the anatomic donors and their families for the generous bequeathal of their own or their loved ones' remains. We recognize and honor the ultimate gift, that is, donating one's body for the purposes of educating future health care providers. We are eternally grateful.

Without the leadership of a dedicated and patient development team, *LIR Anatomy* may have faded into the sunset. Crystal Taylor, thank you for trusting Ron and me to create an educational product that upholds the quality of the LIR name. I applaud and appreciate your ability to remain flexible yet firm in your leadership role as Senior Acquisitions Editor, allowing *LIR Anatomy* to come to fruition organically over the past 4 years. I also want to thank you for choosing Kelly Horvath as the freelance Development Editor on this project. I knew, when I signed on, that I would gain a publication, but I never imagined that I would also gain a lifelong colleague and friend in Kelly. Kelly, thank you for your honesty, hard work, countless phone meetings, vivid storytelling, constant support, and friendship. You kept me sane and confident through the past 2 years, and I am so very grateful to be on this team with you.

I also thank the other members of the Wolters Kluwer team who worked behind the scenes to help turn this project into a book. They include Andrea Vosburgh, Internal Development Editor; Jeremiah Kiely, Editorial Coordinator; and Marian Bellus, Production Project Manager. A special thank-you must go to Art Director Jen Clements, who worked miracles to turn our artistic vision into reality. She went above and beyond, putting lots of long hours as well as diligence and care into the art program.

I would like to recognize the clinicians and educators who provided valuable radiologic images and consulting to ensure that the clinical application text and figures were accurate and informative—specifically, interventional and diagnostic radiologists Dr. Michael Berry, Dr. Gregory Lewis, and Dr. Douglas Shusterman (Eastern Radiology, Greenville, NC) and Dr. Michael Meuse (Carolina HealthCare System, Charlotte, NC). Your conscientious contributions to the radiologic components of *LIR Anatomy* are very much appreciated.

I would also like to thank Dr. Robert Hartman, Clinical Assitant Professor of Pediatrics at the Brody School of Medicine for providing the beautiful ultrasound images of pediatric heart defects.

Thank you to the medical and allied health students who took pride and time in preparing clean, complete dissections (Chapters 4 and 7) and were actively involved in developing practice questions (Chapters 8 and 9). Across multiple disciplines, I'd like to thank a small group of students, many of whom have now graduated and moved on to their professional careers. Thank you Dr. Jinal Desai and Dr. Dan-Thanh Nguyen (MD) for your creative and engaging clinical vignette–style practice questions. For assistance with dissections, I'd like to thank my friend and colleague, Dr. Emily Askew; Dr. Amalia Kondyles, Dr. Brandon Kovash, and Dr. Marisa Lee (DPT); Richard Khang; Dr. Samantha Sellers (PhD); and Dr. Asem Rahman (MD). I would also like to acknowledge and thank future-doctor Gabrielle Kattan, for lending her hand modeling skills to Chapter 7.

We also recognize and thank the Brody School of Medicine and the University of California San Francisco School of Medicine for permission to use histology light micrographs from each institution's slide collections.

To Dr. M. Alex Meredith (Medical College of Virginia, Richmond, VA), thank you for sharing your artistic depiction of an area so many learners (and teachers) struggle to imagine and explain—the pterygopalatine fossa. Your willingness to contribute your art and vision of this space has better informed not only *LIR Anatomy* but also countless learners who have passed through our classrooms and laboratories.

Thank you to my parents for their love and encouragement through this process and life in general. You raised me in a nurturing environment, where I was taught to seize my moment, and that approach to life continues to serve me well. Thank you for instilling in me confidence, work ethic, and a love for learning. Those traits have turned this vision into a reality.

Finally, I would like to acknowledge the unyielding support of my husband, Danny. Over the course of coauthoring and designing *LIR Anatomy*, we grew our family from just the two of us to a family of four. Danny, without your encouragement and love, the idea of writing a book while working full time and raising two small children would have seemed impossible. You helped me believe it was possible, and I am forever grateful for your role in the whole process.

Preface

In all living forms, structure dictates function. Take the human skeleton, for example—a bony core that serves as a mobile, yet protective scaffold onto which our tissues are successively layered, producing our adaptable, fluid bodies. In each unique tissue, intricate cells and fibers flow together to fill a role—movement, transport, protection, stability, nutrition, procreation, storage, intelligence, sensation, life, and, ultimately, death.

From a young age, I was in awe of the way these structures coexist and function together within a single vessel. Even in light of variation or anomaly, the human body almost always finds a way to grow, evolve, and accommodate within its own environment. It is truly a marvel to be studied and celebrated.

The study of anatomy is a journey across the microscopic landscape of cells and tissues into the macroscopic topography of organ systems. Much like the estuaries of eastern North Carolina, anatomy comprises small structures merging to form larger structures and functioning within a physiologic ebb and flow. Just as small creeks fill grooves carved into earth and merge to form tributaries and rivers, histologic examination of human tissue shows how cells and microscopic structures merge and coordinate as larger organs. Just as rivers expand into sounds and eventually flow out to sea, human organs integrate as body systems. The estuary represents the place where the river meets the sea, an intersection seen in the study of the human body where histology meets gross anatomy.

This intersection of histology and gross anatomy is underpinned by embryology. These three streams of anatomic science converge in a novel way in the first edition of *LIR Anatomy* to better elucidate the structural and functional details of the human body. So unique in its layout, *LIR Anatomy* regionally integrates embryology, gross anatomy, and histology together in a single source to highlight the important relationships that exist across these topics.

Purpose: Since its inception, *LIR Anatomy* has been designed to precipitate those "ah-ha" moments that occur when learners follow related topics along a continuum of time and space. As the puzzle begins to come together, learners build on their understanding in a more integrative fashion. Studies show that thoughtful integration of topics leads to deeper learning and retention. This theory underpins the shift of many medical schools from traditional to integrated curricula. *LIR Anatomy* augments this approach to learning with writing that is engaging, well-organized, and informative.

Audience: *LIR Anatomy* is written as a detailed review text with medical students in mind. From day 1 of medical school, students must integrate basic science topics and organize them to promote learning and retention. In the short term, medical students are most concerned with performance on licensing exams. The integration of all three anatomic science topics—embryology, gross anatomy, and histology—provides learners with a valuable resource for immediate exam preparation and future clinical reference.

Although succinct enough for review purposes, *LIR Anatomy* is comprehensive in its treatment of the anatomic science triumvirate, making it an appropriate primary text in allied health programs that incorporate these topics.

Art: *LIR Anatomy* art brings the text to life with interactive figures that walk the reader through processes and concepts in a systematic, comprehensible manner. Images are further invigorated with strategically placed tips and mnemonics in the series' signature dialogue bubbles. Figures also include directional labels to assist readers in orientation to structures on a two-dimensional page. Clear, crisp histologic images display unique tissue characteristics across systems, while color-coded schematic embryologic figures take readers through the step-wise process of human development.

The hallmark of *LIR Anatomy* art is its cadaveric specimens, which were carefully dissected just for this book, photographed, and then digitally enhanced to present realistic yet idealized views of the inside of the human body. Coloring, labeling, and "narration" highlight the arrangement of gross anatomic structures in a more three-dimensional format.

Format: *LIR Anatomy* is designed to be both narrative and concise. The outline-format chapters are organized by anatomic region and further subdivided into easy-to-digest sections. Each chapter follows a similar progression, with embryology presented up front, followed by gross anatomy and histology. This approach allows readers to integrate topics, while continuing to support the traditional, regional method common to the study of anatomic sciences. This two-pronged system allows for easy adoption across different curricular models.

Features: *LIR Anatomy* incorporates a variety of features to facilitate integrative learning within a clinical context.

- **Clinical applications (blue boxes):** Learning anatomy out of context is like fishing without a lure—you aren't going to catch anything! Each chapter provides high-yield clinical anatomy applications in blue boxes that give readers insight into the utility of the content in practice. Additionally, clinical applications illustrate how important a solid foundational knowledge in the anatomic sciences is in the diagnosis of common pathologies and injuries.
- **Knowledge morsels (green boxes):** Whether it is a helpful mnemonic or a stand-out structural or functional detail, green boxes are incorporated in each chapter to augment learning. These tidbits of information reinforce and supplement both the main text and the adjacent figures.
- **Dialogue bubbles:** Dialogue bubbles have been added to figures to remind readers of important relationships, further integrate topics, highlight clinically significant information, and provide learners with helpful study tips. As readers process the figures, they can imagine the authors taking a moment to interject and engage in a discussion. Readers should use these memorable dialogues as prompts for further thought and discussion in each chapter.
- **Study questions:** Board-style practice questions on high-yield topics are included at the end of each chapter for self-assessment. These questions are written to address the first three levels of Bloom's taxonomy—knowledge, understanding, and application. Many questions are presented in clinical-vignette style to provide opportunity for learners to practice applying knowledge in a low-stakes environment before sitting for licensing exams.

—Kelly M. Harrell, PhD, MPT

Contents

Anatomy Foundations

1

I. OVERVIEW

A thorough evaluation of the anatomical sciences involves the intersection of three subjects—gross anatomy, embryology, and histology. This review text integrates all three anatomical subjects into a region-based model divided into back, thorax, abdomen, pelvis, upper limb, lower limb, neck, and head and cranial nerves chapters. While maintaining this overall integration within each body region, each chapter is subdivided to cover gross anatomy, embryology, and histology in discrete chunks that help delineate the content. In order to fully understand the content in each chapter, a foundation of anatomical terminology and an overview of organ-system organization are required, as this introductory chapter is designed to provide. Gross anatomy body systems are covered here, while body regions are covered in chapters corresponding to relevant anatomy. Select clinical conditions are interspersed throughout chapters in Clinical Application boxes to connect anatomy to clinical practice. In addition, a brief discussion of radiographic anatomy at the end of this chapter provides learners with basic radiologic terminology to aid in orientation to diagnostic images included throughout the text.

A. Anatomical position

Anatomical position refers to the body position in which an individual is standing upright with the head and toes facing forward, the upper limbs adjacent to the sides of the body with the palms facing forward, and the lower limbs close together with feet parallel (Fig. 1.1).

B. Anatomical planes

Four imaginary planes are used in anatomical descriptions: **median**, **sagittal**, **frontal (coronal)**, and **transverse (axial) planes** (see Fig. 1.1). The median plane is a vertical plane that passes longitudinally through the midline of the body and divides the body into the right and left halves. The sagittal planes are vertical planes that pass longitudinally through the body parallel to the median plane. The frontal (coronal) planes are vertical planes that pass through the body at right angles to the median plane and divide the body into the front (anterior or ventral) and back (posterior or dorsal) parts. The transverse planes are horizontal planes that pass through the body at right angles to the median plane and divide the body into upper (superior) and lower (inferior) parts.

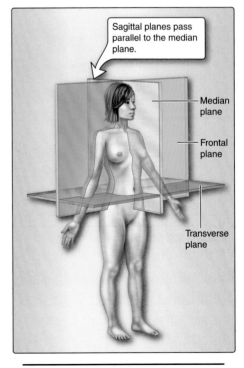

Sagittal planes pass parallel to the median plane.

Median plane

Frontal plane

Transverse plane

Figure 1.1
Anatomical planes.

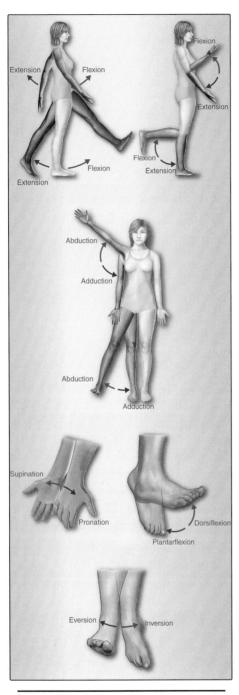

Figure 1.2
Anatomical movements.

Table 1.1: Terms of Relationship

Term	Description
Medial	Refers to a structure nearer to the median plane
Lateral	Refers to a structure farther from the median plane
Proximal	Refers to a structure nearer a limb attachment
Distal	Refers to a structure farther from a limb attachment
Bilateral	Refers to paired structures having right and left members
Unilateral	Refers to unpaired structures that occur only on one side
Ipsilateral	Refers to a structure that occurs on the same side as another structure
Contralateral	Refers to a structure that occurs on the opposite side as another structure

C. Anatomical terms of relationship

The terms *superior* and *cranial* refer to a structure nearer the cranium. The terms *inferior* and *caudal* refer to a structure nearer the foot. The terms *posterior* and *dorsal* refer to the back surface of the body. The terms *anterior* and *ventral* refer to the front surface of the body. [**Note:** In this text, "cranial," "caudal," "dorsal," and "ventral" are used only in the context of embryology.] Other important terms are presented in Table 1.1.

D. Anatomical terms of movement

As shown in Figure 1.2, *flexion* describes a movement that decreases the angle between the bones, whereas *extension* describes a movement that increases the angle between the bones. Except when referring to the digits, *abduction* describes a movement away from the median plane (as in the upper limb moving away from the body), whereas *adduction* describes a movement toward the median plane (as in the upper limb moving toward the body). *Pronation* describes a rotation in the forearm from the anatomical position so that the palm of the hand faces posteriorly, and *supination* describes a rotation in the forearm whereby the pronated hand returns to the anatomical position so that the palm of the hand faces anteriorly. *Dorsiflexion* describes flexion at the ankle joint as in lifting the toes off the ground, and *plantarflexion* describes flexion at the ankle joint as in lifting the heel off the ground. *Eversion* describes a movement of the foot whereby the sole moves away from the median plane, whereas *inversion* describes a movement of the foot whereby the sole of the foot moves toward the median plane. Finally, movements that are unique to the hands and feet, particularly the digits of the hands, are shown in Table 1.2.

II. INTEGUMENTARY SYSTEM

The integumentary system consists of the **skin** and **epidermal derivatives** (or **epidermal appendages**). Skin forms the outer covering of the body and is the largest organ of the body, accounting for 15%–20% of the total body weight. Epidermal derivatives include **sweat** and **sebaceous glands**, **hair** and **hair follicles**, and **nails**.

A. Functions

Collectively, skin and epidermal derivatives regulate body temperature and water loss, provide a nonspecific barrier to external environmental factors (e.g., microorganisms), synthesize vitamin D, absorb ultraviolet

Table 1.2: Terms of Movement of the Hands and Feet

Term	Movement Described	
Flexion of the digits	Fingers move toward the palm, flexing at the MCP and IP joints	
Extension of the digits	Fingers return from flexion to anatomical position, extending at the MCP and IP joints	
Abduction of the digits	Fingers spread away from a neutral-positioned third finger (middle finger) or the toes from a neutral-positioned second toe	
Adduction of the digits	Fingers "un-spread" back toward a neutral-positioned third finger (middle finger) or the toes toward a neutral-positioned second toe	
Opposition of the thumb	Thumb touches the pad of another finger	
Reposition of the thumb	Thumb returns from opposition to anatomical position	
Abduction of the thumb	Thumb moves away from the fingers in the sagittal plane	
Adduction of the thumb	Thumb moves toward the fingers in the sagittal plane	
Flexion of the thumb	Thumb moves toward the fingers in the frontal plane	
Extension of the thumb	Thumb moves away from the fingers in the frontal plane	

IP = interphalangeal, MCP = metacarpophalangeal.

(UV) irradiation, convey sensory information, play a role in antigen presentation, and secrete sweat and sebum.

B. Skin

In general, skin consists of three layers, **outer epidermis**, **middle dermis**, and **deep hypodermis** or **subcutaneous layer**.

1. **Outer epidermis:** The outer epidermis is an epithelial layer classified as a keratinized stratified squamous epithelium. On the basis of the comparative thickness of the epidermis, skin is classified as either **thick skin** (found on palms of the hands or soles of the feet) or **thin skin** (covering the rest of the body), as shown in Figures 1.3 and 1.4.

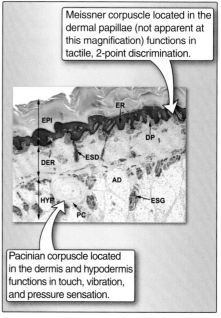

Meissner corpuscle located in the dermal papillae (not apparent at this magnification) functions in tactile, 2-point discrimination.

Pacinian corpuscle located in the dermis and hypodermis functions in touch, vibration, and pressure sensation.

Figure 1.3

Thick skin. AD = adipose tissue, DER = dermis, DP = dermal papillae, EPI = epidermis, ER = epidermal ridge, ESD = eccrine sweat gland duct, ESG = eccrine sweat gland, HYP = hypodermis, PC = Pacinian corpuscle.

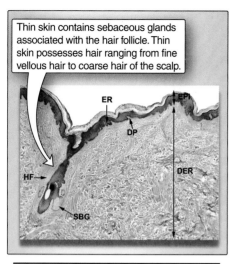

Thin skin contains sebaceous glands associated with the hair follicle. Thin skin possesses hair ranging from fine vellous hair to coarse hair of the scalp.

Figure 1.4
Thin skin. DER = dermis,
DP = dermal papillae, EPI = epidermis,
ER = epidermal ridge, HF = hair follicle,
SBG = sebaceous gland.

2. **Dermis**: The junction between the epidermis and dermis is irregular, whereby **epidermal ridges** protrude into the underlying dermis, and **dermal papillae** protrude into the overlying epidermis (see Fig. 1.3). The dermis is composed of the **papillary layer** and **reticular layer**. The superficial papillary layer (i.e., the dermal papillae) consists of loose connective tissue with fibroblasts, types I and III collagen fibers, and thin elastic fibers. The deeper reticular layer consists of dense, irregular connective tissue with fibroblasts, type I collagen, and thick elastic fibers. In addition, skin contains a number of epidermal derivatives (also called **epidermal appendages**): **eccrine** and **apocrine sweat glands**, **sebaceous glands**, **hair follicles** (and **arrector pili muscles**), and **nails**.

C. **Epidermal derivatives**

1. **Eccrine sweat glands and duct**: These simple, coiled tubular glands are involved in the secretion of **water**, **electrolytes**, **urea**, and **ammonium**. The duct opens onto the skin surface as **sweat pores**. The eccrine sweat glands function in the regulation of body temperature and emotional sweating.

2. **Apocrine sweat glands and duct**: These simple, coiled tubular glands are involved in the secretion of **proteins**, **carbohydrates**, **ammonia**, **lipid**, and **organic compounds**. The duct opens onto the skin surface in the axilla, mons pubis, and anal regions. The apocrine sweat glands function in the production of a malodorous body scent.

3. **Sebaceous glands and duct**: These simple acinar glands are involved in the secretion of **sebum** (i.e., lipid and cell debris). The short duct opens into the upper portion of a hair follicle into the **pilosebaceous canal**. The sebaceous glands function in the lubrication of the skin and play a role in teenage acne.

4. **Hair follicles**: These form as epidermal cells and grow into the underlying dermis during early embryonic development. The deepest part of the hair follicle becomes round-shaped and is called the **hair bulb**. The hair bulbs are invaginated by connective tissue called the **dermal papillae**, which are infiltrated by blood vessels and nerve endings. Epidermal cells within the hair bulb form an area containing **epidermal stem cells** called the **germinal matrix**. The continuous proliferation and differentiation of germinal matrix cells at the tip of the dermal papilla is responsible for the formation and growth of the **hair shaft**, a long, slender filament that extends above the surface of the epidermis.

5. **Nail**: The nail is a translucent plate (called the **nail plate**) of closely compacted **hard keratin** formed by the proliferation and keratinization of epithelial cells within the **nail matrix**. The nail matrix is a V-shaped area located under a fold of skin called the **proximal nail fold**. The only portion of the nail matrix that is grossly visible is the **lunula**, a half moon–shaped whitish area. At the outer edge of the proximal nail fold is the **eponychium** or **cuticle**. The nail rests on top of the nail bed. At the fingertip, the nail and the nail bed fuse to form the **hyponychium**, which protects the nail matrix from bacterial and fungal invasion. The dermis beneath the nail bed is highly vascular, which contributes to the pink color seen through the nail, and is a clinically useful indicator of the degree of oxygenation of blood.

III. SKELETAL SYSTEM

The skeletal system is divided into the **axial skeleton** and the **appendicular skeleton** (Fig. 1.5). The axial skeleton consists of bones of the cranium (or skull), hyoid bone, ribs, sternum, vertebrae, and sacrum. The appendicular skeleton consists of the bones of the upper and lower limbs, shoulder girdle, and pelvic girdle. The skeleton is composed of **cartilage** and **bone**.

A. Cartilage

The three types of cartilage include **hyaline cartilage, elastic cartilage**, and **fibrocartilage**.

1. **Hyaline cartilage**: Hyaline cartilage is found in fetal skeletal tissue, epiphyseal growth plates, articular surface of synovial joints, costal cartilages, nasal cartilage, laryngeal cartilage, tracheal cartilage rings, and bronchial cartilage plates. Its main features are **cells**, including **chondrogenic cells, chondroblasts,** and **chondrocytes**; a **ground substance**, containing **proteoglycans** (e.g., **aggrecan, decorin, biglycan,** and **fibromodulin**), **hyaluronan, multiadhesive glycoproteins** (e.g., **chondronectin, tenascin**), and **water (interstitial fluid)**; and **fibers**, including **types II, VI, IX, X,** and **XI collagen** (Fig. 1.6).

2. **Elastic cartilage**: Elastic cartilage is found in the pinna of the external ear, external auditory meatus, auditory tube, epiglottis, corniculate cartilage of the larynx, and cuneiform cartilage of the larynx. Its main features are similar to those of hyaline cartilage (Fig. 1.7). However, the distinguishing feature of elastic cartilage is the presence of **elastic fibers** along with **type II collagen fibers**. Elastic cartilage is generally stained with a special stain (i.e., Verhoeff) that colors elastic fibers black.

3. **Fibrocartilage**: Fibrocartilage is found in intervertebral disks, symphysis pubis, articular disks of the temporomandibular and sternoclavicular joints, menisci of the knee joint, and insertion of tendons. Its main features are similar to that of hyaline cartilage (Fig. 1.8). However, the distinguishing features of fibrocartilage include the absence of a perichondrium, more extracellular matrix than cells, and the presence of types I and II collagen fibers.

B. Bone

Bones can be classified according to their shape. **Long bones** are tubular (e.g., humerus), and **short bones** are cuboidal (e.g., bones of the wrist and ankle). **Flat bones** serve a protective function (e.g., bones of the cranium). **Irregular bones** have various shapes (e.g., bones of the face), and **sesamoid bones** form in certain tendons (e.g., patella bone of the knee). Visual inspection of a bone reveals various **bone markings**, created by the attachment of tendons, ligaments, and fascia or by the close proximity of an artery to the bone or where an artery enters the bone, and **bone formations** caused by the passage of a tendon to a joint to improve its leverage. The main features of bone are **cells (osteoprogenitor cells, osteoblasts, osteocytes,** and **osteoclasts)**, a **ground substance (proteoglycans, hyaluronan, multiadhesive glycoproteins, vitamin K–dependent proteins,** and a **mineral**

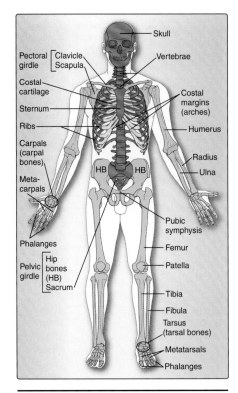

Figure 1.5
Skeletal system comprises the axial skeleton (red) and the appendicular skeleton (green) as well as articular (blue) and costal (yellow) cartilage.

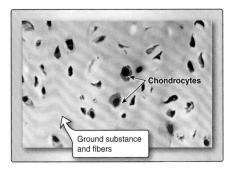

Figure 1.6
Hyaline cartilage.

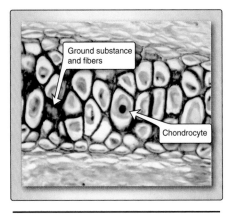

Figure 1.7
Elastic cartilage.

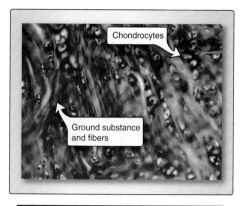

Figure 1.8
Fibrocartilage.

component of **hydroxyapatite crystals** [Ca$_{10}$ (PO$_4$)$_6$ OH$_2$]), and **fibers** that include **types I** and **V collagen**.

1. **Lamellar bone**: Comprising virtually all bone in a healthy adult, lamellar bone is therefore sometimes referred to as **mature bone**. (**Woven bone** comprises bone during embryonic development, bone remodeling, and bone repair and is therefore sometimes referred to as **immature bone**.) Lamellar bone (compared with woven bone) is characterized by an ordered arrangement of osteocytes, a reduced amount of ground substance, a regular parallel arrangement of collagen fibers organized into lamellae or layers, and increased mineralization. It is divided into two types: **compact bone** and **spongy bone** (Fig. 1.9).

> Although collagen fibers are oriented in a parallel arrangement within a single lamella, they alternate from lamella to lamella, creating an overall zig-zag appearance.

a. **Compact bone**: As shown in Figure 1.9, compact bone consists predominately of **osteons** (or **Haversian systems**). The osteon is the basic unit of compact bone and consists of an **osteonal (Haversian) canal** and **perforating (Volkmann) canals** through

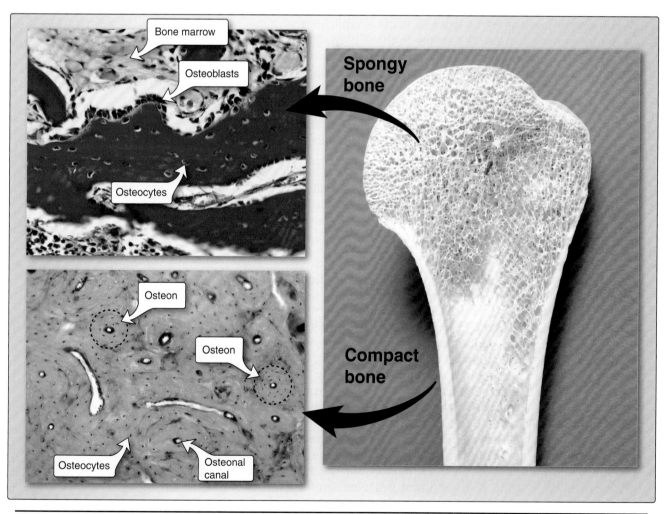

Figure 1.9
Spongy and compact bone.

which blood vessels and nerves travel, **concentric lamellae** (layers) of mineralized extracellular matrix that surround the osteonal canal, **collagen fibers** that are oriented in a parallel arrangement within a single lamella, **osteocytes** whose cell bodies reside in **lacunae** and whose cell processes extend through **canaliculi**, and a **cement line** that surrounds each osteon.

b. **Spongy bone**: Spongy bone consists predominately of a meshwork of internal struts called **trabeculae** (see Fig. 1.9). The lamellae in spongy bone are arranged in a stacked pattern (i.e., one layer on top of another layer), rather than in the concentric pattern found in the osteon of compact bone.

IV. MUSCULAR SYSTEM

Muscles of the human body comprise three types: **cardiac, smooth, and skeletal** (Fig. 1.10; see also Fig. 3.52A). Cardiac muscle forms the walls of the heart. Cardiac muscle cells are striated but smaller than skeletal

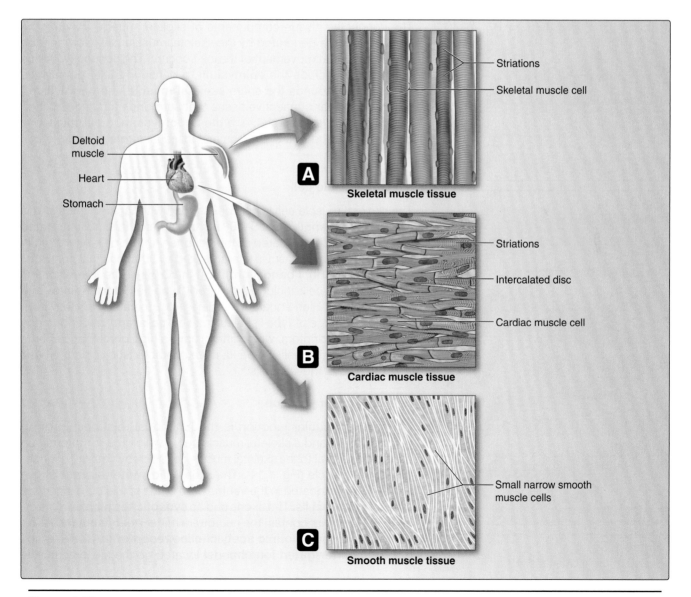

Figure 1.10
Muscle tissue. A, Skeletal muscle. B, Cardiac muscle. C, Smooth muscle.

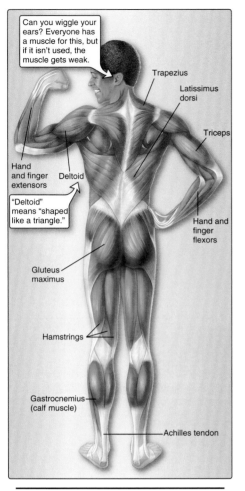

Figure 1.11
Skeletal muscles.

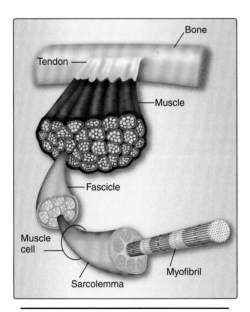

Figure 1.12
Skeletal muscle organization.

muscle cells and have a single nucleus per cell. Smooth muscle is primarily found in the walls of hallow viscera and blood vessels. Smooth muscle cells lack striations, have one nucleus per cell, and are small and narrow in appearance. Cardiac and smooth muscle are detailed in Chapters 3 and 4, respectively.

The gross Skeletal muscle cells are striated and converge to form skeletal muscles of varied shapes and sizes (Fig 1.11). As shown in Table 1.3, skeletal muscles can be described according to their shape. A **skeletal muscle** (e.g., biceps brachii muscle) consists of numerous **fascicles**, which consist of numerous **skeletal muscle cells** (also called **skeletal muscle fibers**). A skeletal muscle cell, in turn, consists of numerous **myofibrils** comprising **thick and thin myofilaments** (Fig. 1.12).

> ‖ **Skeletal muscle → Fascicles → Skeletal muscle cells → Myofibrils → Myofilaments**

A. Connective tissue components

The connective tissue components of skeletal muscle transmit the contractile force generated by the skeletal muscle cell to the tendon and bone so that movement of the joint occurs. The connective tissue components include the **epimysium**, a dense irregular connective tissue that surrounds the entire **skeletal muscle**; the **perimysium**, a dense irregular connective tissue that surrounds a bundle of skeletal muscle cells (**fascicle**); and the **endomysium**, a delicate loose connective tissue that surrounds an individual **skeletal muscle cell** (see Fig. 1.12).

B. Skeletal muscle cell

The skeletal muscle cell is cylinder shaped with tapered ends and is ~2–100 mm in length and 10–100 μm in diameter. It is multinucleated with thin, flat nuclei located at the periphery of the cell. As shown in Figure 1.13, its cytoplasm is characterized by striations that consist of the **A band (dark)**, **I band (light)**, and the **Z disc**. The three types of skeletal muscle cells include **type I (red)**, **type IIa (intermediate)**, and **type IIb (white)**. High-endurance athletes (e.g., marathon runners) have a high percentage of type I skeletal muscle cells, and low-endurance athletes (e.g., sprinters, weightlifters) have a high percentage of type IIb skeletal muscle cells. Type IIa have characteristic of both types I and IIb skeletal muscle cells.

C. Neuromuscular junction

The neuromuscular junction is the junctional relationship of an α-motoneuron and a skeletal muscle cell in which the α-motoneuron transmits a signal to the skeletal muscle cell, thereby causing contraction of the muscle (Fig. 1.14). The axons of **α-motoneurons** whose cell bodies are located in the ventral horn of the spinal cord innervate skeletal muscle cells. The axons end as **synaptic terminals** with synaptic vesicles that contain the neurotransmitter **acetylcholine (ACh)**. ACh binds to the **nicotinic acetylcholine receptor (nAChR)**, which is a **transmitter-gated ion channel** located on the skeletal muscle

Table 1.3: Muscle Shapes

Shape	Muscle Example	
Flat	External oblique muscle of the abdomen	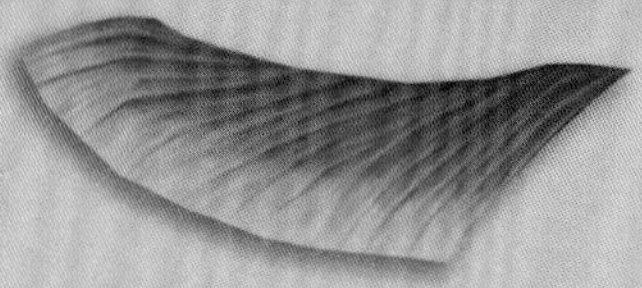
Pennate	Rectus femoris muscle	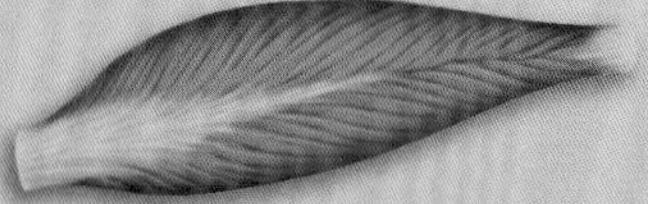
Fusiform	Biceps brachii	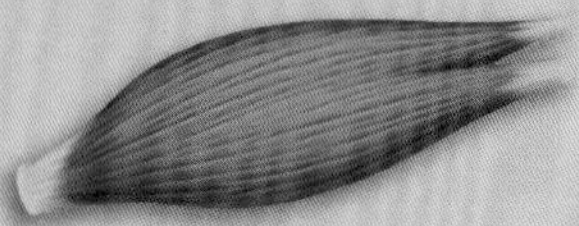
Multiheaded	Triceps brachii	
Convergent	Pectoralis major	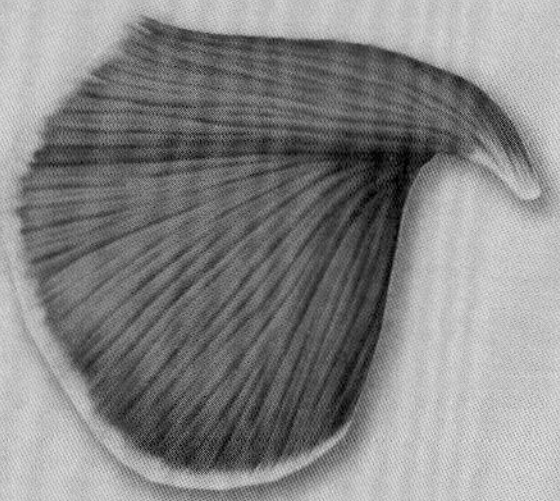
Quadrate	Rectus abdominis	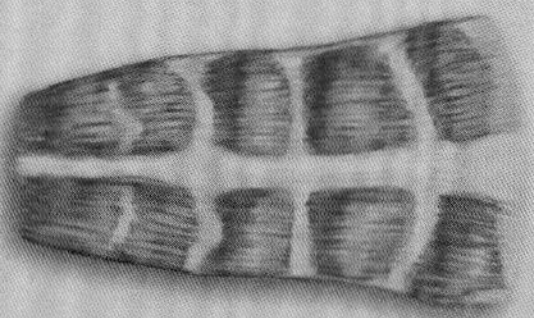
Circular	Orbicularis oculi	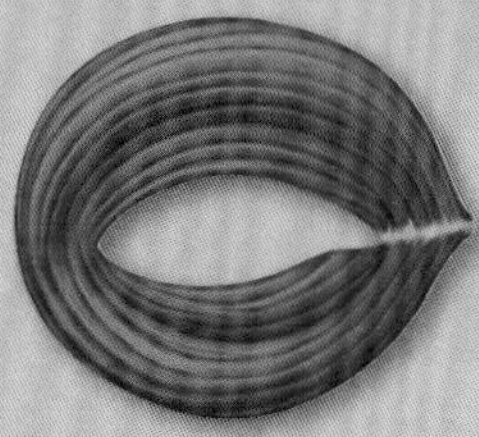
Multibellied	Gastrocnemius	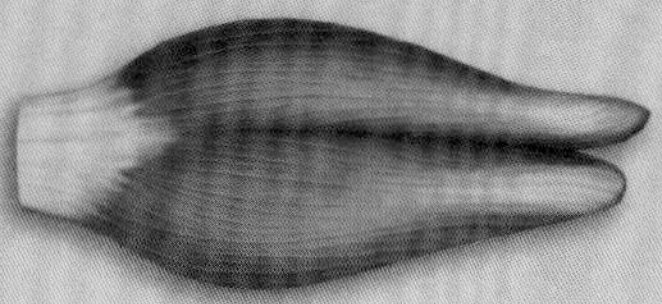

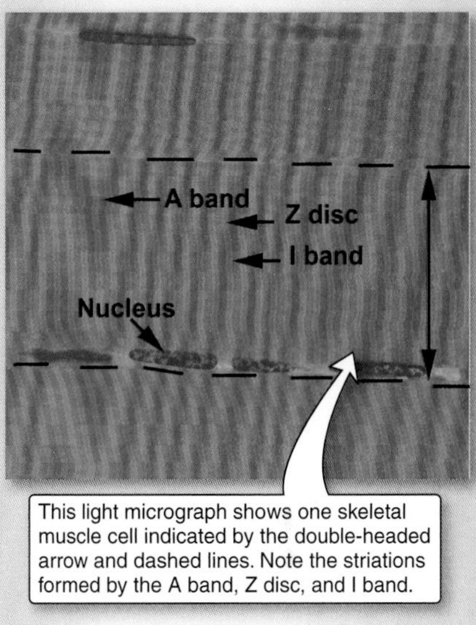
A band
Z disc
I band
Nucleus
This light micrograph shows one skeletal muscle cell indicated by the double-headed arrow and dashed lines. Note the striations formed by the A band, Z disc, and I band.

Figure 1.13
Skeletal muscle cell.

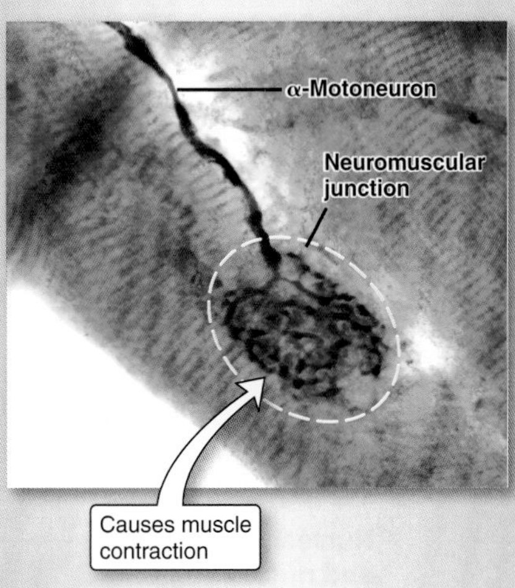
α-Motoneuron
Neuromuscular junction
Causes muscle contraction

Figure 1.14
Neuromuscular junction.

cell. When ACh binds to nAChR, a "gate" opens and allows **Na⁺ influx** into the skeletal muscle cell, causing depolorization.

D. Motor unit

A single axon of an α-motoneuron may innervate 1 to 5 skeletal muscle cells, which forms a **small motor unit**. Or, a single axon of an α-motoneuron may branch and innervate more than 150 skeletal muscle cells, forming a **large motor unit**.

> **‖** A motor unit is the **functional contractile unit** of a gross skeletal muscle, not a skeletal muscle cell.

E. Muscle spindle

As shown in Figure 1.15, the muscle spindle is a small, elongated, encapsulated structure distributed throughout a gross skeletal muscle that senses both **dynamic changes in muscle length** and **static muscle length** as well as activating the **myotactic (stretch) reflex** (e.g., knee jerk reflex). It consists of **nuclear bag cells** and **nuclear chain cells** and is innervated by **type Ia sensory neurons (annulo-spiral endings)**, **type II sensory neurons (flower-spray endings)**, and **γ-motoneurons**.

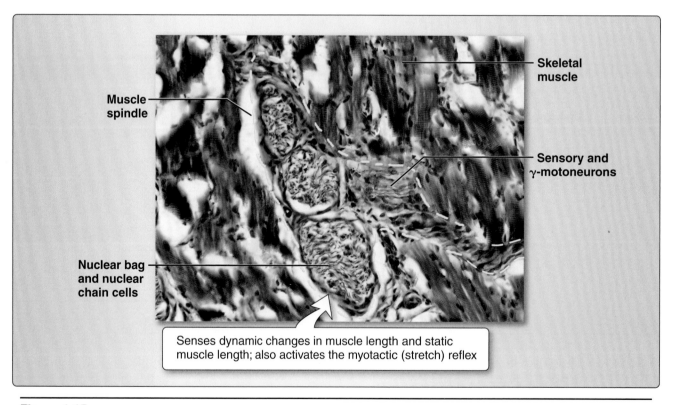

Senses dynamic changes in muscle length and static muscle length; also activates the myotactic (stretch) reflex

Figure 1.15
Muscle spindle (yellow dashed line).

V. CARDIOVASCULAR SYSTEM

The cardiovascular system consists of the **heart** and **blood vessels** that circulate blood throughout the body (Fig. 1.16).

A. Heart

The heart consists of two muscular pumps that divide the blood circulation into two circuits (Fig. 1.17). In the **pulmonary circulation**, the right ventricle pumps low-oxygen blood into the lungs via the **pulmonary arteries** where the blood is oxygenated and then returned to the left atrium of the heart via the **pulmonary veins**. In the **systemic circulation**, the left ventricle pumps highly oxygenated blood through the **systemic arteries** to distribute oxygen and nutrients throughout the body. Low-oxygen blood is returned to the right atrium of the heart via **systemic veins**.

B. Blood vessels

The three general types of blood vessels are **arteries**, **capillaries**, and **veins**, which distribute blood throughout the body. For a summary of blood vessel types, see Figure 1.20.

> Systemic blood flow follows a particular pathway:
>
> Elastic arteries → Muscular arteries → Arterioles → Metarterioles → Capillary bed →
>
> Postcapillary venules → Muscular venules → Collecting venules → Veins of increasing diameter (named veins)

1. **Arteries**: The vascular wall of arteries consists of three concentric layers ("tunics"): **tunica intima**, **tunica media**, and **tunica adventitia** (Fig. 1.18). The tunica intima is the innermost layer and consists of the **endothelium, basal lamina, subendothelial loose connective tissue,** and an **internal elastic lamina**. The tunica media is the middle layer and consists of **smooth muscle cells, type III collagen fibers, elastic fibers,** and an **external elastic lamina**. The tunica adventitia is the outermost layer and consists of **fibroblasts, type I collagen fibers,** and **scattered elastic fibers**. The tunica adventitia of large arteries contains small blood vessels (**vasa vasorum**), small postganglionic sympathetic nerve bundles (**nervi vascularis**), and small **lymph vessels**. In the circulatory system, elastic arteries gradually transition to large muscular arteries (i.e., no line demarcates them). In the region of transition, the amount of elastic fibers in the tunica media decreases, whereas the amount of smooth muscle whereas the amount of smooth muscle in the tunica media increases.

   a. **Elastic artery**: Elastic arteries function primarily as **conduction arteries**; that is, they conduct blood from the heart to the muscular arteries. Elastic arteries are distinguished by a tunica media with a prominent elastic fiber component that consists of concentric layers of **fenestrated elastic lamellae** (or sheets).

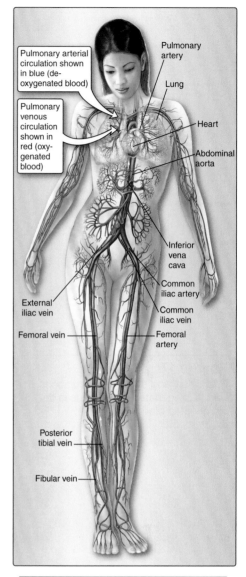

Figure 1.16
Cardiovascular system.

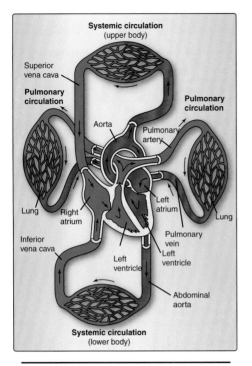

Figure 1.17
Pulmonary and systemic circulations. Red is oxygenated blood; blue is de-oxygenated blood.

They receive blood under high systolic pressure from the heart and keep the blood circulating while the heart pumps intermittently. Elastic arteries distend during systole and recoil during diastole. Examples include the **pulmonary trunk**, **aorta**, **common carotid arteries**, **subclavian arteries**, and **common iliac arteries**.

b. **Muscular artery**: Muscular arteries function primarily as **distribution arteries**. They have a tunica media with a prominent smooth muscle component that controls the distribution of blood to organs and tissues of the body. Examples include the **axillary**, **ulnar**, **radial**, and **femoral arteries**.

c. **Arteriole**: Arterioles function primarily as **resistance vessels**. They regulate blood flow to the capillary beds. The contraction of the one or two layers of smooth muscle cells in the tunica media increases the vascular resistance and thereby reduces blood flow to the capillary bed. The arterioles offer the greatest resistance to the flow of blood from the heart to the peripheral tissues and therefore play a role in the regulation of **arterial blood pressure**.

d. **Metarteriole**: A metarteriole is the terminal branch of the arterial system and flows directly into the capillary bed. It has a thickened smooth muscle cell layer that acts as a **precapillary sphincter**, regulating blood flow to the capillary bed.

2. **Capillaries**: The vascular wall of a capillary consists of an **endothelium**, a **basal lamina**, and **pericytes**. A pericyte is a cell that has contractile properties and can proliferate in response to tissue injury to act as a stem cell during angiogenesis. The capillary forms a small tube with a diameter that allows for the passage of red blood cells one at a time. Capillaries function primarily as **exchange vessels**. The capillary is the principle site of exchange of water, oxygen, carbon dioxide, glucose, amino acids, proteins, metabolites, and waste products between the blood and cells.

a. **Continuous capillary**: A continuous capillary consists of a single layer of endothelial cells joined by a **zonula occludens** (**tight junction**). It is surrounded by a continuous basal lamina and is found in the lung, muscle, thymus (blood–thymus barrier), nervous system (blood–brain barrier), connective tissue, and exocrine glands.

b. **Fenestrated capillary**: As shown in Figure 1.19, a fenestrated capillary consists of a single layer of endothelial cells joined by a **fascia occludens** (a tight junction that extends only partially around the perimeter of the cell creating small slit-like intercellular spaces). It is surrounded by a continuous basal lamina and has numerous **fenestrae** (or **pores**). The fenestrae are generally bridged by a **diaphragm**. They are found in the kidney (except that in the kidney glomerulus the fenestrated capillary has no diaphragms), lamina propria of the intestine, choroid plexus of the brain, choriocapillaris of the eye, and endocrine glands.

c. **Discontinuous capillary (sinusoid)**: A discontinuous capillary consists of a single layer of endothelial cells joined by a **fascia occludens**. Like fenestrated capillaries, it has numerous **fenestrae**, but its basal lamina is discontinuous. They are found in the liver, bone marrow, and spleen.

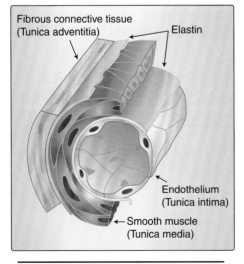

Figure 1.18
Blood vessel structure.

3. **Veins**: Like arteries, the vascular wall of veins consists of three concentric tunics. The tunica media of veins is thinner than that of arteries, and the tunica adventitia is thicker. Veins have **valves** that are projections of the tunica intima. The transport of blood back to the heart via veins depends on the contraction of skeletal muscles and valves that ensure one-way flow of blood.

   a. **Postcapillary venule**: The vascular wall of a postcapillary venule (~0.2 mm in diameter) consists of an **endothelium**, a **basal lamina,** and **pericytes**. The postcapillary venule is the principal site of action for vasoactive agents (e.g., histamine, serotonin) resulting in the **extravasation of fluid** during inflammation and allergic reactions, **migration of inflammatory leukocytes** (i.e., **diapedesis**), and **migration of lymphocytes** to repopulate the lymph node.

   b. **Muscular and collecting venules**: The vascular wall of a venule consists of three tunics.

   c. **Medium- and large-sized veins**: Medium- and large-sized veins are **high-capacitance** or **reservoir vessels** that contain about 70% of the total blood volume.

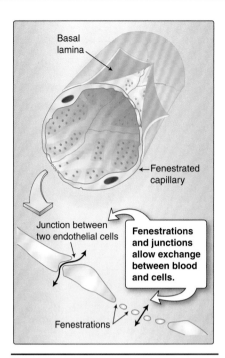

Figure 1.19
Capillary wall structure.

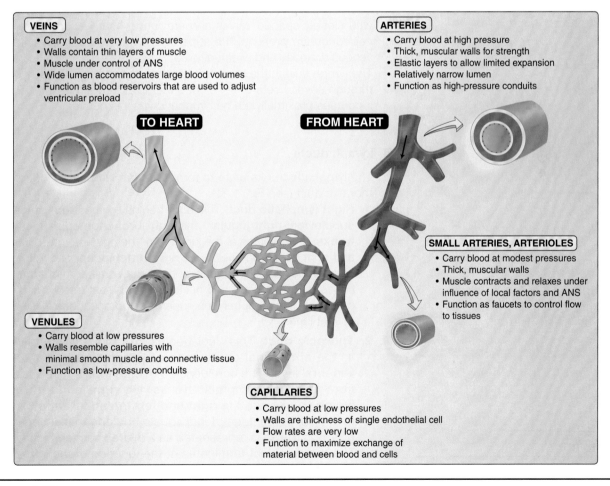

Figure 1.20
Organization of arteries and veins.

The high capacitance of veins can be attributed to the distensibility of their vascular wall; therefore, the content of blood within veins is relatively high.

VI. LYMPHATIC SYSTEM

The lymphatic system comprises an overflow system that drains surplus extracellular tissue fluid and leaked plasma proteins and returns them back into the venous bloodstream. In addition, the lymphatic system functions in the absorption and transport of dietary fat along with immune defense. All regions of the body have lymphatic drainage, even the dural sinuses of the brain. The lymphatic system consists of **lymphatic capillaries**, **superficial** and **deep lymphatic vessels**, **lymphatic trunks**, **right lymphatic duct**, **thoracic duct**, and **superficial** and **deep lymph nodes** (Fig. 1.21).

A. Lymph vessels

The lymphatic capillaries begin blindly in the extracellular spaces of tissues and form a lymphatic plexus intertwined with a capillary plexus. The lymphatic vessels in general are a bodywide network of vessels with closely spaced valves and are found nearly everywhere blood capillaries are present. The superficial lymphatic vessels follow the venous drainage and eventually drain into the deep lymphatic vessels. The lymph fluid in the superficial and deep lymphatic vessels passes through several sets of series of superficial or deep lymph nodes as it courses proximally. Large lymphatic vessels converge to form lymphatic trunks.

B. Lymph ducts

The lymphatic trunks unite to form the right lymphatic duct and the thoracic duct (see Fig. 1.21).

1. **Right lymphatic duct**: This duct begins by the union of the **right subclavian**, **right jugular**, and **right bronchomediastinal lymph trunks**. It terminates at the junction of the right internal jugular vein and right subclavian vein (i.e., **right brachiocephalic vein**) at the base of the neck. The right lymphatic duct drains lymph from the 1) right side of the head and neck, 2) right breast (medial and lateral quadrant), 3) right upper limb/superficial thoracoabdominal wall, and 4) right lung.

2. **Thoracic duct**: This duct begins in a majority of individuals as the **abdominal confluence of lymph trunks** at the L1/L2 vertebral level. The confluence of lymph trunks receives lymph from four main lymphatic trunks: the **right and left lumbar lymph trunks** and the **right and left intestinal lymph trunks**. In a small percentage of individuals, the abdominal confluence of lymph trunks is represented as a dilated sac (**cisterna chyli**). The thoracic duct terminates at the junction of the left internal jugular vein and left subclavian vein (i.e., **left brachiocephalic vein**) at the base of the neck. The thoracic duct drains lymph

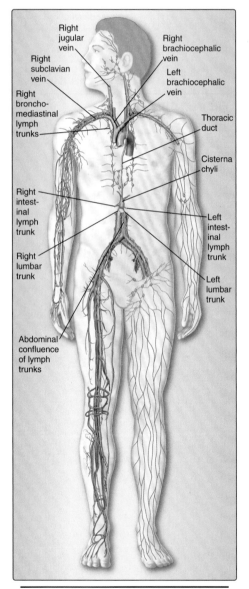

Figure 1.21
Lymphatic system.

from 1) the left side of the head and neck, 2) left breast, 3) left upper limb/superficial thoraco-abdominal wall, and 4) all the body below the diaphragm.

C. Lymph nodes

The lymph nodes are bean-shaped glands that lie in the course of the lymphatic vessels (see Fig. 1.21). They **filter** and **monitor lymph** for various antigens.

1. **Layers:** The lymph node consists of the **outer cortex**, **inner cortex**, and **medulla** (Fig. 1.22). The outer cortex contains a number of cell types: **mature** (or **virgin**) **IgM⁺** and **IgD⁺ B lymphocytes**, **follicular dendritic cells**, **macrophages**, and **fibroblasts** (or **reticular cells**). The inner cortex differs in that, instead of B lymphocytes, it contains **mature T lymphocytes**. The medulla contains all of the cell types contained in the outer and inner cortices as well as **plasma cells**.

2. **Lymphatic drainage**: **Afferent lymphatic vessels** carry lymph, which enters the lymph node on the convex surface (Fig. 1.23). The lymph percolates through the **subcapsular**, **trabecular**, and finally the **medullary sinuses**. The medullary sinuses coalesce into the **efferent lymphatic vessel** that exits at the hilus. A majority of B lymphocytes and T lymphocytes exit the lymph node via the **efferent lymphatic vessel**.

3. **Blood supply**: Arterioles enter the lymph node at the hilus, give off some branches in the medulla, and then travel to the cortex where they form a capillary network. The capillaries drain into **postcapillary venules** (also called **high endothelial venules**) within the inner cortex where a majority of the B lymphocytes and T lymphocytes enter the lymph node via the postcapillary venules. The postcapillary venules drain into small venules within the medulla and then larger venules that exit at the hilus (see Fig. 1.23).

VII. NERVOUS SYSTEM

The nervous system can be **anatomically** divided into the **central nervous system** (**CNS**) and the **peripheral nervous system** (**PNS**). The nervous system can also be **functionally** divided into the **somatic nervous system**, which controls voluntary activities by innervating skeletal muscle, and the **autonomic** (or **visceral**) **nervous system** (**ANS**), which controls involuntary activities by innervating viscera, smooth muscle, cardiac muscle, and glands.

A. Neuron

The neuron is the structural and functional unit of the nervous system. It has the capacity to receive impulses from other neurons or from receptor organs (i.e., a sensory function) as well as to transmit impulses to other neurons or to effector organs (i.e., a motor function). A neuron consists of a **perikaryon (soma)**, **dendrites**, and an **axon** (Figs. 1.24 and 1.25). The perikaryon is the cell body of the neuron and contains the nucleus along with the organelles. The dendrites receive information from other neurons or from the environment and

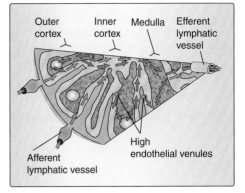

Figure 1.22
Lymph node organization.

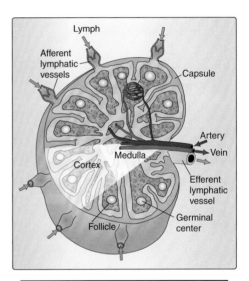

Figure 1.23
Lymph drainage through a lymph node.

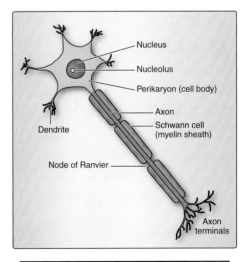

Figure 1.24
Neuron.

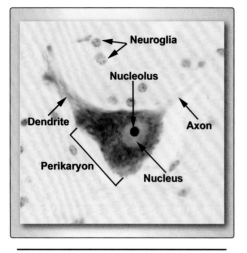

Figure 1.25
Light micrograph of a neuron.

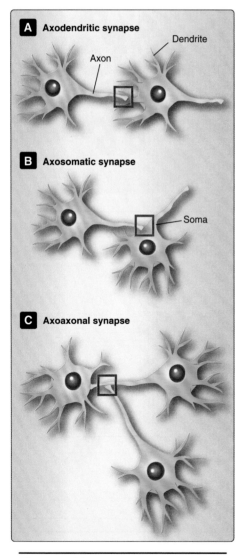

Figure 1.26
A to C, Types of synapses.

transmit the information toward the perikaryon. The axon generates, propagates, and transmits an **action potential**.

B. Synapse

A synapse is a specialized junction by which neurons communicate with one another. The three main types are the **axodendritic synapse** between an axon and a dendrite, the **axosomatic synapse** between an axon and the perikaryon (soma), and the **axoaxonic synapse** between an axon and another axon (Fig. 1.26). Synapses consist of **pre- and postsynaptic components** and the **synaptic cleft** (Fig. 1.27).

1. **Presynaptic**: This component is characterized morphologically by the presence of 40- to 60-nm-diameter **synaptic vesicles** that contain a neurotransmitter. The presynaptic cell membrane contains **voltage-gated Ca^{2+} channels** that open when a depolarization reaches the synaptic terminal and that allow an **influx of Ca^{2+}** from the extracellular milieu. The influx of Ca^{2+} causes the docking of synaptic vesicles at the presynaptic membrane and the release of neurotransmitter into the synaptic cleft (Fig. 1.28). The synaptic cleft is a 20- to 30-nm space between the presynaptic and postsynaptic membranes. This is where the neurotransmitter is released into in order to bind to its receptor on the postsynaptic membrane.

2. **Postsynaptic**: This component is characterized morphologically by the presence of the **postsynaptic density** located just beneath the postsynaptic cell membrane (see Fig. 1.28). The postsynaptic cell membrane contains either **transmitter-gated ion channels** or **G protein–linked receptors** that bind a specific neurotransmitter.

C. Central Nervous System

The Central nervous system (CNS) consists of the **brain** and the **spinal cord**. When examining the brain or spinal cord with the unaided eye, the **white matter** and **gray matter** can be distinguished (Fig. 1.29). The appearance of the white matter is due to the abundance of myelinated axons, whereas the appearance of the gray matter is due to the scarcity of myelinated axons. The neuropil is a broad term used to describe the unmyelinated and myelinated axons that form a synapse-rich meshwork in the gray matter, "and includes dendrites and neuroglial cell processes".

1. **Cells**: CNS neuroglia include **astrocytes**, **oligodendrocytes**, **microglia**, and **ependymal cells** (Fig. 1.30). The astrocyte has numerous functions, some of which include 1) projects foot processes to capillaries that contribute to the blood–brain barrier, 2) plays a role in the metabolism of neurotransmitters, and 3) buffers the [K+] of the CNS extracellular space. The oligodendrocyte produces a **myelin sheath** that surrounds and insulates a portion of an axon. The junction between adjacent oligodendrocyte processes on an axon is called the **node of Ranvier**. The microglia have a phagocytic function and proliferate in regions of injury or disease whereby they are then called **reactive microglia**. The ependymal cells line the ventricles of the brain and the central canal of the spinal cord.

2. **Meninges**: CNS connective tissue components called the **meninges** protect the underlying brain and spinal cord; provide a framework for arteries, veins, and dural sinuses; and enclose a fluid-filled space called the subarachnoid space. The meninges include the **dura mater**, **arachnoid mater**, and **pia mater**.

   a. **Dura mater**: The tough/durable outermost meningeal component contains blood vessels and nerves.

   b. **Arachnoid mater**: The middle meningeal component is divided into two parts: **arachnoid barrier cell layer** and the **arachnoid trabeculae**. The arachnoid barrier cell layer is composed of **fibroblasts** but no **collagen fibrils**. The arachnoid trabeculae are composed of **tentacle-shaped fibroblasts** and **collagen fibrils** that closely associate with the fibroblast tentacles. The fibroblast tentacles extend from the arachnoid barrier cell layer to the pia mater, thereby bridging the **subarachnoid space**, which contains **cerebrospinal fluid**.

   c. **Pia mater**: The innermost component of the meninges closely follows the surface topography of the brain and spinal cord. The pia mater is composed of a **single** or **multiple layers of fibroblasts** and **collagen fibrils**. It is separated from the neural tissue of the brain and spinal cord by the **glial-limiting membrane** formed by astrocytes.

D. Peripheral nervous system

The Peripheral nervous system (PNS) consists of **31 pairs of spinal nerves/ganglia** and **12 pairs of cranial nerves/ganglia**. A typical spinal nerve contains bundles of axons that carry either motor information or sensory information (Fig. 1.31). The axons have **variable diameters (1–20 μm)** as well as **variable amounts of myelination** (high myelination → intermediate myelination → no myelination). The neuronal perikarya of the axons that carry motor information are located in the spinal cord, brainstem, or brain. For example, the neuronal perikarya of an α-motoneuron whose axon ends at the neuromuscular junction are located in the ventral horn of the spinal cord. The neuronal perikarya of the axons that carry sensory information are located in ganglia. For example, the neuronal perikaryon of a sensory neuron associated with a Pacinian corpuscle is located in the dorsal root ganglion.

1. **Cells**: Neuroglia of the PNS include the **Schwann cell** and the **satellite cell**. A Schwann cell may produce a **myelin sheath** around an axon, thereby forming a myelinated axon. The junction between adjacent myelinating Schwann cells is called the **node of Ranvier** (see Fig. 1.30). In addition, a Schwann cells may produce **cytoplasmic extensions** around an axon, thereby forming an unmyelinated axon. The satellite cell surrounds the neuronal perikarya located within sensory, sympathetic, and parasympathetic ganglia.

2. **Connective tissue components**: The connective tissue components of a spinal nerve hold the axons within a spinal nerve together in bundles (see Fig. 1.31). The **epineurium** is a dense irregular connective tissue that surrounds the entire peripheral nerve (e.g., the sciatic nerve). The **perineurium** is a specialized

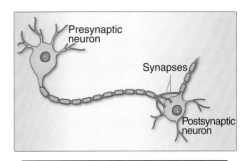

Figure 1.27
Pre- and postsynaptic neurons.

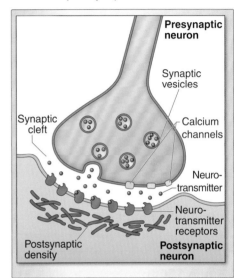

Figure 1.28
Synapse.

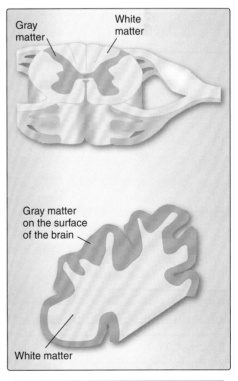

Figure 1.29
White and gray matter.

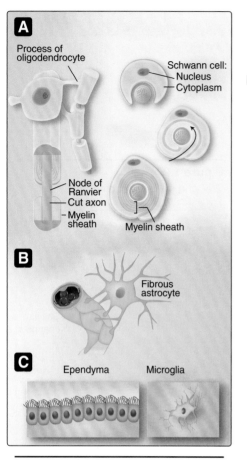

Figure 1.30
Neuroglia. A, Oligodendrocytes
and Schwann cells. B, Astrocytes.
C, Ependyma and microglia.

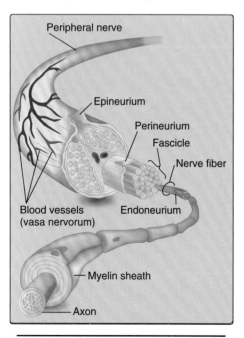

Figure 1.31
Peripheral nerve structure.

type of connective tissue that surrounds a bundle of axons called a **fascicle**. The **endoneurium** is a delicate, loose connective tissue that surrounds an individual **axon**.

E. Autonomic nervous system

The ANS has **visceromotor** and **viscerosensory components** (although traditionally only the visceromotor component has been emphasized). The **hypothalamus** has central control of the ANS, coordinating all ANS actions. The ANS can be subdivided into **sympathetic (thoracolumbar)** and **parasympathetic (craniosacral) divisions**.

1. **Sympathetic (thoracolumbar; T_1–L_2/L_3) division**: The visceromotor component of the sympathetic nervous system has a *fight or flight* or **catabolic function** that is necessary in **emergency situations** in which the body needs a sudden burst of energy, and the whole system tends to "go off together" (Fig. 1.32). It is a two-neuron chain that consists of a **preganglionic sympathetic neuron** and a **postganglionic sympathetic neuron** following this general pattern: short preganglionic neuron → ganglion → long postganglionic neuron → effector organ. The exception to this arrangement is found in the sympathetic **splanchnic nerves** (which are detailed in Chapters 3 and 4, where the thorax and abdomen are covered, respectively), where the pattern is long preganglionic neuron → prevertebral ganglion → short postganglionic neuron → effector organ. The viscerosensory component carries **visceral pain sensation** from **nociceptors** located in viscera to the CNS (Fig. 1.33). Nociceptors are free nerve endings that respond to pathologic stimuli such as myocardial infarction, appendicitis, and gastrointestinal cramping or bloating. Visceral pain sensation is carried almost exclusively by the viscerosensory component of the sympathetic nervous system. It is poorly localized because nociceptor density is low, nociceptor fields are large, and its projection to higher CNS levels is widespread.

2. **Parasympathetic (craniosacral; CNs III, VII, IX, and X and S_2–S_4) division**: The visceromotor component of the parasympathetic nervous system has a *rest and digest* or **anabolic function** that is necessary to conserve energy, restore body resources, and get rid of wastes (Fig. 1.34). The whole visceromotor component of the parasympathetic nervous system does not "go off together" but, instead, specific activities are initiated when appropriate. It is a two-neuron chain that consists of a **preganglionic parasympathetic neuron** and a **postganglionic parasympathetic neuron** following this general pattern: long preganglionic neuron → ganglion → short postganglionic neuron → effector organ. The viscerosensory component carries 1) **arterial oxygen tension (P_aO_2)** and **arterial pH** information from chemoreceptors, 2) **blood pressure** information from baroreceptors, 3) **visceral pressure** and **movement sensation** from rapidly adapting mechanoreceptors, 4) **visceral stretch sensation** from slowly adapting mechanoreceptors, 5) **osmolarity** information from osmoreceptors, and 6) **temperature** from internal thermal receptors (Fig. 1.35).

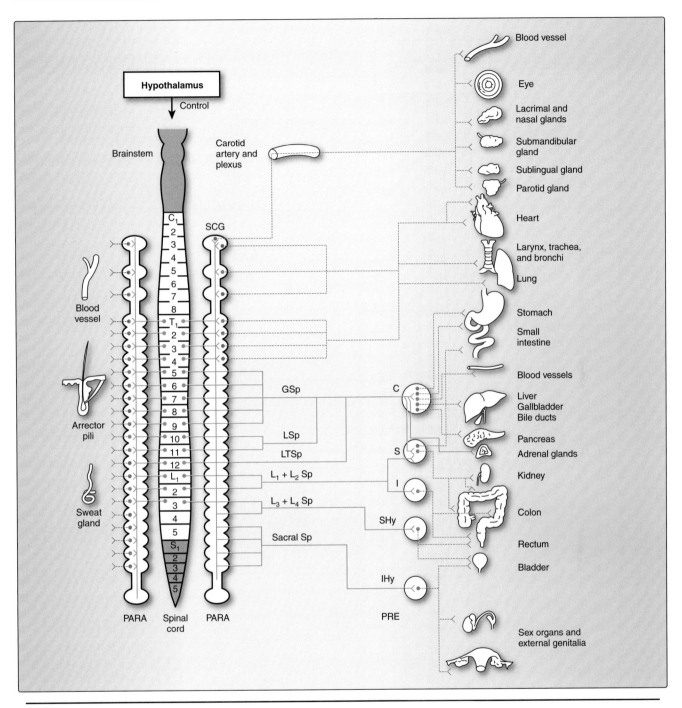

Figure 1.32

Visceromotor component of the sympathetic system. Preganglionic sympathetic neurons (solid line; green), postganglionic sympathetic neurons (dashed line; orange). C = celiac ganglion, GSp = greater thoracic splanchnic nerve, I = inferior mesenteric ganglion, IHy = inferior hypogastric plexus, LSp = lesser thoracic splanchnic nerve, LTSp = least thoracic splanchnic nerve, PARA = paravertebral chain ganglia, PRE = prevertebral ganglia, S = superior mesenteric ganglion, SCG = superior cervical ganglion, Shy = superior hypogastric plexus, Sp = splanchnic nerve.

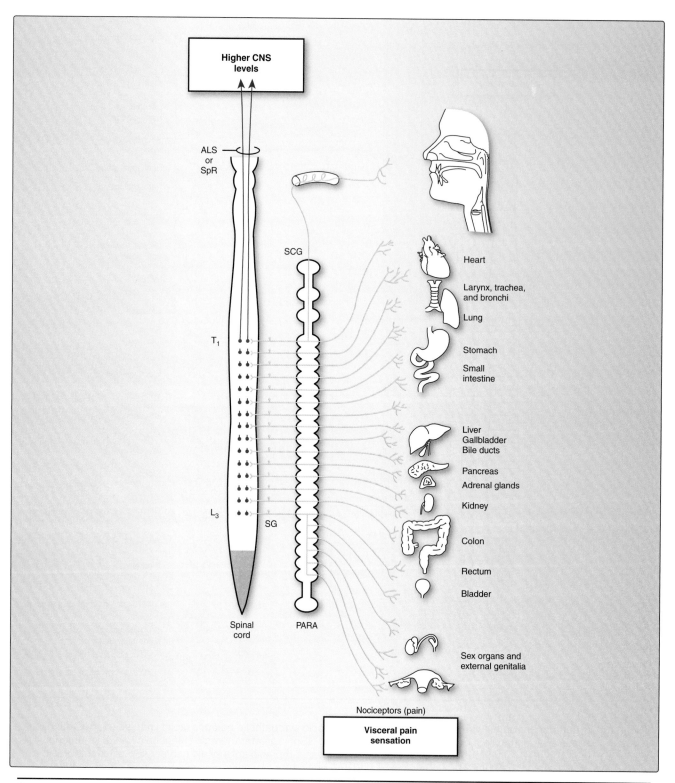

Figure 1.33
Viscerosensory component of the sympathetic system (visceral pain sensation). The sensory neuron (yellow) has its perikaryon in the spinal ganglia (SG). This neuron sends a peripheral process to the viscera that ends as a free nerve ending (or nociceptor) and sends a central process into the spinal cord, which synapses with a neuron within the spinal cord (red). This neuron (red) projects axons to higher CNS levels. ALS = anterolateral system, CNS = central nervous system, PARA = paravertebral chain ganglia, SCG = superior cervical ganglion, SpR = spinoreticular tract.

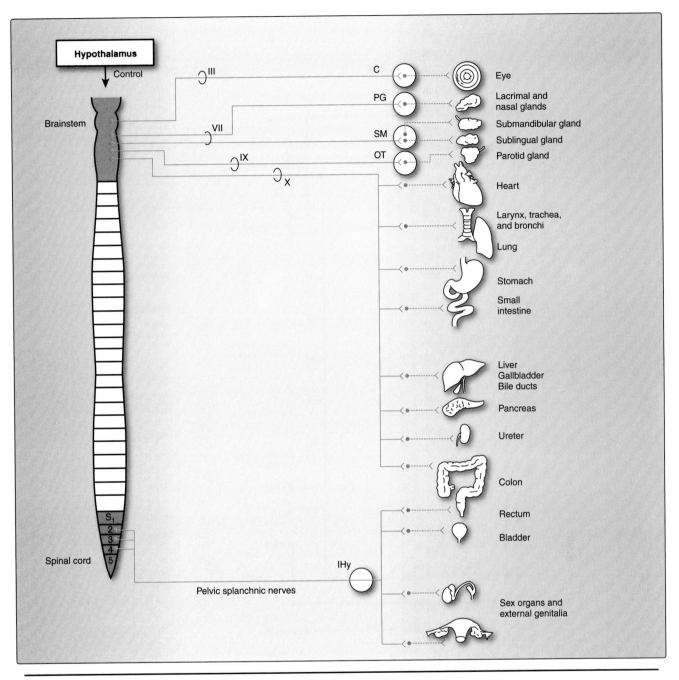

Figure 1.34
Visceromotor component of the parasympathetic system. Preganglionic parasympathetic neurons (solid line; green), postganglionic parasympathetic neurons (dashed line; orange). C = ciliary ganglion, PG = pterygopalatine ganglion, SM = submandibular ganglion, OT = otic ganglion, IHy = inferior hypogastric plexus, cranial nerves III, VII, IX, X.

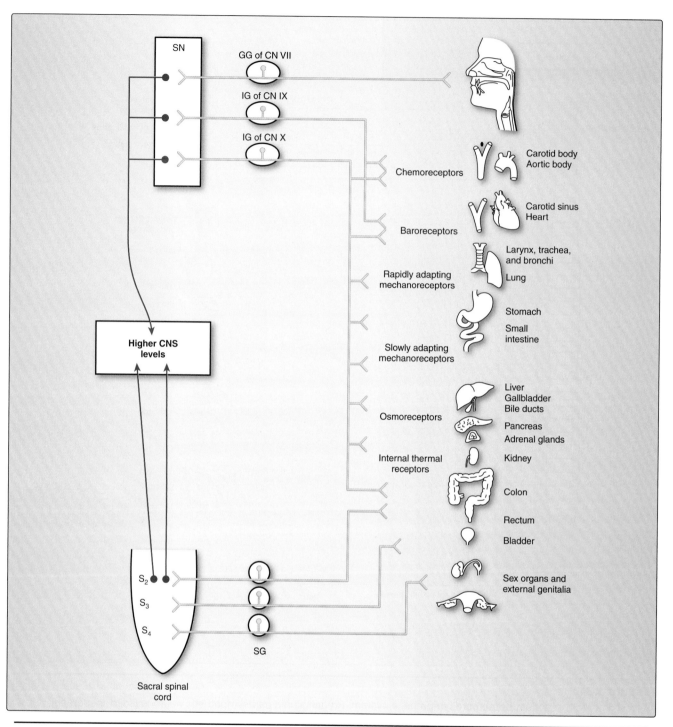

Figure 1.35

Viscerosensory component of the parasympathetic system. The sensory neuron (yellow) has its perikaryon in the posterior root ganglion, geniculate ganglion (GG) of CN VII, inferior (petrosal) ganglion (IG) of CN IX, or the inferior (nodose) ganglion (IG) of CN X. This neuron sends a peripheral process to the viscera that ends as various receptors and sends a central process into the spinal cord or solitary nucleus (SN), which synapses with a neuron within the spinal cord or the SN (red). These neurons (red) project axons to higher CNS levels. CN = cranial nerve, CNS = central nervous system, SG = spinal ganglia.

VIII. RADIOLOGY

Radiologic anatomy utilizes diagnostic medical imaging to study the structure and function of the human body. Diagnostic images are included throughout the text to illustrate normal and pathologic anatomy in a clinical context. Combining gross anatomical dissections, schematic illustrations, and diagnostic medical images promotes integration of gross and clinical anatomy topics. Early exposure to radiologic anatomy not only aids in the understanding of gross anatomical relationships, but also improves the learner's understanding of foundational radiology concepts and terms and familiarizes the learner with basic radiologic modalities.

A. Modalities

The following types of imaging modalities are presented throughout the text.

1. **X-ray/plain film**: Images are formed by x-rays that are passed through tissue onto a film/detector. This modality allows for excellent penetration of all structures and good imaging of bone and lungs. Soft tissues like fat and muscle are not well visualized on plain film.

2. **Ultrasound (US)**: Sound waves are passed through tissue to produce an image based on the rate of reflection back to the transducer. This modality allows for excellent distinction between cystic and solid structures, but does not penetrate through bone or gas.

3. **Computed tomography (CT)**: Three-dimensional images are rendered from a data set produced by a rotating x-ray beam. This modality allows for excellent visualization of soft tissue, gas, bone, and large vessels.

4. **Magnetic resonance imaging (MRI)**: Three-dimensional images are produced by radio waves passed through tissue in an extremely powerful magnetic field. This modality allows for excellent imaging of bones and soft tissues (CNS, musculoskeletal system).

B. Orientation

Once the modality has been identified, develop a systematic approach to looking at radiographs. First, orientation to the image is key, and information about radiographic position, projection, and view is provided to aid in this task. Keeping these basic terms and concepts in mind will help the learner establish correct image orientation and, in turn, better appreciate the anatomy pictured in the radiologic images within each chapter.

1. **Position**: Position refers to the general position of the patient or the side of the patient closest to the film/detector. For this text, assume the patient is upright, unless otherwise noted (e.g., recumbent, supine, prone).

2. **Projection**: Projection refers to the direction of x-rays in relation to the patient and film/detector (Fig. 1.36). Common projection terms include the following:

   a. **Anteroposterior (A/P) projection**: The x-rays travel from an anterior position, through the patient to reach the x-ray film/detector that is posterior to the patient.

   b. **Posteroanterior (P/A) projection**: The x-rays travel from a posterior position, through the patient to reach the film/detector that is anterior to the patient.

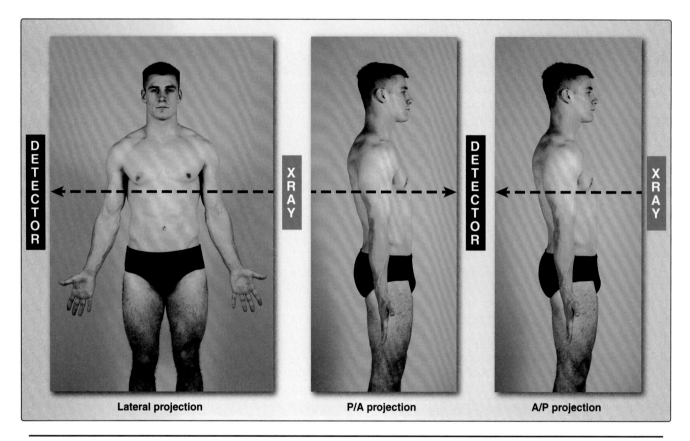

| Lateral projection | P/A projection | A/P projection |

Figure 1.36
Radiologic projections. Black dashed arrow indicates direction of x-ray beam.

    c. Lateral projection: The x-ray travels from one side, through the patient to reach the film/detector on the contralateral side (e.g., left to right).

3. **View**: The most common descriptor noted in the text, view provides information about plane and axis orientation.

    a. Anteroposterior view: An A/P view describes the image as if the viewer is facing the patient; thus, the left side of the image coincides with the right side of the viewer's body.

    b. Lateral view: A lateral view describes the image as if the viewer is looking at the image from the side, rather than from the front.

    c. Views in CT and MRI: For CT and MRIs, the specific plane is commonly included to aid in orientation to structures. For example, an MRI of the knee joint is typically viewed from a sagittal view to best visualize the internal structures (e.g., cruciate ligaments). CT images are commonly described as axial to denote an image through the long axis of the body (in the transverse plane), although CT images can also be rendered in the sagittal and coronal planes. When viewing an axial CT image, remember that it is an inferior view, meaning that the patient's feet are coming out of the plane of the image and the head into the plane of the image. Therefore, the left side of the image corresponds to the right side of the patient.

Back

I. OVERVIEW

The back represents the posterior region of the trunk that is continuous with the neck and extends inferiorly to the level of the pelvis. [**Note:** For the purpose of completeness, the cervical spine (neck) is included in this chapter.] The back is the main component of the axial skeleton, onto which appendicular skeletal structures (limbs) are fixed through bony articulations and ligament and muscle attachments. From superficial to deep, back structures include skin, subcutaneous tissue, deep fascia, muscles, ligaments, vertebrae, ribs, spinal cord and meninges, spinal nerves, and blood vessels.

II. OSTEOLOGY

Back stability is provided by the **vertebral column** or spine, which is divided into **cervical**, **thoracic**, **lumbar**, **sacral**, and **coccygeal** regions. As shown in Figure 2.1, the adult vertebral column typically contains 33 vertebrae: 7 cervical, 12 thoracic, 5 lumbar, 5 sacral (fused), and 3–5 coccygeal (fused). Vertebrae are separated by fibrocartilaginous intervertebral discs and united through a series of joints, ligaments, and capsules. Functionally, the vertebral column serves to protect the spinal cord and spinal nerves and support body weight superior to the pelvis. It also allows for varying degrees of motion and plays an integral part in posture and gait. Most spinal motion occurs superior to the sacral level and is further dictated by articular orientation and bony attachments (e.g., ribs in the thoracic region). Spinal motion includes extension, flexion, lateral side-bending, rotation, and circumduction.

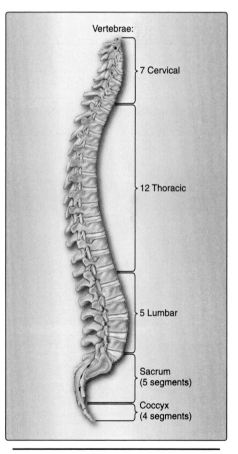

Figure 2.1
Vertebral column.

Clinical Application 2.1: Spondylosis

Spondylosis is the degeneration of the vertebral column. It most often occurs in the cervical region, although it can also be seen in the thoracic and lumbar regions. The etiology is not well defined, although patient age is a strong element in the development of spondylosis, which most often affects the geriatric patient population. Vertebral discs and facet joints are most vulnerable to degenerative changes, leading to narrowing of disc space/weakening of annulus fibrosis, and bone spur formation, respectively. De-generative changes can also affect the adjacent posterior longitudinal ligament, which increases the risk of spinal cord compression as a result of disc herniation. Subsequent myelopathy and/or radiculopathy may also occur. Neurological symptoms—motor and sensory—associated with myelopathy and radiculopahty commonly drive patients to seek medical attention.

Sacrum

Lateral view

Spondylosis. Lumbosacral plain film radiograph revealing narrowing of disc space at the L3/L4 level (*).

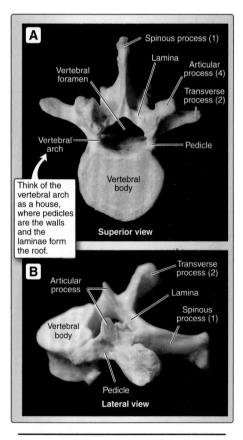

Figure 2.2
General vertebral structures.

A. Vertebrae

A **vertebra** is generally arranged as a weight-bearing **body** anteri-orly, a **vertebral (neural) arch** and **spinous process** posteriorly, and **transverse processes** laterally. **Articular processes** project superiorly and inferiorly (Fig. 2.2).

1. **Vertebral body:** The **vertebral body** is the weight-bearing portion of the vertebra and also serves as the site for intervertebral disc attachment. Body size and shape vary throughout the length of the vertebral column.

2. **Vertebral arch:** The **vertebral arch** protects the spinal cord and is formed by two **pedicles** that project posteriorly from the body and two **laminae** that meet in the midline at the spinous process.

3. **Vertebral foramen:** The **vertebral canal** houses the spinal cord and is formed by the collection of **vertebral foramen** along the length of the spine. Right and left sets of superior and inferior articular processes project from the junction of the pedicles and laminae.

Clinical Application 2.2: Laminectomy

A **laminectomy** is a surgical procedure that involves removal of a spinous process and associated laminae and pedicles at one or more vertebral levels. This procedure is performed to create more space in the vertebral canal, thus relieving pressure on the spinal cord and spinal nerve roots. Pressure is often caused by spinal stenosis (narrowing of the canal) as a result of a space-occupying lesion, such as excess bony growth, tumor formation, or disc herniation.

4. **Vertebral notches:** Laterally, superior and inferior **vertebral notches** present as indentations posterior to the vertebral body.

 a. **Intervertebral foramina:** The inferior and superior vertebral notches of adjacent vertebrae combine to form paired **intervertebral foramina** at each spinal level. Spinal nerves and vasculature travel through intervertebral foramina on each side of the column.

 b. **Sacral foramina:** In the sacral region, spinal nerves exit the canal through **anterior** and **posterior sacral foramina**.

5. **Processes:** Muscles and ligaments attach to both spinous and transverse processes. Transverse processes in the thoracic region also articulate with ribs posteriorly and support the thoracic cage.

B. Regional characteristics

Regionally, vertebrae have distinct structural characteristics that further dictate function. For example, articular processes are oriented in different planes to allow or limit spinal mobility. Variations in size and shape can also allow for transmission of neural structures, such as the **cervical** and **lumbar spinal cord enlargements**, in respective regions.

1. **Cervical (C1–C7):** As shown in Figures 2.3 and 2.4, cervical vertebrae feature a small body and a large, triangular vertebral foramen. A **foramen transversarium** in the transverse processes accommodates vertebral vessels and sympathetic plexuses. Articular processes are oriented in the horizontal (transverse) plane. Spinous processes in C3–C5 are short and bifid (divided into two equal parts). Unique cervical vertebrae are described as follows.

 a. **C1 (atlas):** This ring-like vertebra has neither body nor spinous process. It articulates with occipital condyles through two lateral masses (atlanto-occipital joint) and has a small anterior facet for articulation with the dens (odontoid process) of C2.

 b. **C2 (axis):** This vertebra is strong, featuring a dens that projects superiorly to articulate with C1 (pivot joint).

 c. **C7 (vertebra prominens):** This vertebra with its long, prominent spinous process makes a reliable surface landmark.

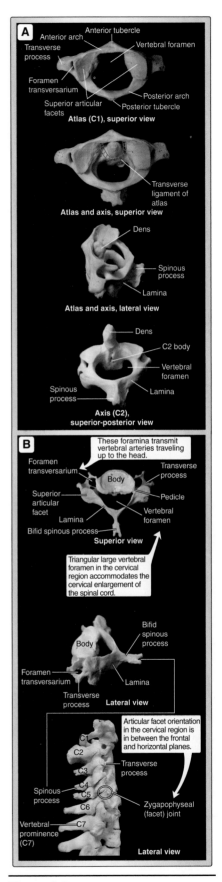

Figure 2.3
A, Atlas (C1) and axis (C2). B, Cervical vertebrae features.

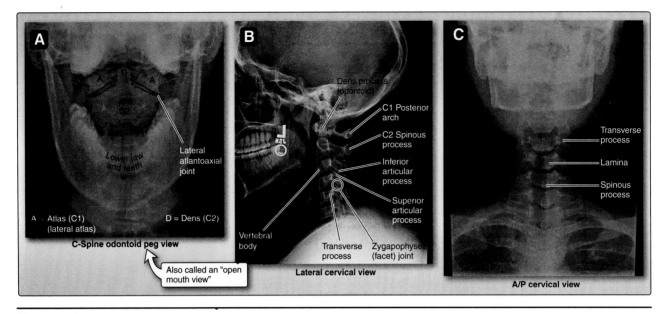

Figure 2.4
Cervical plain film views (A–C).

2. **Thoracic (T1–T12):** As shown in Figures 2.5 and 2.6, thoracic vertebrae feature a heart-shaped body with **costal demifacets** for articulation with the heads of ribs and a small, circular vertebral foramen. In T1–T10 vertebrae, transverse processes have **costal facets** for articulation with rib tubercles, articular processes oriented in the frontal (coronal) plane, and long posteroinferiorly sloping, overlapping spinous process.

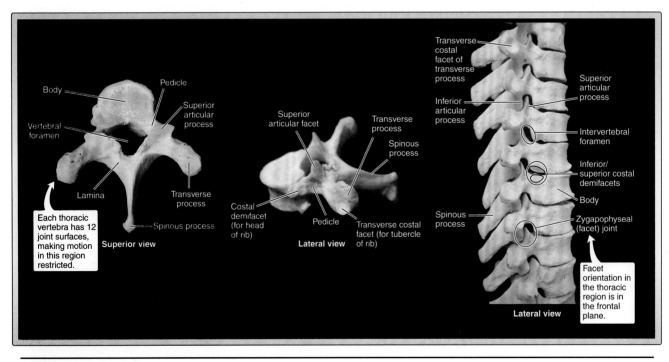

Figure 2.5
Thoracic regional features.

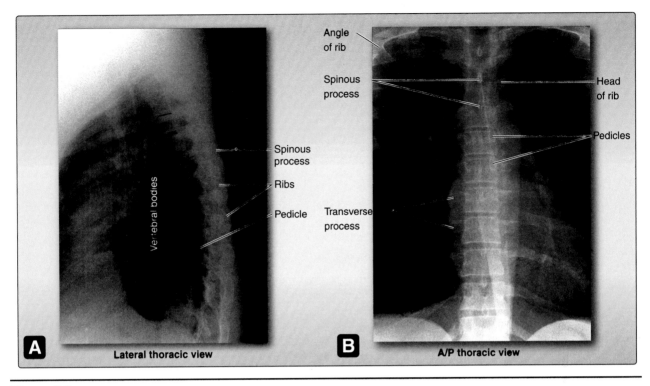

Figure 2.6
Thoracic plain film views (A and B).

3. **Lumbar (L1–L5):** As shown in Figures 2.7 and 2.8, lumbar vertebrae have large, kidney-shaped bodies and large, triangular vertebral foramina. Their articular facets are oriented in the sagittal plane, and they have short, hatched-shaped spinous processes. A **mammillary process** is located on the superior articular process.

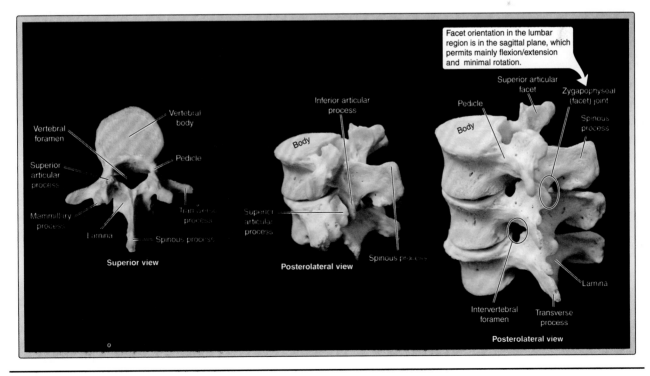

Figure 2.7
Lumbar regional features.

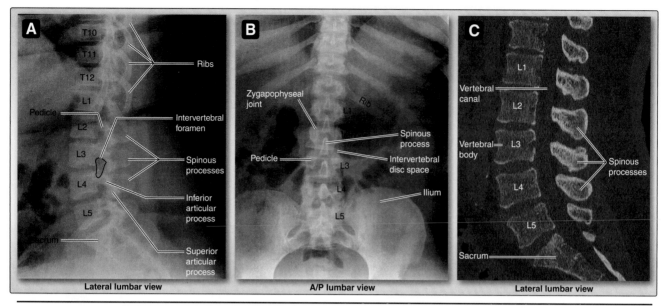

Figure 2.8
Plain film, A/B and computed tomography (CT), C.

4. **Sacral (S1–S5):** This fused, wedge-shaped bone is concave anteriorly and convex posteriorly. It features anterior and posterior foramina and a sacral canal and hiatus (Fig. 2.9).

5. **Coccygeal:** This beak-like bone comprises three to five small, fused vertebrae. It is a tail-like structure at the caudalmost region of the vertebral column.

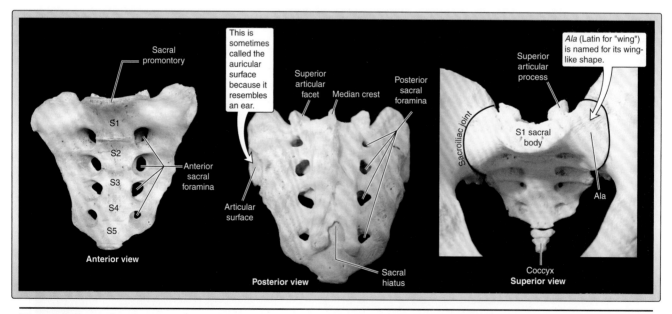

Figure 2.9
Sacral and coccygeal regional features.

Clinical Application 2.3: Dislocation

Vertebral dislocation without fracture most often occurs in the cervical region because of the horizontal orientation of articular facets. Pure dislocation in the thoracic and lumbar regions is less common and occurs in conjunction with additional factors, such as fracture, pathology, or congenital malformation. Some examples of dislocations with fractures are:

- **Spondylolysis (Scottie dog fracture):** This stress fracture of the pars interarticularis is most commonly observed in young athletes at the L4 or L5 level. Anterior displacement at the level of fracture may occur (spondylolisthesis).
- **Spondylolisthesis:** Anterior displacement of the vertebral body in relation to the inferior vertebral body causes include fracture (spondylolysis), pathology, degeneration, and congenital malformation. This typically occurs at the lumbosacral junction.

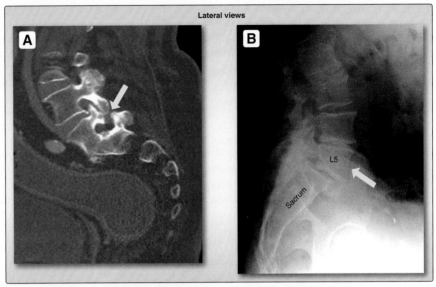

A, Spondylolysis. Lateral CT showing fracture of the L5 pars interarticularis, indicated by the yellow arrow. B, Plain film showing anterior position of L5 on sacrum, indicated by the yellow arrow.

C. Intervertebral discs

As shown in Figure 2.10, fibrocartilage **intervertebral discs** are arranged between all presacral vertebrae, except for between the occiput, atlas (C1), and axis (C2). In the adult, the discs constitute ~25% of the total length of the spine.

1. **Composition:** Each disc consists of an outer **annulus fibrosis** and an inner **nucleus pulposus**.
   The strong outer annulus is made up of 6–10 fibrocartilaginous rings (lamellae) arranged concentrically at opposite angles. The inner nucleus pulposus is a gel-like connective tissue structure with high water content. Collectively, these structures permit spinal movement and transmit loads across each vertebral segment, in addition to binding vertebral bodies together.

2. **Regional characteristics:** Regionally, intervertebral discs vary in shape and thickness. Variations in thickness permit different ranges of motion, while shape is dictated mainly by secondary spinal curvatures (see II.D). For example, in the cervical and lumbar regions, discs are thicker anteriorly, whereas thickness is generally uniform throughout the thoracic spine.

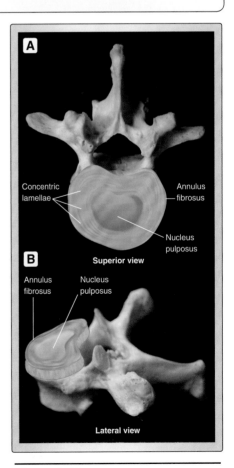

Figure 2.10
Intervertebral disc.

Clinical Application 2.4: Vertebral Fractures

In general, vertebral fractures involve compression of the vertebral body following a quick, forceful flexion event, such as a motor vehicle accident. If the force is great enough, fracture can be accompanied by anterior displacement of the vertebra on the adjacent inferior vertebra (traumatic spondylolisthesis) and ligament damage. Specific vertebral fractures include:

- **Chance fracture (seat-belt injury):** This anterior compression fracture is accompanied by a transverse fracture through posterior vertebral structures, including the spinous process and vertebral arch, caused by excessive flexion. This most commonly occurs at the T12/L1 interface in the pediatric population and can be accompanied by intra-abdominal injuries (not shown).
- **Jefferson fracture:** This burst fracture of the C1 vertebra with at least two points of fracture is often associated with headfirst diving into shallow water. Ligament damage (transverse ligament of the atlas) may also be present and require more aggressive immobilization and surgical treatment.
- **Hangman fracture:** This bilateral fracture through the vertebral arch of C2 (axis) often occurs just posterior to the articular facets when force is applied to a hyperextended neck and can result in C2 traumatic spondylolisthesis and spinal cord injury.
- **Teardrop fracture:** This hyperflexion injury in the cervical spine is characterized by the avulsion of a triangular bony fragment from the anteroinferior region of the vertebral body. The spine superior to the fracture becomes unstable and tilts anteriorly, potentially causing injury to the spinal cord.

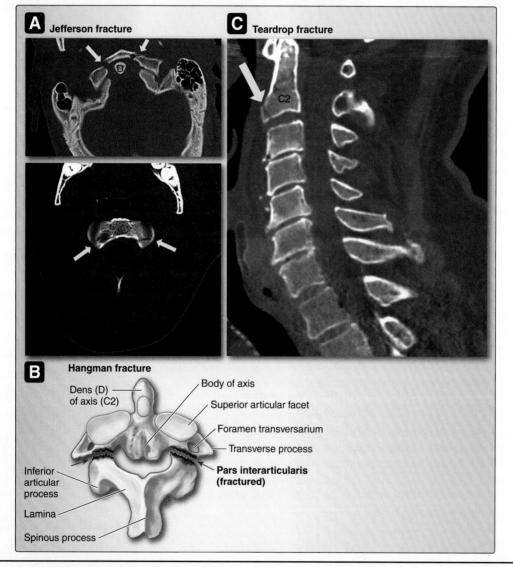

A, Jefferson fracture. Transverse CT at atlantoaxial joint level; yellow arrows showing bilateral fractures in anterior arch of atlas (C1), D, dens. B, Hangman fracture. Transverse CT at C2 level; yellow arrows showing bilateral fractures posterior to articular facets of C2. C, Teardrop fracture. Lateral cervical spine CT; yellow arrow indicating site of fracture.

Clinical Application 2.5: Disc Herniation

The intervertebral disc is vulnerable to degenerative changes that compromise its structural integrity. Tears in the outer annulus fibrosus can lead to herniation or protrusion of the gelatinous inner nucleus pulposus into the vertebral canal. Herniation most often occurs in a posterior or posterolateral direction insofar because the posterior longitudinal ligament is weaker and narrower than its anterior counterpart. Disc herniation in the posterior direction can impinge on the spinal cord, whereas the more common posterolateral herniation impinges on spinal nerve roots. In the cervical spine, a herniation affects spinal nerve roots at that level (C3/C4 herniation would affect C3), whereas in the lumbar region, a herniation affects the spinal nerve root at the level below (L3/L4 herniation would affect the L4 spinal nerve root). Symptoms can include localized and radiating pain (in the affected dermatome), muscle weakness, and reflex changes.

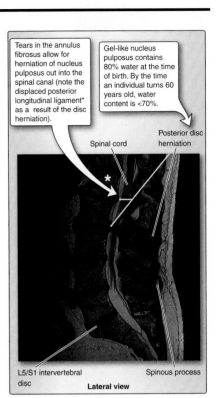

Tears in the annulus fibrosus allow for herniation of nucleus pulposus out into the spinal canal (note the displaced posterior longitudinal ligament* as a result of the disc herniation).

Gel-like nucleus pulposus contains 80% water at the time of birth. By the time an individual turns 60 years old, water content is <70%.

Spinal cord

Posterior disc herniation

L5/S1 intervertebral disc

Spinous process

Lateral view

Herniated disc. Lumbar MRI showing significant disc herniation at L1/L2 and L2/L3 levels.

D. Curvatures

In the adult, there are four distinct spinal curvatures, which are described as being either primary or secondary (Fig. 2.11). **Primary curvatures** include those in the thoracic and sacral regions. These are concave anteriorly and represent curvatures that develop during the fetal period. **Secondary curvatures** are found in the cervical and lumbar regions and are concave posteriorly. Cervical and lumbar curvatures develop as an infant begins to hold his or her head erect and walk, respectively. Deviations from normal spinal curvatures may lead to clinical impairments in the back.

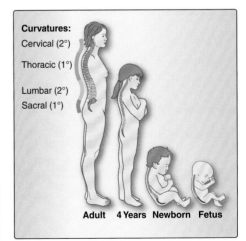

Curvatures:
Cervical (2°)
Thoracic (1°)
Lumbar (2°)
Sacral (1°)

Adult   4 Years   Newborn   Fetus

Figure 2.11

Primary (1°) and secondary (2°) spine curvatures. Normal curvatures of the spine from fetus to adult.

Clinical Application 2.6: Aging and Disc Health

With aging, the structural integrity of the intervertebral disc is at risk. These changes occur in concert with decreases in vertebral body bone density. Disc dehydration associated with changes in nucleus pulposus content is observed over time as well as thickening of the annulus fibrosus. These changes decrease the mobility of the disc and increase risk of injury.

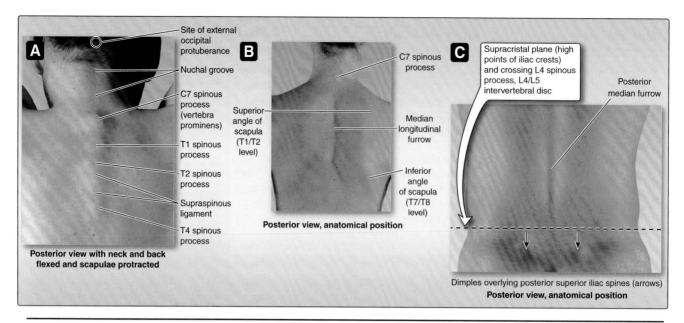

Figure 2.12
Back surface anatomy (A–C).

E. Surface anatomy

Clinicians need to have a solid understanding of back surface anatomy to detect abnormalities (Fig. 2.12A–C). Along the midline of the back is a recess called the **posterior median furrow**, which overlies vertebral spinous processes. Spinous processes project posteriorly and are best observed when a patient's spine is in a flexed position.

1. **Cervical region:** The spinous process of C7 (vertebra prominens) is often the most visible in this region. The spinous process of T1 can also be very distinct and easily mistaken for C7. Superior to C7, a thick nuchal ligament overlies the cervical spinous processes of C2–C6, making it difficult but not impossible to palpate at these levels.

2. **Thoracic region:** Here, spinous processes are longer and slope inferiorly. Because of this arrangement, palpation of a thoracic spinous process does not always correspond to vertebral body level. The **superior angle of the scapula** typically corresponds to the T1/T2 spinous process level, while the **inferior angle of the scapula** lies at the T7/T8 level.

3. **Lumbar region:** Lumbar spinous processes are large and easily palpated with the patient in a flexed position. The **L4 spinous process** lies at the level of the **iliac crest**, which is an important landmark for spinal anesthesia and lumbar puncture procedures.

4. **Sacral region:** Sacral spines of the first three fused segments can be palpated. Commonly, a small dimple representing the **posterior superior iliac spine** can be visualized at the level of the **S2** spinous process.

Clinical Application 2.7: Excessive Spinal Curvatures

Deviation from the normal primary and secondary spinal curvatures can cause functional impairments. These deviations may be positional or congenital and include:

- **Kyphosis:** This excessive thoracic curvature appears more convex posteriorly and often occurs in the geriatric population as a result of degenerative changes in the spine and poor posture.
- **Lordosis:** This excessive lumbar curvature appears more concave posteriorly and is associated with an anteriorly rotated pelvis and accompanying shortening of hip flexor muscles (e.g., iliopsoas). This is often seen in individuals who carry more weight anteriorly and often in late pregnancy.
- **Scoliosis:** This abnormal lateral curvature of the spine involves both lateral bending and rotation of the spine, creating a lateral concavity. The spine laterally bends toward the side of the concavity and rotates to the opposite side. This is often seen in adolescent girls and causes can be either postural/positional or congenital.

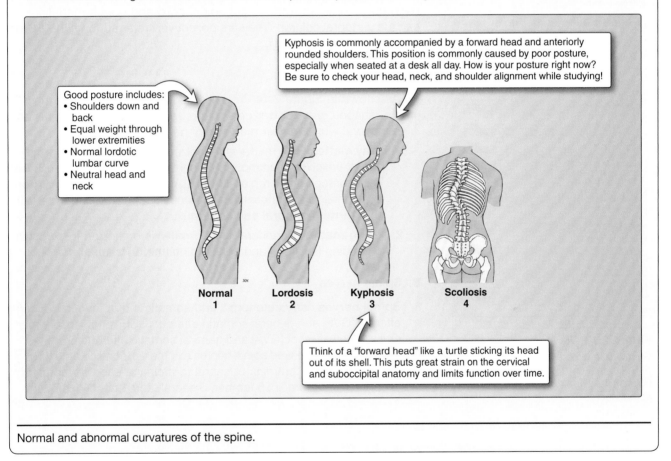

Good posture includes:
- Shoulders down and back
- Equal weight through lower extremities
- Normal lordotic lumbar curve
- Neutral head and neck

Kyphosis is commonly accompanied by a forward head and anteriorly rounded shoulders. This position is commonly caused by poor posture, especially when seated at a desk all day. How is your posture right now? Be sure to check your head, neck, and shoulder alignment while studying!

Normal 1 **Lordosis** 2 **Kyphosis** 3 **Scoliosis** 4

Think of a "forward head" like a turtle sticking its head out of its shell. This puts great strain on the cervical and suboccipital anatomy and limits function over time.

Normal and abnormal curvatures of the spine.

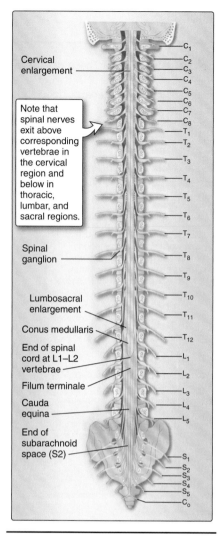

Cervical enlargement

Note that spinal nerves exit above corresponding vertebrae in the cervical region and below in thoracic, lumbar, and sacral regions.

Spinal ganglion

Lumbosacral enlargement

Conus medullaris

End of spinal cord at L1–L2 vertebrae

Filum terminale

Cauda equina

End of subarachnoid space (S2)

C_1
C_2
C_3
C_4
C_5
C_6
C_7
C_8
T_1
T_2
T_3
T_4
T_5
T_6
T_7
T_8
T_9
T_{10}
T_{11}
T_{12}
L_1
L_2
L_3
L_4
L_5
S_1
S_2
S_3
S_4
S_5
C_o

Figure 2.13
Spinal cord. Posterior schematic image of the spinal cord within the vertebral column (laminae removed) and exiting spinal nerves.

III. SPINAL CORD

Housed and protected within the vertebral column, the **spinal cord** spans from the foramen magnum to approximately the L2 vertebral level in the adult (Fig. 2.13). As part of the **central nervous system** (**CNS**), the spinal cord serves as a reflex center and conducts motor and sensory signals between the brain and the body. The vertebral column also contains vasculature, adipose, and meningeal layers, which supply and protect the spinal cord, respectively. The spinal cord is cylindrical in shape with enlargements in the cervical and lumbar regions to accommodate for upper and lower limb innervation, respectively. Distally, the spinal cord tapers and ends at L2 as the **conus medullaris**. Multiple spinal **nerve rootlets** emerge from the distal spinal cord and conus medullaris to exit the vertebral column. They are collectively referred to as the **cauda equina** (Latin for *horse tail*).

A. Internal organization

As shown in Figure 2.14, in cross section, the spinal cord has an "H"-shaped **gray matter** core made up of neuronal cell bodies and peripheral **white matter** made up of nerve fibers (axons).

1. **Gray matter:** Gray matter is organized into **anterior** and **posterior horns**, which contain motor and sensory cell bodies, respectively. The thoracolumbar region (T_1–L_2/L_3) also features a **lateral horn** that contains preganglionic sympathetic cell bodies organized into an **intermediolateral cell column**.

2. **White matter:** Peripheral white matter is organized into specific ascending (sensory) and descending (motor) tracts.

B. Spinal nerves

Spinal nerves carry autonomic and somatic motor (general visceral efferent [GVE] and general somatic efferent [GSE]) and sensory (general visceral afferent [GVA] and general somatic afferent [GSA]) nerve fibers. Thirty-one paired spinal nerves exit the vertebral column through the intervertebral foramina or sacral foramina at each vertebral level (8 cervical, 12 thoracic, 5 lumbar, 5 sacral, and 1 coccygeal).

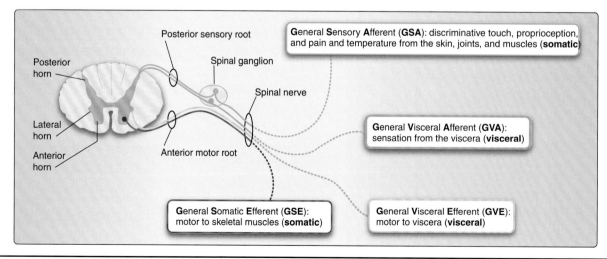

Figure 2.14
Cross section of the spinal cord with spinal nerve components.

Owing to the differential growth of the spinal cord and vertebral column, the spinal cord segment that gives rise to a single spinal nerve does not always lie adjacent to the corresponding vertebral level (see Fig. 2.27).

1. **Anterior** and **posterior rootlets:** These arise from the spinal cord laterally, representing motor and sensory fibers, respectively (see Fig. 2.14). Rootlets converge to form **nerve roots**, which contain autonomic and somatic motor (anterior root) or sensory (posterior root) components.

2. **Pseudounipolar sensory neurons:** Cell bodies for these are housed in the **spinal ganglion** (posterior root ganglion) that is contained in the posterior root (Fig. 2.15).

3. **Multipolar motor neurons:** Cell bodies for these are found in the anterior horn of the spinal cord, and their axons form the anterior root.

4. **Rami:** Once the spinal nerve has exited the vertebral column, it splits into an **anterior** and a **posterior ramus**. Anterior rami provide motor and sensory innervation to the skin, muscles, vasculature, and joints of the trunk and extremities, while the posterior rami innervate intrinsic back muscles, associated vasculature, and overlying skin.

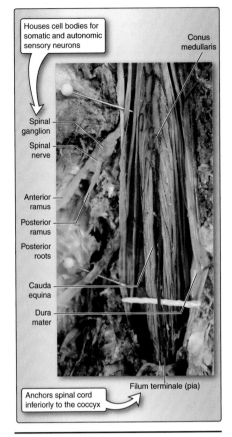

Figure 2.15
Cadaveric image showing caudal spinal cord structures (laminae removed).

Clinical Application 2.8: Lumbar Puncture and Spinal Anesthesia

A **lumbar puncture** is performed to obtain cerebrospinal fluid (CSF) in the subarachnoid space. In the adult patient, this is typically performed at the L3/L4 or L4/L5 level. At this level, risk of injury to the spinal cord is decreased, which ends at the L2 vertebral level. To localize the L4 level, palpate the iliac crests and move to the midline. The patient is then flexed forward in a sitting or side-lying position to widen the space between the spinous processes above or below L4. A needle is inserted through the supraspinous ligament and into the lumbar cistern to obtain a CSF sample for analysis.

Spinal anesthesia (nerve block) can be administered into the epidural (extradural) space at the L3/L4 or L4/L5 level in a procedure similar to a lumbar puncture. Anesthesia bathes the spinal nerves in this region, causing a loss of sensation inferior to the level of administration. To affect sacral spinal nerves, anesthesia can be injected via the sacral canal or posterior sacral foramina.

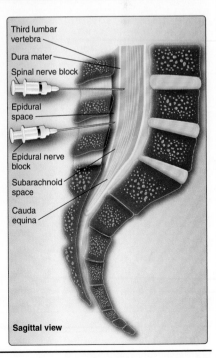

Lumbar puncture and spinal anesthesia.

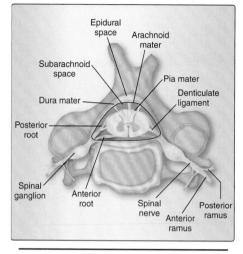

Figure 2.16
Cross-sectional view of spinal meninges and spaces.

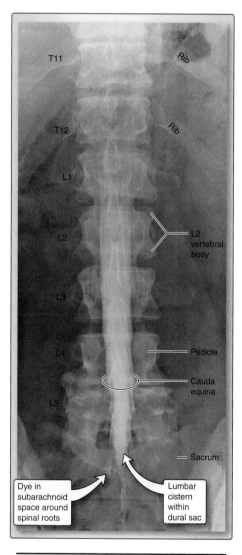

Figure 2.17
Lumbosacral myelography.

C. Meninges

Spinal meninges include the **dura mater**, **arachnoid mater**, and **pia mater**, which collectively surround, support, and protect the spinal cord and spinal nerve roots (Fig. 2.16). See Chapter 1, page 17 for histology of the meninges.

1. **Dura mater:** The dura mater (Latin for *tough mother*) is the outermost layer and is a thick, tough covering. An **epidural (extradural) space** separates the dura from the boundaries of the vertebral foramen that is filled with adipose and a spinal venous plexus. Spinal dura mater is continuous with the cranial dura mater and extends inferiorly to the level of S2, forming a tube-like **dural sac** (Fig. 2.17).

2. **Arachnoid mater:** Deep to the dura mater is the arachnoid mater, a delicate, web-like layer that creates a **subarachnoid space** filled with **cerebrospinal fluid (CSF)**. CSF bathes and protects the spinal cord and nerve roots within the vertebral canal. The subarachnoid space also contains arterial and venous branches that nourish the spinal cord. Under normal conditions, the arachnoid and dura are closely associated, obliterating the **subdural space** between these two layers. However, bleeding can occur into this space, forming a subdural hematoma. A widened subarachnoid space exists below the level of the conus medullaris between vertebral levels L2–S2. This space, referred to as the **lumbar cistern**, lies within the dural sac and contains CSF and the cauda equina.

3. **Pia mater:** The innermost meningeal layer, the pia mater, is closely adhered to the spinal cord. Two specializations of pia mater function to anchor the spinal cord within the vertebral canal: **Denticulate ligaments** are extensions of pia that project laterally at each vertebral foramen level and anchor into the inner surface of the dura mater, separating anterior and posterior rootlets (Fig. 2.18). The **filum terminale** is an extension of pia from the tip of the conus medullaris that extends inferiorly to attach on the coccyx, acting as a caudal anchor for the spinal cord.

IV. VASCULATURE AND INNERVATION

A. Vasculature

Vascular supply to the spinal cord and vertebral column originates from a number of sources (Fig. 2.19).

1. **Arterial supply:** Arterial supply to the spinal cord and vertebral column includes branches of segmental spinal arteries along the length of the cord/column.

   a. **Medullary arteries:** The singular **anterior spinal artery** and paired **posterior spinal arteries** originate from the **vertebral arteries** and run the length of the spinal cord. Spinal arteries receive collateral circulation from a series of **segmental medullary**

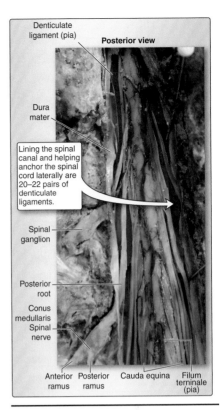

Figure 2.18
Cadaveric image showing spinal meninges (laminae removed).
Dura = pink, pia specializations = red.

arteries that originate from vertebral, deep cervical, ascending cervical, posterior intercostal, lumbar, and lateral sacral arteries. The largest of these is the **great anterior segmental medullary artery (artery of Adamkiewicz)**, which serves the lower two thirds of the spinal cord.

b. **Radicular arteries: Radicular arteries** supply the meningeal coverings and spinal nerve roots, but do not anastomose with spinal arteries.

c. **Periosteal** and **equatorial branches** supply arterial blood to the vertebral column (Fig. 2.20). Spinal branches also contribute to the bone surrounding the spinal canal. These branches arise from cervical (vertebral and ascending cervical arteries) and segmental arteries in the thoracic and lumbar regions (posterior intercostal, subcostal, lumbar, iliolumbar, and sacral arteries).

2. **Venous drainage:** Venous drainage of the vertebral column arises from **spinal veins** that originate from surrounding **internal** and **external venous plexuses**. These veins drain into segmental thoracic and lumbar veins as well as vertebral veins in the cervical region. Venous drainage occurs through three **anterior** and three **posterior spinal veins** and a series of **anterior** and **posterior medullary** and **radicular veins**. These veins communicate with the internal vertebral venous plexus, which is continuous with the dural venous sinuses in the cranial vault.

B. Innervation

In general, the vertebral column receives innervation from spinal nerves, specifically **meningeal branches** (Fig. 2.21). These branches supply intervertebral discs, periosteum, ligaments, dura mater, and spinal blood vessels. In addition, each zygapophyseal (facet) joint is innervated by **articular medial branches** of posterior rami from adjacent spinal nerves, giving the synovial joint a dual innervation.

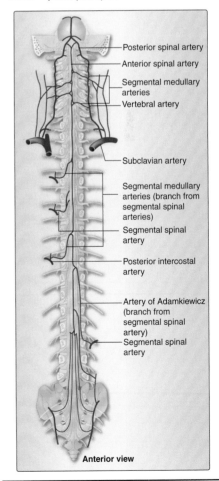

Figure 2.19
Primary arterial blood supply of the spinal cord.

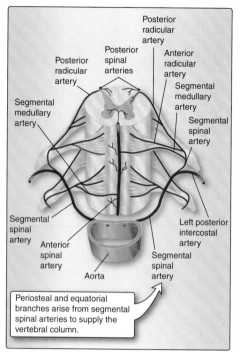

Figure 2.20
Cross section through spinal cord showing internal and external arterial supply.

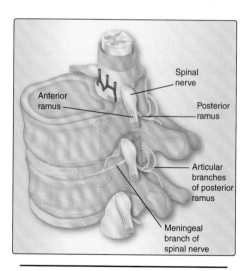

Figure 2.21
Neurovascular supply to the vertebral column.

V. EMBRYOLOGY

The CNS (brain and spinal cord) begins to form in **week 3** of development during which time the process of **neurulation** occurs (Fig. 2.22). Neurulation refers to the formation and closure of the neural tube in which **bone morphogenetic protein 4 (BMP-4)**, **noggin** (an inductor protein), **chordin** (an **inductor protein**), **fibroblast growth factor 8**, and **neural cell adhesion molecule** play a role.

A. Somitomeres

The paraxial mesoderm is a thick plate of mesoderm that organizes into segments called **somitomeres**, which form in a craniocaudal sequence. The somitomeres one to seven do not form somites but contribute mesoderm to the head and neck region (i.e., the pharyngeal arches). The remaining somitomeres condense in a craniocaudal sequence to form 42–44 pairs of somites of the trunk region. The somites closest to the caudal end eventually disappear, to give a final count of ~**35 pairs** of somites.

1. **Somites:** The paraxial mesoderm on either side of the midline (neural tube) gives rise to the somites, which, in turn, soon differentiate into an **sclerotome** and a **dermamyotome** (Fig. 2.23).

   a. **Sclerotome:** During week 4 of development, the mesodermal cells from the sclerotome migrate and condense in three areas: around the **notochord**, around the **neural tube**, and into the **lateral body wall**.

      [1] **Sclerodermal cells:** The sclerodermal cells around the notochord form the **centrum**, which develops into the **adult vertebral body**. The sclerodermal cells around the neural tube form the **vertebral arches**, which develop into the **adult pedicles**, **laminae**, **spinous process**, **articular processes**, and the **transverse processes**. The sclerodermal cells in the lateral body wall form the costal processes, which develop into the **adult ribs**.

      [2] **Mesodermal and notochordal cells**: The space between the vertebral bodies is filled with mesodermal cells that contribute to the formation of the **intervertebral disc**. The notochord regresses in the area of the vertebral body, but persists in the intervertebral disc. As mentioned, each intervertebral disc consists of the nucleus pulposus and the annulus fibrosis. The nucleus pulposus is a remnant of the embryonic **notochord**. By age 20 years, all notochordal cells have degenerated such that all notochordal vestiges in the adult are limited to just a noncellular matrix. The annulus fibrosis is an outer rim of **fibrocartilage** derived from **mesoderm** found between the vertebral bodies.

      [3] **Sclerotome resegmentation**: As development continues, each sclerotome splits into a **cranial portion** with a low cell density and a **caudal portion** with a high cell density (Fig. 2.24). The boundary between the cranial portion and the caudal portion is marked by an **intersegmental fissure**

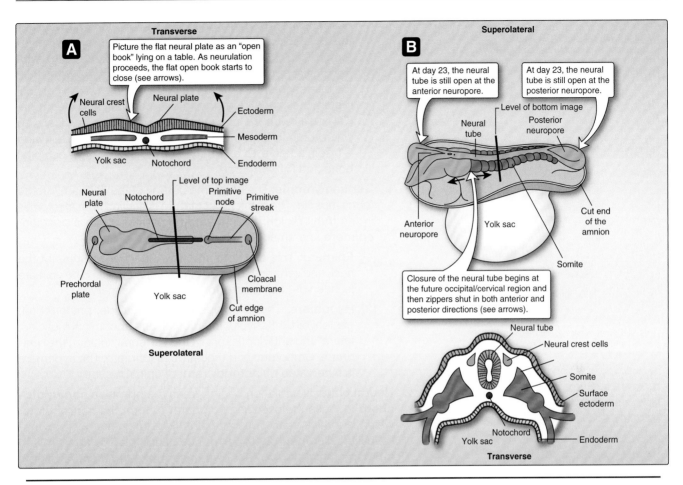

Figure 2.22

Neurulation. The formation and closure of the neural tube. A, Day 20. B, Day 23.

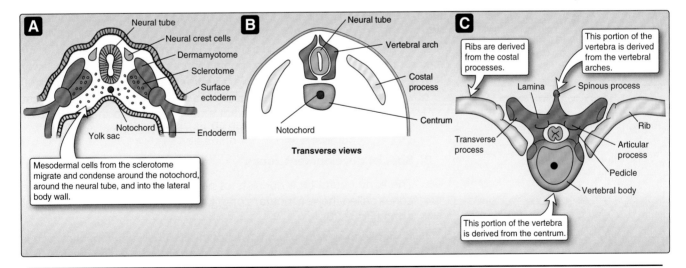

Figure 2.23

Embryologic formation of vertebrae. A, At about day 28, mesodermal cells from the sclerotome migrate and condense in three areas: around the notochord, around the neural tube, and into the lateral body wall. B, The formation of the centrum, vertebral arches, and the costal processes. C, The adult derivatives of the centrum, vertebral arches, and the costal processes.

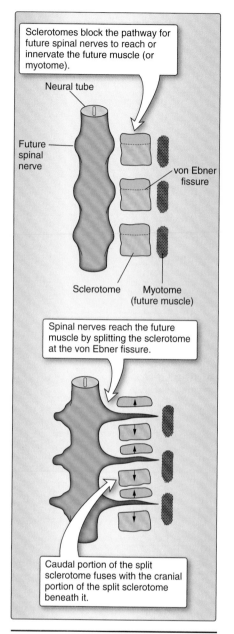

Figure 2.24
Resegmentation of the sclerotomes.

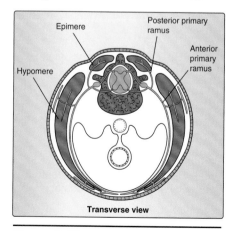

Figure 2.25
Development of the trunk musculature.

or **von Ebner fissure**. These fissures provide pathways for the developing spinal nerves to reach their respective myotomes. The caudal portion of each sclerotome fuses with the cranial portion of the sclerotome beneath it, resulting in the intersegmental position of the vertebrae. In the cervical region, the caudal portion of the fourth occipital sclerotome (O4) fuses with the cranial portion of the first cervical (C1) sclerotome to form the base of the occipital bone, allowing C1 spinal nerve to exit between the base of the occipital bone and C1 vertebrae.

b. **Dermamyotome:** The myotome portion of the dermamyotome forms **muscle**. The **trunk musculature** is derived from myotomes in the trunk region. Each myotome partitions into a posterior **epimere** and an anterior **hypomere** (Fig. 2.25).

[1] **Epimere:** This develops into the extensor muscles of the neck and vertebral column (e.g., erector spinae). The epimere is innervated by **posterior rami** of spinal nerves.

[2] **Hypomere:** This develops into the scalene, prevertebral, geniohyoid, infrahyoid, intercostal, and abdominal muscles; lateral and anterior flexors of the vertebral column; the quadratus lumborum; and the pelvic diaphragm. The hypomere is innervated by **anterior rami** of spinal nerves.

2. **Neural plate:** Neurulation begins when the **primitive node/notochord** induces the overlying ectoderm to form the **neural plate**, which is a thick plate of pseudostratified, columnar neuroepithelial cells called **neuroectoderm**. The neural plate is shaped with a broad cranial portion that gives rise to the brain and a narrow caudal portion that gives rise to the spinal cord.

3. **Neural tube:** The neural plate begins to fold during week 4 of development to form a closed **neural tube**. The closure of the neural tube begins at the future occipital/cervical region and then proceeds in both anterior and posterior directions. This closure continues until the most anterior end (i.e., the **anterior neuropore**) and the most posterior end (i.e., the **posterior neuropore**) close. If the anterior neuropore fails to close, upper neural tube defects occur (e.g., **anencephaly**). If the posterior neuropore fails to close, lower neural tube defects occur (e.g., **spina bifida with myeloschisis**). As the neural tube folds, some cells differentiate into **neural crest cells**. The lumen of the neural tube gives rise to the **ventricular system** of the brain and **central canal** of the spinal cord.

B. Special development zones

The early neural tube consists of neuroectoderm arranged in three zones called the **ventricular zone**, **intermediate zone**, and **marginal zone** (Fig. 2.26).

1. **Ventricular zone:** Two waves of proliferation/differentiation occur here. The first wave gives rise to **neuroblasts**, which migrate into the intermediate zone. The second wave gives rise to **glioblasts**, which migrate into the intermediate and marginal zones. The remaining neuroectoderm gives rise to the **ependymocytes** that line the central canal of the spinal cord.

2. **Intermediate zone:** After migration, the neuroblasts differentiate into **neurons**, and the glioblasts differentiate into **astrocytes** and

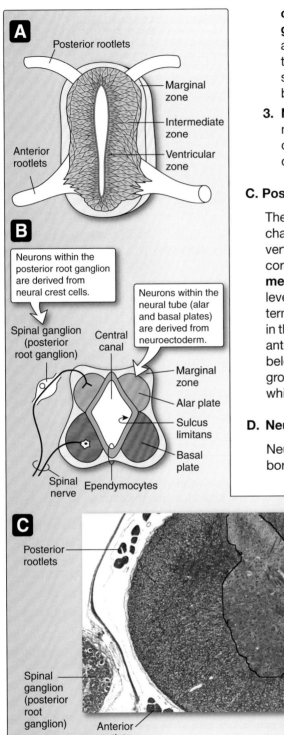

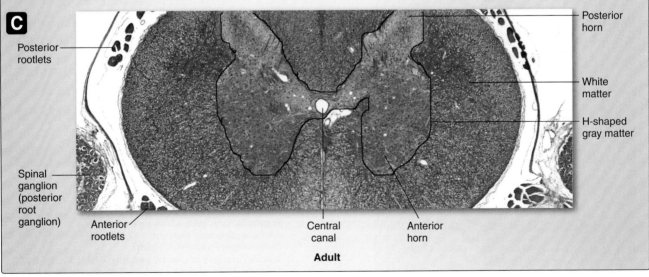

oligodendrocytes. The intermediate zone forms the H-shaped **gray matter** of the spinal cord, which is divided into the **alar plate** and the **basal plate**. The alar plate becomes the **posterior horn** of the spinal cord. The basal plate becomes the **anterior horn** of the spinal cord. Both the alar plate and the basal plate are separated by a longitudinal groove called the **sulcus limitans**.

3. **Marginal zone:** The marginal zone contains axons that arise from the neurons within the intermediate zone. In addition, the marginal zone contains glioblasts that differentiate into astrocytes and oligodendrocytes. The marginal zone forms the **white matter** of the spinal cord.

C. Positional changes

The position of the spinal cord in relationship to the vertebral column changes due to the disparate growth between the spinal cord and vertebral column (Fig. 2.27). At week 8 of development, the spinal cord extends the length of the vertebral canal. At birth, the **conus medullaris** (the tapered lower end of the spinal cord) extends to the level of the third lumbar vertebra (**L3**). In adults, the conus medullaris terminates at the **L1–L2 interspace**. The disparate growth also results in the formation of the **cauda equina** that consists of the posterior and anterior roots from L3 to coccygeal vertebral levels and that descends below the level of the conus medullaris. Additionally, this disparate growth results in the formation of the non-neural **filum terminale** (pia), which anchors the spinal cord inferiorly to the coccyx.

D. Neural crest cell formation

Neural crest cells differentiate from cells located along the lateral border of the neural plate, which is mediated by BMP-4 and BMP-7.

Figure 2.26
A and B, Further development of the neural tube. C, Posterior and anterior horns of the adult spinal cord.

This space allows for respiratory sounds to be heard clearly because of thinning of back musculature. Patient is asked to fold the arms across chest and flex forward to better reveal this space.

Testing trapezius function is a quick way to assess the integrity of cranial nerve (CN) XI (accessory). Ask the patient to shrug the shoulders and test muscle strength. Asymmetry indicates a potential lesion of CN XI.

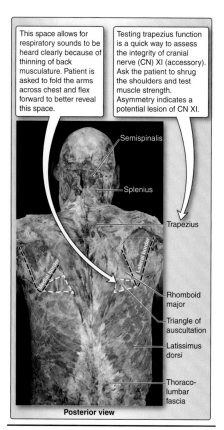

Posterior view

Figure 2.28
Back musculature.

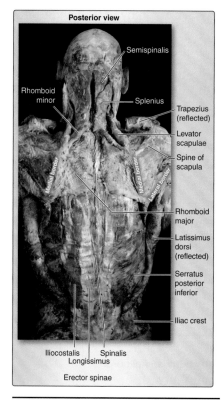

Posterior view

Figure 2.29
Superficial, intermediate, and deep back musculature (trapezius and latissimus dorsi reflected bilaterally).

When performing a lumbar puncture, the needle should be inserted below the level at which the spinal cord ends (conus medullaris).

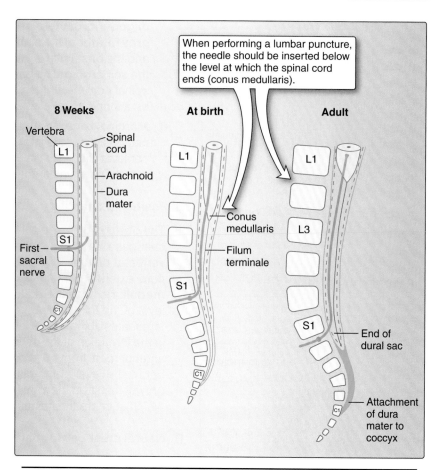

Figure 2.27
Positional changes of the spinal cord in relation to the vertebral column are shown at 8 weeks of development, at birth, and in the adult.

They can be generally divided into **cranial neural crest cells** and **trunk neural crest cells** based on their prolific migration throughout the embryo to both the cranial and trunk regions. Neural crest cells ultimately differentiate into a wide array of adult cells and structures, as indicated in Table 2.1.

Table 2.1: Adult Cells and Structures Formed From Neural Crest Cells

Neural Crest Cells	Adult Cells and Structures
Cranial region	**Pharyngeal arch, skeletal, and connective tissue components** *Bones of the neurocranium* *Pia and arachnoid* *Parafollicular C cells of the thyroid* *Aorticopulmonary septum* *Odontoblasts (dentin of teeth)* *Sensory ganglia of cranial nerves (CNs) V, VII, IX, and X* *Ciliary (CN III), pterygopalatine (CN VII), submandibular (CN VII), and otic (CN IX) parasympathetic ganglia*
Trunk region	**Melanocytes** *Schwann cells* *Chromaffin cells of adrenal medulla* *Posterior root ganglia* *Paravertebral sympathetic chain ganglia* *Prevertebral sympathetic ganglia* *Enteric parasympathetic ganglia of the gut (Meissner and Auerbach; CN X)* *Abdominal/pelvic cavity parasympathetic ganglia*

VI. MUSCULATURE

Back musculature can be divided into **intrinsic** and **extrinsic muscle groups**, based on developmental origin. Muscles of the back are further arranged into superficial, intermediate, and deep groups (Figs. 2.28 and 2.29). Extrinsic muscles are found in the superficial and intermediate groups and are innervated by anterior rami, while intrinsic muscles make up the deep group and are innervated by posterior rami. The exception to this is the trapezius, which is innervated by cranial nerve XI, the accessory nerve.

A. Superficial group

Superficial back muscles originate from the spine and insert onto the upper limb (see Chapter 7). This group comprises two layers: the first layer includes the **latissimus dorsi** and the **trapezius muscles**. The second layer includes the **rhomboid major** and **minor** and **levator scapulae muscles** (see Figs. 2.28 and 2.29).

B. Intermediate group

Intermediate back muscles function to assist respiration and proprioception and to receive segmental innervation (anterior rami) and vascularization. This group includes the serratus posterior superior and inferior muscles (see Fig. 2.29).

C. Deep group

Deep back muscles are native to the back, meaning during development, they originated posteriorly and remained in this position (Fig. 2.30; see also Fig. 2.29). This group is innervated by segmental posterior rami and function bilaterally to maintain an upright, extended spine and unilaterally to side-bend and rotate the spine. This group is further subdivided into superficial, intermediate, and deep layers.

1. **Superficial layer:** The V-shaped **splenius** (**cervicis** and **capitis**) **muscles** on the posterior neck resemble a bandage (Latin for *bandage*). They originate from the midline nuchal ligament and C7–T6 spinous processes and insert onto the mastoid process, superior nuchal line, and the cervical transverse processes (tubercle).

Clinical Application 2.10: Back Pain

Back pain, particularly low back pain, is one of the most common health complaints. Sources of low back pain include fibroskeletal (sprain), meningeal, synovial, muscular (strain), and nervous tissues. Common causes of low back pain include degenerative disc changes, poor posture, improper lifting technique, and abdominal muscle weakness/imbalance. Obtaining a thorough history of symptoms as well as a complete physical examination will help to create a focused differential diagnosis.

- **Sprains** in the spine involve ligament damage or damage at the osseoligament interface. Pain associated with sprains in the spine can be reproduced with end of range movements of the vertebral column.
- **Strains** involve overstretching or microtearing of back muscle fibers. Strains in the spine most often occur in the lumbar region, especially in postural muscles of the erector spinae group. Pain associated with strains in the spine is often caused by inflammation and subsequent muscle spasms, especially with movement. Spasms can lead to a physiologic muscle-holding pattern, which may cause spinal malalignment and increased pain. Most cases of low back pain are caused by a muscle strain.

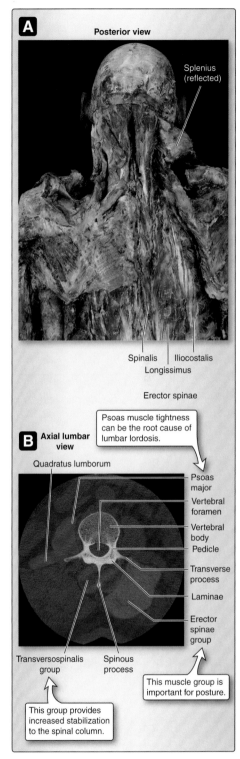

A Posterior view

Splenius (reflected)

Spinalis | Iliocostalis
Longissimus
Erector spinae

Psoas muscle tightness can be the root cause of lumbar lordosis.

B Axial lumbar view

Quadratus lumborum

Psoas major
Vertebral foramen
Vertebral body
Pedicle
Transverse process
Laminae
Erector spinae group

Transversospinalis group | Spinous process

This muscle group is important for posture.

This group provides increased stabilization to the spinal column.

Figure 2.30
A, Cervical and thoracic levels showing deeper dissection on the right sides of the cadaver (rhomboid major and minor are reflected on right side).
B, Lumbar level computed tomography (CT) scan showing intrinsic back muscle orientation.

2. **Intermediate layer: Erector spinae muscles** are a collection of three muscles that originate from a broad tendon arising from the posterior iliac crest, sacrum, sacroiliac and sacrospinous ligaments and lumbar and sacral spinous processes. They run superiorly along the vertebral column. Arranged medially to laterally, these muscles act as the primary extensor of the spine.

   a. **Spinalis (thoracis, cervicis, and capitis) muscles:** These insert onto spinous processes.

   b. **Longissimus (thoracis, cervicis, and capitis) muscles:** These insert onto ribs, transverse processes, and the mastoid process.

   c. **Iliocostalis (lumborum, thoracic, and cervicis) muscles:** These insert onto the angles of ribs and cervical transverse processes.

3. **Deep layer:** The **transversospinales muscle group** collectively originates from transverse processes and inserts onto spinous processes superiorly. Functionally, these muscles act as spinal stabilizers. This group includes the following muscles, progressing from superficial to deep.

   a. **Semispinalis (capitis) muscle:** This muscle spans five vertebral segments.

   b. **Multifidus muscle:** This muscle spans three vertebral segments.

   c. **Rotatores muscle:** This muscle spans one vertebral segment.

VII. JOINTS AND LIGAMENTS

Joints of the vertebral column include both **synovial** and **symphysis** type articulations (Fig. 2.31). Anteriorly, adjacent vertebral bodies are joined by interposed intervertebral discs (symphysis type), allowing for weight bearing and contributing to the strength of the spine.

A. Joints

Posteriorly, zygapophyseal joints (synovial type) occur between the articular processes bilaterally, and orientation of the articular facets dictates regional type and range of motion. Finally, craniovertebral joints join the base of the skull and cervical spine. These joints are further supported through a series of ligaments.

1. **Symphysis joints:** Anteriorly, adjacent vertebral bodies are joined by intervertebral discs. Intervertebral discs are present at all presacral levels except between the occiput, atlas (C1), and axis (C2). These joints are formed between the annulus fibrosus of the disc and a thin layer of hyaline cartilage on the articular surface of the vertebral body.

2. **Synovial joints:** Synovial plane joints are supported by an articular capsule and allow for gliding in different planes, depending on the spinal region. For example, in the cervical spine, these joints are oriented between the horizontal (transverse) and frontal (coronal) planes, allowing for a wide range of motion. Conversely, lumbar facet joints are oriented in the sagittal plane, allowing mainly spinal flexion and extension with minimal side-bending and rotation.

   a. **Zygapophyseal joints (facet joints):** Posteriorly, **zygapophyseal joints** occur between superior and inferior articular processes on either side of the vertebral arch of adjacent vertebrae.

   b. **Craniovertebral joints:** These include the **atlanto-occipital joint** between the **occipital condyles** and C1 (atlas) and the **atlantoaxial**

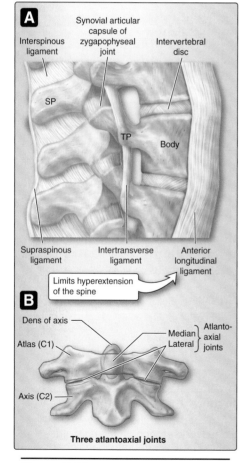

Figure 2.31
Zygapophyseal (facet) joints.
A, Lumbar region. B, Atlantoaxial joints.
SP = spinous process, TP = transverse process.

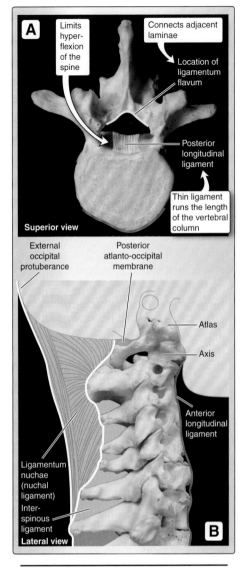

Figure 2.32
Vertebral ligaments. A, Lumbar spine. B, Cervical spine.

joint between C1 and C2 (axis). The atlanto-occipital joint permits head nodding (e.g., nodding "yes"), whereas the atlantoaxial joint allows for head rotation (e.g., "no" movement). Rotation at the atlantoaxial joint occurs around the axis of the dens of C2.

B. Ligaments

The vertebral column is supported by a series of ligaments that limit excessive spinal motion (Fig. 2.32). The **anterior longitudinal ligament** spans from the occipital tubercle to the sacrum over the anterior and lateral surfaces of vertebral bodies and discs. This ligament is wide and strong and prevents hyperextension of the spine. The **posterior longitudinal ligament** runs along the posterior surface of the vertebral bodies and discs from the axis to the sacrum and coccyx. This ligament is thin and provides little resistance to disc herniation, especially in the lumbar region. It prevents hyperextension.

1. **Posterior ligaments:** The **supraspinous ligament** runs over the tips of the spinous processes, connecting adjacent spines. In the cervical region, the supraspinous ligament is replaced by the **nuchal ligament**, which has higher elastic connective tissue content and forms a strong midline band of tissue that is easily palpated.

2. **Segmental ligaments:** These span between various vertebral structures and include the **interspinous** and **intertransverse ligaments**, between the spinous and transverse processes, respectively. The **ligamentum flavum** connects adjacent laminae, forming the posterior wall of the vertebral canal.

3. **Ligaments of the craniovertebral joints:** These include anterior and **posterior atlanto-occipital** and **tectorial membranes**, **alar ligaments**, and the **cruciate ligament (transverse ligament of atlas and longitudinal bands)**. The transverse ligament of the atlas is crucial in maintaining the atlantoaxial joint position and in keeping the dens of C2 from being driven posteriorly into the spinal cord or superiorly into the brainstem (see Fig. 2.3).

4. **Inferior ligaments:** A series of strong ligaments anchor the spine to the pelvis, including the **iliolumbar** and **sacroiliac ligaments**.

Chapter Summary

- Neurulation begins when the primitive node/notochord induces the overlying ectoderm to form the neural plate.

- The neural plate begins to fold during week 4 of development to form a closed neural tube.

- The early neural tube consists of neuroectoderm arranged in three zones called the ventricular, intermediate, and marginal zones.

- The position of the spinal cord in relationship to the vertebral column changes due to the disparate growth between the spinal cord and vertebral column.

- Neural crest cells differentiate from cells located along the lateral border of the neural plate and can be generally divided into two groups: cranial neural crest cells and trunk neural crest cells.

- During week 4 of development, the mesodermal cells from the sclerotome migrate and condense in three areas: around the notochord, around the neural tube, and into the lateral body wall.

- Trunk musculature is derived from myotomes in the trunk region. Each myotome partitions into a posterior epimere and an anterior hypomere.

- The adult vertebral column typically contains 33 vertebrae: 7 cervical, 12 thoracic, 5 lumbar, 5 sacral (fused), and 3–5 coccygeal (fused).

- Functionally, the vertebral column serves to protect the spinal cord and spinal nerves and support body weight superior to the pelvis. It also allows for varying degrees of motion and plays an integral part in posture and gait.

- The general arrangement of a vertebra is a weight-bearing body anteriorly, a vertebral (neural) arch and spinous process posteriorly, and transverse processes laterally. Articular processes project superiorly and inferiorly.

- Intervertebral discs consist of an outer annulus fibrosis and an inner nucleus pulposus. Collectively, these structures permit spinal movement and transmit loads across each vertebral segment, in addition to binding vertebral bodies together. Disc herniation typically occurs in the posterior or posterolateral direction.

- Deviation from the normal primary and secondary spinal curvatures can cause functional impairments. These deviations include kyphosis, lordosis, and scoliosis.

- The anterior and posterior longitudinal ligaments prevent hyperextension and hyperflexion of the spine, respectively. The transverse ligament of the atlas is crucial in maintaining the atlantoaxial joint position and in keeping the dens of C2 from being driven posteriorly into the spinal cord or superiorly into the brainstem.

- In adults, the spinal cord ends at the L2 level, and the dural sac ends at the S2 level. Therefore, lumbar puncture and spinal anesthesia procedures are typically performed just above or below L4 to avoid damage to the spinal cord.

- Spinal nerve roots combine to form a spinal nerve, which carries autonomic and somatic motor (general visceral efferent [GVE] and general somatic efferent [GSE]) and sensory (general visceral afferent [GVA] and general somatic afferent [GSA]) nerve fibers. Thirty-one paired spinal nerves exit the vertebral column through the intervertebral foramina or sacral foramina (8 cervical, 12 thoracic, 5 lumbar, 5 sacral, and 1 coccygeal).

- Spinal meninges include the dura mater, arachnoid mater, and pia mater, which collectively surround, support, and protect the spinal cord and spinal nerve roots. Cerebrospinal fluid (CSF) is located in the subarachnoid space.

- Arterial supply to the spinal cord is meager. Injury to the great anterior segmental medullary artery (artery of Adamkiewicz) can eliminate blood supply to the inferior two thirds of the spinal cord and cause paralysis (paraplegia).

- Extrinsic back muscles are found in the superficial and intermediate groups and are innervated by anterior rami, while intrinsic muscles (erector spinae and transversospinales groups) make up the deep group and are innervated by posterior rami.

- Back pain is one of the most common health problems. Common causes of low back pain include degenerative disc changes, poor posture, improper lifting technique, and abdominal muscle weakness/imbalance.

Study Questions:

Choose the ONE correct answer.

2.1 Which of the following structures is derived from neural crest cells?

    A. Sclerotome

    B. Posterior root ganglia

    C. Dermamyotome

    D. Somites

    E. Somitomeres

Correct answer = B. Neural crest cells differentiate from cells located along the lateral border of the neural plate and migrate throughout the embryo. The paraxial mesoderm on either side of the neural tube gives rise to the somitomeres, which later condense to form somites. The somites then differentiate into the sclerotome and dermamyotome.

2.2 A 1-week newborn female is admitted with fever, vomiting, drowsiness, and pale, blotchy skin. Upon physical inspection, you also observe rapid, labored breathing and abnormal grunting sounds. You suspect meningitis and order a lumbar puncture to collect cerebrospinal fluid. During the procedure, you take into account the length of the spinal cord at birth. Which of the following vertebral levels denotes the location of the conus medullaris in this newborn?

    A. L1

    B. L2

    C. L3

    D. T12

    E. S1

Correct answer = C. At birth, the tapered lower end of the spinal cord called the conus medullaris reaches to L3. At week 8 of development, the spinal cord extends the entire length of the vertebral canal. In the adult, the conus medullaris terminates at the L1–L2 interspace.

The following clinical scenario corresponds to Questions 2.3 and 2.4.

A 55-year-old male patient presents to a clinic with complaints of low back pain that is localized to the lumbar region to the right of the median furrow. He does not complain of any numbness or tingling into his lower limbs. The patient explains that he has been helping his mother move over the past week and thinks he may have strained his back. You palpate just lateral to his lumbar spinous processes and note tenderness, swelling, and warmth on the right side more than the left. Upon visual inspection, you notice that he is carrying a significant amount of weight anteriorly in his abdomen, and his lumbar curvature is accentuated.

2.3 What is the clinical term for this patient's accentuated lumbar curvature?

    A. Kyphosis

    B. Scoliosis

    C. Lordosis

    D. Spondylosis

    E. Spondylolisthesis

Correct answer = C. Lumbar curvature is concave posteriorly. People who carry excess weight anteriorly (e.g., in obesity or late-term pregnancy), they may present with an increased lumbar curvature, termed lumbar lordosis.

2.4 Sensory input from the skin overlying the back musculature is mediated through which of the following nerves/ nerve structures?

    A. Anterior root

    B. Anterior ramus

    C. Sympathetic trunk

    D. Posterior root

    E. Lateral horn of the spinal cord

Correct answer = D. Sensory receptors in the skin send impulses proximally through the posterior primary ramus, spinal nerve, and posterior root before entering the posterior horn of the spinal cord. These pseudounipolar neurons have a peripheral and central process, and their cell bodies are housed within the posterior root ganglion.

The following clinical scenario corresponds to Questions 2.5 and 2.6.

A 22-year-old male patient is admitted to the emergency department after sustaining injuries from diving head-first into shallow water. A computed tomography (CT) scan is ordered to assess possible cervical spine and traumatic head injuries, and it clearly shows fractures of the anterior arch of C1.

2.5 Which of the following spinal ligaments is most likely damaged in this patient?

A. Interspinous ligament
B. Supraspinous ligament
C. Ligamentum flavum
D. Transverse ligament
E. Denticulate ligament

Correct answer = D. The transverse ligament of the atlas helps maintain the position of the dens on the inner surface of the anterior arch of C1 (atlas). A bilateral fracture through the anterior arch of C1 would most likely injure this ligament.

2.6 What is the clinical name for this type of fracture?

A. Jefferson fracture
B. Spondylolisthesis
C. Tear drop fracture
D. Hangman fracture
E. Chance fracture

Correct answer = A. A Jefferson fracture is a burst fracture of the C1 vertebra with at least two points of fracture. It is often associated with headfirst diving into shallow water.

2.7 A 36-year-old full-term pregnant patient is admitted into the hospital in active labor. While she is in triage being monitored, her baby is discovered to be in distress, necessitating a cesarean delivery. She is taken to the operating room where she is met by the anesthesiologist, who will be performing a spinal epidural. What bony landmark would the anesthesiologist use to find the appropriate entry level for the spinal epidural?

A. Anterior superior iliac spine
B. Iliac crests
C. Posterior superior iliac spine
D. Twelfth rib
E. Ischial spine

Correct answer = B. The adult spinal cord terminates at approximately the L2 vertebral level. The iliac crests represent the L4 level, well below the conus medullaris. Accessing the epidural space below L2 limits any chance of accidental injury to the spinal cord.

2.8 A 75-year-old male is being seen for cervical spinal stenosis. Additionally, CT scan of his spine revealed spondylolisthesis of C4 on C5, likely due to age and degeneration. The orientation of the articular facets in this region is also a contributing factor to the spondylolisthesis. Which of the following statements best describes the facet orientation in the cervical spine?

A. In the frontal plane
B. In the horizontal plane
C. Oblique plane between sagittal and frontal
D. In the sagittal plane
E. In the coronal plane

Correct answer = B. Each vertebral region is characterized by the orientation of their facets. In the cervical region, facets are primarily oriented in the horizontal plane, which makes vertebral dislocation much more common in this region, as opposed to the thoracic and lumbar regions. Facet orientation also dictates the type and amount of movement that will occur in that region.

Thorax

3

I. OVERVIEW

The thorax represents the axial region that extends between the neck and the muscular diaphragm. It is characterized by a bony, expandable cage that protects important cardiopulmonary and gastrointestinal (GI) viscera while permitting respiratory movements. The bony thoracic cage is made up of paired ribs (12) that primarily connect the thoracic vertebrae posteriorly with the sternum anteriorly. The thoracic cavity contains the heart, lungs, esophagus, and other associated structures. These contents are organized into three main regions: right and left pulmonary cavities and a midline mediastinum. While some structures are self-contained in the thoracic cavity, others pass through the thorax from the neck to reach the abdominal cavity.

II. THORACIC WALL

The thoracic wall is semi-rigid in its construction, allowing for movement of the ribs with respiration, while also creating a protective cage for thoracic viscera. The inner surface of the wall is lined with a serous parietal pleural layer, which, along with a visceral layer, creates two pleural cavities within the thoracic cage.

A. Osteology

The thoracic cage is formed by a combination of bony and cartilaginous structures, including the sternum, 12 pairs of ribs and costal cartilages, and thoracic vertebrae 1–12 with associated intervertebral discs (Fig. 3.1).

1. **Sternum:** From superior to inferior, the three parts of the sternum are the **manubrium**, **body**, and **xiphoid process**. The manubrium articulates laterally with the clavicle (sternoclavicular joint) and first costal cartilage and inferiorly with the body. The junction between the manubrium and body is a palpable landmark known as the **sternal angle** (of Louis) (Fig. 3.2).

> The **sternal angle** is a reliable landmark in the thorax. An imaginary line drawn posteriorly from the sternal angle through the intervertebral disc between T4 and T5 divides the central thorax into superior and inferior mediastinal regions.

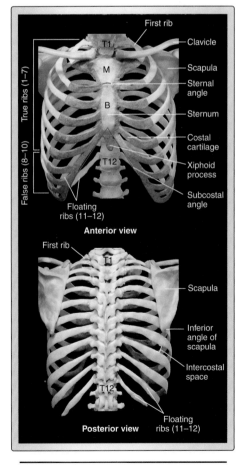

Figure 3.1
Thoracic cage, bony and cartilaginous components. B = body of sternum, M = manubrium of sternum.

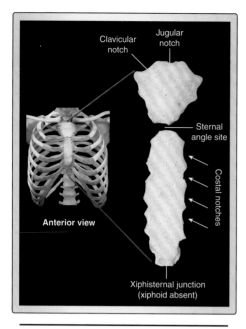

Figure 3.2
Sternum.

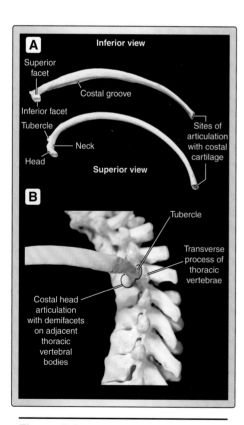

Figure 3.3
General rib features. A, Rib parts. B,
Costal articulation at thoracic spine.

2. **Ribs:** Ribs are classified as true (1st–7th), false (8th–10th), or floating (11th–12th), based on direct, indirect, or no articulation by costal cartilage to the sternum, respectively. Floating ribs have no connection to the sternum, as they terminate in the abdominal wall musculature. General rib features include the following (Fig. 3.3):

   a. **Head:** The head articulates with demifacets on the bodies of adjacent thoracic vertebrae. The inferior head facet articulates with the vertebrae that correspond to the rib numerically.

   b. **Neck:** The neck connects head to tubercle region and is not present in 11th–12th ribs.

   c. **Tubercle:** At the transition between neck and body, the tubercle articulates with the corresponding thoracic transverse process and serves as an attachment site for ligamentous support.

   d. **Body:** This thin, flat, long portion of the rib is marked by the **costal angle** laterally and an internal **costal groove** that contains intercostal neurovascular bundle. The distal, anterior end of body articulates with costal cartilages, which, in turn, articulate with the sternum.

> An **accessory cervical rib** (1% of population) may articulate with the C7 vertebra and potentially contribute to thoracic outlet syndrome, in which pressure is placed on the subclavian artery or lower brachial plexus trunk or both. Symptoms include numbness, tingling in C_7–C_8 nerve root distribution, pain, and temperature changes in the upper limb.

3. **Thoracic vertebrae:** Twelve thoracic vertebrae contribute to the posterior boundary of the thoracic cage (see Fig. 3.3). Thoracic processes serve as attachment sites for ligamentous, muscular, capsular, and costal structures. For a more detailed description of thoracic vertebrae anatomy and clinical considerations, refer to Chapter 2.

4. **Thoracic apertures:** Thoracic apertures mark the superior and inferior boundaries of the thoracic cage. The small, kidney-shaped **superior thoracic aperture** (thoracic inlet) is bound by the manubrium (anteriorly), 1st rib pair (laterally), and T1 vertebral body (posteriorly). It allows for structural continuity between the neck and thorax. The large, irregularly shaped **inferior thoracic aperture** is bound by the xiphoid process (anteriorly), costal arch and 12th rib pairs (laterally), and T12 vertebral body (posteriorly). While the muscular diaphragm closes off the inferior thoracic aperture, openings within the diaphragm allow for communication of structures between the thorax and abdomen (Fig. 3.4).

5. **Movement:** Respiration requires that the thoracic cage be able to expand (increase volume) and retract (decrease volume) to facilitate

Clinical Application 3.1: Rib Fracture

Fracture of the rib typically occurs at the costal angle as a result of crushing or traumatic injury. Visceral pleura and lungs are at risk of injury from exposed fractured rib end, which can result in pneumothorax (see Clinical Application 3.9). If indicated, surgical intervention (rib plating) involves stabilizing fractures with hardware to limit deformity and improve respiratory function

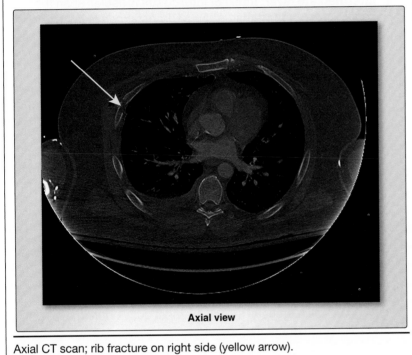

Axial view

Axial CT scan; rib fracture on right side (yellow arrow).

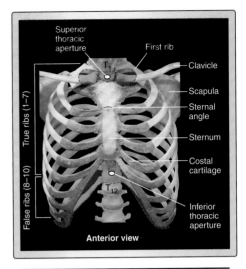

Figure 3.4
Thoracic apertures.

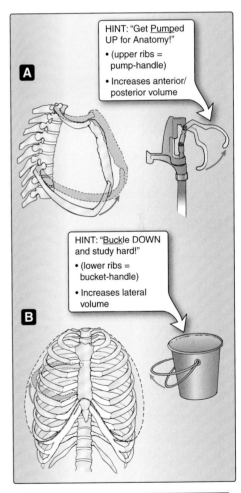

Figure 3.5
Thoracic cage movements. A, Pump-handle movement. B, Bucket-handle movement.

inspiration and expiration, respectively. Articulations between the vertebrae, ribs, costal cartilages, and sternum, in conjunction with contraction and relaxation of the muscular diaphragm, allow for thoracic cage movement and volume changes in three planes (Fig. 3.5).

a. **Anterior/posterior plane:** Analogous to a water pump handle, anterior/posterior volume changes involve the upward rotational movement of ribs 1–6 and anterior movement of the sternum.

b. **Lateral plane:** Like a bucket handle, lateral volume changes involve elevation of the lower ribs, where the lateral portions swing superolaterally.

c. **Superior/inferior plane:** Superior/inferior volume changes involve contraction and relaxation of the muscular diaphragm, in which contraction flattens the muscle to increase volume and relaxation resumes its dome-shaped appearance.

B. Musculature

The intrinsic muscles of the thoracic wall assist in respiration and are arranged in three layers—superficial, intermediate, and deep. These

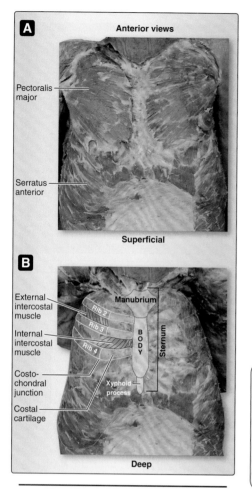

Figure 3.6
Anterior thoracic wall musculature.
Cadaveric specimens. (Pectoralis major,
pectoralis minor, and serratus anterior
muscles reflected bilaterally in B).

muscles receive innervation and blood supply from corresponding intercostal nerves (thoracic anterior rami), arteries, and veins (Fig. 3.6).

1. **Superficial layer: External intercostal muscles** span the intercostal space from the tubercle to the costochondral junctions, running in an inferomedial direction from superior to inferior ribs. The muscle is replaced anteriorly by external intercostal membranes along the costal cartilage to the sternum.

2. **Intermediate layer: Internal intercostal muscles** span the intercostal space from the sternum and costal cartilages posteriorly to the angle of the ribs, running in an inferolateral direction from superior to inferior ribs. The muscle is replaced posteriorly by internal intercostal membranes.

3. **Deep layer: Innermost intercostal** and **transversus thoracis muscles** represent this incomplete layer. Innermost intercostal muscles are most developed posterolaterally and may span one or two intercostal spaces. Those muscles spanning two intercostal spaces are called **subcostal muscles**. Transversus thoracis muscles consist of four to five paired slips of muscle that attach between the posterior surface of the inferior sternum to superior costal cartilages.

> **A general rule for main intercostal muscle function is that it is opposite of muscle name!**
> External intercostal muscles—most active during inspiration (remember EX-IN).
> Internal intercostal muscles—most active during expiration (remember IN-EX).

4. **Diaphragm:** Although not an intrinsic muscle of the thoracic wall, the **diaphragm** is the most important respiratory muscle. This dome-shaped muscle arises from the costal margins of the inferior thoracic aperture and upper lumbar vertebrae. The strong central tendon of the diaphragm serves as a common insertion point for the peripheral fibers. With inspiration, the diaphragm flattens and then assumes its relaxed dome shape during expiration. The diaphragm has three posterior openings to allow for passage of the inferior vena cava (IVC), esophagus, and aorta at vertebral levels T8, T10, and T12, respectively.

> **An easy way to remember the vertebral levels: "I Eat Apples at 8, 10, and 12."**
> I = inferior vena cava, E = esophagus, A = aorta.

5. **Accessory respiratory muscles:** Muscles that contribute to the thoracic wall and aid respiratory function include serratus posterior superior, serratus posterior inferior, and levator costarum. These muscles may also play an important role in proprioception of the thoracic cage.

6. **Axioappendicular, neck, and abdominal muscles:** Muscles that have attachments to the ribs, sternum, and costal cartilages also contribute to the structure and stability of the thoracic cage. These muscles include pectoralis major, pectoralis minor, subclavius, scalenes, serratus anterior, external abdominal oblique, internal abdominal oblique, transversus abdominis, and rectus abdominis. These muscles are detailed in Chapters 4, 7, and 9.

C. Innervation

Thoracic spinal nerves 1–11 give rise to 11 paired thoracic anterior rami known as **intercostal nerves**. The T_{12} anterior rami pair travel inferior to the 12th rib and are known as **subcostal nerves**. At the angle of the rib, a typical intercostal nerve travels between the innermost and internal intercostal muscles along the costal groove with intercostal veins and arteries. The arrangement of the intercostal neurovascular bundle is such that, from superior to inferior, their order is vein, artery, and nerve (mnemonic = VAN) (Fig. 3.7).

1. **Intercostal nerves:** These nerves provide innervation to the skin and muscle of the thoracic wall. Along their course, intercostal nerves give off **lateral** and **anterior cutaneous branches** to the areas of skin that correspond to thoracic dermatomes T_1–T_{11}. As a result of upper limb development, T_1 and T_2 spinal nerve dermatome distribution is also found along the medial arm and forearm.

2. **Muscular and sensory branches:** Muscular branches arise along the course of the intercostal nerves to innervate the muscles of the thoracic wall. Sensory branches also arise to mediate sensation from peripheral portions of the diaphragm and diaphragmatic and costal pleura. The diaphragm receives motor innervation from the **phrenic nerve** (C_3–C_5).

⏸ C_3, C_4, C_5 keep the diaphragm alive!

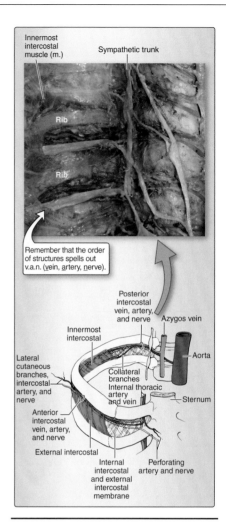

Remember that the order of structures spells out v.a.n. (vein, artery, nerve).

Figure 3.7
Intercostal neuromuscular bundle. Intercostal space showing bundle distribution (bottom). Posterior thoracic wall showing bundle orientation and path (top).

Clinical Application 3.2: Accessing the Intercostal Space

During procedures like thoracentesis and intercostal nerve blocks, care must be taken to avoid damaging the main neurovascular bundle (in costal groove) and smaller collateral bundle within the intercostal space. For thoracentesis (removal of fluid from pleural cavity), needle placement should occur just superior to the superior rib border and extend into the costodiaphragmatic recess in the pleural cavity. For complete anesthesia, multiple injections between the intermediate and deep intercostal muscle layers may be warranted for intercostal nerve blocks, as adjacent dermatomes tend to overlap in the thoracic region.

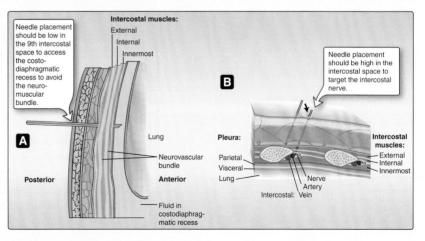

Accessing the intercostal space. A, Needle placement for thoracentesis (patient upright). B, Needle placements for intercostal nerve block (patient supine).

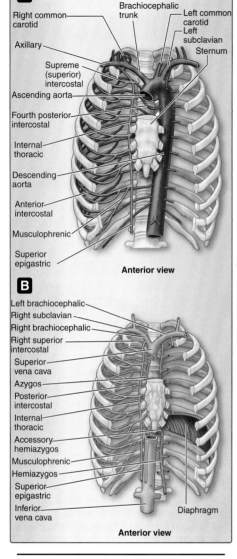

A

Right common carotid
Brachiocephalic trunk
Left common carotid
Left subclavian
Axillary
Sternum
Supreme (superior) intercostal
Ascending aorta
Fourth posterior intercostal
Internal thoracic
Descending aorta
Anterior intercostal
Musculophrenic
Superior epigastric

Anterior view

B

Left brachiocephalic
Right subclavian
Right brachiocephalic
Right superior intercostal
Superior vena cava
Azygos
Posterior intercostal
Internal thoracic
Accessory hemiazygos
Musculophrenic
Hemiazygos
Superior epigastric
Inferior vena cava
Diaphragm

Anterior view

Figure 3.8
Intercostal blood supply. A, Arterial distribution. B, Venous distribution.

D. Vasculature

Intercostal arteries arise primarily from either the thoracic aorta as posterior intercostal arteries or the **internal thoracic** (internal mammary) arteries as anterior intercostal arteries. Posterior and anterior intercostal arteries anastomose with each other. Each of the 11 intercostal spaces receives blood supply from posterior and anterior intercostal arteries and collateral branches that arise from posterior intercostal arteries. The **subcostal arteries** supply a small area inferior to the 12th rib (Fig. 3.8). Eleven pairs of posterior and anterior **intercostal veins** drain the thoracic wall primarily by way of the azygos venous system or internal thoracic veins, respectively. **Subcostal veins** drain a small area inferior to the 12th rib.

III. BREAST

The most prominent surface feature of the anterior thorax is the **breast**. Both males and females have breasts, although breast development and function differ between the sexes.

A. Embryology

During week 4, a pair of epidermal (ectoderm) thickenings called the **mammary ridges** form on both sides of the embryo. The mammary ridges extend from the axilla to the inguinal region. The mammary ridges normally disappear below the axilla in humans. During week 7, the mammary ridge at the site of the future breast forms a **primary bud**, which invaginates into the underlying dermis (mesoderm). During week 10, the primary bud branches into several **secondary buds**. The secondary buds will lengthen and branch throughout the remainder of gestation and eventually canalize to form **15–25 lactiferous ducts**. At birth, the mammary gland consists of 15–25 rudimentary lactiferous ducts that open into a small surface depression called the **mammary pit**. The mammary pit is converted to an everted nipple as the underlying dermis (mesoderm) proliferates within a few weeks after birth. The skin surrounding the nipple forms the **areola** (Fig. 3.9).

The Tanner stages of breast development are guidelines in assessing whether a female adolescent is developing normally:

Stage I: Breasts have papillae elevations only.
Stage II: Breasts have palpable buds and the areolae enlarge.
Stage III: Breasts show elevation of contours and the areolae enlarge.
Stage IV: Breasts form secondary areolar mounds.
Stage V: Breasts show an adult breast contour, the areolae recess to the general contour of the breast, and the nipples project.

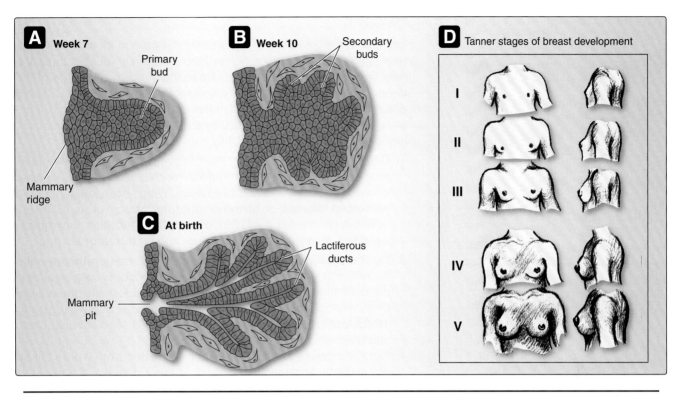

Figure 3.9
Embryology of breast. A, Week 7. B, Week 10. C, At birth. D, Tanner stages of breast development.

B. Anatomy

Although present in both males and females, breasts are more prominent in females as they contain well-developed **mammary glands** and variable amounts of adipose tissue.

1. **Mammary glands:** These are arranged into **lobules** (15–25) within the female breast. Lobules are supported by **suspensory ligaments** (Cooper's ligaments) that anchor into the overlying dermis. Mammary glands in men are nonfunctional. The female breast is in the superficial fascia of the chest, typically between the 2nd and 6th intercostal spaces, overlying the deep pectoral fascia and pectoralis major and minor muscles (Fig. 3.10).

2. **External features:** These include the **nipple** and **areola**. The nipple is surrounded by the pigmented circular areola and can vary in size and prominence. The male nipple serves as a reliable landmark for the 4th intercostal space. However, due to the varying amounts of adipose in the female breast, the nipple is not a reliable surface landmark. Rather, the **inferior mammillary fold** (inferior cutaneous crease) is often used to locate the 6th intercostal space in the female.

> The nipple may occasionally remain depressed (called an **inverted nipple**).
> Supernumerary nipples (called **polythelia**) or supernumerary breasts (called **polymastia**) may form along the line of the mammary ridge.

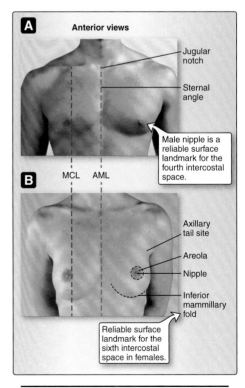

Figure 3.10
Breast. A, Male. B, Female.
AML = anterior median line,
MCL = midclavicular line.

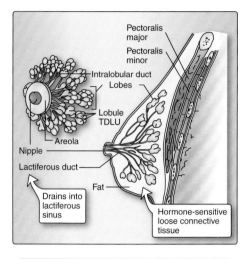

Figure 3.11
Organization of mammary gland.
TDLU = Terminal ductule lobular unit.

C. Histology

The mammary gland within the breast is a compound, tubuloalveolar gland that develops as downgrowths of the skin epidermis along the **milk line**, which runs from the axilla to the groin on each side of the torso. The mammary gland remains **inactive** until pregnancy, during which time the mammary gland matures functionally and morphologically. This maturation is controlled by estrogen, progesterone, prolactin, and placental lactogen (Fig. 3.11).

1. **Composition:** The mammary gland is composed of **15–25 irregular-shaped lobes** that are separated from each other by dense, irregular connective tissue and adipose tissue. Within each lobe, there are numerous **lobules** or **terminal ductule lobular units (TDLUs)**. A TDLU comprises a **cluster of terminal ductules, hormone-sensitive loose connective tissue**, and an **intralobular duct**.

2. **Ductal system:** The alveoli surrounded by **myoepithelial cells** secrete milk, which empties into **intralobular ducts** lined by simple cuboidal epithelium and then into larger **interlobular ducts** lined by simple columnar epithelium. The interlobular ducts merge into **15–25 lactiferous sinuses** lined by stratified cuboidal epithelium and then into **15–25 lactiferous ducts** lined by keratinized stratified squamous epithelium. The lactiferous ducts open onto the tip of the nipple arranged in a ring.

3. **Stages:** At birth, the mammary gland consists of 15–25 rudimentary lactiferous ducts that open into a small surface depression called the **mammary pit**. The mammary gland remains relatively inactive until puberty, when the female progresses through basically four stages (Fig. 3.12).

   a. **Puberty stage:** During puberty, the duct system comprises a modest network of ducts that branch into the connective tissue and end with a **terminal end bud**. The terminal end bud is a mass of epithelial cells (i.e., no lumen).

   b. **Virgin adult stage:** The duct system now comprises a fairly advanced network of branching ducts that have grown in length and end in a **cluster of terminal ductules**.

   c. **Pregnancy stage:** During pregnancy, a prolific network of branching ducts have grown and elongated. This proliferation of the duct system takes place at the expense of the connective tissue and adipose tissue in the breast, which concurrently decreases during pregnancy (Figure 3.13). Eventually, the characteristic structure of the mammary gland takes shape, comprising **numerous lobules** or **TDLUs, interlobular ducts, lactiferous sinuses**, and **lactiferous ducts**.

      [1] **Alveoli:** In addition, the terminal ductules differentiate and form secretory **alveoli** that are surrounded by **myoepithelial cells**.

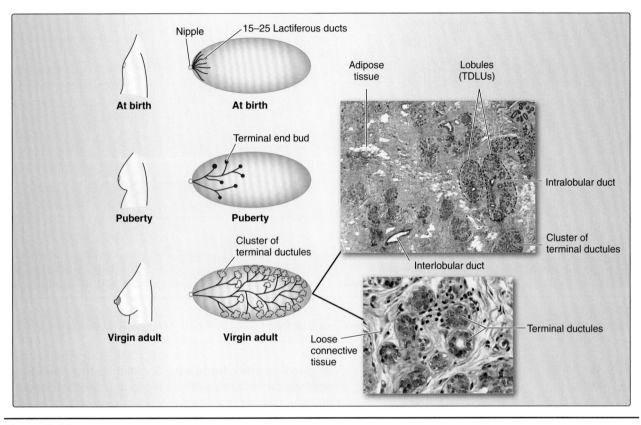

Figure 3.12
Histology of breast and mammary gland stages, birth through virgin adult. TDLUs = terminal ductule lobular units.

[2] **Colostrum:** The ducts and alveoli distend as alveoli secrete **colostrum**. Plasma cells, lymphocytes, and eosinophils infiltrate the connective tissue at this time.

d. **Lactation stage:** Because the alveoli become active in **milk production** and **milk secretion** at this stage, their lumina become filled with milk. Numerous lipid droplets and secretory granules containing dense aggregates of milk proteins can be observed ultrastructurally at the apical end of the alveolar epithelial cells. Human breast milk is produced 1–3 days after childbirth.

[1] **Breast milk contents:** Breast milk contains a substantial amount of lipid, protein, lactose, vitamins, and secretory immunoglobulin A (which affords temporary enteric passive immunity).

[2] **Milk letdown:** Although milk is produced continuously by the alveoli (milk production), it is delivered only in response

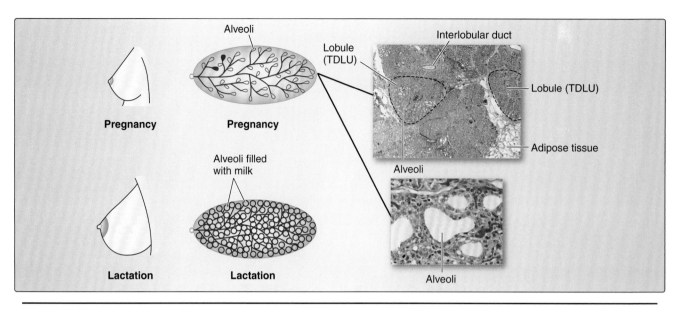

Figure 3.13
Histology of breast and mammary gland stages, pregnancy, and lactation. TDLUs = terminal ductule lobular units.

to suckling (**milk letdown**). Suckling stimulates afferent neurons that relay the information to the hypothalamus such that the following actions occur: 1) **oxytocin** is released from the neurohypophysis, which causes the contraction of myoepithelial cells and milk letdown, and 2) **prolactin-inhibiting hormone** (**dopamine**) is inhibited, which causes the release of **prolactin** from the adenohypophysis and further milk production.

D. Vasculature

The breast receives arterial blood supply primarily from branches of the internal thoracic (medial mammary branches), lateral thoracic (lateral mammary branches), thoracoacromial (pectoral branches), and anterior intercostal (perforating branches) arteries. Venous drainage of the breast occurs mainly through tributaries of the axillary artery, with minimal drainage into the internal thoracic veins.

E. Lymphatics

Lymphatic drainage of the breast is very important to understand in the context of breast cancer metastasis. A network of lymphatic vessels drains the glandular tissue first into a delicate **subareolar plexus**, just deep to the nipple. The subareolar plexus is continuous with the **circumareolar plexus**, which communicates with the contralateral breast. Approximately 75% of lymph drainage travels laterally toward the axillary lymph nodes, particularly the pectoral group of nodes. Lymph then travels proximally toward the subclavicular nodes and eventually into the right or left lymphatic duct. Approximately 25% of lymph drainage occurs medially by way of the **parasternal nodes** along the lateral borders of the sternum. These nodes also communicate to contralateral nodes, which may allow for metastasis from one breast to the other (Fig. 3.14).

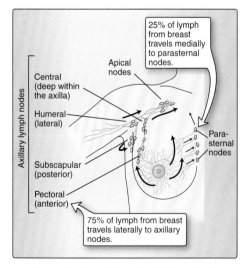

Figure 3.14
Breast lymphatic drainage. Black arrows indicate direction of flow.

Clinical Application 3.3: Breast Carcinoma (Cancer)

Carcinoma of the breast typically arises from the epithelial cells of the mammary gland lactiferous ductal system (adenocarcinomas). This type of cancer is malignant and can metastasize through the lymphatic system (most common), venous system, and by direct invasion of adjacent tissue. Lymphatic metastasis typically occurs through axillary lymph nodes, which drain 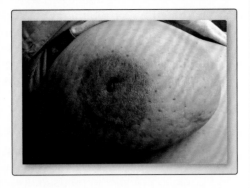 ~75% of lymph from the breast. Breast cancer most often metastasizes to bone, lungs, brain, or liver. Common signs of breast cancer include acute asymmetry, skin dimpling, pitting edema (peau d'orange sign), abnormal breast contours, nipple inversion, redness, nipple discharge (blood; milk when not pregnant/breastfeeding), and palpable mass in breast or axilla. Mammography—radiographic examination of breast tissue—is often used to detect abnormal masses in the breast. If cancer is suspected, a biopsy may be performed to determine whether cancer is present and to what extent. Treatment may include radiation, chemotherapy, and mastectomy, which involves surgical excision of affected tissue. Traditionally, a radical mastectomy involved removal of the pectoral muscles, fascia, adipose, breast tissue, and adjacent lymph nodes. Current practice attempts to spare surrounding tissue and target only the tumor and any additional affected tissue. Care should be taken during a mastectomy to avoid damaging the long thoracic nerve, which runs along the lateral border of the breast in the midaxillary line. Damage to the long thoracic nerve causes ipsilateral winging of the scapula due to paralysis of serratus anterior muscle.

Classic clinical features of inflammatory breast cancer: erythema, edema (peau d'orange), enlargement.

F. Surface anatomy

Palpation of important surface landmarks in the thorax is often warranted during a thorough physical assessment. In addition, imaginary directional lines allow for consistent and reliable anatomical description in the thorax (Fig. 3.15).

1. **Bony landmarks:** Important bony landmarks include the following.

   a. **Sternoclavicular joint:** This is used to assess musculoskeletal impairment.

   b. **Jugular (suprasternal) notch:** This is used to assess aortic pathology.

   c. **Sternal angle:** This is a demarcation between superior and inferior mediastinal regions.

   d. **Xyphoid process:** The T_6 dermatome overlies this process.

   e. **Costal margin:** This is used to assess for hepatomegaly (liver enlargement).

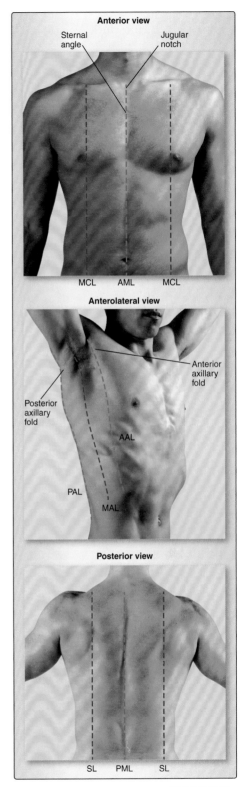

Figure 3.15

Thoracic surface anatomy. AAL = anterior axillary line, AML = anterior median line, MAL = midaxillary line, MCL = midclavicular line, PAL = posterior axillary line, PML = posterior median line, SL = scapular line.

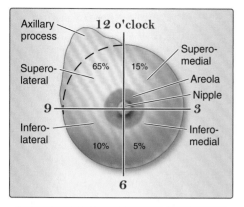

Figure 3.16
Breast quadrants. Percentages indicate incidence of pathology in each quadrant.

2. **Directional lines:** These include the anterior midsternal lines; clavicular lines (bilateral); anterior, mid-, and posterior axillary lines; and the posterior median line (see Fig. 3.15).

3. **Quadrants:** For examination and diagnostic purposes, the breast is divided into four quadrants: **superior lateral** (with axillary process), **superior medial**, **inferior lateral**, and **inferior medial**. Imaginary vertical (12 o'clock–6 o'clock) and horizontal (9 o'clock–3 o'clock) lines are drawn through the middle of the nipple (Fig. 3.16).

> A systematic approach to palpation of the breast should be taken to ensure a thorough assessment. The pads of digits 2–4 should be used, keeping fingers flat and applying enough pressure to assess various levels of depth. Always remember to include the axillary process. Two common methods are:
> **Spiral method**: Palpate outwardly from nipple using concentric circles.
> **Vertical strips method**: Palpate medial to lateral in a superior/inferior strip pattern.

IV. THORACIC CAVITY

The thoracic cavity is encased by the thoracic walls and houses thoracic viscera (lungs, heart, esophagus, and trachea) and associated neurovascular structures. The space can be divided into two independent pleural cavities and a centralized mediastinum. Within the mediastinum is the pericardial cavity, which contains the heart and roots of the great vessels. The thoracic cavity is partitioned off from the abdominal cavity by the muscular diaphragm.

A. Embryology

The **intraembryonic coelom** is a single continuous cavity that forms when spaces coalesce within the lateral mesoderm and form a horseshoe-shaped space that opens into the chorionic cavity (extraembryonic coelom) on the right and left sides. The intraembryonic coelom provides the needed room for the growth of various organs in the thorax and abdomen. The intraembryonic coelom gets partitioned during development into the definitive adult body cavities called the **pleural cavity, pericardial cavity**, and **peritoneal cavity** (Fig. 3.17). How does the embryo divide one continuous cavity (i.e., the intraembryonic coelom) into three separate adult cavities (i.e., pleural, pericardial, and peritoneal)? The answer is that the embryo forms two partitions called the paired **pleuropericardial membranes** and the **diaphragm**.

1. **Paired pleuropericardial membranes:** These sheets of somatic mesoderm separate the pericardial cavity from the pleural cavities. These membranes develop into the definitive **fibrous pericardium** surrounding the heart.

The diaphragm undergoes positional changes during development. During week 4, the developing diaphragm becomes innervated by the **phrenic nerves**, which originate from C_3, C_4, and C_5 and pass through the pleuropericardial membranes. This explains the definitive location of the phrenic nerves associated with the fibrous pericardium.

2. **Diaphragm:** The diaphragm separates the pleural cavities from the peritoneal cavity.

   a. **Position:** By week 8, an apparent **descent of the diaphragm to L1** occurs because of the rapid growth of the neural tube. The phrenic nerves are carried along with the "descending diaphragm," which explains their unusually long length in the adult.

   b. **Formation:** The diaphragm is formed through the fusion of tissue from four different sources.

      [1] **Septum transversum:** This thick mass of mesoderm is located between the primitive heart tube and the developing liver. The septum transversum is the primordium of the **central tendon of the diaphragm** in the adult.

      [2] **Paired pleuroperitoneal membranes:** These appear to develop from the dorsal and dorsolateral body wall by an unknown mechanism.

Clinical Application 3.4: Congenital Diaphragmatic Hernia

A congenital diaphragmatic hernia is a herniation of abdominal contents into the plural cavity caused by a failure of the pleuroperitoneal membrane to develop or fuse with the other components of the diaphragm. A congenital diaphragmatic hernia is most commonly found on the left posterolateral side and is usually life-threatening because abdominal contents compress the lung buds, causing pulmonary hypoplasia. Clinical features in the newborn include an unusually flat abdomen, breathlessness, severe dyspnea, peristaltic bowel sounds over the last chest, and cyanosis. It can be detected prenatally using ultrasonography.

A/P view

Pediatric patient with congenital posterolateral diaphragmatic hernia on the left. The mediastinum is displaced to the right by the intestinal loops present in the left chest. A/P = anterior/posterior.

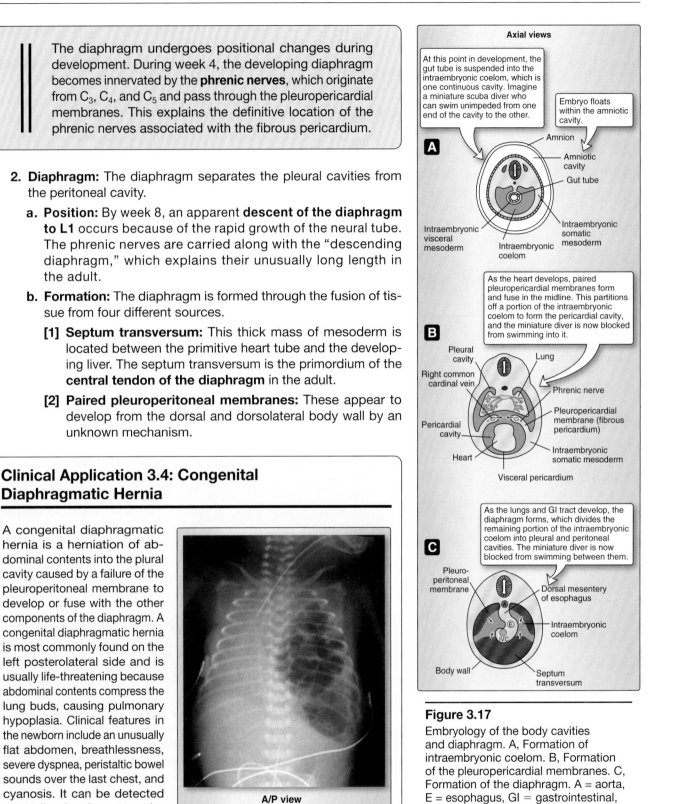

Figure 3.17
Embryology of the body cavities and diaphragm. A, Formation of intraembryonic coelom. B, Formation of the pleuropericardial membranes. C, Formation of the diaphragm. A = aorta, E = esophagus, GI = gastrointestinal, IVC = inferior vena cava.

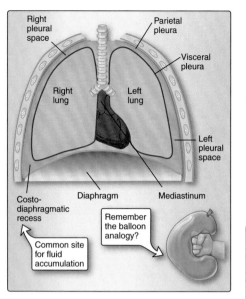

Figure 3.18
Pleurae and pleural cavity. Layers of pleura lining lung (visceral) and thoracic cage (parietal) surfaces. Lower left corner illustrates the balloon analogy.

[3] **Dorsal mesentery of the esophagus:** Invaded by myoblasts, this forms the crura of the diaphragm in the adult.

[4] **Body wall:** This contributes muscle to the peripheral portions of the definitive diaphragm.

B. Pleurae

The thoracic cavity houses a right and left **pleural sac**, each containing the right or left lung, respectively (Fig. 3.18). These pleural sacs are formed by a continuous serous membrane that lines either the inner surface of the thoracic cavity (**parietal pleura**) or the surface and fissures of the lung (**visceral pleura**).

> The pleural sac can be visualized like a fist pushed into an inflated balloon, where your fist is representing the lung. In this "balloon analogy," the outer surface of the balloon not touching your fist represents the parietal pleura (see Fig. 3.18). The surface of the balloon in contact with your fist is the visceral pleura, and the air/space between these two surfaces represents the pleural cavity. Your wrist represents the root of the lung, where these two layers are continuous.

1. **Anatomy:** Pleural layers are continuous with one another at the root of the lungs, forming pleural reflections that assist in anchoring respiratory viscera. The space between the parietal and visceral pleura is the **pleural cavity**. This space contains a small amount of serous fluid to allow for smooth movement during respiration.

   a. **Parietal pleura:** Parietal pleura is described based on the surface it is covering—costal, mediastinal, diaphragmatic, and cervical (around apex of lung). A thin layer of connective tissue—**endothoracic fascia**—separates the costal parietal pleura from the internal surface of the thoracic cage (ribs and intercostal muscles).

   b. **Visceral pleura:** Visceral pleura lines the lungs and follows lung fissures along their entirety.

   c. **Pleural recesses:** These are spaces that occur at the limits of the pleural cavity where regions of parietal pleura are continuous. The **costodiaphragmatic recess** is located where the inferior margin of the costal parietal pleura meets the outer margin of the diaphragmatic parietal pleura. The **costomediastinal recess** occurs where the anterior costal parietal pleura and mediastinal pleura meet. During inspiration and expiration, lung tissue moves in and out of these spaces. These spaces are clinically important, as they can be accessed without risk of lung tissue damage (see Clinical Application 3.2).

2. **Vasculature:** Arteries that supply the thoracic wall and diaphragm also supply the parietal pleurae, including **intercostal**, **internal thoracic**, and **musculophrenic arteries**. Venous drainage of parietal pleurae occurs by way of veins that accompany the above

---

Clinical Application 3.5: Pleural Effusion

Pleural effusion is caused by an accumulation of excess fluid within the pleural space, thus between the parietal and visceral pleurae. Pleural effusions can be categorized as transudative or exudative in origin. Transudative effusions are most commonly caused by heart failure, whereas exudative effusions are commonly caused by vascular or lymphatic blockage, lung trauma, inflammation, and tumor. Chest x-ray or computed tomography scan may confirm effusion. Treatment includes thoracentesis to remove excess fluid and implementation of preventive measures based on the principle cause of effusion.

---

arteries. Visceral pleura is supplied by **bronchial arteries**; however, venous return occurs by way of pulmonary veins rather than bronchial veins. This small amount of deoxygenated blood has no effect on the oxygenated pulmonary blood returning to the heart.

3. **Innervation:** Sensory innervation from parietal pleurae is mediated by the **phrenic** (diaphragmatic part) and **intercostal nerves**. Parietal pleura is pain sensitive, often referring pain over intercostal spaces proximal to the injury. Sensory innervation from visceral pleura is mediated by sympathetic and parasympathetic autonomic (general visceral afferent [GVA]) fibers of the pulmonary plexus. Visceral pleura is pain insensitive.

4. **Lymphatics:** Lymph from parietal pleurae drains into thoracic wall nodes, including intercostal, mediastinal, parasternal, and phrenic. Lymph from visceral pleura drains into the **superficial lymphatic plexus** just deep to the visceral pleura. Lymph then travels to **bronchopulmonary nodes** in the lung hilum before draining into **tracheobronchial lymph** nodes at the tracheal bifurcation. (See C.6. for a more detailed description.)

C. Trachea and lungs

Lungs are the main respiratory viscera, responsible for oxygenation of blood at the interface of alveoli and pulmonary capillaries. Each lung (right and left) is contained within a pleural sac. These sacs are separated from each other by the mediastinum and, therefore, do not communicate. Although the respiratory tract begins in the head, it continues into the thoracic cavity as the trachea and bronchial tree associated with each lung.

1. **Embryology:** The respiratory diverticulum initially is in open communication with the foregut, which means that the respiratory system and the digestive system are in open communication in early embryologic development. This open communication is closed off by indentations of visceral mesoderm called the **tracheoesophageal folds**. When the tracheoesophageal folds fuse in the midline to form the **tracheoesophageal septum**, the foregut is divided into the trachea anteriorly and esophagus posteriorly.

   a. **Respiratory diverticulum:** During week 4, the **respiratory diverticulum**, which consists of **endoderm**, forms in the anterior wall (or floor) of the primitive foregut and is the first sign in the development of the respiratory system (Fig. 3.19). The respiratory diverticulum protrudes into the surrounding **visceral mesoderm**. The distal end of the respiratory diverticulum enlarges to form the **lung bud**, which is also surrounded by visceral mesoderm. The lung bud divides into two **bronchial buds** that

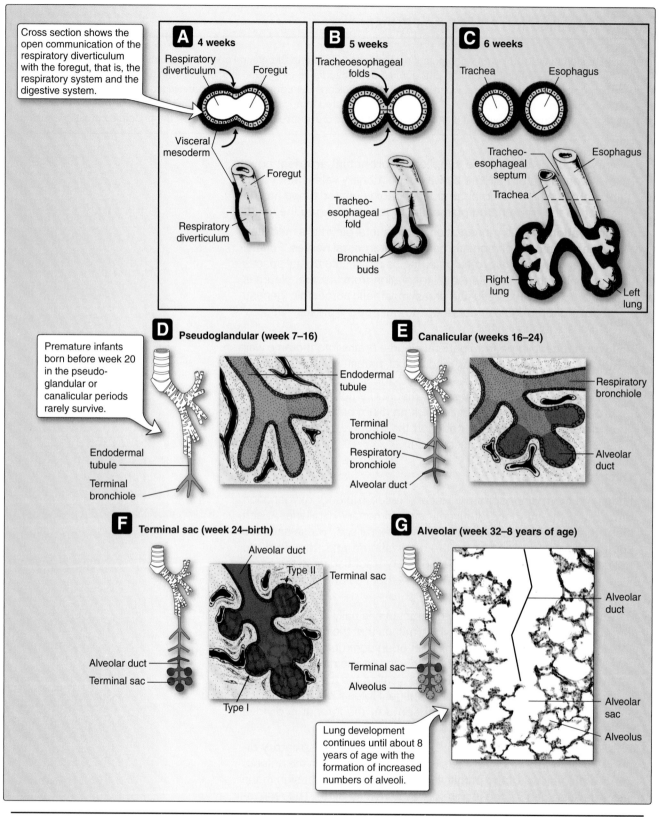

Cross section shows the open communication of the respiratory diverticulum with the foregut, that is, the respiratory system and the digestive system.

A 4 weeks
Respiratory diverticulum
Foregut
Visceral mesoderm
Foregut
Respiratory diverticulum

B 5 weeks
Tracheoesophageal folds
Tracheoesophageal fold
Bronchial buds

C 6 weeks
Trachea
Esophagus
Tracheoesophageal septum
Esophagus
Trachea
Right lung
Left lung

Premature infants born before week 20 in the pseudoglandular or canalicular periods rarely survive.

D Pseudoglandular (week 7–16)
Endodermal tubule
Endodermal tubule
Terminal bronchiole

E Canalicular (weeks 16–24)
Respiratory bronchiole
Terminal bronchiole
Respiratory bronchiole
Alveolar duct
Alveolar duct

F Terminal sac (week 24–birth)
Alveolar duct
Type II
Terminal sac
Alveolar duct
Terminal sac
Type I

G Alveolar (week 32–8 years of age)
Alveolar duct
Terminal sac
Alveolus
Alveolar sac
Alveolus

Lung development continues until about 8 years of age with the formation of increased numbers of alveoli.

Figure 3.19
Embryologic formation of the respiratory system. A–C, Relationship between developing trachea and esophagus. D–G, Stages of lung development.

Clinical Application 3.6: Tracheoesophageal Fistula

A **tracheoesophageal fistula** is an abnormal communication between the trachea and esophagus that results from improper division of foregut by the tracheoesophageal septum. It is generally associated with **esophageal atresia**, which will then result in **polyhydramnios**. The most common type of tracheoesophageal fistula is an **esophageal atresia with a tracheoesophageal fistula at the distal third end of the trachea**.

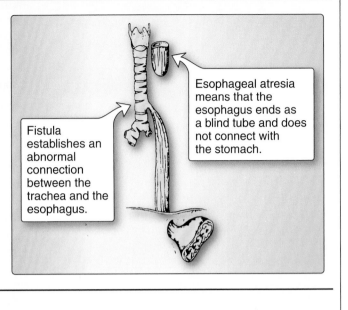

Fistula establishes an abnormal connection between the trachea and the esophagus.

Esophageal atresia means that the esophagus ends as a blind tube and does not connect with the stomach.

Tracheoesophageal fistula.

are also surrounded by visceral mesoderm. The bronchial buds branch into airway channels that progressively decrease in size. These airway channels include the **main (primary), lobar (secondary), segmental (tertiary), subsegmental bronchi**, and all the **smaller airway channels**. This means that the respiratory system forms from both endoderm and mesoderm.

b. **Trachea:** The epithelium that lines the trachea and the tracheal glands are derived from **endoderm** associated with the foregut. The tracheal smooth muscle, connective tissue, and C-shaped cartilage rings are derived from the surrounding **visceral mesoderm**.

c. **Bronchi:** In week 5, the bronchial buds enlarge to form the **main (primary) bronchi**. These subdivide into **lobar (secondary) bronchi** (three on the right side and two on the left side, corresponding to the lobes of the adult lung). The lobar bronchi further subdivide into **segmental (tertiary) bronchi** (10 on the right side and 9 on the left side), which further subdivide into **subsegmental bronchi**. The segmental bronchi are the primordia of the **bronchopulmonary segments**, which are morphologically and functionally separate respiratory units of the lung. The bronchial epithelium and glands are derived from **endoderm**. The bronchial smooth muscle, connective tissue, and cartilage are derived from **visceral mesoderm**.

d. **Primitive pleural cavity:** As the bronchi continue to grow and develop, the lungs expand laterally and caudally into a space known as the **primitive pleural cavity**. The visceral mesoderm covering the outside of the lungs develops into **visceral pleura**, and the somatic mesoderm covering the inside of the body wall develops into **parietal pleura**. The space between the visceral and parietal pleura is called the **pleural cavity**.

e. **Lungs:** The fetal and postnatal development of the lungs is divided into four periods.

[1] Pseudoglandular period (weeks 7–16): During this period, the developing lung resembles an exocrine gland. The numerous **endodermal tubules** are lined by simple columnar epithelium and are surrounded by visceral mesoderm containing a modest capillary network. Each endodermal tubule branches into a number of **terminal bronchioles**. At this point, respiration is not possible, and premature infants cannot survive.

[2] Canalicular period (weeks 16–24): During this period, the terminal bronchioles branch into a number of **respiratory bronchioles** that subsequently branch into a number of **alveolar ducts**. The terminal bronchioles, respiratory bronchioles, and alveolar ducts are now lined by a **simple cuboidal epithelium** and are surrounded by visceral mesoderm containing a prominent capillary network. Premature infants born before week 20 rarely survive.

[3] Terminal sac period (weeks 24 to birth): During this period, terminal **sacs** bud off the alveolar ducts and then dilate and expand into the surrounding mesoderm. The terminal sacs are separated from each other by connective tissue called **primary septa**. The simple cuboidal epithelium within the terminal sacs differentiates into **type I pneumocytes** (thin, flat cells that make up part of the blood–air barrier) and **type II pneumocytes** (which produce surfactant). The terminal sacs are surrounded by mesoderm containing a rapidly proliferating capillary network. The capillaries make intimate contact with the terminal sacs and thereby establish a **blood–air barrier** with the type I pneumocytes. Premature infants born between week 25 and week 28 can survive with intensive care.

Clinical Application 3.7: Neonatal Respiratory Distress Syndrome

Neonatal respiratory distress syndrome is caused by a deficiency of surfactant, which may occur due to prolonged intrauterine asphyxia, maternofetal hemorrhage, in premature infants, in infants of diabetic mothers, and in multiple-birth infants. A deficiency of surfactant prevents the newborn from inflating the lungs with air. Pathologic findings include hemorrhagic edema within the lung, atelectasis (collapse of alveoli), widely dilated air spaces, and **hyaline membrane disease** characterized by eosinophilic material consisting of proteinaceous fluid (fibrin, plasma) and necrotic cells.

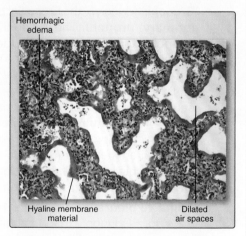

Neonatal respiratory distress syndrome.

Clinical Application 3.8: Pulmonary Hypoplasia

Pulmonary hypoplasia (PH) is a poorly developed bronchial tree with abnormal histology. PH classically involves the right lung in association with right-sided obstructive congenital heart defects. PH can also be found in association with **congenital diaphragmatic hernia** (i.e., herniation of abdominal contents into the thorax), which compresses the developing lung. PH can also be found in association with **bilateral renal agenesis**, or **Potter syndrome**, which causes an insufficient amount of amniotic fluid (oligohydramnios) to be produced, which, in turn, increases pressure on the fetal thorax.

[4] **Alveolar period (week 32–8 years of age):** During this period, terminal sacs are partitioned by connective tissue called **secondary septa** to form adult **alveoli**. About 20–70 million alveoli are present at birth. About 300–400 million alveoli are present by age 8 years. The major mechanism for the increase in the number of alveoli is formation of secondary septa that partition existing alveoli. After birth, the increase in the size of the lung is due to an increase in the number of respiratory bronchioles.

2. **Lung anatomy:** The lungs are housed in the thorax, each within a separate pleural sac. Recall that visceral pleura covers the external surface of the lung, including into the fissures.

   a. **Common features:** In general, each lung has the following features (Fig. 3.20).

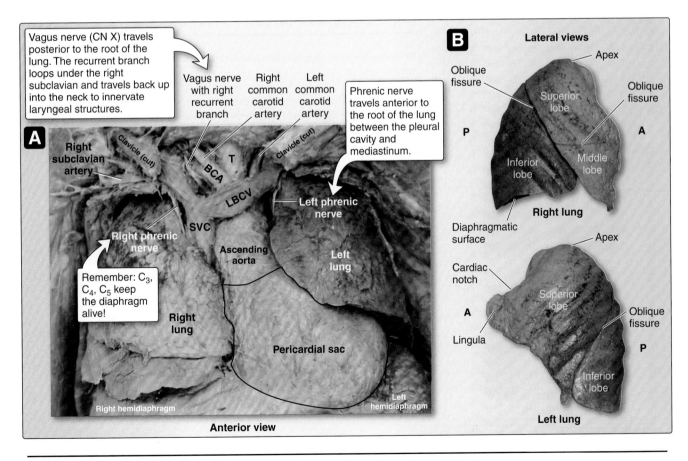

Figure 3.20
Lung features. A, In situ with mediastinal structures. B, Cadaveric specimens (lungs removed from body). A = anterior, LBCV = left brachiocephalic vein, SVC = superior vena cava, T = trachea, P = posterior.

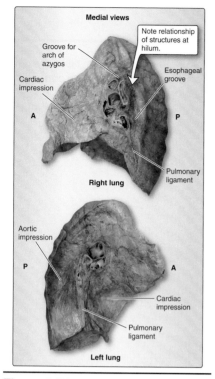

Figure 3.21

Hilum of lungs and impressions.
Blue = pulmonary arteries,
red = pulmonary veins, yellow = bronchi,
A = anterior, P = posterior.

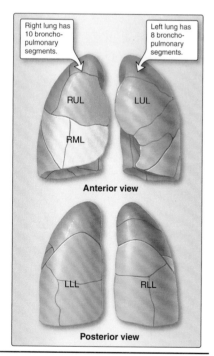

Figure 3.22

Bronchopulmonary segments. Segments indicated by lines within each lobe.
Pink = upper lobes, yellow = middle lobe, blue = lower lobes, LLL = left lower lobe, LUL = left upper lobe, RLL = right lower lobe, RML = right middle lobe, RUL = right upper lobe.

[1] **Surfaces:** Each lung has a costal, mediastinal, and diaphragmatic (base) surface.

[2] **Borders:** Each lung has an anterior, inferior, and posterior border.

[3] **Apex:** The superior portion of each lung extends into the root of the neck, forming the apex.

[4] **Hilum:** This is the medial point of entry/exit for bronchi, vessels, and nerves (Fig. 3.21).

[5] **Root:** The root of each lung is a collection of structures entering/exiting the lung at the hilum. It is the structural junction of visceral and parietal pleurae.

b. **Unique features:** Separately, the right and left lungs have the following unique features (Fig. 3.22).

[1] **Right lung:** The right lung has three lobes: superior, inferior, and middle. It has two fissures—horizontal and oblique. Impressions of the right lung include cardiac, superior vena cava (SVC), arch of the azygos vein, azygos vein, and the esophagus.

[2] **Left lung:** The left lung has just two lobes, superior and inferior, and one oblique fissure. Its impressions are cardiac,

Clinical Application 3.9: Pneumothorax

Pneumothorax (collapsed lung) occurs when the parietal pleura is compromised, and air is allowed into the pleural cavity. The normal air pressure that is present within the pleural cavity is decreased, thereby causing the air-filled lung tissue to recede in size. Symptoms include significant difficulty breathing and chest pain. Treatment commonly involves placement of a chest tube to remove excess air. Surgery may also be an option in the event that the chest tube does not fix the problem completely.

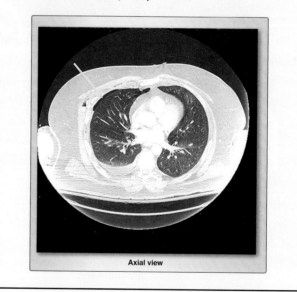

Axial view

Pneumothorax. Air in right pleural cavity indicated by yellow arrow.

arch of the aorta, and the descending aorta. The left lung also has two notches, a cardiac notch and a lingual notch (homologue to middle right lobe).

> A stethoscope is used to **auscultate** lung (breath) sounds across all anterior and posterior lung fields. Breath sounds vary depending on airway diameter. **Percussion** of the thorax is performed to determine whether underlying lung tissue is air-filled, fluid-filled, or solid, producing a resonate, dull, or flat sound, respectively. These techniques are critical for respiratory assessment.

3. **Tracheal and bronchial tree anatomy:** The **trachea** begins in the neck at the inferior boundary of the larynx and extends into the thorax anterior to the esophagus, through the superior thoracic aperture (Fig. 3.23). The skeleton of the trachea is composed of C-shaped cartilaginous rings that are open posteriorly, maintaining patency while permitting some flexibility.

   a. **Primary bronchi:** At the sternal angle, the trachea bifurcates into right and left **primary (main) bronchi** (see Fig. 3.23). The right primary bronchus is oriented in a more vertical position and is wider and shorter than the left. The left primary bronchus passes anterior to the esophagus and inferior to the aortic arch in a more horizontal orientation. Primary bronchi enter their respective lungs at the hilum, along with pulmonary arteries and veins, lymphatic vessels, and bronchial arteries. The **carina** is a ridge of cartilage that serves as an important visual landmark at the tracheal bifurcation.

   b. **Secondary and tertiary bronchi and terminal bronchioles:** Branching of the bronchial tree continues at the hilum of the lung. Primary bronchi divide into multiple **secondary (lobar) bronchi** corresponding to the number of lobes—three on the right, two on the left. Branching continues into **tertiary (segmental) bronchi** to supply each **bronchopulmonary segment** and continues down to the level of **terminal bronchioles**.

4. **Vasculature:** The lungs receive poorly oxygenated blood from two large **pulmonary arteries** that arise from the pulmonary trunk (Fig. 3.24). Pulmonary arteries are contained within the root of the lung and branch into lobar and segmental arteries, traveling adjacent to bronchial tree branches. Paired **pulmonary veins** (superior and inferior) carry oxygen-rich blood from each lung to the left atrium of the heart. These veins originate at the capillary level and join to eventually form intersegmental veins that unite to form the pulmonary veins. **Bronchial arteries** supply lung parenchyma and root structures, while **bronchial veins** drain the structures supplied by the bronchial arteries near the root of the lung. The remaining deoxygenated blood is removed by the pulmonary veins.

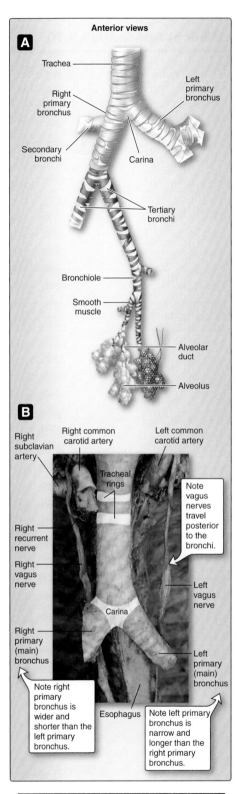

Figure 3.23
Trachea and bronchial tree. A, Distal trachea and bronchial tree. B, Cadaveric specimen of trachea and primary bronchi.

Clinical Application 3.10: Tracheobronchial Foreign Body Aspiration

Foreign body aspiration (FBA) is a potentially fatal event due to potential airway obstruction and is a common cause of morbidity and mortality in children. Due to its vertical orientation and wider diameter, aspirated objects most often lodge in the right primary bronchus or one of its branches. If a bronchoscopy is warranted to assess the position of the foreign body, the carina is visualized as an important anatomical landmark.

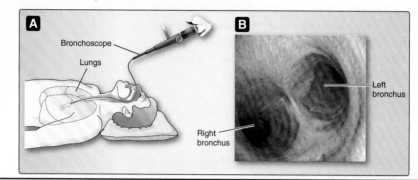

Tracheobronchial foreign body aspiration. A, Bronchoscopy. B, Internal view of airway at tracheal bifurcation.

- Left superior pulmonary vein—drains left superior lobe.
- Left inferior pulmonary vein—drains left inferior lobe.
- Right superior pulmonary vein—drains right superior and middle lobes.
- Right inferior pulmonary vein—drains right inferior lobe.

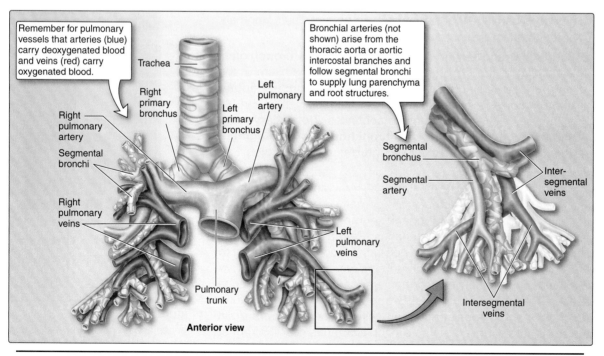

Figure 3.24
Respiratory blood supply. Pulmonary and segmental vessels.

Clinical Application 3.11: Obstructive and Restrictive Lung Diseases

Obstructive lung diseases are characterized by elevated airway resistance, primarily during expiration, due to airway narrowing. Airway narrowing may be caused by smooth muscle hypertrophy in airway walls, increase luminal mucus secretions, or diseased lung tissue surrounding airway branches. Examples of obstructive lung disease include chronic bronchitis, asthma, cystic fibrosis, and emphysema. Chronic obstructive pulmonary disease (COPD) involves a combination of chronic bronchitis and emphysema.

Restrictive lung diseases are characterized by restriction in lung expansion during inhalation; therefore, the lung is described as being "stiff." Total lung capacity is limited in restrictive lung diseases. Examples of conditions that cause restrictive lung disease include pulmonary fibrosis, asbestosis, sarcoidosis, significant scoliosis, and select neuromuscular diseases, such as amyotrophic lateral sclerosis (ALS) and muscular dystrophy.

Lung diseases are commonly diagnosed by radiologic studies, pulmonary function testing, bronchoscopy, and biopsies. Difficulty breathing and a chronic cough are two common symptoms for both types of lung disease.

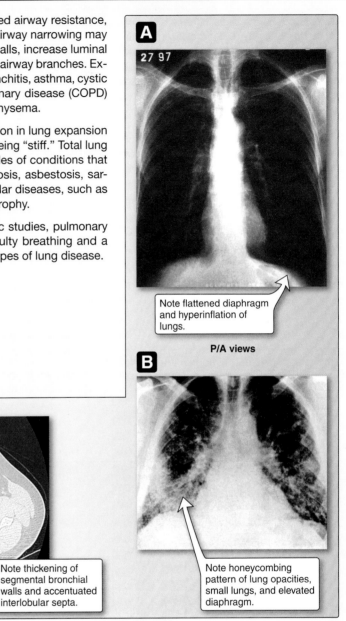

Note flattened diaphragm and hyperinflation of lungs.

P/A views

Axial view

Note thickening of segmental bronchial walls and accentuated interlobular septa.

Note honeycombing pattern of lung opacities, small lungs, and elevated diaphragm.

Obstructive and restrictive lung diseases. A, Plain film radiograph of obstructive lung disease. B, Plain film radiograph of restrictive lung disease. C, CT image of chronic obstructive pulmonary disease (COPD). P/A = posterior/anterior.

5. **Innervation:** Respiratory structures receive autonomic innervation (general visceral efferent, GVA) from the **pulmonary plexus** (Fig. 3.25). This plexus lies anterior and posterior to the root of each lung. The **anterior pulmonary plexus** is located anterior to the tracheal bifurcation and is continuous with the deep cardiac plexus anteriorly and the **posterior pulmonary plexus** posteriorly. Sympathetic and parasympathetic fibers contribute to the formation of the pulmonary plexus.

Clinical Application 3.12: Pulmonary Embolism

Pulmonary embolism refers to the blockage of a pulmonary artery and its branches by a blood clot (embolus) that has traveled to the lung(s) from a deep vein thrombosis (DVT) in the lower limb or pelvis. Blocked vessels decrease blood oxygen levels and can be life-threatening. Severity depends on the size of the embolus, with larger emboli blocking main vessels—potentially fatal—and small emboli leading to pulmonary hypertension over time. Sedentary or bedridden patients are typically at higher risk for developing DVTs and must be monitored closely. Thrombolytic therapies may help to break up the clot, and anticoagulant ("blood thinners") therapy may help to prevent future clot development.

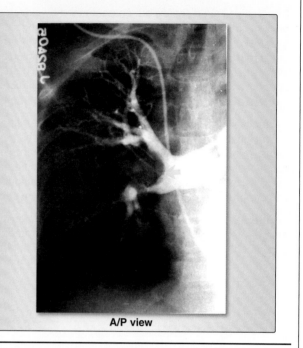

A/P view

Pulmonary embolism. Pulmonary arteriogram shows a large "saddle embolus" (yellow arrow head) at the vessel bifurcation, and downstream decreased perfusion in the middle and lower lobes as a result. A/P = anterior/posterior.

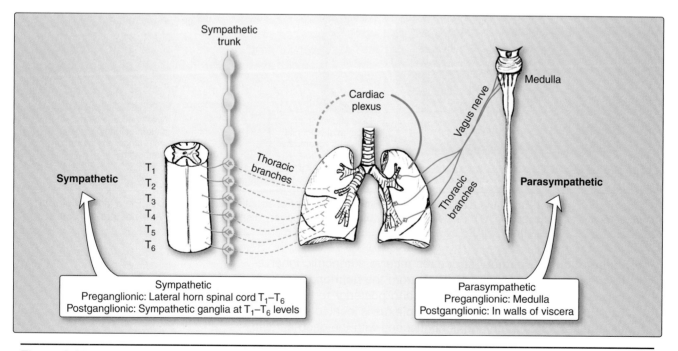

Figure 3.25
Pulmonary plexus. Autonomic innervation of respiratory structures.

a. **Sympathetic fibers:** Postganglionic fibers arise from the cardiac plexus and thoracic sympathetic trunk ganglia (T_1–T_6). Sympathetic stimulation causes bronchodilation and decreased mucous secretions.

b. **Parasympathetic fibers:** Preganglionic fibers arise from the cardiac plexus and direct branches of the right and left vagus nerves (cranial nerve X). Parasympathetic stimulation causes bronchoconstriction and increased mucous secretions. Postganglionic parasympathetic neurons are in the walls of the viscera.

6. **Lymphatics:** The lymphatics of the lung are clinically important in terms of lung cancer metastasis (Fig. 3.26). The lymphatic system in the lung is divided into continuous superficial and deep plexuses.

a. **Superficial plexus:** The superficial plexus lies deep to visceral pleura. It drains lung parenchyma and visceral pleura first into bronchopulmonary lymph nodes at the hilum of the lung.

b. **Deep plexus:** The deep plexus is located in submucosa of bronchi and surrounding connective tissue. It drains primarily lung root structures first through pulmonary lymph nodes before draining into bronchopulmonary lymph nodes.

c. **Lymph flow:** Lymph from **bronchopulmonary lymph nodes** drains to superior and inferior **tracheobronchial lymph nodes** situated around the tracheal bifurcation. Lymphatic vessels coalesce into **right** and **left bronchomediastinal trunks** that ultimately drain into the venous system at the junction between subclavian and jugular veins (venous angle).

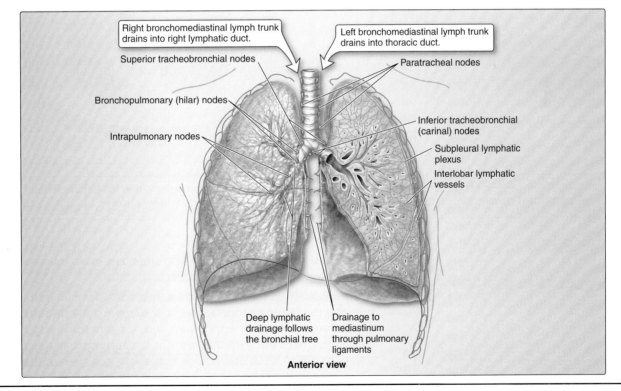

Figure 3.26
Lymphatic drainage of lungs.

Clinical Application 3.13: Lung Carcinoma

In both men and women, lung cancer is the leading cause of death, accounting for ~25% of all annual cancer deaths. Lung cancer can be classified as either non–small-cell carcinoma (84%) or small-cell carcinoma (13%). Non–small-cell carcinoma can be further divided into adenocarcinoma (most common in women), squamous cell carcinoma (poor prognosis), or large-cell carcinoma.

Small cell carcinoma occurs almost always in smokers, has the worst prognosis, and often metastasizes early. Signs and symptoms typically do not present until later stages, but patients commonly describe a chronic cough, shortness of breath, angina, and recurrent bouts of pneumonia or bronchitis.

Lung tumor growth into surrounding structures can lead to Horner syndrome (cervical sympathetic ganglia involvement), superior vena cava syndrome, dysphagia (esophagus involvement), voice hoarseness (vagus nerve/recurrent branch involvement), and diaphragm paralysis (phrenic nerve involvement).

Structural or positional changes in the carina during bronchoscopy are indicative of tumor growth around the tracheal bifurcation. Treatment options include radiotherapy, chemotherapy, surgery, and palliative care. Primary lung cancer most commonly metastasizes to the brain, liver, and bone.

Lateral view

Axial view

Carcinoma of the lungs. A, Plain film radiograph showing the nodule (yellow arrows) anterior within the left upper lobe consistent with bronchogenic carcinoma. B, CT with cancerous mass in left upper lobe (yellow arrow).

7. **Tracheal histology:** The trachea is organized into a mucosa, submucosa, and adventitia (Fig. 3.27).

   a. **Mucosa:** The mucosa of the trachea consists of an **epithelium** and the **lamina propria**. The epithelium is a **pseudostratified ciliated columnar epithelium** and, for simplicity, is generally called **respiratory epithelium**. The lamina propria of the trachea consists of loose connective tissue with **collagen and elastic fibers** and diffuse lymphatic tissue referred to as **bronchus-associated lymphatic tissue** (**BALT**).

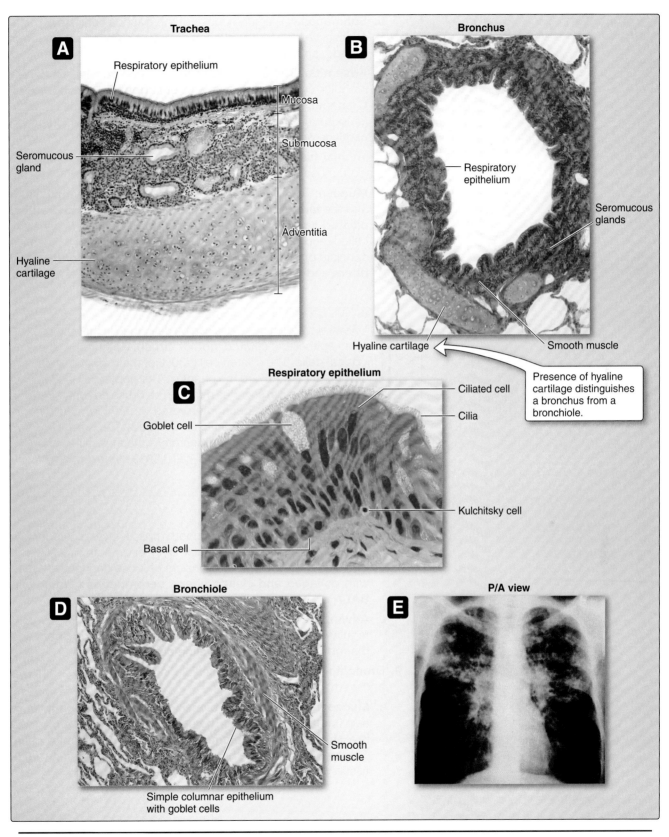

Figure 3.27
Histology of the respiratory system. A, Trachea. B, Bronchus. C, Respiratory epithelium. D, Bronchiole. E, Cystic fibrosis. Plain film radiograph shows hyperinflation bilaterally, reduced heart size due to pulmonary compression, cyst formation, and atelectasis (collapsed alveoli) bilaterally.

    b. Submucosa: The submucosa of the trachea consists of loose connective tissue with **collagen** and **elastic fibers**, **seromucous glands**, and **BALT**.

    c. Adventitia: The adventitia of the trachea consists of dense, irregular connective tissue with **collagen** and **elastic fibers**, **C-shaped hyaline cartilage rings**, and the **trachealis muscle** (smooth muscle) that spans the dorsal ends of the C-shaped cartilage rings.

8. Bronchial histology: A bronchus is organized into a mucosa, smooth muscle layer, submucosa, and adventitia.

    a. Mucosa: The mucosa of a bronchus consists of an **epithelium** and the **lamina propria**. The epithelium is a **pseudostratified ciliated columnar epithelium** and, for simplicity, is generally called **respiratory epithelium**. The lamina propria of a bronchus consists of loose connective tissue with **collagen and elastic fibers** and **BALT**.

> Several different cell types can be described in the respiratory epithelium: **ciliated**, **goblet**, **brush**, **Kulchitsky**, and **basal cells**. The ciliated cell ($\cong$30% of the total cells) has cilia that beat toward the pharynx. The goblet cell ($\cong$30% of the total cells) secretes mucus. The brush cell contains microvilli and has been interpreted as an intermediate stage in the differentiation to ciliated cells. The Kulchitsky cell is an endocrine cell and secretes catecholamines and peptide hormones. The basal cell ($\cong$30% of the total cells) functions as a stem cell.

    b. Smooth muscle layer: The smooth muscle layer of a bronchus consists of a prominent circular layer of smooth muscle. The submucosa of a bronchus consists of loose connective tissue with **collagen and elastic fibers**, **seromucous glands**, and **BALT**.

    c. Adventitia: The adventitia of a bronchus consists of dense, irregular connective tissue with **collagen** and **elastic fibers** and **discontinuous plates of hyaline cartilage**.

9. Bronchiole histology: A bronchiole is organized into a mucosa and a smooth muscle layer.

    a. Mucosa: The mucosa of a bronchiole consists of an **epithelium** and the **lamina propria**. The epithelium in a large bronchiole is a **simple ciliated columnar epithelium with goblet cells**. The lamina propria of a bronchiole consists of loose connective tissue with **collagen and elastic fibers** and **BALT**.

b. Smooth muscle layer: The smooth muscle layer of a bronchiole consists of a prominent circular layer of smooth muscle.

> **Cystic fibrosis (CF)** is caused by production of abnormally thick mucus by seromucous glands and goblet cells lining the respiratory tract (see Fig. 3.27E). This results clinically in obstruction of airways and recurrent bacterial infections. CF is an autosomal-recessive genetic disorder.

10. **Terminal and respiratory bronchiole histology:** Both terminal and respiratory bronchioles are organized into a mucosa and a smooth muscle layer (Fig. 3.28).

    a. **Mucosa:** The mucosa consists of an **epithelium** and **lamina propria**. The epithelium is a **simple ciliated cuboidal epithelium with Clara cells**. The lamina propria consists of loose connective tissue with **collagen and elastic fibers**.

    b. **Smooth muscle layer:** The smooth muscle layer consists of an incomplete circular layer of smooth muscle.

> Clara cells secrete:
> * A **lipoprotein** that acts as a surface-active agent that prevents luminal adhesion
> * **CC16 (Clara cell 16) protein** used as a marker of pulmonary function in bronchopulmonary lavage fluid and serum
> * **Surfactant-associated proteins (SPs) A, B**, and **D, proteases, antimicrobial peptides, cytokines, chemokines**, and **mucins** that contribute to the extracellular material lining the airspaces
> The Clara cell also detoxifies airborne toxins using the cytochrome P450 system and functions as a stem cell.

Terminal bronchiole marks the end of the conduction portion of the respiratory system, hence the name. This means that from the trachea to the terminal bronchiole, air is only conducted. That is, no O_2/CO_2 gas exchange occurs.

Respiratory bronchiole marks the beginning of the respiratory portion of the respiratory system, hence the name. This means that O_2/CO_2 gas exchange begins here and continues to the alveoli.

Terminal bronchioles

Respiratory bronchioles

Alveolar ducts

Alveoli

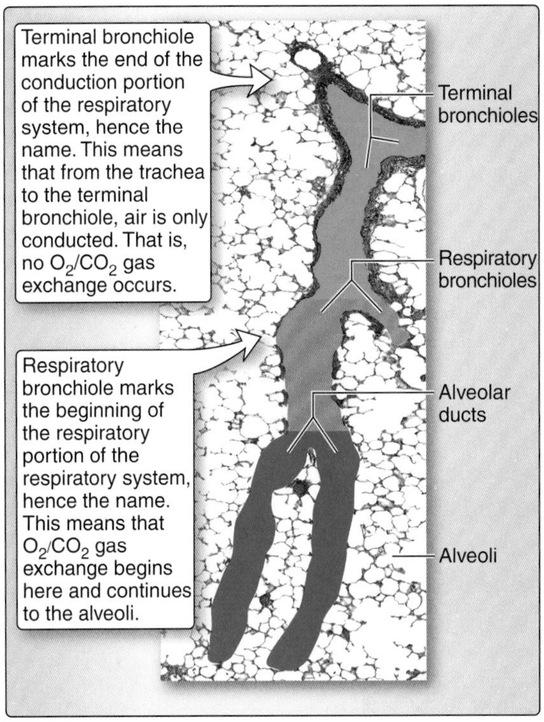

Figure 3.28
Histology of the respiratory system. Terminal bronchiole, respiratory bronchiole, and alveolar duct.

11. **Alveolar duct histology:** An **alveolar duct** is organized into a **mucosa** and a **smooth muscle layer**. The mucosa of an alveolar duct consists of an **epithelium** and **lamina propria**. The epithelium of an alveolar duct is a **simple squamous epithelium**. The lamina propria of an alveolar duct consists of loose connective tissue with **collagen and elastic fibers**.
The smooth muscle layer of an alveolar duct consists of smooth muscle "knobs" because numerous alveoli perforate its wall.

12. **Alveolar histology:** An **alveolus** is organized into a **mucosa** only (Fig. 3.29). The mucosa of an alveolus consists of an **epithelium** and the **lamina propria**. The epithelium of an alveolus is composed of a **type I pneumocyte**, **type II pneumocyte**, and an **alveolar macrophage**. The lamina propria of an alveolus consists of loose connective tissue with **collagen and elastic fibers** that comprises the alveolar septum.

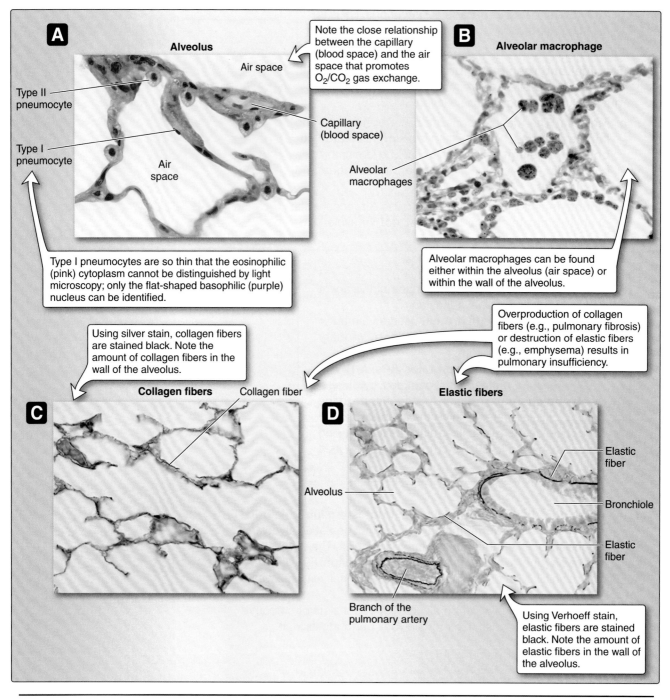

Figure 3.29
Histology of the respiratory system. A, Alveolus. B, Alveolar macrophage. C, Collagen fibers. D, Elastin fibers.

An alveolus is a thin-walled, polyhedron-shaped chamber that is continuous with the alveolar duct. It is surrounded by a network of capillaries that brings blood in close proximity to the air so that gas exchange between the blood and air can occur.

a. **Type I pneumocyte:** The type I pneumocyte is a simple squamous epithelial cell that lines the alveolus. It has no mitotic capacity. Adjacent type I pneumocytes are joined by zonula occludens (tight junctions).

b. **Type II pneumocyte:** The type II pneumocyte is a cuboidal-shaped cell with a round-shaped nucleus. Its cytoplasm contains rough endoplasmic reticulum, polyribosomes, a Golgi complex, smooth endoplasmic reticulum, mitochondria, and distinctive **lamellar bodies** that store surfactant. Type II pneumocytes have a high mitotic capacity, thereby functioning as stem cells to regenerate the alveolar lining. Hyperplasia of type II pneumocytes is an important marker of alveolar injury and repair of alveoli. Type II pneumocytes secrete **surfactant**.

Surfactant is composed of:

- **Dipalmitoylphosphatidylcholine**, which is the strongest-acting surfactant lipid molecule
- **Phosphatidylcholine, phosphatidylglycerol, neutral lipids**, and **cholesterol**
- **SPs A, B, C, D**

Surfactant reduces the elastance or collapsing force in the lung by reducing the surface attraction between opposing alveolar walls.

c. **Alveolar macrophage:** Alveolar macrophages are found within the alveolar septum or within the alveolus where they phagocytize inhaled dust, bacteria (e.g., *Mycobacterium tuberculosis*), degraded surfactant, or red blood cells that may enter the alveolus in heart failure (i.e., hemosiderin-laden "heart failure cells"). Alveolar macrophages within alveoli may pass upward along the bronchial tree toward the pharynx where they are expectorated or swallowed.

d. **Blood–air barrier:** This is where diffusion of O_2 and CO_2 occurs (Fig. 3.30). The components of the blood–air barrier include **surfactant**, **type I pneumocyte cytoplasm**, **basal lamina**, and **endothelium cytoplasm** lining a continuous capillary.

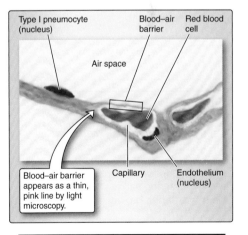

Figure 3.30
Histology of the respiratory system. Blood–air barrier.

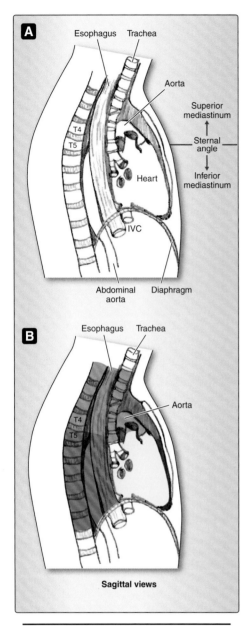

Figure 3.31
Mediastinum. A, Division between superior and inferior mediastinal compartments at sternal angle. B, Mediastinal subdivisions. IVC = inferior vena cava; red = posterior, yellow = middle, blue = anterior, brown = superior.

D. Mediastinum

As shown in Figure 3.31, the **mediastinum** lies centrally in the thoracic cavity, between the two pleural cavities (lateral), the sternum and thoracic vertebral bodies (anterior/posterior), and the superior thoracic aperture and diaphragm (superior/inferior). The mediastinum contains thoracic viscera and associated neurovascular and lymphatic structures, except for the lungs. For descriptive purposes, this region is divided into superior and inferior compartments. The **inferior mediastinum** is further divided into anterior, middle, and posterior sections. As previously mentioned, the **sternal angle** is a palpable landmark on the anterior thoracic wall, marking the junction between the manubrium and body of the sternum. This junction also marks the imaginary dividing line between the superior and inferior mediastinal compartments.

1. **Superior mediastinum:** The **superior mediastinum** extends from the superior thoracic aperture to the imaginary horizontal plane between the sternal angle and T4/T5 intervertebral disc (Figs. 3.32 and 3.33). The superior mediastinum is continuous with the retropharyngeal space of the neck. The contents of the superior mediastinum are as follows:

    a. **Thymus:** This lymphoid gland is typically more prominent in children.

    b. **Brachiocephalic veins (right and left):** These are formed by the junction of Internal jugular and subclavian veins on the right and left sides.

    c. **Superior vena cava:** The SVC is formed by the junction of right and left brachiocephalic veins and delivers blood to the right atrium.

    d. **Arch of the azygos vein:** The SVC receives the arch of the azygos vein.

    e. **Aortic arch with branches (brachiocephalic trunk, left common carotid, left subclavian arteries):** Aortic arch branches supply head, neck and upper limbs structures. The obliterated ductus arteriosus (ligamentous arteriosus) connects the inferior surface of the arch to the superior surface of the pulmonary trunk and is closely associated with the left recurrent branch of the vagus nerve.

    f. **Vagus nerve:** These pass posterior to the root of each lung, and right and left recurrent branches are found just inferior to the right subclavian artery and arch of the aorta, respectively. This inconsistency is due to changes that occur during embryologic development of major vessels.

    g. **Phrenic nerves (C_3–C_5):** These pass anterior to the root of each lung.

    h. **Trachea:** The trachea extends into the thorax from the neck through the superior thoracic aperture, just anterior to the esophagus.

    i. **Esophagus:** The esophagus is located posterior to the trachea and anterior to thoracic vertebral bodies.

    j. **Thoracic duct:** This large lymphatic vessel lies between the esophagus and left vagus nerve ("duck between two gooses"; see Fig. 3.35).

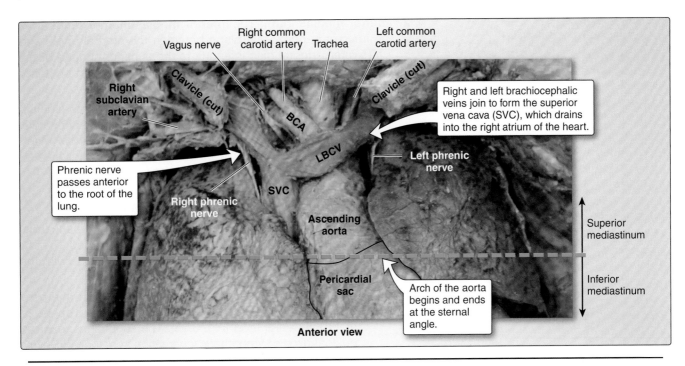

Figure 3.32
Superior mediastinum (with heart/lungs). Cadaveric specimen. BCA = brachiocephalic artery, LBCV = left brachiocephalic vein.

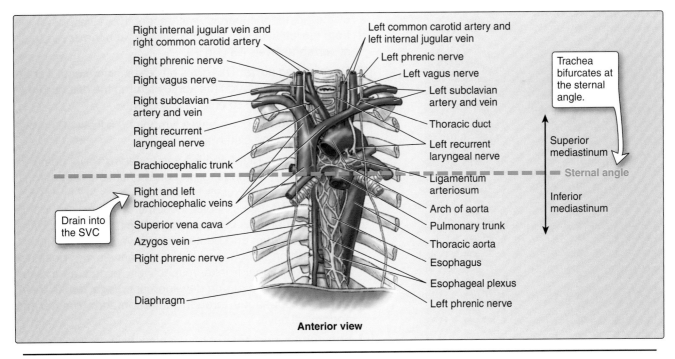

Figure 3.33
Superior mediastinum (heart/lungs removed). SVC = superior vena cava.

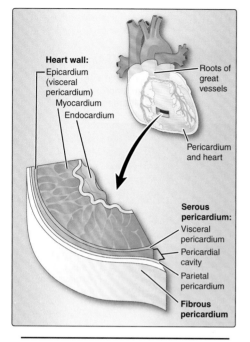

Heart wall:
- Epicardium (visceral pericardium)
- Myocardium
- Endocardium

Roots of great vessels

Pericardium and heart

Serous pericardium:
- Visceral pericardium
- Pericardial cavity
- Parietal pericardium

Fibrous pericardium

Figure 3.34
Middle mediastinum, including heart wall and pericardium layers.

2. **Inferior mediastinum:** The **inferior mediastinum** extends from the imaginary horizontal plane between the sternal angle and T4/T5 intervertebral disc inferiorly to the superior surface of the diaphragm. It is subdivided into anterior, middle, and posterior mediastinal regions.

a. **Anterior:** The smallest of the inferior compartments sits just posterior to the body of the sternum, anterior to the pericardial cavity. In children, the thymus extends into this compartment. The internal thoracic vessels are the main contents of the anterior mediastinum.

b. **Middle:** This compartment contains the pericardium, heart, and roots of the great vessels entering/leaving the heart (Fig. 3.34).

c. **Posterior:** This compartment lies posterior to the pericardial cavity and anterior to the thoracic vertebral bodies T5–T12 (Fig. 3.35). The posterior mediastinum is continuous with the superior mediastinum and contains the following.

[1] **Esophagus:** The esophagus travels posterior to the pericardial sac to reach the abdomen through the diaphragm at T10 vertebral level (Fig. 3.36). The esophagus receives postganglionic sympathetic innervation from thoracic levels along its course and preganglionic parasympathetic innervation from vagus nerves.

[2] **Azygos venous system:** The azygos vein receives posterior intercostal veins to drain the right posterior thoracic wall. On the left, the accessory hemiazygos and hemiazygos veins receive tributaries from the left upper and middle portions of the posterior thoracic wall, respectively. Venous blood from the left side typically crosses to reach the azygos vein at vertebral levels T8 and T9.

[3] **Descending aorta:** This gives off posterior intercostal arteries and travels through the aortic hiatus in the diaphragm at vertebral level T12 to enter the abdomen.

[4] **Thoracic duct:** This receives lymph at the level of the diaphragm from the cisterna chyli.

[5] **Vagus nerves:** Right and left vagus nerves travel posterior to the root of the lungs, giving off branches to the cardiac and pulmonary plexuses (see Figs. 3.25, 3.36, and 3.51). Right and left vagus nerves become plexiform at the mid to lower esophagus before reconjoining to form the anterior (left vagus nerve) and posterior (right vagus nerve) trunks. The transition of right and left vagus nerves into posterior and anterior vagal trunks, respectively, occurs as a result of foregut rotation during development. Vagal trunks travel with the esophagus through the diaphragm to enter the abdominal cavity.

[6] **Splanchnic nerves:** Thoracic splanchnic nerves are preganglionic sympathetic nerves that arise from spinal levels T_6–T_9 (greater splanchnic nerve), T_{10}–T_{11} (lesser splanchnic nerve), and T_{12} (least splanchnic nerve). Thoracic splanchnic nerves provide sympathetic innervation to abdominal viscera and vasculature.

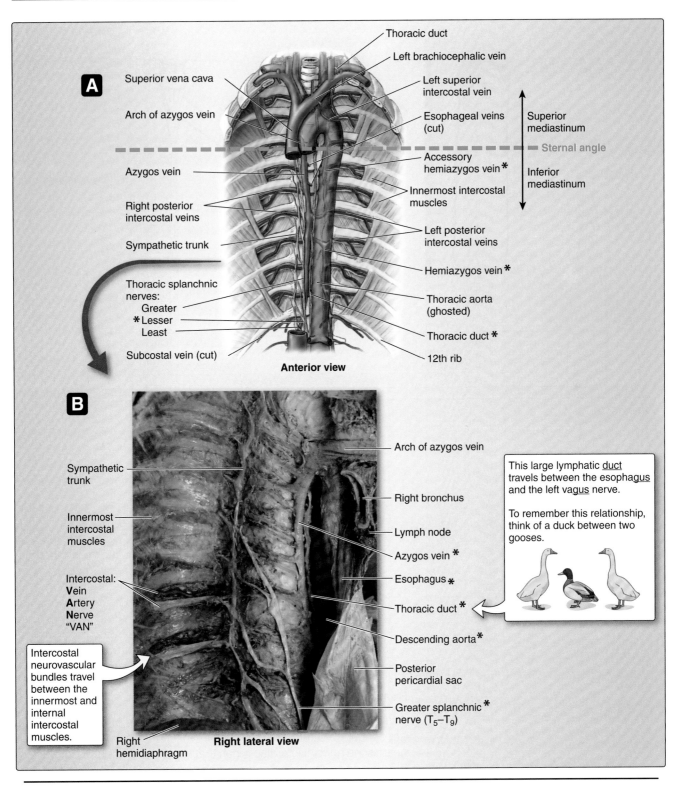

A

Superior vena cava

Arch of azygos vein

Azygos vein

Right posterior
intercostal veins

Sympathetic trunk

Thoracic splanchnic
nerves:
    Greater
  *Lesser
    Least

Subcostal vein (cut)

Thoracic duct

Left brachiocephalic vein

Left superior
intercostal vein

Esophageal veins
(cut)

Accessory
hemiazygos vein *

Innermost intercostal
muscles

Left posterior
intercostal veins

Hemiazygos vein *

Thoracic aorta
(ghosted)

Thoracic duct *

12th rib

Superior
mediastinum

Sternal angle

Inferior
mediastinum

Anterior view

B

Sympathetic
trunk

Innermost
intercostal
muscles

Intercostal:
Vein
Artery
Nerve
"VAN"

Intercostal
neurovascular
bundles travel
between the
innermost and
internal
intercostal
muscles.

Right
hemidiaphragm

Arch of azygos vein

Right bronchus

Lymph node

Azygos vein *

Esophagus *

Thoracic duct *

Descending aorta*

Posterior
pericardial sac

Greater splanchnic *
nerve (T$_5$–T$_9$)

Right lateral view

This large lymphatic <u>duct</u>
travels between the esoph<u>agus</u>
and the left va<u>gus</u> nerve.

To remember this relationship,
think of a duck between two
gooses.

Figure 3.35

Posterior mediastinum. A, Blue-dotted line indicates upper limit of posterior mediastinum. Esophagus removed.
B, Cadaveric specimen showing mediastinal (*) and posterior thoracic wall structures.

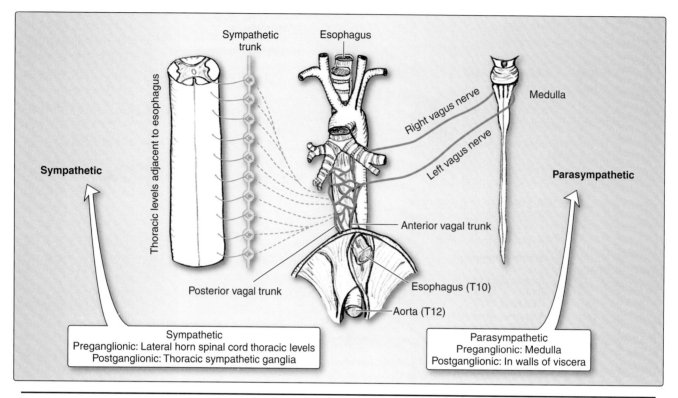

Figure 3.36
Esophageal plexus. Esophagus and aorta pass through diaphragm at indicated vertebral levels.

3. **Adjacent structures:** Select structures in the thoracic cavity are not contained within the mediastinum. For example, the phrenic nerves and pericardiacophrenic vessels run along between the mediastinal pleurae and pericardium; however, they are not considered a part of the middle mediastinum. The IVC enters the thoracic cavity through the diaphragm (at the T8 level) to join the right atrium of the heart, but it is not considered in the middle mediastinum. Finally, the thoracic sympathetic trunks lie on either side of the thoracic vertebral bodies and are, therefore, outside the posterior mediastinal boundary. However, the splanchnic nerves that arise from the sympathetic trunks course anteriorly over the vertebral bodies of T5–T12; thus, these nervous structures are contained within the posterior mediastinum.

E. **Heart**

As previously mentioned, the heart and the roots of its great vessels are contained within a pericardial sac in the middle mediastinum. The heart is the principle cardiac organ that functions to circulate deoxygenated blood to the lungs and oxygenated blood throughout the body. The heart develops from a single heart tube before transitioning into a four-chambered organ, consisting of right and left atria and ventricles.

1. **Embryology:** The heart is the first organ to function, beginning to beat at day 21 and beginning to pump blood at day 25. Conceding that the embryologic formation of the heart is extremely complex,

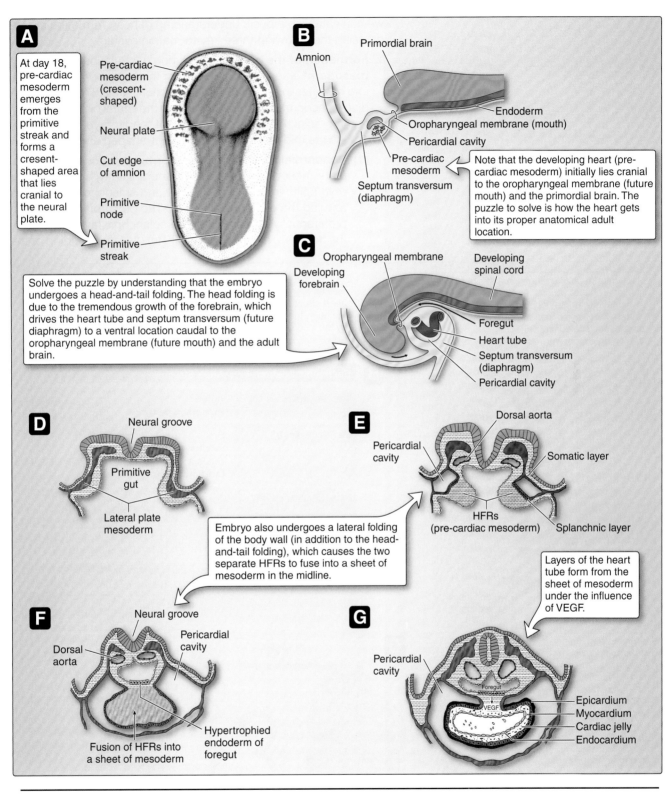

A At day 18, pre-cardiac mesoderm emerges from the primitive streak and forms a cresent-shaped area that lies cranial to the neural plate.

Pre-cardiac mesoderm (crescent-shaped)

Neural plate

Cut edge of amnion

Primitive node

Primitive streak

B Primordial brain

Amnion

Endoderm

Oropharyngeal membrane (mouth)

Pericardial cavity

Pre-cardiac mesoderm

Septum transversum (diaphragm)

Note that the developing heart (pre-cardiac mesoderm) initially lies cranial to the oropharyngeal membrane (future mouth) and the primordial brain. The puzzle to solve is how the heart gets into its proper anatomical adult location.

Solve the puzzle by understanding that the embryo undergoes a head-and-tail folding. The head folding is due to the tremendous growth of the forebrain, which drives the heart tube and septum transversum (future diaphragm) to a ventral location caudal to the oropharyngeal membrane (future mouth) and the adult brain.

C Oropharyngeal membrane

Developing forebrain

Developing spinal cord

Foregut

Heart tube

Septum transversum (diaphragm)

Pericardial cavity

D Neural groove

Primitive gut

Lateral plate mesoderm

E Dorsal aorta

Pericardial cavity

Somatic layer

HFRs (pre-cardiac mesoderm)

Splanchnic layer

Embryo also undergoes a lateral folding of the body wall (in addition to the head-and-tail folding), which causes the two separate HFRs to fuse into a sheet of mesoderm in the midline.

Layers of the heart tube form from the sheet of mesoderm under the influence of VEGF.

F Neural groove

Pericardial cavity

Dorsal aorta

Fusion of HFRs into a sheet of mesoderm

Hypertrophied endoderm of foregut

G Pericardial cavity

Foregut

VEGF

Epicardium

Myocardium

Cardiac jelly

Endocardium

Figure 3.37

Heart tube formation. A, Dorsal view. B and C. Sagittal views. D–G. Cross-sectional views. HFRs = heart-forming regions, VEGF = vascular endothelial growth factor.

we can establish a basic understanding of heart formation by addressing the following three key formation events.

a. **Formation of the heart tube:** During gastrulation, **precardiac mesoderm** emerges from the upper third of the primitive streak and migrates in a cranial–lateral direction (Fig. 3.37). The precardiac mesoderm becomes localized to the lateral plate mesoderm in the cranial region on both sides of the embryo and extends across the midline forming a crescent-shaped area.

[1] **Pericardial cavity and heart-forming regions:** The lateral plate mesoderm located in the cranial region of the embryo splits into a somatic layer and splanchnic layer, thus forming the **pericardial cavity**. The precardiac mesoderm preferentially migrates into the splanchnic layer and forms the **heart-forming regions** (**HFRs**). As lateral folding of the

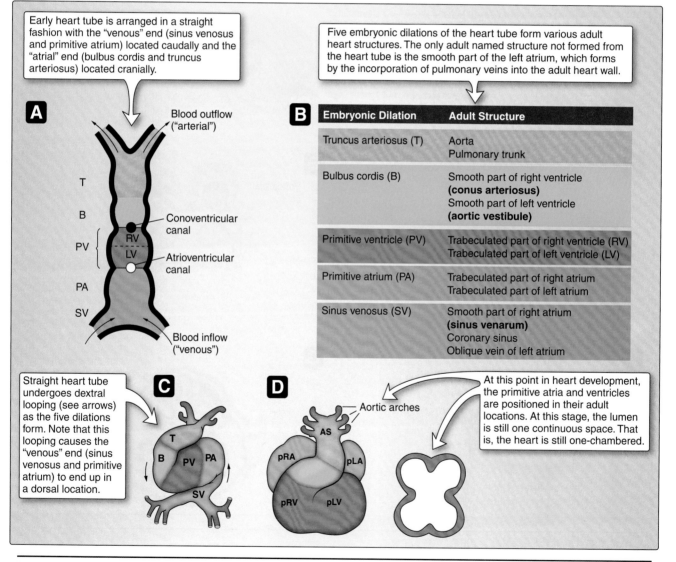

Figure 3.38
Dilations and dextral looping. A, Coronal view. B, Adult derivative table. C, Dextral looping. D, Final adult placement of primitive atria and ventricles (no partitioning). AS = aortic sac, p = primitive.

embryo occurs, the HFRs and the pericardial cavities fuse in the midline and form a continuous sheet of mesoderm surrounded by a single pericardial cavity.

[2] Endocardium, myocardium, and epicardium: Hypertrophied foregut endoderm secretes **vascular endothelial growth factor**, which induces the sheet of mesoderm to form discontinuous vascular channels that remodel into a single **endocardial tube** (i.e., the **endocardium**). The mesoderm that surrounds the endocardium forms the **myocardium**, which secretes a layer of extracellular matrix proteins called the **cardiac jelly**. The mesoderm that lines the coelomic wall near the liver migrates into the cardiac region and forms the **epicardium**.

b. Formation of the heart dilations and dextral looping: The five dilations that form along the length of the heart tube are called the: 1) truncus arteriosus, 2) bulbus cordis, 3) primitive ventricle, 4) primitive atrium, and 5) sinus venosus (Fig. 3.38). These five dilations will eventually develop into the adult structures of the heart. In addition, dextral looping (i.e., bending to the right side) occurs concurrently as the dilations form, which brings the presumptive chambers of the future heart into their correct spatial relationship to each other.

c. Formation of the heart septa: By day 28, dextral looping is complete, and the heart is a one-chambered structure (i.e., if you cut the heart open, the lumen is one continuous space). The puzzle the embryo now needs to solve is how to partition one continuous space (i.e., a one-chambered heart) into four separate spaces (i.e., a four-chambered heart). The answer to the puzzle is the formation of four heart septa.

[1] Atrioventricular septum: The atrioventricular (AV) septum begins to form when the **dorsal AV cushion** and the **ventral AV cushion** enlarge and approach each other due to a proliferation of cells within the endocardium (Fig. 3.39). The dorsal AV cushion and the ventral AV cushion eventually fuse with each other in the center of the heart to form the AV septum. The AV septum partitions the AV canal into the **right AV canal** and the **left AV canal**. The AV septum is important because the other three septa grow toward and fuse with the AV septum.

[2] Atrial septum: As shown in Figure 3.40, the atrial septum begins to form when the crescent-shaped **septum primum** develops in the roof of the primitive atrium and grows toward the AV cushions (or the future AV septum). The **foramen primum (first opening)** is located between the free edge of the septum primum and the AV cushions and eventually closes when the septum primum fuses with the AV cushions. As the septum primum fuses with the AV cushions, small perforations in upper portion of the septum primum coalesce to form the **foramen secundum (second opening)**. A second crescent-shaped **septum secundum** develops in the roof of the primitive atrium to the right side of the septum primum and also grows toward the AV cushions. The **foramen ovale**

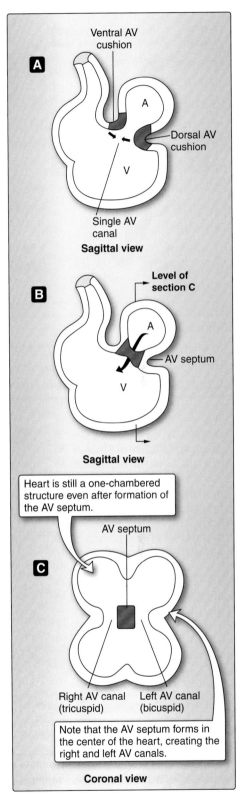

Figure 3.39
Atrioventricular (AV) septum formation (A–C).

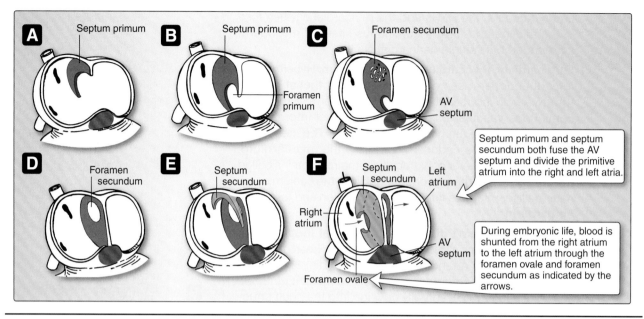

Figure 3.40
Atrial septum formation (A–F). AV = atrioventricular.

Clinical Application 3.14: Persistent Common AV Canal Heart Defect

A persistent common atrioventricular (AV) canal heart defect is caused by a failure of fusion of the dorsal AV cushion and ventral AV cushion. This results in a condition in which the common AV canal fails to partition into the right AV canal and the left AV canal, so that a large opening exists in the center of the heart. Consequently, the tricuspid and bicuspid valves are represented by one valve (a common AV valve) common to both sides of the heart.

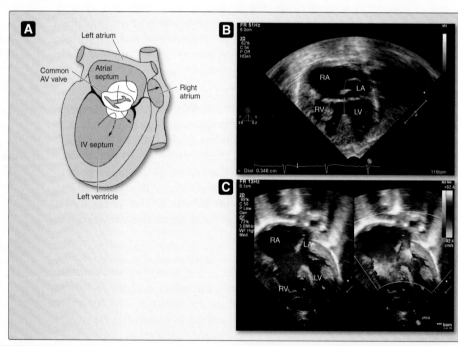

Persistent common atrioventricular (AV) canal heart defect. A, Schematic drawing of persistent common AV canal. Note septal defects in both atrial and ventricular septa. B, Pediatric ultrasound. Systolic view of the endocardial cushion defect showing both the primum atrial septal defect and the inlet ventricular septal defect, at birth. The primum atrial septal defect is measured in this image, and note how there is no tissue between the defect and the valve. The green line demonstrates the inlet ventricular septal defect. This infant also has a secundum atrial septal defect marked by the red line. C, Color compare diastolic view of the same endocardial cushion defect with color-flow Doppler at 6 weeks of age. Note the asymmetry of the right atrium and ventricle due to significant flow through the atrial and ventricular septal defects. The superimposed color of red and yellow indicates that the blood is flowing from the left atrium and ventricle into the right atrium and ventricle through the atrial and ventricular septal defects. IV = interventricular, LA = left atrium, LV = left ventricle, RA = right atrium, RV = right ventricle.

Clinical Application 3.15: Atrial Septal Defects

Atrial septal defects (ASDs) are noted on auscultation with a loud S1 and a wide, fixed, split S2 and are characterized by left to right shunting of blood. ASD types include:

1. **Foramen secundum defects:** caused by excessive resorption of septum primum or septum secundum or both. This results in a condition in which there is an opening between the right and the left atria. Some defects can be tolerated for a long time, with clinical symptoms manifesting as late as the third decade of life. It is the most common, clinically significant ASD.

2. **Common atrium:** caused by the complete failure of septum primum and secundum to develop, resulting in the formation of only one atrium.

3. **Probe patent foramen ovale:** caused by the incomplete anatomic fusion of septum primum and secundum. It is present in ~25% of the population and typically has no clinical significance.

4. **Premature closure of foramen ovale:** occurs during prenatal life and results in hypertrophy of right side of heart and underdevelopment of the left side of the heart.

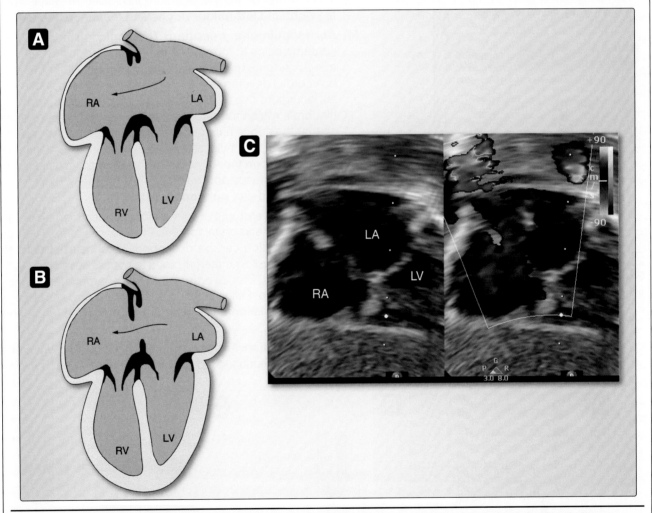

Atrial septal defects. A, Schematic common atrium. B, Schematic foramen secundum defect. C, Pediatric ultrasound. Color compare systolic view of the secundum atrial septal defect. Note how there is tissue between the defect and the valve. The superimposed color of red indicates that blood flow is flowing from the left atrium into the right atrium. LA = left atrium, LV = left ventricle, RA = right atrium, RV = right ventricle.

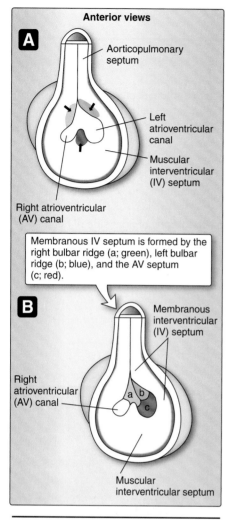

Anterior views

Figure A labels: Aorticopulmonary septum; Left atrioventricular canal; Muscular interventricular (IV) septum; Right atrioventricular (AV) canal

Membranous IV septum is formed by the right bulbar ridge (a; green), left bulbar ridge (b; blue), and the AV septum (c; red).

Figure B labels: Membranous interventricular (IV) septum; Right atrioventricular (AV) canal; Muscular interventricular septum

Figure 3.41
Interventricular (IV) septum formation (A and B).

(i.e., the **opening in the septum secundum**) is located in the lower portion of the septum secundum. Later in life, the septum primum and septum secundum anatomically fuse to complete the formation of the atrial septum and to obliterate the foramen ovale and foramen secundum. The fused portion of the septum is called the **fossa ovale**.

[3] **Interventricular septum:** As shown in Figure 3.41, the interventricular (IV) septum begins to form when the **muscular IV septum** develops in the floor of the primitive ventricle and grows toward the AV cushions (or the future AV septum). The **IV foramen** is located between the free edge of the muscular IV septum and the AV cushions and allows for communication between the right ventricle and left ventricle. The IV foramen is closed by the **membranous IV septum**, which forms by the proliferation and fusion of tissue from the **right** and **left bulbar ridges** and the **AV cushions**.

[4] **Aorticopulmonary septum:** The aorticopulmonary (AP) septum begins to form when the **truncal ridges** (within the truncus arteriosus) and the **bulbar ridges** (within the bulbus cordis) develop due to a proliferation of cells within the endocardium (Fig. 3.42). Later, neural crest cells from the hindbrain region migrate into the truncal and bulbar ridges so that the ridges enlarge and approach each other. As the ridges do so, they twist around each other in a spiral manner and fuse to form the AP septum. The AP septum divides the truncus arteriosus and bulbus cordis (or the outflow tract) into the **aorta** and **pulmonary trunk**.

d. **Circulatory system:** With a foundational understanding of the complexities of heart development, the nuances of fetal versus newborn circulation can be described. Fetal heart structures described above allow maternal blood to bypass developing fetal viscera (lungs and liver) in order to provide appropriate nutrients for growth in utero. Following birth, these fetal structures change to permit oxygenation and filtering of blood by the lungs and liver, respectively.

[1] **Fetal circulation:** As shown in Figure 3.43, highly oxygenated and nutrient-enriched blood from the mother is distributed to

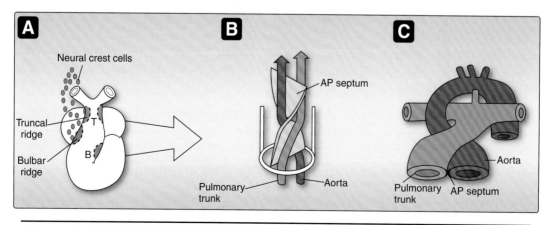

Figure 3.42
Aorticopulmonary (AP) septum formation (A–C).

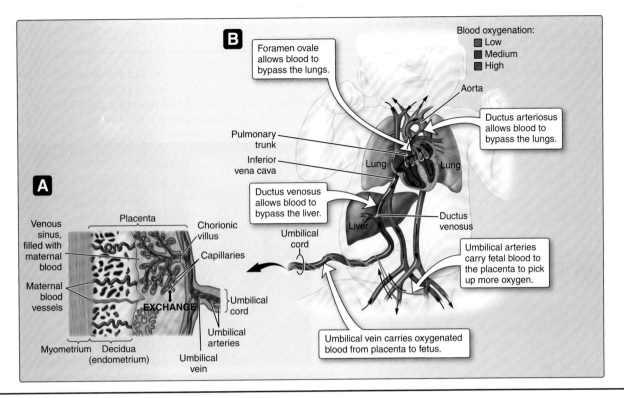

Figure 3.43
Fetal circulation. A, Magnification of placental structures and arrangement. B, Circulatory anatomy of the fetus. Arrows indicate direction of blood flow between placenta and fetus.

Clinical Application 3.16: Ventricular Septal Defect

A **membranous ventricular septal defect** (**VSD**) is the most common type of defect involving the IV septum. A membranous VSD is caused by faulty fusion of the **right** and **left bulbar ridges** and **AV cushions**. This results in an opening in the IV septum that allows for the free flow of blood between the right and left ventricles. A large membranous VSD is initially associated with a left–right shunting of blood, increased pulmonary blood flow, and pulmonary hypertension.

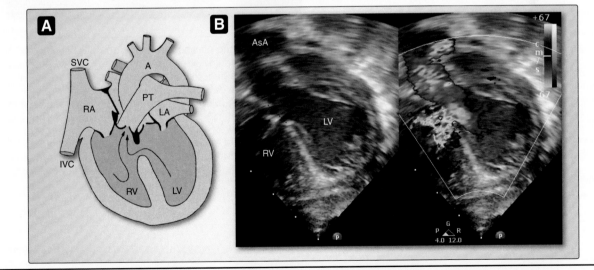

Ventricular septal defect (VSD). A, Schematic VSD. B, Pediatric ultrasound. Color compare systolic view of the perimembranous ventricular septal defect. The dotted line shows the boundary of the defect. Note how the defect line "touches" the right side of the aortic valve annulus (dash dot blue line). The superimposed color shows blood being ejected out the aortic valve and into the ascending aorta in blue. The yellow and red colors indicate the blood flow is going from the left ventricle through the ventricular septal defect and into the right ventricle. A = aorta, AsA = ascending aorta, IVC = inferior vena cava, LA = left atrium, LV = left ventricle, PT = pulmonary trunk, RA = right atrium, RV = right ventricle, SVC = superior vena cava.

Clinical Application 3.17: Tetralogy of Fallot

Tetralogy of Fallot (TF) is caused by an abnormal neural crest cell migration such that a skewed development of the AP septum occurs. TF results in a condition in which the pulmonary trunk exhibits a small diameter and the aorta exhibits a large diameter. TF is characterized by four classic malformations: **pulmonary stenosis**, **right ventricular hypertrophy**, **overriding aorta**, and **ventricular septal defect**. TF is associated clinically with **marked cyanosis (right–left shunting of blood)**.

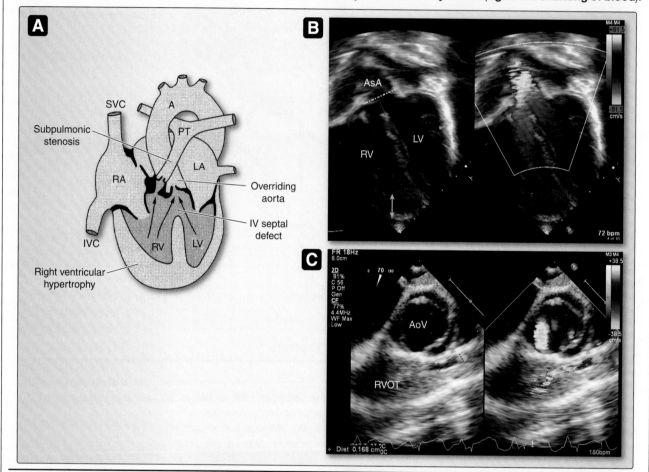

Tetralogy of Fallot. A, Schematic figure labeled with main features. B, Pediatric ultrasound. Color compare systolic view of the ventricles and aorta in a patient with tetralogy of Fallot. The red-dotted line shows the boundary of the ventricular septal defect. Note how the aorta is overriding the defect—the defect line is directly under the center of the aortic valve annulus (dash dot line, compare with the perimembranous ventricular septal defect). The muscle of the right ventricle near the apex (green arrows) is much thicker than the free wall of the left ventricle (blue line with dots). The superimposed color shows blood being ejected from both ventricles out the aorta, indicative of deoxygenated blood from the right ventricle going out the aorta. C, Transesophageal systolic color compare systolic view of the aortic valve and right ventricular outflow tract. Note how narrow and stenotic the right ventricular outflow tract appears compared to the aortic valve annulus, seen on face. The pulmonary valve annulus is severely small (red-dotted line). The superimposed color that is seen in the right ventricular outflow tract shows a long segment of severe stenosis leading up to the severely hypoplastic and stenotic pulmonary valve. A = aorta, AoV = aortic valve, AsA = ascending aorta, IV = interventricular, IVC = inferior vena cava, LA = left atrium, LV = left ventricle, PT = pulmonary trunk, RA = right atrium, RV = right ventricle, RVOT = right ventricular outflow tract, SVC = superior vena cava.

the fetus from the placenta via the **left umbilical vein**. [Note: Highly oxygenated blood is carried by the left umbilical *vein*, not by an artery]. From the left umbilical vein, blood enters the liver, where most of the blood bypasses the hepatic sinusoids by coursing through the **ductus venosus** to enter the IVC. From the IVC, blood enters the right atrium, where most of the blood bypasses the right ventricle by coursing through the **foramen ovale** to enter the left atrium. From the left atrium, blood enters the left ventricle and is delivered to fetal tissues via the aorta. Poorly oxygenated and nutrient-poor fetal blood returns to the placenta via **right and left umbilical arteries**. Although most of the blood bypasses the right ventricle, some blood does enter the right ventricle. The blood in the right ventricle enters the pulmonary trunk, but most of the blood bypasses the fetal lungs by coursing through the **ductus arteriosus**.

Because of the course fetal blood takes through the ductus arteriosus, the fetal lungs receive only a minimal amount of blood for growth and development, and this blood is returned to the left ventricle via pulmonary veins.

[2] **Newborn circulation:** The circulatory changes that occur at birth are facilitated by a **decrease in right atrial pressure** due to occlusion of placental circulation and by an **increase in left atrial pressure** due to increased pulmonary venous return. The circulatory changes include closure and *formation of adult remnants* of the following: left umbilical vein (*ligamentum teres*), ductus venosus (*ligamentum venosum*), foramen ovale (*fossa ovale*), right and left umbilical arteries (*medial umbilical ligaments*), and the ductus arteriosus (*ligamentum arteriosum*).

2. **Anatomy:** The heart is contained within a **fibrous pericardial sac**.

   a. **Pericardium:** The fibrous pericardium is continuous with the covering of the great vessel roots superiorly and is anchored inferiorly to the central tendon of the diaphragm (see Fig. 3.34). Mediastinal pleura covers the lateral outer surfaces of the fibrous sac, along with varying amounts of adipose. The **phrenic nerves** and **pericardiacophrenic vessels** course anterior to the root of the lung within the adipose and parietal pleura on way to the diaphragm. The inner surface of the fibrous pericardial sac is covered with a **parietal serous pericardium**, while a **visceral serous pericardial** layer covers the heart's surface. The **pericardial cavity** is a potential space that occurs between these two serous layers and contains a small amount of serous fluid.

   [1] **Sinuses:** At two locations, reflections of visceral serous pericardium are continuous with the parietal serous pericardium (Fig. 3.44). These reflections create sinuses. The **transverse pericardial sinus** occurs where the aorta and pulmonary trunk emerge from the heart and is located posterior to these vessels and anterior to the SVC. The **oblique pericardial sinus** occurs posterior to the heart where the SVC, IVC, and pulmonary veins enter the heart.

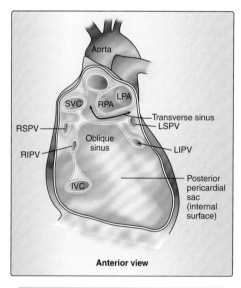

Anterior view

Figure 3.44
Pericardial sinuses. Heart removed. IVC = inferior vena cava, LIPV = left inferior pulmonary vein, LPA = left pulmonary artery, LSPV = left superior pulmonary vein, RIPV = right inferior pulmonary vein, RPA = right pulmonary artery, RSPV = right superior pulmonary vein, SVC = superior vena cava.

Clinical Application 3.18: Cardiac Tamponade

Cardiac tamponade is described as compression on the heart in the pericardial sac. Symptoms include a significant drop in blood pressure, difficulty breathing, and lightheadedness. This may occur as a result of fluid buildup between the heart and the unyielding fibrous pericardial sac. The increase in pressure on the heart is potentially fatal and must be decompressed by pericardiocentesis (fluid drainage) to avoid organ damage and ultimately failure. This procedure involves inserting a needle into the pericardial cavity at the level of the fifth or sixth intercostal space adjacent to the sternum, or at the left subcostal angle. Cardiac tamponade should be considered an emergency and treated immediately.

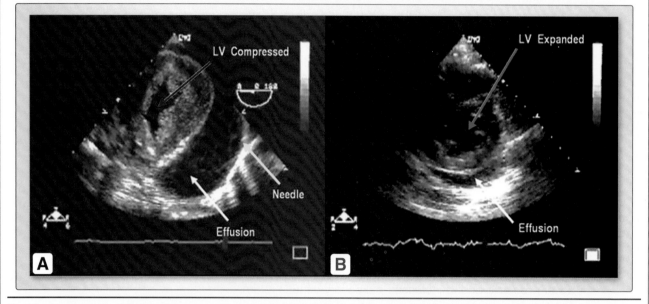

Cardiac tamponade. Echocardiogram. A, Note pericardial effusion (white arrow) and left ventricular (LV) compression (red arrow) associated with cardiac tamponade. Needle (yellow arrow) accessing pericardial cavity. B, Comparison following pericardiocentesis. LV response (blue arrow).

[2] **Blood supply:** The pericardium receives blood supply mainly from **pericardiacophrenic** and **musculophrenic arteries**. **Azygos** and **internal thoracic vein** tributaries control venous return. It is innervated by the **phrenic nerve** and branches of the **cardiac plexus**, although the visceral serous pericardium is pain insensitive.

b. **External features:** The heart can be described as having four **borders**, an **apex**, and a **base** (Figs. 3.45 and 3.46). It is roughly pyramid shaped and oriented with its apex facing anterolaterally toward the left side of the body and base facing posteriorly.

[1] **Borders:** The borders of the heart are primarily made up of the right atrium (right and inferior), left ventricle (left), and the roots of the great vessels (superior).

[2] **Apex and base:** The **apex** of the heart is primarily made up of the left ventricle and the **base** the left atrium.

[3] **Sulci:** Several sulci characterize the surface of the heart, including **coronary** and **IV sulci**.

[4] **Auricles: Right** and **left auricles** are ear-like appendages extending from the surface of the right and left atria, respectively. These vestigial structures represent portions of the primitive

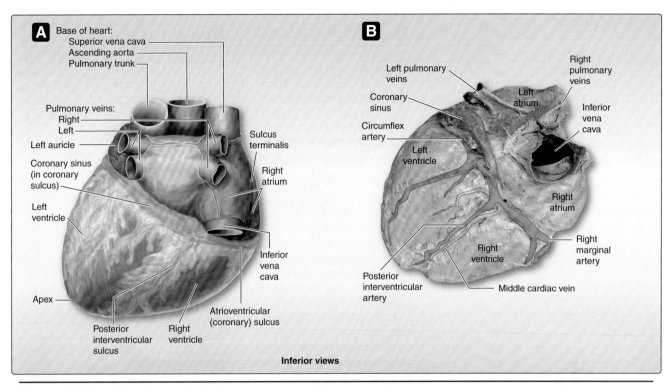

Figure 3.46

A. Posterior external features of the heart. B. Cadaveric specimen with vasculature visible.

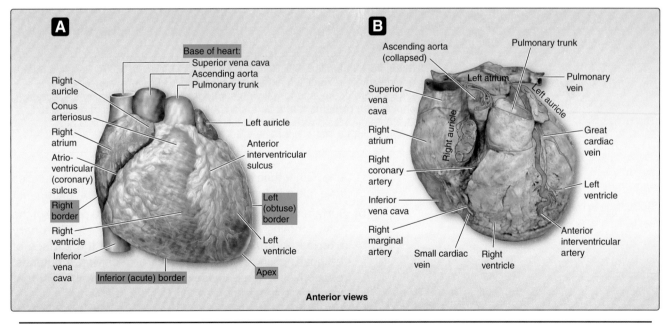

Figure 3.45

Anterior external features of the heart. A, Blue boxes indicate borders/boundaries. B, Cadaveric specimen with vasculature visible.

Clinical Application 3.19: Myocardial Infarction

Myocardial infarct (MI), or "heart attack," occurs when the heart is deprived of blood and oxygen, often because of a blocked coronary artery. Death of heart tissue can cause referred pain in the chest, shoulder, mid-thoracic back, and the arm—the left arm in particular. Additional symptoms include diaphoresis (excessive sweating), nausea, vomiting, shortness of breath, and fatigue. An MI should be treated immediately, as it can lead to irreversible tissue damage and possibly death. A common treatment for blocked coronary arteries is angioplasty with placement of a single or multiple stents. For more complex cases, a coronary artery bypass graft (CABG) may be indicated, in which an intact vessel (often the internal thoracic artery) is used to bypass the blocked vessel.

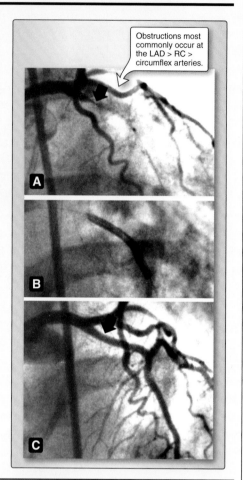

Obstructions most commonly occur at the LAD > RC > circumflex arteries.

Myocardial infarction (MI). Primary angioplasty for acute MI. A, Baseline total occlusion of proximal left anterior descending (LAD) (yellow arrow head) 2 hours into acute anterior MI with cardiogenic shock. B, Primary angioplasty shown with placement of a perfusion balloon across the area of occlusion. C, Postangioplasty with no residual stenosis (red arrow head) and brisk antegrade flow. RC = right coronary.

atria. Other than increasing the capacity of the atria, auricles have minimal functional significance in the adult heart.

[5] **Surface:** Along with visceral pericardium, the surface of the heart contains varying degrees of adipose tissue. **Coronary arteries** and **cardiac veins** course along the surface of the heart, giving rise to branches or receiving tributaries, respectively. These vessels often travel within sulci that correspond to partitions of underlying chambers.

c. **Arterial supply:** The heart receives blood from the **right** and **left coronary arteries** and their branches (see Figs. 3.45 and 3.46). Coronary arteries arise from **aortic sinuses** in the ascending aorta, just superior to the aortic value cusps. As oxygenated blood is expelled from the left ventricle to the aorta, a small portion of that blood is distributed to the structures of the heart by coronary arteries. Branching patterns can vary significantly.

[1] Right coronary: This artery begins at right aortic sinus and travels to the right in the coronary sulcus to the posterior surface of the heart. Major branches include **sinoatrial (SA) nodal**, **right marginal** (travels along inferior border), **AV nodal**, and **posterior IV** (travels in posterior IV sulcus) **arteries**.

[2] Left coronary: This artery begins at the left aortic sinus and travels a short distance to the left between the pulmonary trunk and left auricle before bifurcating into the **circumflex artery**, which travels around to the posterior surface of heart and **anterior IV artery** (left anterior descending), which travels in the anterior IV sulcus and gives rise to a left marginal branch.

> At the apex of the heart, posterior and anterior IV arteries anastomose.

d. **Venous drainage:** Venous blood from the heart is drained by a series of **cardiac veins** that travel with adjacent arteries (see Figs. 3.45 and 3.46). The **great**, **middle**, and **small cardiac veins** run with the anterior IV, posterior IV, and right marginal arteries, respectively. These veins drain into the **coronary sinus**, which returns venous blood to the right atrium. A collection of small **anterior cardiac veins** arises from the right ventricular wall and bypasses the coronary sinus to drain directly into the anterior wall of the right atrium.

e. **Chambers:** The four chambers of the heart are the **right atrium**, **right ventricle**, **left atrium**, and **left ventricle**. The right side of the heart receives deoxygenated systemic blood and distributes it to the lungs. The left side of the heart receives oxygenated blood from the lungs and distributes it to the head and body. **Valves** and **septa** partition these four chambers, allowing unidirectional flow and sidedness, respectively. To better visualize the direction of blood flow and the structures associated with each chamber, imagine tracing a drop of blood from the right atrium to the thoracic aorta (Fig. 3.47).

> Deoxygenated Blood from the head, neck, and thoracic cage enters the right atrium through the **SVC**, while blood from the abdomen, pelvis, and lower limbs enters through the **IVC**. Deoxygenated Blood from the heart primarily enters the right atrium through the coronary sinus.

[1] Right atrium: This chamber receives blood from the SVC and IVC, coronary sinus, and anterior cardiac veins (Fig. 3.48). The inner surface has smooth (**sinus venarum**) and rough (**pectinate muscle**) portions, which as separated partially by a vertical ridge of tissue called the **crista terminalis**. Externally,

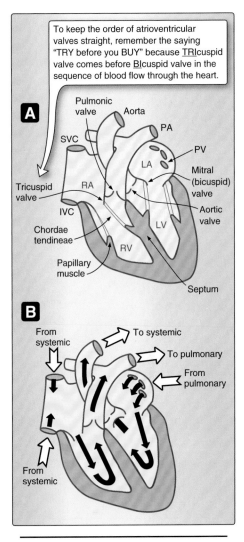

Figure 3.47
Cardiac circulation. A, Internal view of heart chambers and valves. B, Direction of blood flow. External flow (white arrowheads); internal flow (black arrows). IVC = inferior vena cava, LA = left atrium, LV = left ventricle, PA = pulmonary artery, PV = pulmonary vein, RA = right atrium, RV = right ventricle, SVC = superior vena cava.

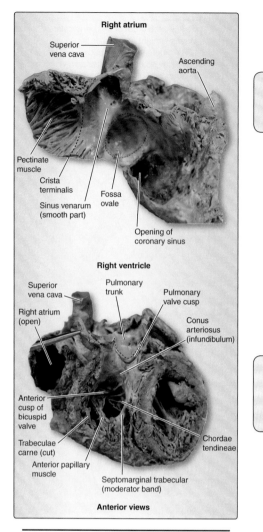

Figure 3.48
Right internal heart structures.

this ridge is represented by the **sulcus terminalis**. Within the sinus venarum is a small oval depression called the **fossa ovalis**—a remnant of the once patent foramen ovale.

 Blood is expelled from the right atrium through the **tricuspid valve** to the right ventricle.

[2] **Right ventricle:** The inner surface is characterized by rough, **trabeculae carne muscle** and a set of **papillary muscles** that correspond to each value cusp (anterior, posterior, septal). Extending from the muscular portion of the **IV septum** to the anterior pupillary muscle is a ridge of tissue called the **septomarginal trabeculae** (moderator band), which transmits the right bundle branch of the heart's intrinsic conduction system. Two adjacent cusps are tethered to one papillary muscles by string-like structures called **chordae tendineae**. The smooth membranous portion of the IV septum—**conus arteriosus**—extends superiorly toward the pulmonary valve.

Blood is expelled from the right ventricle through the **pulmonary value** to the **pulmonary trunk**, which divides into **right** and **left pulmonary arteries** headed to the lungs.

[3] **Left atrium:** Oxygenated Blood returns to the left atrium from the lungs although paired **pulmonary veins** (right and left superior and inferior). The left atrium makes up the base of the heart. The inner surface is primarily smooth, less the pectinate muscle inside the left auricle. The **valve of the foramen ovale** is also visible from the inside of the left atrium (Fig. 3.49).

Blood is expelled from the left atrium through the **bicuspid (mitral) valve** to the left ventricle.

[4] **Left ventricle:** The inner surface of the left ventricle is like that of the right ventricle, in terms of structures present—**papillary muscles** (anterior and posterior), **trabeculae carneae**, and **chordae tendineae**. The muscular walls of the ventricle are thicker than those of the right ventricle, which aids in overcoming systemic blood pressure during left ventricular contraction. A smooth area—**aortic vestibule**—is located superiorly, adjacent to the **aortic valve**.

Oxygenated Blood is expelled from the left ventricle through the **aortic valve** to the ascending aorta and distributed to the head, neck, and body by way of aortic branches.

f. Heart sounds: Contrary to popular belief, heart sounds are not produced by heart contractions, but rather the closure of valves during systolic stages of the cardiac cycle (Fig. 3.50). Clinically, heart sounds can be heard best with a stethoscope at predictable thoracic surface locations, as follows.

[1] **Tricuspid valve:** Sounds from the tricuspid valve can be heard at the fifth or sixth intercostal space near the left sternal border.

[2] **Pulmonary valve:** Sounds from the pulmonary valve can be heard at the second intercostal space, at the left sternal border.

[3] **Bicuspid (mitral) valve:** Sounds from the mitral valve can be heard at the fifth intercostal space in the left midclavicular line.

[4] **Aortic valve:** Sounds from the aortic valve can be heard at the second intercostal space, at the right sternal border.

> Heart sounds are often described as "lub-dub," in which the "lub" refers to closure of the tricuspid and bicuspid valves at the start of ventricular systole (contraction), and "dub" refers to closure of the pulmonary and aortic valves at the end of ventricular systole. "Lub" is the first heart sound and often referred to as S1. "Dub" is the second heart sound and often referred to as S2.

g. Innervation: The heart has its own intrinsic conduction system, which is further regulated by the autonomic nervous system.

[1] **Intrinsic conduction system:** In the heart's conduction system, a wave of depolarization originates at the **SA (sinoatrial) node**, which is the intrinsic pacemaker of the heart (Fig. 3.51). The SA node is located in the wall of the right atrium, adjacent to the SVC. The initial impulse is spread through the atrial walls, causing coordinated contraction before reaching the **AV (atrioventricular) node**, which is located posteriorly between the atria and ventricles. From the AV node, the impulse travels through the **AV bundle** (bundle of His) located in the IV septum before bifurcating into **right** and **left bundle branches**, which distribute to right and left ventricles, respectively. Subendocardial branches distribute to papillary muscles and to the muscular myocardium to control valve closure and ventricular wall contraction, respectively.

[2] **Autonomic regulation:** Autonomic regulation of heart function occurs through sympathetic and parasympathetic components of the **cardiac plexus** (Fig. 3.52). The cardiac plexus is a mixed plexus, described as having superficial and deep components. Postganglionic sympathetic fibers arise from the sympathetic trunk at levels T_1–T_5, while preganglionic parasympathetic fibers are supplied through the right and left vagus nerves (cardiac branches). In general, sympathetic stimulation will increase heart rate and force of contraction and cause vasodilation of coronary arteries. Parasympathetic

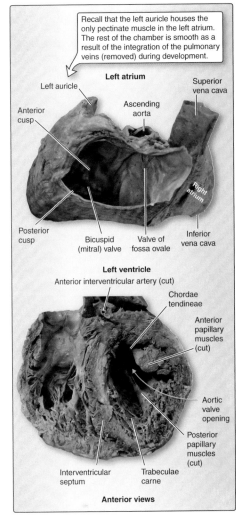

Recall that the left auricle houses the only pectinate muscle in the left atrium. The rest of the chamber is smooth as a result of the integration of the pulmonary veins (removed) during development.

Figure 3.49
Left internal heart structures.

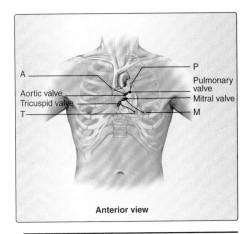

Figure 3.50
Heart sounds. Letters indicate proper placement for heart auscultation sites (blue circles). A = aortic valve, M = mitral (bicuspid) valve, P = pulmonary valve, T = tricuspid valve.

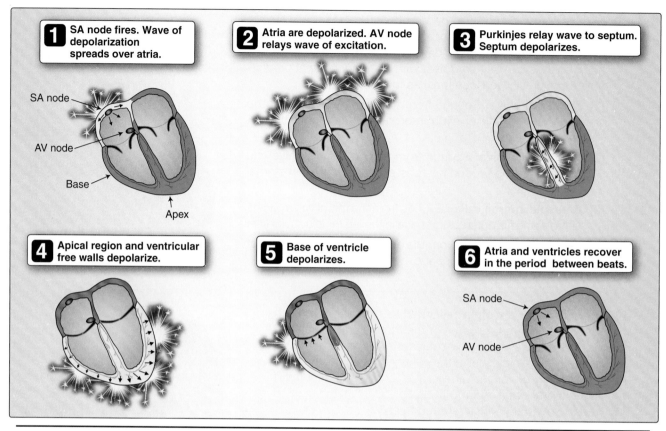

Figure 3.51
Steps in the heart conduction system. AV = atrioventricular, SA = sinoatrial.

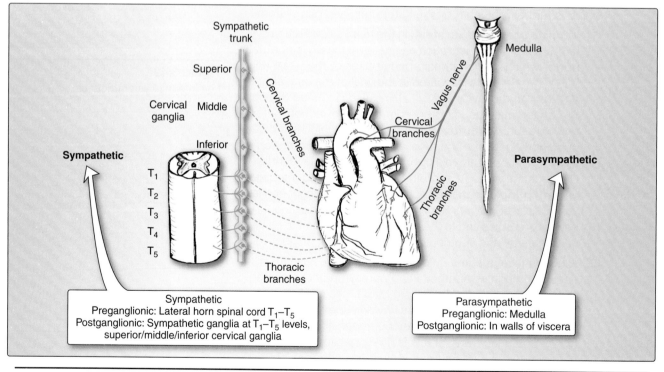

Figure 3.52
Cardiac plexus.

stimulation decreases heart rate and force of contraction and causes vasoconstriction of coronary arteries.

h. Histology: The pericardial cavity is surrounded by the **fibrous pericardium**, which is a dense connective tissue layer that is continuous with the **tunica adventitia** of the blood vessels entering and leaving the heart (see Fig. 3.34). The heart wall in all four chambers of the heart consists of three layers: **endocardium**, **myocardium**, and **epicardium**.

[1] Endocardium: The endocardium is the innermost layer of the heart wall and is thickest in the atria and thinnest in the ventricles. It is continuous with the **tunica intima** of the blood vessels entering and leaving the heart. It is composed of **endothelium**, a **basal lamina**, and a **loose connective tissue layer** (Fig. 3.53).

(a) Endothelium: This simple squamous epithelium lines the inside of the heart chambers and abuts the blood.

(i) Subendocardium: The **subendocardial layer** is a layer of connective tissue that lies beneath the endocardium and contains **blood vessels, autonomic nerve bundles**, and **Purkinje cells**.

(ii) Purkinje cell: The Purkinje cell is a **modified cardiac muscle cell** that is specialized for **conduction** (not contraction). The Purkinje cell is not a neuron. Purkinje cells comprise the **AV bundle** (bundle of His) and right and left bundle branches that travel in the subendocardium and then terminate as an intramural network of Purkinje cells within the myocardium. Purkinje cells are arranged end to end in long rows. They have irregular borders often with

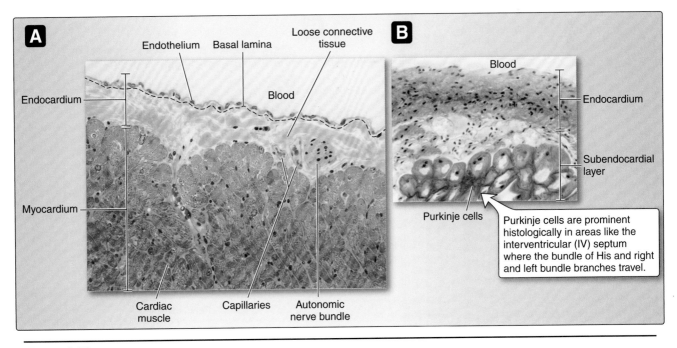

Figure 3.53
Histology of the heart. A, Endocardium. B, Subendocardial layer.

large extensions that protrude into a neighboring Purkinje cell that increases the surface area for cell-to-cell contact. They are connected to each other by intercalated discs. The Purkinje cell has only scattered myofibrils, abundant mitochondria, and a high content of glycogen.

(b) **Basal lamina:** The basal lamina lies beneath the endothelium.

(c) **Loose connective tissue layer:** This layer consists of scattered fibroblasts, collagen fibers, and elastic fibers.

[2] **Myocardium:** The myocardium is the middle layer of the heart wall and is thickest in the ventricles and thinnest in the atria (Fig. 3.54). It is continuous with the tunica media of the blood vessels entering and leaving the heart. The myocardium contains a number of different cell types: **cardiac muscle** (most abundant), **Purkinje, myocardial endocrine**, and **cardiac nodal cells**.

(a) **Cardiac muscle cell:** The cardiac muscle cell is a branching, cylinder-shaped cell that ends in finger-like projections that interdigitate with neighboring cardiac muscle cells. In many cases, a cardiac muscle cell will branch and join two or more neighboring cardiac muscle cells. The cardiac muscle cell is surrounded by a basal lamina and the endomysium. It has a single nucleus located at the center of the cell with a distinctive juxtanuclear region. It is characterized by striations (although not as prominent as in a skeletal muscle cell) that consist of **A bands** (dark), **I bands** (light), and **Z discs**. In addition, **intercalated discs** are conspicuous.

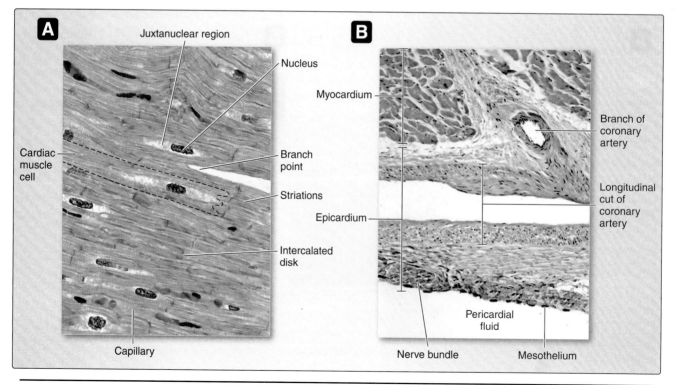

Figure 3.54
Histology of the heart. A, Myocardium. B, Epicardium.

(b) Intercalated disc: This is a highly specialized attachment site that exits between neighboring cardiac muscle cells. It is located along the finger-like projections at the ends of a cardiac muscle cell that interdigitate with neighboring cardiac muscle cells. An intercalated disc consists of a **fascia adherens**, a **macula adherens (desmosome)**, and a **gap junction (nexus)**.

[3] Epicardium: The epicardium is the outermost layer of the heart wall. It consists of three components: **mesothelium**, simple squamous epithelium that lines the inside of the pericardial cavity and abuts the pericardial fluid in the pericardial cavity; **basal lamina** lying beneath the mesothelium; and a **loose connective tissue layer** consisting of scattered fibroblasts, numerous adipocytes, collagen fibers, and elastic fibers. The coronary arteries, cardiac veins, and autonomic nerve bundles travel within this connective tissue layer.

V. POSTERIOR THORACIC WALL

Structures of the posterior thoracic wall are those not contained within pleural cavities or mediastinal compartments, but rather lie deep to the endothoracic fascia (Fig. 3.55). Structures of the posterior thoracic wall include:

- Branches of the thoracic (descending) aorta—posterior intercostal arteries
- Tributaries of the azygos venous system—posterior intercostal veins

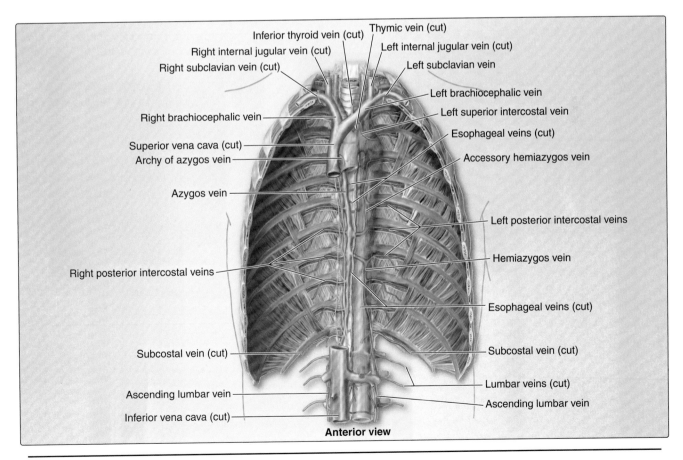

Figure 3.55
Posterior thoracic wall. Aorta ghosted to highlight azygos system.

- Thoracic sympathetic trunks with rami communicantes
- Anterior rami (intercostal nerves)
- Subcostal muscles—innermost intercostal muscles that span more than one intercostal space

Intercostal veins, arteries, and nerves travel in the intercostal space between the internal and innermost intercostal muscles. Bilateral thoracic sympathetic trunks run vertically just lateral to thoracic vertebral bodies T1 through T12. Gray and white rami communicantes connect the sympathetic trunk to spinal nerves at each spinal level in this region.

VI. THORAX IMAGING

The plain film chest radiograph is among the most frequently ordered diagnostic procedures (Fig. 3.56). Therefore, gaining a solid understanding of the normal anatomy of the lungs, pleurae, heart and bony structures of the thorax is essential for evaluating radiographs of this region. In general, a standard chest radiograph includes two views—PA (posterior/anterior) and lateral (see Fig. 1.36). This allows for proper localization of structures, foreign bodies, masses, etc.

CT scans of the thorax allow for a more three-dimensional view of the thoracic viscera (heart and lungs) and adjacent structures and may allow for better detection of pathology that could be missed in a plain film radiograph (Fig. 3.57). Interpretation of any chest radiograph requires an in-depth understanding of the anatomy of the thorax. Intravenous or oral contrast may be used to differentiate specific thoracic structures, especially vasculature.

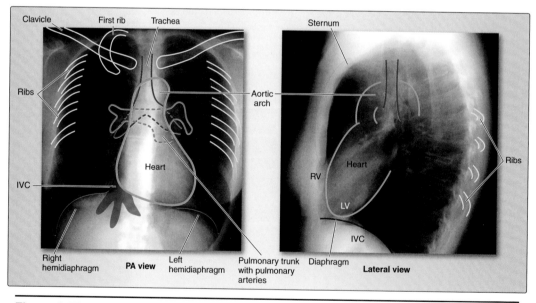

Figure 3.56
Plain film. IVC = inferior vena cava, LV = left ventricle, RV = right ventricle, PA = posterior anterior.

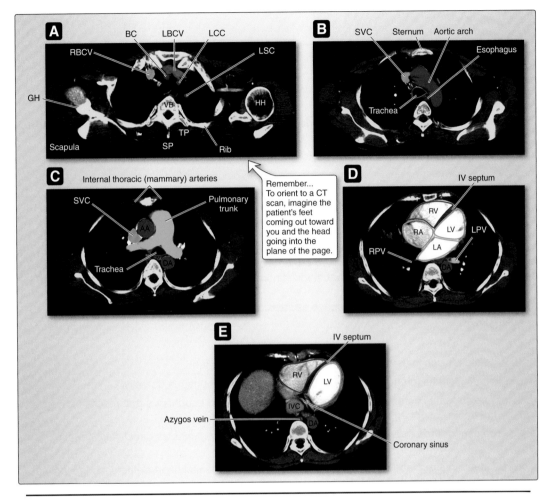

Figure 3.57

CT axial images. A–E arranged from superior to inferior. AA = ascending aorta, BC = brachiocephalic artery, DA = descending aorta, GH = glenohumeral joint, HH = humeral head, IV = interventricular, IVC = inferior vena cava, LA = left atrium, LBCV = left brachiocephalic vein, LCC = left common carotid artery, LPV = left pulmonary vein, LSC = left subclavian artery, LV = left ventricle, RA = right atrium, RBCV = right brachiocephalic vein, RPV = right pulmonary vein, RV = right ventricle, SP = spinous process, SVC = superior vena cava, TP = transverse process, VB = vertebral body.

Chapter Summary

Body Cavities and Diaphragm

- The intraembryonic coelom gets partitioned during development into the definitive adult body cavities called the pleural cavity, pericardial cavity, and peritoneal cavity.

- The paired pleuropericardial membranes and the diaphragm divide the intraembryonic coelom into the three separate adult cavities.

- The paired pleuropericardial membranes fuse in the midline and form the definitive fibrous pericardium.

- The diaphragm is formed by the fusion of the septum transversum, the paired pleuroperitoneal membranes, the dorsal mesentery of the esophagus, and the body wall.

- The diaphragm is innervated by the phrenic nerve (C_3-C_5) and is the main respiratory muscle in the body. It separates the thoracic and abdominal cavities but allows for passage of large structures like the abdominal aorta, inferior vena cava and esophagus.

- The thoracic wall is made up of intercostal musculature and ribs, which collectively provide a semi-rigid, expandable cage that protects thoracic viscera while allowing for movement during respiration.

- The thoracic cavity contains two pleural cavities and a central mediastinum, which if further divided into superior and inferior portions.

- Anterior rami in the thoracic region travel in the intercostal space as intercostal nerves and innervate adjacent intercostal muscles and overlying skin.

Respiratory

- The respiratory diverticulum is the first sign in the development of the respiratory system.

- The tracheoesophageal septum divides the foregut into the trachea ventrally and esophagus dorsally.

- A tracheoesophageal fistula is an abnormal communication between the trachea and esophagus that results from improper division of foregut by the tracheoesophageal septum.

- The fetal and postnatal development of the lungs is divided into four periods: pseudoglandular, canalicular, terminal sac, and alveolar periods.

- Pulmonary hypoplasia can be found in association with right-sided obstructive congenital heart defects, congenital diaphragmatic hernia, or bilateral renal agenesis (Potter syndrome).

- Neonatal respiratory distress syndrome is caused by a deficiency of surfactant, which prevents the newborn from inflating their lungs with air.

- Cell types in the respiratory epithelium include: ciliated, goblet cell, brush, Kulchitsky, and basal cells.

- In the thorax, the respiratory system consists of the trachea, bronchial tree, right and left lungs and associated pleural cavity structures. The esophagus travels posterior to the trachea through the superior and inferior mediastinal regions.

- The trachea travels through the superior mediastinum and bifurcates at the sternal angle.

- The pleural cavity is a space formed between parietal and visceral pleural layers. A small amount of serous fluid is found within this space to decrease friction during respiration.

- The right primary bronchus is wider, shorter and more vertically oriented than the left, making it a common site for foreign body aspiration.

- The right lung has three lobes (upper, middle, lower) and 10 bronchopulmonary segments. The left lung has 2 lobes (upper, lower) and 8 bronchopulmonary segments.

- The pulmonary plexus provides mixed autonomic innervation to respiratory structures. Sympathetic innervation increases bronchodilation and decreases mucous secretions.

- Oxygen exchange occurs at the microscopic interface between pulmonary arteries (deoxygenated blood) and pulmonary veins (oxygenated blood).

- Clara cells secrete a lipoprotein that acts as a surface-active agent to prevent luminal adhesion.

- CC16 (Clara cell 16) protein is used as a marker of pulmonary function in bronchopulmonary lavage fluid and serum.

- Surfactant-associated proteins (SPs) A, B, and D; proteases, antimicrobial peptides; cytokines; chemokines; and mucins contribute to the extracellular material lining the airspaces.

- Clara cells also detoxify airborne toxins using the cytochrome P450 system and functions as stem cells.

Chapter Summary (*continued*)

- The epithelium of an alveolus is composed of a type I pneumocyte, type II pneumocyte, and an alveolar macrophage.
- Type I pneumocytes are simple squamous epithelial cell that line the alveolus and participates in the formation of the blood–air barrier.
- Type II pneumocytes secrete surfactant, which is stored in lamellar bodies.
- Surfactant is composed of dipalmitoylphosphatidylcholine, phosphatidylcholine, phosphatidylglycerol, neutral lipids, cholesterol, and SPs A, B, C, D.
- The components of the blood–air barrier include surfactant, type I pneumocyte cytoplasm, basal lamina, and endothelium cytoplasm.

Heart

- Pre-cardiac mesoderm forms a crescent-shaped area in the cranial region of the embryo.
- Pre-cardiac mesoderm develops into heart-forming regions (HFRs) on either side of the embryo, which fuse in the midline to form a continuous sheet of mesoderm surrounded by the pericardial cavity.
- The five dilations that form along the length of the heart tube are: 1) truncus arteriosus, 2) bulbus cordis, 3) primitive ventricle, 4) primitive atrium, and 5) sinus venosus. They will eventually develop into the adult structures of the heart.
- The heart tube undergoes dextral looping (bending to the right side).
- The atrioventricular (AV) septum forms in the center of the heart as the dorsal AV cushion and ventral AV cushion fuse.
- The atrial septum forms via the septum primum and the septum secundum.
- The interventricular (IV) septum forms via the muscular IV septum and the membranous IV septum.
- The aorticopulmonary (AP) septum forms from neural crest cells that migrate into the truncal ridges and the bulbar ridges. The AP septum develops in a spiral manner and divides the truncus arteriosus and bulbus cordis (or the outflow tract) into the aorta and pulmonary trunk.
- The heart is located, along with the pericardium, in the middle mediastinum, with the roots of the great vessels marking the superior boundary of that space.
- The heart is a four-chamber organ, including right and left atria and ventricles, with the right side of the heart receiving deoxygenated blood to be sent to the lungs and the left side of the heart receiving oxygenated blood to be sent to the body and head.
- The heart has an intrinsic conduction system that is further regulated by the autonomic nervous system.
- Right and left coronary arteries supply the heart, while cardiac veins drain the heart, primarily by way of the coronary sinus. The right atrium receives venous blood through the superior vena cava, inferior vena cava, coronary sinus and anterior cardiac veins.
- The aortic arch begins and ends at the boundary between superior and inferior mediastina, a plane called the sternal angle, which runs from the sternal articulation of the manubrium and body posteriorly through the T4/T5 intervertebral disc.
- The endocardium is the innermost layer of the heart and is continuous with the tunica intima of the blood vessels entering and leaving the heart.
- The subendocardial layer contains small blood vessels, autonomic nerve bundles, and Purkinje cells of the conduction system.
- Purkinje cells are modified cardiac muscle cells specialized for conduction.
- The myocardium is the middle layer of the heart and is continuous with the tunica media of blood vessels entering and leaving the heart.
- The myocardium consists of predominately cardiac muscle cells.
- Cardiac muscle cells are branching, cylinder-shaped cells with a single, centrally located nucleus and striations (A band, I band, and Z disc) along with intercalated discs that attach neighboring cardiac muscle cells.
- The intercalated disc consists of a fascia adherens, a macula adherens (desmosome), and a gap junction (nexus).
- The epicardium is the outermost layer of the heart that abuts the pericardial cavity.
- The pericardial cavity is filled with pericardial fluid and is surrounded by the fibrous pericardium, which is continuous with the tunica adventitia of blood vessels entering and leaving the heart.

Chapter Summary (*continued*)

Breast Development

- The mammary ridges are epidermal (ectoderm) thickenings that form on both sides of the embryo during week 4.
- The primary buds invaginate into the underlying dermis (mesoderm) during week 7.
- The secondary buds form during week 10, whereby they lengthen and branch throughout the remainder of gestation.
- The secondary buds canalize to form 15–25 lactiferous ducts.
- Both males and females have breasts, though female breasts are more prominent with the presence of functional mammary glands and varying degrees of adipose.
- The male nipple can be used as a reliable surface landmark for the fourth intercostal space.
- Lymph from the breast either travels laterally to pectoral nodes (75%) or medially to parasternal nodes (25%), which can communicate to opposite breast. This is a potential pathway for breast cancer metastasis.
- The mammary gland is composed of 15–25 irregular-shaped lobes that empty into 15–25 lactiferous sinuses, 15–25 lactiferous ducts, and ultimately onto the nipple.
- A lobule or, terminal ductule lobular unit (TDLU), comprises a cluster of terminal ductules, hormone-sensitive loose connective tissue, and an intralobular duct.
- The duct system of the mammary gland at the puberty stage is composed of a modest network of ducts that branch into the connective tissue and end with a terminal end bud.
- At the virgin adult stage, it comprises a fairly advanced network of branching ducts that have grown in length and end in a cluster of terminal ductules.
- At the pregnancy stage, it is composed of a prolific network of branching ducts that have grown in length. In addition, the terminal ductules differentiate and form secretory alveoli, which are surrounded by myoepithelial cells.
- During the lactation stage, lumen of the alveoli become filled with milk, as the alveoli become active in milk production and milk secretion at this stage.

Study Questions:

Choose the ONE correct answer.

3.1   Which of the following manifestations occurs in polythelia?

    A. Supernumerary nipples along the midline
    B. Supernumerary breasts along the midline
    C. Supernumerary breasts along the mammary ridge
    D. Supernumerary nipples along the mammary ridge
    E. Supernumerary nipples near the clavicle.

Correct answer = D. Polythelia refers to supernumerary nipples found along the mammary ridge

3.2   The respiratory diverticulum initially is in open communication with the primitive foregut. Which of the following embryonic structures is responsible for separating these two structures?

    A. Laryngotracheal groove
    B. Posterior esophageal folds
    C. Laryngotracheal diverticulum
    D. Tracheoesophageal septum
    E. Bronchopulmonary segment

Correct answer = D. When the tracheoesophageal folds fuse in the midline, they form the tracheoesophageal septum. This septum is responsible for separating the adult trachea ventrally from the esophagus dorsally.

3.3   A faulty fusion of the right and left bulbar ridges and the atrioventricular (AV) septum will result in which of the following?

A. Common ventricle
B. Common atrium
C. Tetralogy of Fallot
D. Membranous ventricular septal defect (VSD)
E. Muscular VSD

Correct answer = D. Faulty fusion of the right and left bulbar ridges and AV cushions will cause membranous VSD. A membranous VSD is the most common type of defect involving the interventricular septum.

3.4   Tetralogy of Fallot (TF) is a cardiac malformation that involves which of the following septa?

A. Aorticopulmonary (AP) septum
B. Atrial septum
C. Atrioventricular (AV) septum
D. Muscular Interventricular (IV) septum
E. Membranous Interventricular (IV) septum

Correct answer = A. TF involves the skewed development of the aorticopulmonary (AP) septum. TF results in a condition in which the pulmonary trunk exhibits a small diameter and the aorta exhibits a large diameter.

3.5   An 8-day-old baby boy presents with a history of complete loss of breath at times and of turning blue on a number of occasions. If the baby is placed in an upright or sitting position, his breathing improves. Physical examination reveals an unusually flat stomach when he is lying down. Auscultation demonstrates no breath sounds on the left side of the thorax. What is the diagnosis?

A. Physiologic umbilical herniation
B. Esophageal hiatal hernia
C. Tetralogy of Fallot
D. Congenital diaphragmatic hernia
E. Tricuspid atresia

Correct answer = D. The loss of breath and cyanosis result from pulmonary hypoplasia associated with congenital diaphragmatic hernia. Placing the baby in an upright position will reduce the hernia somewhat and ease the pressure on the lungs, thereby increasing the baby's comfort. The baby's stomach is flat (instead of the plump belly of a normal newborn) because the abdominal viscera have herniated into the thorax. Auscultation reveals no breath sounds on the left side because of pulmonary hypoplasia.

4 Abdomen

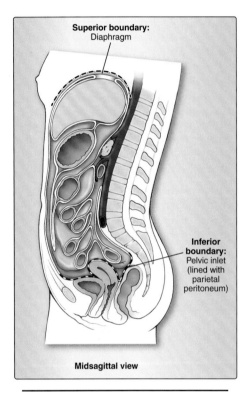

Superior boundary:
Diaphragm

Inferior boundary:
Pelvic inlet
(lined with
parietal
peritoneum)

Midsagittal view

Figure 4.1
Abdomen boundaries.

I. OVERVIEW

The abdomen represents the axial region that extends between the muscular diaphragm and the bony pelvis and contains important gastrointestinal (GI), renal, and endocrine viscera and glands. It is characterized by a multilayered anterolateral muscular wall, which allows for varying degrees of expansion, and is lined internally by parietal and visceral peritoneum, thus creating a peritoneal cavity. Abdominal contents are partially protected by the bony thoracic cage superiorly and the bony pelvis inferiorly (Fig. 4.1).

II. ABDOMINAL WALL

For diagnostic and descriptive purposes, the abdomen can be divided into regions or quadrants externally, which allow for consistent anatomical localization internally. Nine topographic abdominal regions are bound by imaginary vertical lines through the **midclavicular planes** bilaterally and horizontal lines through **subcostal** and **transtubercular planes**. Quadrants are bound by an imaginary vertical line through the median plane and horizontal line through the **transumbilical plane**. The **umbilicus** is the most prominent external feature of the abdominal wall, located midway between the xiphoid process and pubic symphysis (Fig. 4.2).

A. Anterolateral abdominal wall

Unlike the thoracic wall, the anterolateral abdominal wall is primarily made up of layers of soft tissue, including fascia, adipose, muscle, and peritoneum. For descriptive purposes, these structures contribute to the lateral and anterior walls of the abdomen.

1. **Lateral abdominal wall:** Laterally, the abdominal wall is characterized by the layering of three flat abdominal muscles on either side—**external oblique**, **internal oblique**, and **transversus abdominis** (Fig. 4.3). Collectively, these muscles provide support to pelvic viscera. External and internal oblique muscles also perform trunk rotation and flexion.

   a. **External oblique:** This muscle originates from the external surfaces of ribs 5–12 and inserts onto the anterior iliac crest, pubic tubercle, and linea alba.

   b. **Internal oblique:** This muscle originates from the iliac crest and thoracolumbar fascia and inserts onto the pectin pubis (by the conjoint tendon), linea alba, and ribs 10–12.

   c. **Transversus abdominis:** This muscle originates from the internal surfaces of the costal cartilages associated with ribs 7–12, the

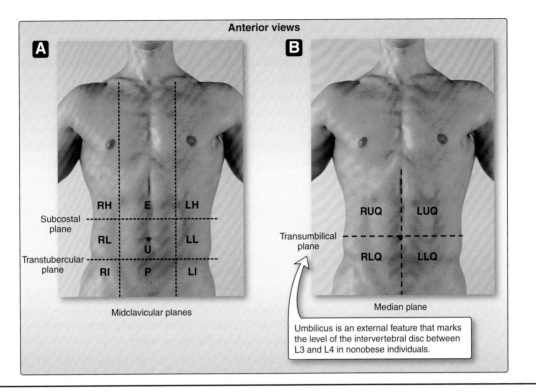

Figure 4.2
Abdomen regional (A) and quadrant (B) organization. E = epigastric, LH = left hypogastric, LI = left inguinal, LL = left lateral (lumbar), LLQ = left lower quadrant, LUQ = left upper quadrant, P = pubic, RH = right hypogastric, RI = right inguinal, RL = right lateral (lumbar), RLQ = right lower quadrant, RUQ = right upper quadrant, U = umbilical.

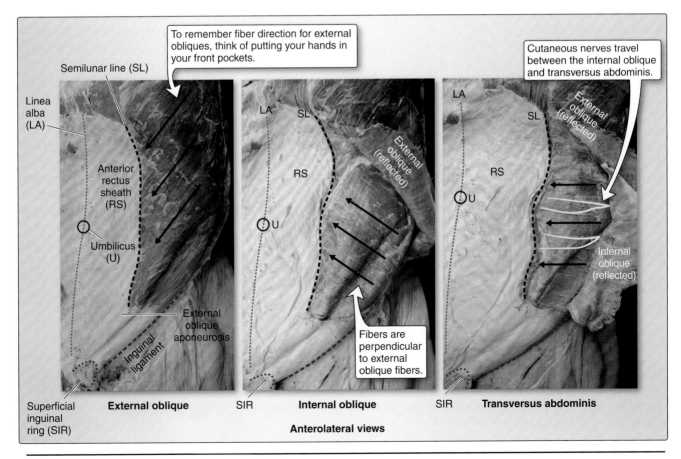

Figure 4.3
Lateral abdominal wall muscles. Left side of abdominal wall. Note arrows illustrate muscle fiber direction.

Table 4.1: General Arrangement of Anterolateral Wall Layers From Superficial to Deep

Lateral Layers	Anterior Layers
Skin	Skin
Superficial fascia, Camper (fatty), and Scarpa (membranous)	Superficial fascia, Camper, and Scarpa
External oblique muscle	Anterior rectus sheath (aponeuroses of external and internal oblique muscles)
Internal oblique muscle	Rectus abdominis muscle
Transverse abdominis muscle	Posterior rectus sheath (aponeuroses of internal oblique and transverse abdominis muscles)
Transversalis fascia	Transversalis fascia
Extraperitoneal adipose	Extraperitoneal adipose
Pa Parietal peritoneum	Parietal peritoneum

iliac crest, and thoracolumbar fascia and inserts onto the pubic crest, pectin pubis (by the conjoint tendon), and linea alba.

   d. **Layers:** The general arrangement of layers from superficial to deep is presented in Table 4.1.

2. **Anterior abdominal wall:** Anteriorly, the abdominal wall is characterized by the **umbilicus**, **rectus abdominis**, and **pyramidalis** muscles; **rectus sheath**; and the midline **linea alba** (Fig. 4.4). The rectus sheath is composed of the aponeuroses of the three flat muscles and encapsulates the rectus abdominis muscle and inferior epigastric arteries and veins. In conjunction with the lateral flat muscles, rectus abdominis flexes the trunk and provides support to abdominal viscera as well as aids in pelvic tilt control. It is characterized by perpendicular **tendinous intersections** along its length, which anchor the muscle to the internal surface of the anterior rectus sheath. Pyramidalis is considered insignificant in the support of the anterior wall, although it functions to tense the linea alba. It is often used as a landmark for abdominal surgeries.

   a. **Rectus abdominis:** This muscle originates from the pubic crest and symphysis and inserts superiorly onto the xiphoid process and costal cartilages of ribs 5–7.

   b. **Pyramidalis:** This muscle originates from the anterior pubis and pubic ligament and inserts in the linea alba.

Umbilical hernias in newborns occur at the site of an incompletely closed umbilicus. Herniation of peritoneum, fat, or bowel may occur. Unlike omphaloceles, umbilical hernias do not involve failed return of intestines from the umbilical cord back into the abdominal cavity.

---

   c. **Layers:** Anteriorly, the general arrangement of layers from superficial to deep is presented in Table 4.1. This arrangement changes at the midway point between the umbilicus and pubic symphysis, due to the transition of aponeuroses. At this level, all three aponeuroses travel anterior to the rectus abdominis muscle, leaving only the transversalis fascia to line the posterior surface of the muscle. This interruption in the dense connective tissue sheath not only allows for the transmission of inferior epigastric vessels, but also creates a weakness in the anterior body wall (Fig. 4.5).

Clinical Application 4.1: Gastroschisis

Gastroschisis is a rare congenital condition in which a full-thickness defect in the anterior abdominal wall—typically to the right of the umbilicus—remains due to nonclosure during lateral body wall folding. This defect allows for abdominal viscera—typically the small intestine—to protrude into the amniotic cavity in utero. Unlike an omphalocele, extruded viscera associated with gastroschisis are not covered by peritoneum and umbilical cord covering. Therefore, the surface of the viscera is in direct contact with the amniotic fluids, which may cause tissue damage, dilation, and wall thickening. Gastroschisis can be detected with fetal ultrasound. Postnatal surgical reduction of eviscerated bowel and closure of abdominal wall defect are indicated.

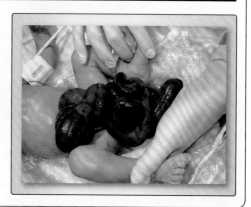

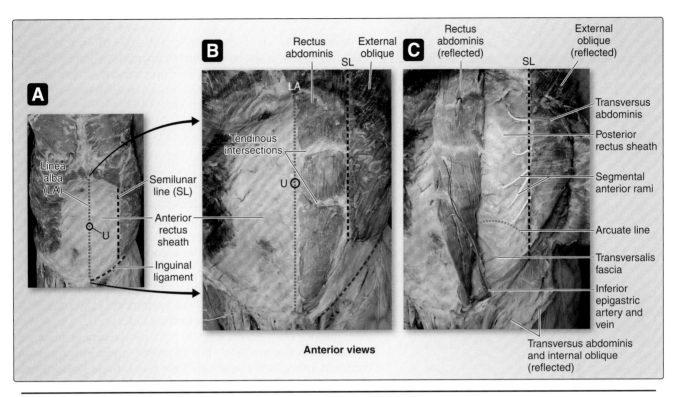

Anterior views

Figure 4.4
Anterior abdominal wall structures. A, Rectus sheath intact. B, Left anterior rectus sheath removed to reveal rectus abdominis. C, Left rectus abdominis muscle reflected to right to reveal posterior rectus sheath and associated structures.

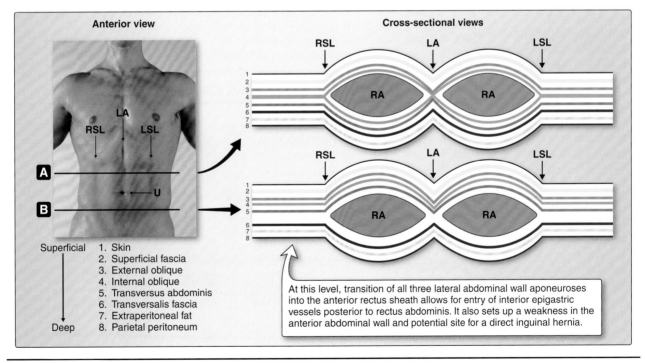

At this level, transition of all three lateral abdominal wall aponeuroses into the anterior rectus sheath allows for entry of interior epigastric vessels posterior to rectus abdominis. It also sets up a weakness in the anterior abdominal wall and potential site for a direct inguinal hernia.

Figure 4.5
Anterolateral abdominal wall layers and rectus sheath. A, Cross section superior to umbilicus. B, Cross section inferior to arcuate line. LA = linea alba, LSL = left semilunar line, RA = rectus abdominis, RSL = right semilunar line, U = umbilicus.

Paracentesis involves passing a needle through the structures of the abdominal wall to access the peritoneal space for excess fluid removal. This procedure is performed in the midline either anteriorly through the linea alba or laterally through the muscular wall.

3. **Innervation:** These muscles and the overlying skin and fascia receive innervation from segmental anterior rami from thoracic and upper lumber spinal nerves (T_6–T_{12}, L_1–L_2).

4. **Blood supply and lymphatics:** The abdominal wall has extensive venous, arterial, and lymphatic networks. This rich vascular arrangement provides important anastomotic flow to the region (Fig. 4.6).

   a. **Veins:** The venous plexus found in the subcutaneous tissue is made up of tributaries inferiorly from the **femoral vein (superficial epigastric** and **superficial circumflex iliac)** and **external iliac vein (inferior epigastric)**, laterally from the **axillary vein (lateral thoracic)**, superiorly from the **superior epigastric/internal thoracic veins**, and posteriorly from the 11th **posterior intercostal** and **subcostal veins**. **Paraumbilical veins**—tributaries from the hepatic portal vein—anastomose with the tributaries in the paraumbilical region to allow for important collateral flow if there is a blockage. This is one of a few areas in the body where there is a portal–caval anastomosis.

   b. **Arteries:** The principle arterial supply for the anterolateral abdominal wall is maintained by branches of the **internal thoracic**

Clinical Application 4.2: Caput Medusae

Caput medusae is a clinical presentation that occurs as a result of portal hypertension. Blood flow in the portal vein is reversed and forced into the caval system at sites of portal–caval anastomoses. Varicosities observed in caput medusae occur around the umbilical anastomosis, where paraumbilical veins in the subcutaneous fascia of the anterior abdominal wall become distended. This clinical diagnosis is named for the appearance of the varicosities, which resemble the head of the Medusa—a character in Greek mythology whose hair was made of venomous serpents.

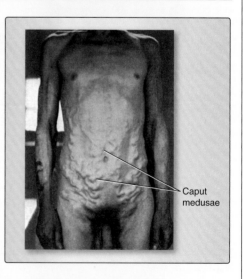

Caput medusae

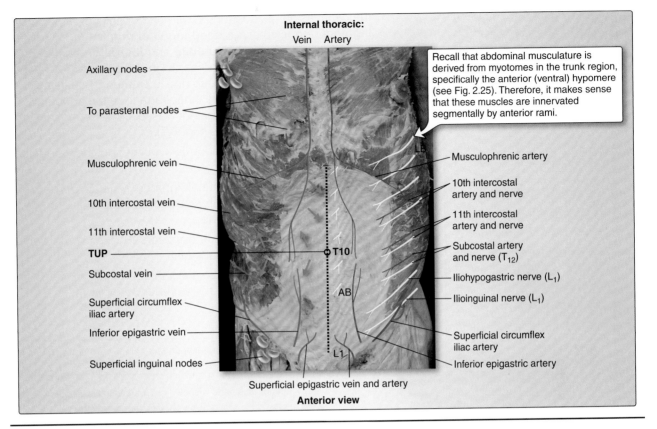

Internal thoracic:
Vein   Artery

Axillary nodes

To parasternal nodes

Recall that abdominal musculature is derived from myotomes in the trunk region, specifically the anterior (ventral) hypomere (see Fig. 2.25). Therefore, it makes sense that these muscles are innervated segmentally by anterior rami.

Musculophrenic vein

10th intercostal vein

11th intercostal vein

TUP

Subcostal vein

Superficial circumflex iliac artery

Inferior epigastric vein

Superficial inguinal nodes

Musculophrenic artery

10th intercostal artery and nerve

11th intercostal artery and nerve

Subcostal artery and nerve (T$_{12}$)

Iliohypogastric nerve (L$_1$)

Ilioinguinal nerve (L$_1$)

Superficial circumflex iliac artery

Inferior epigastric artery

Superficial epigastric vein and artery

Anterior view

T10

AB

L1

LB

Figure 4.6
Abdominal wall blood supply and lymphatics. Right side shows arterial and nervous supply. Left side shows venous drainage and direction of lymph drainage (green arrows). Superficial venous network not pictured. T10 marks the dermatome around the umbilicus. L1 marks the dermatome at the pubic symphysis. AB = anterior branch of thoracoabdominal nerves, LB = lateral branch of thoracoabdominal nerves, TUP = transumbilical plane.

(**musculophrenic** and **superior epigastric**), external iliac (**inferior epigastric** and **deep circumflex iliac**), and femoral (superficial circumflex iliac and superficial epigastric) arteries. **Posterior intercostal** (10th and 11th) and **subcostal** arteries—branches of the aorta—provide additional supply primarily to the lateral portion of the abdominal wall. The superior and inferior epigastric arteries pierce the rectus sheath to enter the space and supply the rectus abdominis muscle directly.

c. **Lymphatics:** Superficial lymphatic vessels superior to the transumbilical plane drain superiorly to axillary lymph nodes (primarily) and parasternal lymph nodes (secondarily). Superficial lymphatic vessels inferior to the transumbilical plane drain inferiorly into superficial inguinal lymph nodes. Deep lymphatic vessels travel with the network of deep veins and drain into lumbar, external iliac, and internal iliac nodes.

B. Inguinal region

The inguinal region lies along the inferior border of the anterolateral abdominal wall and represents the area of passageway (inguinal canal) for the testes/spermatic cord and round ligament of the uterus in the male and female, respectively.

1. **Inguinal canal:** The **inguinal canal** is a passageway bounded by structures that make up the anterolateral abdominal wall. Imagine

the canal as an oblique tunnel with two openings—a **superficial inguinal ring** (exit) and a **deep inguinal ring** (entrance). The superficial ring is framed by **medial** and **lateral crural fibers** and **intracrural fibers** that arise as an interruption of the external oblique aponeurosis. The deep ring is created by an invagination of transversalis fascia on the inner surface of the abdominal wall just lateral to the inferior epigastric vessels. The boundaries of the inguinal canal are as follows (Fig. 4.7).

a. **Anterior:** The anterior boundary of the inguinal canal is the external oblique aponeurosis.

b. **Inferior (floor):** The inguinal ligament (inferior border of the external oblique aponeurosis) and lacunar ligament (medial) comprise the inferior border.

c. **Posterior:** Posteriorly, the transversalis fascia and conjoint tendon border the inguinal canal.

d. **Superior (roof):** Arching fibers of internal oblique and transversus abdominis muscles form the superior border.

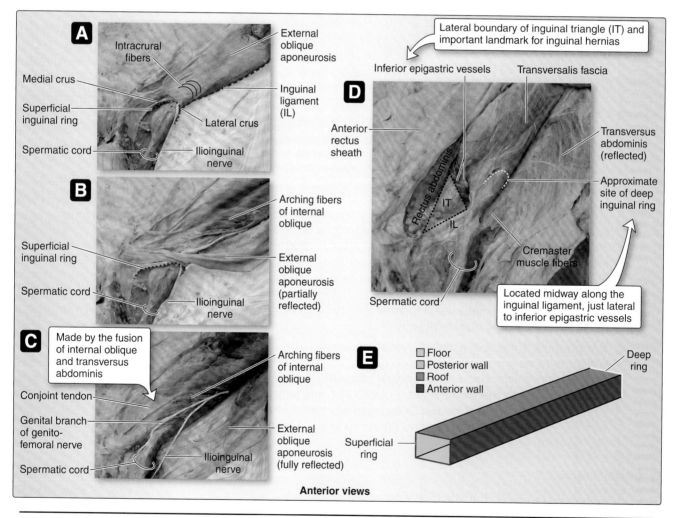

Anterior views

Figure 4.7

Inguinal canal. Layers from superficial A to deep D (A–D). E. Schematic representation of inguinal canal boundaries.

Clinical Application 4.3: Inguinal Hernia

An inguinal hernia results from abdominal contents—typically small bowel—protruding through the abdominal body wall in the inguinal region. Inguinal hernias are described as being either **direct** or **indirect**. A direct inguinal hernia occurs medial to the inferior epigastric vessels, where contents typically protrude through the superficial ring in the inguinal (Hesselbach) triangle. An indirect hernia occurs lateral to the inferior epigastric vessels, where contents protrude through the deep inguinal ring and canal into the scrotum. Direct inguinal hernias are more common in aged males. Indirect inguinal hernias are more common in younger males, often as a result of a **patent processus vaginalis**.

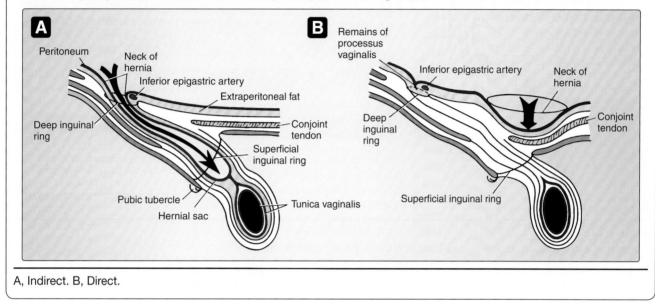

A, Indirect. B, Direct.

C. Spermatic cord and scrotum

Although considered part of the perineum, the scrotum is actually an extension of the lower abdominal wall (Fig. 4.8). Layers of the abdominal wall are represented in the scrotal region and form spermatic cord and testicular coverings. In addition to its coverings, the spermatic cord contains the ductus (vas) deferens, testicular artery, pampiniform venous plexus, deferential vessels, lymphatic vessels, autonomic nerves, and the genital branch of the genitofemoral nerve (L_1–L_2). For additional details on the testes, refer to Chapter 5.

III. PERITONEAL CAVITY

The peritoneal cavity is a potential space between **parietal** and **visceral peritoneal layers** that line the inner surface of the abdominal body wall and abdominal organs (viscera), respectively (Fig. 4.9).

A. Development

Recall that during the fourth week of development, the **intraembryonic coelom** has developed and is being partitioned into **pleural**, **pericardial**, and **peritoneal cavities** (see Fig. 3.17). **Pleuroperitoneal folds** expand medially to begin to close off the right and left **pericardioperitoneal canals**. During this process, the folds thin to become pleuroperitoneal membranes, which will eventually fuse with the **septum transversum** and

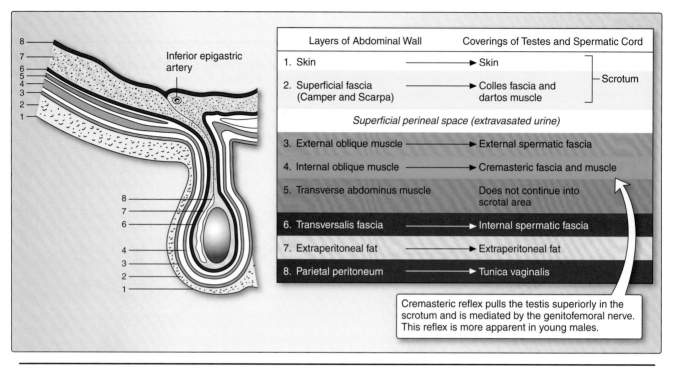

Layers of Abdominal Wall	Coverings of Testes and Spermatic Cord
1. Skin	→ Skin
2. Superficial fascia (Camper and Scarpa)	→ Colles fascia and dartos muscle
Superficial perineal space (extravasated urine)	
3. External oblique muscle	→ External spermatic fascia
4. Internal oblique muscle	→ Cremasteric fascia and muscle
5. Transverse abdominus muscle	Does not continue into scrotal area
6. Transversalis fascia	→ Internal spermatic fascia
7. Extraperitoneal fat	→ Extraperitoneal fat
8. Parietal peritoneum	→ Tunica vaginalis

Inferior epigastric artery

Scrotum

Cremasteric reflex pulls the testis superiorly in the scrotum and is mediated by the genitofemoral nerve. This reflex is more apparent in young males.

Figure 4.8
Scrotum. Corresponding abdominal wall and scrotal/spermatic cord layers.

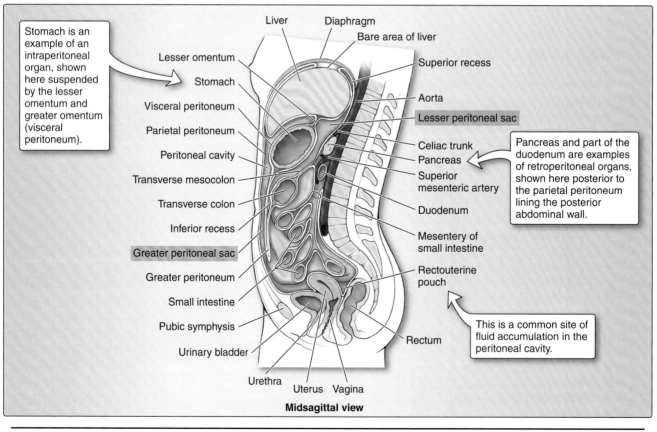

Stomach is an example of an intraperitoneal organ, shown here suspended by the lesser omentum and greater omentum (visceral peritoneum).

Liver
Diaphragm
Bare area of liver
Lesser omentum
Superior recess
Stomach
Aorta
Visceral peritoneum
Lesser peritoneal sac
Parietal peritoneum
Celiac trunk
Peritoneal cavity
Pancreas
Transverse mesocolon
Superior mesenteric artery
Transverse colon
Duodenum
Inferior recess
Mesentery of small intestine
Greater peritoneal sac
Greater peritoneum
Rectouterine pouch
Small intestine
Pubic symphysis
Urinary bladder
Rectum
Urethra   Uterus   Vagina
Midsagittal view

Pancreas and part of the duodenum are examples of retroperitoneal organs, shown here posterior to the parietal peritoneum lining the posterior abdominal wall.

This is a common site of fluid accumulation in the peritoneal cavity.

Figure 4.9
Peritoneal cavity.

dorsal mesentery of the esophagus. This fusion, along with contributions from lateral body wall ingrowth, forms the primitive thoracic diaphragm and partitions the thoracic and abdominal cavities.

1. **Mesentery:** Lateral mesoderm contributes to the development of serous membranes that make up the layers of the peritoneal cavity— **parietal** and **visceral peritoneum**. At the junction of parietal and visceral peritoneum, a double layer of peritoneum, called **mesentery**, exists to suspend or cover viscera and provide a passageway for neurovascular structures to reach abdominal viscera. In the developing human, primitive **ventral** and **dorsal mesenteries (mesogastria)** connect the gut tube to the ventral or dorsal body wall, respectively. In the early stages of development, this arrangement partitions the abdominal cavity into right and left halves. As gut tube development and rotation proceeds, the ventral mesentery remains only in the area of the liver, proximal duodenum, and lesser curvature of the stomach. The dorsal mesentery develops into visceral peritoneum associated with the greater curvature of the stomach, portions of the small and large intestines, spleen, kidney, and diaphragm (Table 4.2). Final positioning of the ventral and dorsal mesenteries contributes to the formation of a small space posterior to the stomach called the **lesser peritoneal sac** (omental bursa), which has limited communication with a larger space that occupies most of the peritoneal cavity called the **greater peritoneal sac**.

2. **Parietal peritoneum:** With the elongation of the trunk, the final position of abdominal contents extends into the true pelvis. Parietal peritoneum also extends into the true pelvis, thus serving as a drape over pelvic viscera. This draping of parietal peritoneum completely closes off the peritoneal cavity in males but allows for communication externally in females by way of the uterine tubes, which are not fully covered by parietal peritoneum (see Fig. 4.1).

B. Anatomy

The peritoneal cavity is formed during development by primitive dorsal and ventral mesenteries. Following birth, the primitive mesenteries are designated as either an omentum or a "ligament" and are named by the structures they span between or surround. Viscera that are suspended in these peritoneal structures are described as **intraperitoneal**, whereas viscera that are only partially covered (one side) by peritoneum and posterior to the parietal peritoneum are described as **retroperitoneal**. These relationships between peritoneum and viscera occur as a result of GI tract development (Table 4.3 and Fig. 4.10, also see Fig. 4.9).

1. **Greater omentum:** The greater omentum is apron-like in appearance and contains variable amounts of fat. Arising from the greater curvature of the stomach, it drapes anterior to the transverse colon and—in varying degrees—the small intestines before doubling back and ascending to attach to the transverse colon. It is further divided into different portions, including the **gastrocolic ligament** (attached to transverse colon), **gastrosplenic ligament** (attached to spleen hilum), and **gastrophrenic ligament** (attached to abdominal surface of the diaphragm).

2. **Lesser omentum:** The lesser omentum spans between the lesser curvature of the stomach and the first part of the duodenum to the

Table 4.2: Dorsal and Ventral Mesentery Derivatives

Dorsal Mesentery Derivatives	Ventral Mesentery Derivatives[a]
Greater omentum (gastrocolic, gastrosplenic, and gastrophrenic ligaments)	Lesser omentum (hepatogastric and hepatoduodenal ligaments)
Splenorenal ligament	Falciform ligament
Mesentery of small intestine	Coronary ligament (right and left triangular ligaments)
Mesoappendix	
Transverse mesocolon	
Phrenicocolic ligament	
Sigmoid mesocolon	

[a]All ventral mesentery derivatives have attachments on the liver.

Table 4.3: Intraperitoneal and Retroperitoneal Viscera

Intraperitoneal Viscera	Retroperitoneal Viscera
Stomach	Second to fourth part of duodenum
First part of duodenum	Ascending colon
Jejunum	Descending colon
Ileum	Rectum
Cecum	Head, neck, and body of pancreas
Appendix	Kidneys
Transverse colon	Ureters
Sigmoid colon	Suprarenal (adrenal) glands
Liver	Abdominal aorta
Gallbladder	Inferior vena cava
Tail of pancreas	
Spleen	

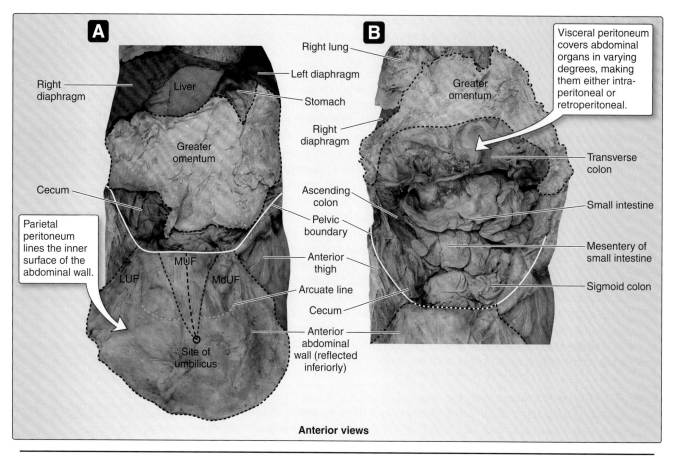

Figure 4.10
Peritoneal structures. Open abdominal cavity. A, Greater omentum in position. B, Greater omentum reflected superiorly.
LUF = lateral umbilical fold, MdUF = medial umbilical fold, MUF = median umbilical fold.

liver. Although the lesser omentum is continuous, it is further distinguished by these attachments into two ligaments—**hepatogastric** and **hepatoduodenal**. The lesser omentum closes off the lesser peritoneal sac anteriorly, and the free edge of the hepatoduodenal ligament serves as a boundary of the omental foramen (foramen of Winslow). The hepatoduodenal ligament also contains the portal triad (common bile duct, proper hepatic artery, and hepatic portal vein), as shown in Figure 4.11.

3. **Splenorenal ligament:** This ligament spans between the hilum of the spleen and the left kidney. The splenic artery travels through this ligament and gives off important branches to portions of the stomach.

4. **Small intestine mesentery:** This fat-laden, fan-shaped mesentery extends from the posterior abdominal wall to suspend the jejunum and ileum. Intestinal vessels and autonomic nerves travel through the mesentery substance to reach the organ walls.

5. **Transverse mesocolon:** This ligament suspends the transverse colon from the posterior abdominal wall and spans across the descending (second part) duodenum and the majority of the pancreas. The gastrocolic ligament is positioned superior and anterior to the transverse mesocolon.

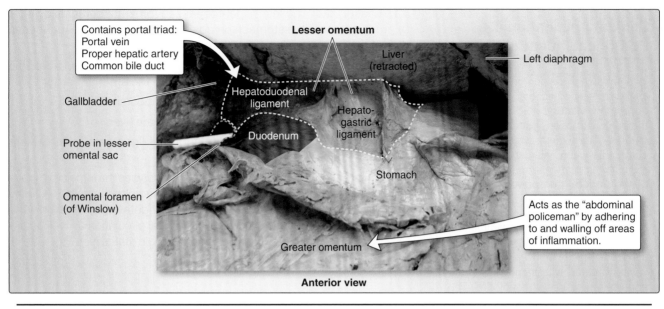

Figure 4.11
Lesser omentum and sac.

6. **Phrenicocolic ligament:** This ligament spans between the left colic (splenic) flexure of the large intestine and the abdominal surface of the left hemidiaphragm. These connections form a "shelf" for the spleen.

7. **Sigmoid mesocolon:** This ligament spans between the inferior, left posterior abdominal wall and the sigmoid colon.

8. **Mesoappendix:** Small in nature, this mesentery spans between the posterior abdominal wall and appendix.

9. **Falciform ligament:** This thin fold of mesentery extends from the anterior liver surface to the internal surface of the anterior abdominal wall. It is sickle-shaped, and its inferior border houses the **ligamentum teres hepatis** (round ligament of the liver), which represents the obliterated umbilical vein.

10. **Coronary ligaments:** A divergence occurs at the superior limit of the falciform ligament on the surface of the liver. This separation of visceral peritoneal layers forms the right and left coronary ligaments. At their most distal extensions, the right and left coronary ligaments reverse in direction to form the **right** and **left triangular ligaments**, respectively. Collectively, these reflections surround an area on the liver—the **bare area**—that lacks visceral peritoneum.

C. Peritoneal sacs

The peritoneal cavity is described as having two sacs—**lesser** and **greater**. The lesser and greater peritoneal sacs communicate by way of the **omental foramen** (foreman of Winslow). The omental foramen is bound posteriorly by the inferior vena cava (IVC) and anteriorly by the portal triad (see Fig. 4.11).

Clinical Application 4.4: Peritoneal Inflammation

Inflammation of the peritoneum can occur as a result of visceral rupture (e.g., appendix), visceral fluid escape into the peritoneal cavity, penetration of the peritoneal cavity (e.g., stab wound), or contact between enlarged viscera and surrounding peritoneum. Inflammation of the parietal peritoneum presents with sharp, localized pain, **rebound tenderness** and reflexive **guarding** with palpation in the area of inflammation. **Peritonitis**—inflammation and infection of the peritoneum—is treated with cavity washout with sterile saline and appropriate course of antibiotics. The greater omentum plays a protective role during inflammation and infection in the peritoneal cavity such that it can isolate and seal off the damaged region and acts as the principle site for migration and proliferation of macrophages and neutrophils.

1. **Lesser sac:** The lesser peritoneal sac (omental bursa) allows for movement of the stomach on posterior structures. The boundaries of the lesser peritoneal sac are as follows.

    a. **Anterior:** The liver, stomach, and lesser omentum (hepatogastric and hepatoduodenal ligaments) form the anterior border.

    b. **Posterior:** The diaphragm forms the posterior border.

    c. **Right:** The right border is formed by the liver.

    d. **Left:** Gastrosplenic and splenorenal ligaments form the left border.

2. **Greater sac:** The greater peritoneal sac occupies the remaining space in the abdomen spanning from the diaphragm to the pelvis. A series of spaces (pouches, recesses, paracolic "gutters") occur within the greater peritoneal sac, allowing for normal circulation as well as accumulation of peritoneal fluids in pathologic states (see Fig. 4.9).

> Excess peritoneal fluids often collect in the rectovesicle pouch in males or the rectouterine pouch (pouch of Douglas) in females. Access to these fluids for diagnostic testing is done through the umbilicus in males and through the posterior fornix of the cervix in females.

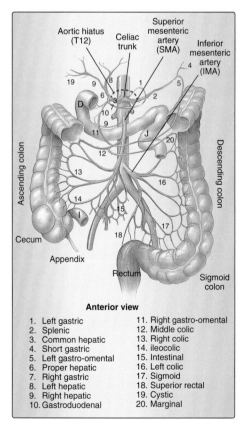

Figure 4.12
Abdominal arterial supply overview.
D = duodenum, I = ileum, J = jejunum.

IV. ABDOMINAL VASCULATURE AND LYMPHATICS

Arterial blood supply to abdominal viscera originates from the abdominal aorta. The thoracic aorta enters the abdomen through the aortic hiatus in the diaphragm at the T12 vertebral level. At this point, it is designated as the abdominal aorta, which extends inferiorly until bifurcating into right and left common iliac arteries at the L4 vertebral level. The abdominal aorta continues inferiorly at the bifurcation in the form of a small, often wanting, median sacral artery. Along the length of the abdominal aorta arise three anterior unpaired branches and multiple paired branches. Venous drainage of structures in the abdominal cavity is unique in that it involves two systems—the portal system and the caval system.

A. Unpaired aortic vessels

Three unpaired branches arise from the anterior surface of the aorta and serve as the primary blood supply to organs associated with the foregut, midgut, and hindgut (Fig. 4.12). To ensure collateral blood flow, select viscera receive branches from more than one of these unpaired branches.

1. **Celiac trunk:** Short in length, the celiac trunk serves as the primary artery to foregut structures (Fig. 4.13). It is the first of the three unpaired vessels to branch from the abdominal aorta, just inferior to the aortic hiatus (T12 level). It almost immediately branches into the left gastric, splenic, and common hepatic arteries.

    a. **Left gastric artery:** The left gastric artery courses to the left half of the lesser curvature of the stomach and gives off a small esophageal branch proximally. It anastomoses along the lesser curvature with the right gastric artery.

Clinical Application 4.5: Abdominal Aortic Aneurysm

Abdominal aortic aneurysm (AAA) is defined as a true aneurysm in which the diameter of the aortic lumen is >50% that of the normal aortic lumen diameter (~2.0 cm), the dilation is segmental, and the full thickness of the vessel is affected. AAAs are described based on their position or involvement with renal vasculature (suprarenal, pararenal, juxtarenal, infrarenal), and most commonly occur between the renal and inferior mesenteric arteries (between L1–L3 vertebral levels). Men are more likely to develop an AAA and cofactors include atherosclerosis, hypertension, family history, and age. Although the majority of patients are asymptomatic, screening is important to limit AAA rupture. Common AAA symptoms prior to rupture include abdominal, back or flank pain, and poor circulation and potential ischemia in lower limbs. A ruptured AAA presents with hypotension, delirium, severe central abdominal pain that may radiate to the spine, and, in ~50% of cases, an abdominal mass with a palpable pulse. Vascular imaging studies are used to confirm the diagnosis and determine a treatment plan. AAA diameter and symptoms dictate management. Open or endovascular surgical repair of an AAA may be indicated in patients who have experienced or are at high risk for AAA rupture.

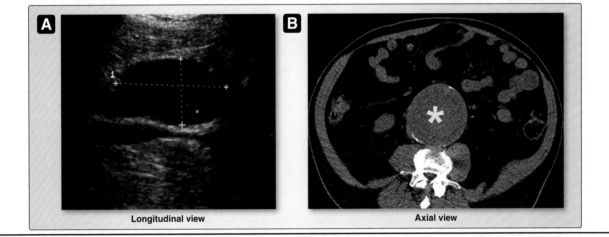

A, Sonographic image showing large AAA. B, CT shows nonruptured aneurysm (*). CT = computed tomography.

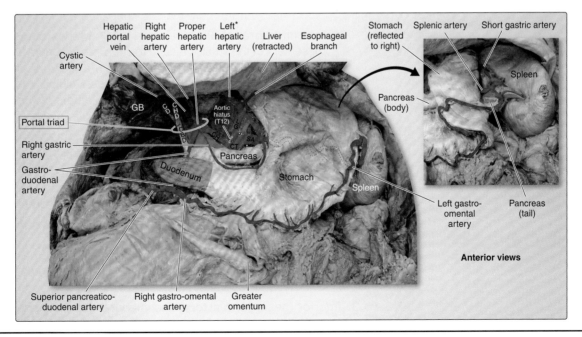

Figure 4.13
Celiac trunk (CT). CBD = common bile duct, CD = cystic duct, CH = common hepatic artery, CHD = common hepatic duct, GB = gallbladder, LG = left gastric, PH = proper hepatic artery, SA = splenic artery. * = variation of left hepatic artery, which typically is a branch of PH.

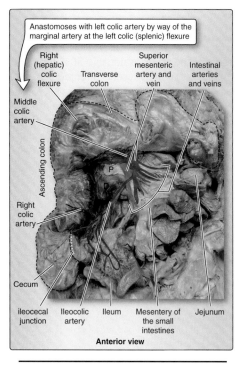

Figure 4.14
Superior mesenteric artery.
D = duodenum, P = pancreas.

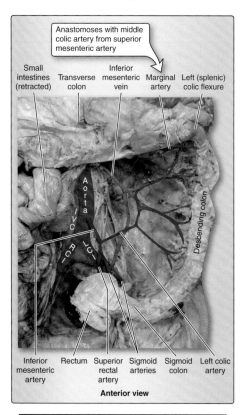

Figure 4.15
Inferior mesenteric artery. IVC = inferior vena cava, LCI = left common iliac artery, RCI = right common iliac artery.

b. **Splenic artery:** This tortuous artery travels to the left, posteriorly to the pancreas and enters the splenorenal ligament before terminating in the hilum of the spleen. Just before entering the spleen, the artery gives off **short gastric** branches superiorly to the fundus of the stomach and a **left gastro-omental** (gastroepiploic) artery to the left greater curvature of the stomach. This will eventually anastomose with the right gastro-omental (gastroepiploic) artery. Additional branches include **dorsal** and **greater pancreatic arteries**.

c. **Common hepatic artery:** This artery courses to the right, toward the liver. It divides into **proper hepatic artery** and **gastroduodenal artery**. Proper hepatic ascends toward the liver and gives off a **right gastric artery** before dividing into **right** and **left hepatic arteries**. Right hepatic artery typically gives rise to the **cystic artery**, which supplies the gallbladder. Gastroduodenal gives off **supraduodenal branches**, descends between the duodenum (first part) and pancreas, and divides into **superior pancreaticoduodenal** and **right gastro-omental** (gastroepiploic) **arteries**.

2. **Superior mesenteric artery:** The superior mesenteric artery (SMA) arises from the aorta, just inferior to the celiac trunk (L1 level), and serves as the primary artery to midgut structures (Fig. 4.14). The artery travels inferiorly and crosses anterior to the left renal vein, pancreas (uncinate process), and the duodenum (third part, horizontal). Within the mesentery of the small intestine, the SMA gives off multiple branches.

a. **Inferior pancreaticoduodenal:** The first branch of the SMA travels superiorly to supply the duodenum and head/uncinate process of the pancreas. It anastomoses with the superior pancreaticoduodenal artery. This is an example of structures receiving blood supply from more than one unpaired aortic arteries.

b. **Intestinal branches:** Multiple (15–18) arteries course in the mesentery of the small intestine to supply the jejunum and ileum. Close to the organ, these vessels form a network of **arterial arcades** that extend into straight vessels called **vasa recta**. The pattern of arcades and vasa recta differs in the jejunum and ileum.

c. **Ileocolic artery:** Found descending into the right lower quadrant, this artery serves as the primary supply to the distal ileum, cecum, and appendix. At the ileocecal junction, it gives off a small **appendicular artery**, which courses through the mesoappendix.

d. **Right colic artery:** This artery can be a direct branch of the SMA or arise from the ileocolic artery. It travels to supply the ascending colon (large intestines).

e. **Middle colic artery:** This artery arises from the proximal SMA and travels in the transverse mesocolon to supply the proximal two thirds of the transverse colon.

3. **Inferior mesenteric artery:** The inferior mesenteric artery arises from the aorta at the L3 level, just inferior to the duodenum (third part), as shown in Figure 4.15. It travels toward the left lower quadrant to supply hindgut structures. Its branches are as follows:

a. **Left colic artery:** This artery supplies the distal third of the transverse colon (by way of the marginal artery) and descending colon.

Clinical Application 4.6: Nutcracker Syndrome

Nutcracker syndrome refers to compression of the left renal vein by the overlying superior mesenteric artery (SMA). The left renal vein courses across the abdominal aorta, just posterior to the SMA to reach the left kidney. Compression limits or occludes drainage of venous blood from the left kidney to the inferior vena cava (IVC). This can cause left flank pain and renal hypertension with subsequent venous rupture within the kidney, resulting in blood in the urine (hematuria). Nutcracker syndrome is different from SMA syndrome (Wilkie syndrome), which compresses the horizontal (third part) of the duodenum, causing visceral rather than vascular obstruction. However, these two syndromes may occur simultaneously.

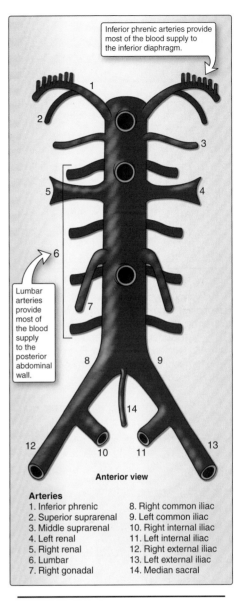

Inferior phrenic arteries provide most of the blood supply to the inferior diaphragm.

Lumbar arteries provide most of the blood supply to the posterior abdominal wall.

Anterior view

Arteries
1. Inferior phrenic
2. Superior suprarenal
3. Middle suprarenal
4. Left renal
5. Right renal
6. Lumbar
7. Right gonadal
8. Right common iliac
9. Left common iliac
10. Right internal iliac
11. Left internal iliac
12. Right external iliac
13. Left external iliac
14. Median sacral

Figure 4.16
Paired aortic branches.

b. **Sigmoid arteries:** This collection of arteries supplies the sigmoid colon.

c. **Superior rectal artery:** This artery supplies the superior rectum and anastomoses with middle and inferior rectal arteries to provide collateral blood flow to the rectum.

B. Paired aortic vessels

As shown in Figure 4.16, paired vessels from the aorta supply the abdominal body wall and paired viscera in the abdominal cavity, such as the kidneys, or viscera that originated in the abdominal cavity during development, such as the gonads (ovaries/testes). The following paired vessels are listed from superior to inferior along the length of the abdominal aorta.

1. **Inferior phrenic arteries:** These supply the diaphragm and gives off superior suprarenal arteries.

2. **Middle suprarenal arteries:** These arise at the L1 level to supply the suprarenal glands.

3. **Renal arteries:** These large vessels arise at the L1 level to supply the kidneys. The right renal artery travels posterior to the IVC to reach the right kidney. Renal arteries also give off **inferior suprarenal arteries**.

4. **Lumbar arteries:** From L1 to L4 levels, four to five paired arteries arise from the aorta to supply the posterior abdominal wall and surrounding spinal structures.

5. **Gonadal arteries:** Ovarian (female) and testicular (male) arteries originate from the abdominal aorta at the L2 level, despite the final position of the ovaries in the pelvis and testes in the scrotum.

C. Portal–caval system

Two venous systems exist in the abdomen. The **portal venous system** is responsible for transporting venous blood from the GI viscera (including pancreas and spleen) to the liver for filtration by way of the hepatic portal vein. The **caval venous system** drains venous blood from structures of the posterior abdominal wall, kidneys, gonads, and suprarenal glands. Important anastomoses between these two systems occur at select sites in the abdomen and pelvis to ensure collateral flow in the event of blockage.

1. **Portal venous system:** The **hepatic portal vein** is most commonly formed by the union of the **superior mesenteric** and

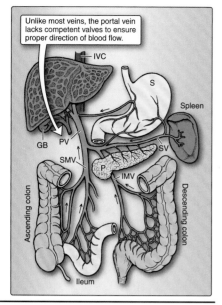

Figure 4.17
Portal venous system. Arrows indicate direction of venous blood flow from viscera to liver by way of the portal vein (PV). GB = gallbladder, IMV = inferior mesenteric vein, IVC = inferior vena cava, P = pancreas, S = stomach, SMV = superior mesenteric vein, SV = splenic vein.

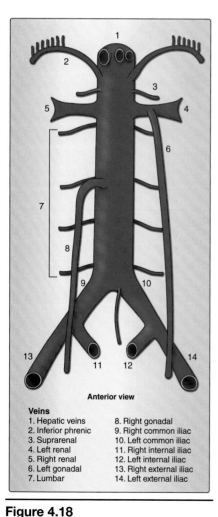

Veins

1. Hepatic veins	8. Right gonadal
2. Inferior phrenic	9. Right common iliac
3. Suprarenal	10. Left common iliac
4. Left renal	11. Right internal iliac
5. Right renal	12. Left internal iliac
6. Left gonadal	13. Right external iliac
7. Lumbar	14. Left external iliac

Figure 4.18
Caval venous system.

splenic veins (Fig. 4.17). The inferior mesenteric vein typically drains into either the splenic vein, superior mesenteric vein, or directly into the union of these vessels. Tributaries of these main vessels collect blood from abdominal viscera to be eventually filtered through the liver. The hepatic portal vein travels in the hepatoduodenal ligament to reach the liver, where it divides into right and left portal veins.

2. **Caval venous system:** The caval venous system is made up of the **IVC** and its tributaries (Fig. 4.18). The IVC is formed by the union of the left and right common iliac veins. In addition to draining blood from the posterior body wall, kidneys, gonads, and suprarenal glands, it receives venous blood from pelvic and perineal structures and the lower limbs. This venous blood bypasses the liver to enter the right atrium of the heart. In the abdomen, the IVC is situated to the right of the aorta, travels posterior to the liver, and receives multiple, short hepatic veins from the liver before piercing the diaphragm at the T8 level to enter the heart.

3. **Portal–caval anastomoses:** Venous anastomoses between these two systems occur in three main regions—the distal esophagus, paraumbilicus, and rectum (Fig. 4.19).

   a. **Esophagus anastomoses:** Tributaries of the left gastric vein (portal system) anastomose with esophageal veins (caval system) of the azygos system.

   b. **Paraumbilical anastomoses:** Paraumbilical veins (portal system) anastomose with superficial veins of the anterolateral abdominal wall (caval system).

   c. **Rectal anastomoses:** Superior rectal veins (portal system) anastomose with middle and inferior rectal veins (caval system).

D. Abdominal lymphatics

Lymph nodes are located throughout the abdomen to receive lymph from abdominal viscera and body wall structures (Fig. 4.20).

1. **Preaortic nodes:** Central collections of preaortic nodes include **celiac, superior mesenteric,** and **inferior mesenteric nodes,** which are located adjacent to the arteries of the same name.

2. **Para-aortic nodes:** Central para-aortic nodes include **right** (caval) and **left** (aortic) **lumbar nodes,** which are located along the length of the IVC and aorta, respectively.

3. **Peripheral nodes:** Peripheral collections of nodes are scattered throughout the mesenteries and along vessels, closer to viscera. These nodes drain centrally.

4. **Cysterna chyli:** Efferents from preaortic nodes (celiac, superior mesenteric, inferior mesenteric) join to form **right** and **left intestinal lymph trunks.** Efferents from lumbar nodes join to form **right** and **left lumbar lymph trunks.** These trunks coalesce at the **abdominal confluence,** the site of a small lymphatic sac called the cysterna chyli. Although commonly less sac-like and more plexiform in appearance, the cysterna chyli sits just inferior to the diaphragm at the aortic hiatus (T12 level). Here, it transitions into the thoracic duct, which continues superiorly in the thoracic cavity.

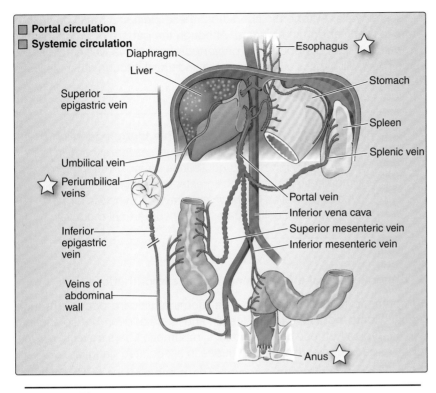

Figure 4.19
Portal–caval anastomoses. Stars indicate site of anastomosis.

V. ABDOMINAL VISCERA INNERVATION

Innervation of the abdominal viscera occurs through an intricate network of autonomic ganglia and plexuses that are organized principally along the anterior surface of the abdominal aorta and along associated paired and unpaired aortic branches (Fig. 4.21, also see Figs. 1.32–1.35). These autonomic structures collectively constitute the **aortic plexus**, which is described as prevertebral (preaortic), as opposed to the paravertebral sympathetic trunks that run on either side of the vertebral bodies. Sympathetic and parasympathetic (general visceral efferent [GVE]) components differ significantly in their origin and slightly in their overall pattern once in the abdominal cavity. In general, both fiber types travel into the abdominal cavity as preganglionic fibers before synapsing on either prevertebral ganglia (sympathetic) or on ganglia in the walls of viscera (parasympathetic).

A. Aortic plexus

The aortic plexus spans between vertebral levels T12 to L3, primarily on the anterior surface of the abdominal aorta. Sympathetic ganglia and mixed (sympathetic and parasympathetic) autonomic fibers that make up subsidiary plexuses are named by the arteries they surround. Named mixed plexuses include **celiac**, **renal**, **intermesenteric**, **inferior mesenteric**, and **superior hypogastric**. Named sympathetic ganglia associated with these plexuses include **celiac**, **superior mesenteric**, **aorticorenal**, and **inferior mesenteric**. These ganglia contain postganglionic sympathetic neurons. Postganglionic parasympathetic neurons are primarily located

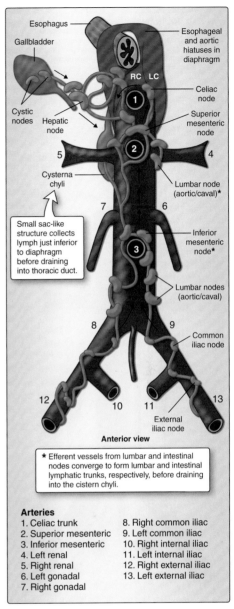

* Efferent vessels from lumbar and intestinal nodes converge to form lumbar and intestinal lymphatic trunks, respectively, before draining into the cistern chyli.

Arteries

1. Celiac trunk	8. Right common iliac
2. Superior mesenteric	9. Left common iliac
3. Inferior mesenteric	10. Right internal iliac
4. Left renal	11. Left internal iliac
5. Right renal	12. Right external iliac
6. Left gonadal	13. Left external iliac
7. Right gonadal	

Figure 4.20
Lymphatics of abdominal viscera. Black arrows indicate general direction of lymphatic flow. LC = left crus, RC = right crus.

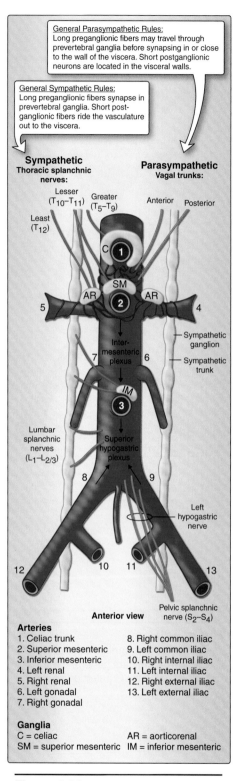

General Parasympathetic Rules:
Long preganglionic fibers may travel through prevertebral ganglia before synapsing in or close to the wall of the viscera. Short postganglionic neurons are located in the visceral walls.

General Sympathetic Rules:
Long preganglionic fibers synapse in prevertebral ganglia. Short post-ganglionic fibers ride the vasculature out to the viscera.

Sympathetic
Thoracic splanchnic nerves:

Lesser
(T_{10}–T_{11}) Greater
(T_5–T_9)

Least
(T_{12})

Parasympathetic
Vagal trunks:

Anterior   Posterior

Sympathetic ganglion

Sympathetic trunk

Inter-mesenteric plexus

Lumbar splanchnic nerves
(L_1–$L_{2/3}$)

Superior hypogastric plexus

Left hypogastric nerve

Pelvic splanchnic nerve (S_2–S_4)

Anterior view

Arteries
1. Celiac trunk
2. Superior mesenteric
3. Inferior mesenteric
4. Left renal
5. Right renal
6. Left gonadal
7. Right gonadal

8. Right common iliac
9. Left common iliac
10. Right internal iliac
11. Left internal iliac
12. Right external iliac
13. Left external iliac

Ganglia
C = celiac
SM = superior mesenteric

AR = aorticorenal
IM = inferior mesenteric

Figure 4.21
General organization and contents of aortic plexus.

in visceral walls. Autonomic fibers from these plexuses travel on vasculature to reach abdominal viscera. Although the pattern of preganglionic sympathetic fiber distribution to prevertebral ganglia is well established, some fibers will bypass adjacent ganglia and travel through other plexuses to reach more lateral or inferior ganglia.

> An interesting exception to the rule that preganglionic sympathetic fibers will synapse in prevertebral ganglia is the case of suprarenal medulla innervation. Preganglionic sympathetic fibers from the greater splanchnic nerve (T_5–T_9) bypass the celiac ganglion and travel to synapse directly on chromaffin cells located in the suprarenal medulla.

B. General visceral efferent innervation, sympathetic

Sympathetic (GVE) innervation of abdominal viscera occurs through preganglionic thoracic (greater, lesser, and least) and lumbar splanchnic nerves. Typically, these preganglionic sympathetic fibers travel to prevertebral (preaortic) plexuses and synapse in associated ganglia.

1. **Thoracic splanchnic nerves:** These nerves have cell bodies that originate in the lateral horn (intermediolateral cell column) of the thoracic spinal cord (T_5–T_{12}).

   a. **Greater splanchnic nerve:** This nerve originates at T_5–T_9 and travels to synapse on postganglionic cell bodies in the celiac ganglion. These fibers distribute primarily on branches of the celiac trunk to reach viscera. In general, these postganglionic fibers distribute to foregut structures in the abdomen.

   b. **Lesser splanchnic nerve:** This nerve originates at T_{10}–T_{11} and travels to synapse on postganglionic cell bodies in the celiac and superior mesenteric ganglia. These fibers may distribute through celiac, superior mesenteric, and renal plexuses to reach viscera. In general, these postganglionic fibers distribute to midgut structures and the kidneys.

   c. **Least splanchnic nerve:** This nerve originates at T_{12} and travels to synapse on postganglionic cell bodies in the aorticorenal ganglia. These fibers distribute through superior renal plexuses to reach viscera.

2. **Lumbar splanchnic nerves:** These nerves have cell bodies that originate in the lateral horn (intermediolateral cell column) of the lumbar spinal cord (L_1–$L_{2/3}$).

   a. **Upper lumbar splanchnic nerves:** These originate at L_1–L_2 and travel to synapse primarily in the inferior mesenteric ganglion. Postganglionic fibers travel through the intermesenteric plexus and distribute along branches of the inferior mesenteric artery to reach viscera. In general, these postganglionic fibers distribute to hindgut structures.

   b. **Lower lumbar splanchnic nerves:** These originate at L_1–L_2 but exit the sympathetic trunk at L_3–L_4 levels. These nerves are not technically part of the aortic plexus. They feed into the superior hypogastric plexus, which provides a thruway for sympathetic fibers to reach pelvic viscera.

C. General visceral efferent innervation, parasympathetic

Parasympathetic (GVE) innervation of abdominal viscera occurs through preganglionic vagus nerves (cranial nerve [CN] X) and pelvic splanchnic nerves (S_2–S_4). Typically, these preganglionic parasympathetic fibers travel through prevertebral (preaortic) plexuses and synapse in the walls of abdominal viscera.

1. **Vagus nerve:** At the distal end of the esophagus, vagal fibers from the esophageal plexus converge to form left and right vagus nerves. With the rotation of the stomach, these nerves assume a more anterior and posterior position, respectively. At this point, they are renamed **anterior** and **posterior vagal trunks**. These preganglionic fibers will bypass prevertebral ganglia and travel within the periarterial plexuses to reach the walls of the viscera. Vagal innervation covers foregut and midgut structures before terminating at the distal third of the transverse colon.

2. **Pelvic splanchnic nerves:** Originating in the gray matter of spinal cord levels S_2, S_3, and S_4, these preganglionic parasympathetic fibers exit the spinal nerve as these levels join the inferior hypogastric plexus, travel through the hypogastric nerves to the superior hypogastric plexus, and distribute along periarterial plexuses associated with hindgut structures (inferior mesenteric artery distribution).

D. General visceral afferent innervation

Afferent pain fibers (general visceral afferent [GVA]) from abdominal viscera up to the midpoint of the sigmoid colon travel back to the sympathetic preganglionic origin. For example, visceral pain from the stomach will travel back to T_6–T_9 spinal cord levels, which represent a portion of the greater splanchnic nerve. Due to the overlap with somatic afferents at these levels, visceral pain can be referred to somatic representations of involved levels—T_6–T_9 dermatomes. Pain from viscera located inferior to the midpoint of the sigmoid colon, as well as subconscious reflex sensations throughout the abdominal viscera, travel back along the path of the pelvic splanchnic nerves (origin: S_2–S_4).

> In general, sympathetic visceromotor function includes decreased peristalsis, decreased gland secretion, vasoconstriction, and closure of sphincters. Parasympathetic visceromotor function includes increased peristalsis, increase gland secretion, vasodilation, and opening of sphincters.

VI. ABDOMINAL VISCERA

Abdominal viscera are associated with the GI, endocrine, and urogenital systems. In this section, GI viscera are described as being either foregut, midgut, or hindgut derivatives and are organized into these three categories. Embryology is presented first, followed by anatomy and histology.

A. General digestive system formation

During week 4, the **primitive gut tube** forms due to the incorporation of the dorsal part of the yolk sac into the embryo with craniocaudal folding and lateral folding of the embryo (Fig. 4.22). The primitive gut tube extends from the **oropharyngeal membrane** cranially to the **cloacal membrane** caudally. The primitive gut tube consists of **endoderm** lining the lumen and surrounding **visceral mesoderm**. The primitive gut tube is divided into the **foregut**, **midgut**, and **hindgut**.

B. Foregut derivatives

The derivatives of the foregut include the **esophagus**, **stomach**, **liver**, **gallbladder/extrahepatic bile ducts**, **pancreas**, and **upper part of the duodenum**. The derivatives of the foregut receive their blood supply from the **celiac trunk**. The foregut is divided into the esophagus dorsally and the trachea ventrally by indentations of the visceral mesoderm called the **tracheoesophageal folds**. When the tracheoesophageal folds fuse in the midline to form the **tracheoesophageal septum**, the foregut is divided into the trachea ventrally and the esophagus dorsally. The esophagus is initially short but lengthens with descent of the heart and lungs. During development, the endodermal lining of the esophagus proliferates rapidly and obliterates the lumen, and later, recanalization occurs.

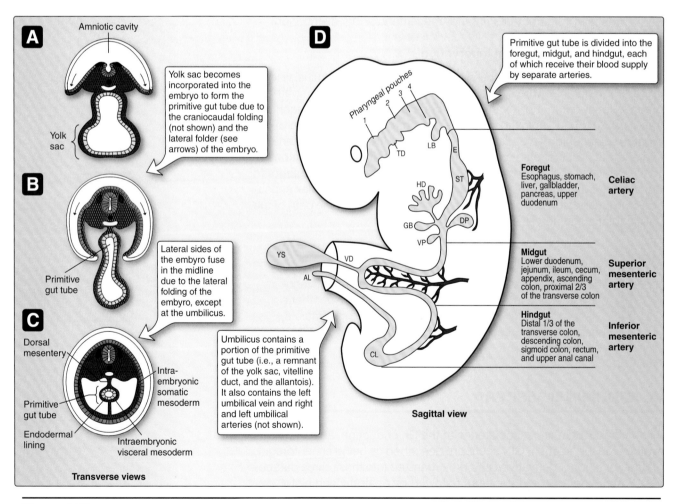

Figure 4.22
Digestive system embryology (A–D). AL = allantois, CL = cloaca, DP = dorsal pancreatic bud, E = esophagus, GB = gallbladder, HD = hepatic diverticulum, LB = lung bud, ST = stomach, TD = thyroid diverticulum, VD = vitelline duct, VP = ventral pancreatic bud, YS = yolk sac.

1. **Esophageal anatomy:** The esophagus is a tube of both skeletal and smooth muscles that extends from the **cricoesophageal muscle** (upper esophageal sphincter) to the cardial orifice of the stomach (Fig. 4.23). This portion of the foregut courses through the thoracic cavity in the superior and inferior (posterior) mediastinal spaces and travels through the **esophageal hiatus**, formed by the right crus of the diaphragm, at T10 vertebral level. The right crus functions as a diaphragmatic sphincter. As it passes through the hiatus, the esophagus widens to join the cardiac region of the stomach at the **gastroesophageal (GE) junction**. Here, the right esophageal border is continuous with the lesser curvature of the stomach, and the left border is interrupted from the fundus of the stomach by the **cardial notch**. The **lower esophageal sphincter (LES)** is found at the GE junction and serves to separate the lower esophagus from the stomach. The LES and diaphragmatic sphincter function together to prevent reflux of stomach contents into the esophagus.

   a. **Blood supply:** The distal esophagus is supplied by the left gastric artery and left inferior phrenic arteries. Venous drainage

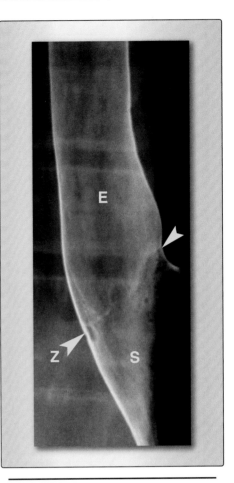

Figure 4.23
Anatomy of lower esophagus and gastroesophageal junction (GE) as shown through a double-contrast barium study. E = esophagus, S = stomach, Z = z-line (yellow arrowheads).

Clinical Application 4.7: Esophageal Varices

Esophageal varices occur in the distal or lower esophagus at the anastomotic site between tributaries of the left gastric vein (portal system) and esophageal veins (caval system). Increased pressure in the portal vein (**portal hypertension**) causes backflow of venous blood into these smaller veins and subsequent dilation. Rupture of these veins can lead to massive bleeding and must be treated as an emergency. Portal hypertension can be caused by cirrhosis of the liver, which severely scars the liver and can cause venous stenosis.

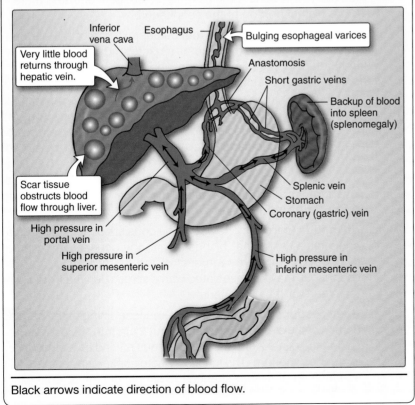

Black arrows indicate direction of blood flow.

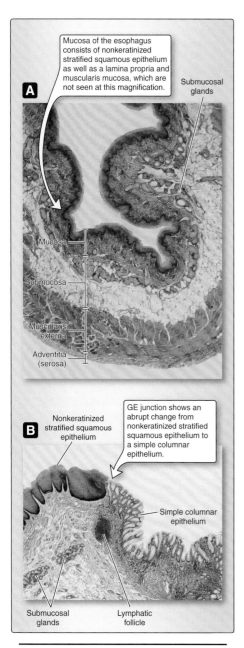

Figure 4.24
Histology of the (A) esophagus and (B)
gastroesophageal (GE) junction.

occurs through both the portal and caval systems by way of the left gastric vein and esophageal veins, respectively.

   b. Innervation: The esophagus receives parasympathetic and sympathetic innervation from vagal trunks and greater splanchnic nerves, respectively. A more detailed description of esophageal innervation can be found in Chapter 3.

   c. Lymphatics: In the abdomen, the distal esophagus drains first into left gastric lymph nodes, which then drain through the preaortic celiac nodes.

2. **Esophageal histology:** The wall of the esophagus consists of four histologic layers, namely, the **mucosa**, **submucosa**, **muscularis externa**, and **adventitia** (**serosa**).

   a. Mucosa: The mucosa of the esophagus consists of an **epithelium**, a **lamina propria**, and a **muscularis mucosa** (Fig. 4.24). The epithelium is a **nonkeratinized stratified squamous epithelium**, except for the distal 2 cm at the gastroesophageal (GE) junction, which is lined by **simple columnar epithelium**. The lamina propria consists of loose connective tissue, blood vessels, and diffuse lymphatic tissue. Within the lamina propria, **mucosal glands** are found concentrated in the terminal portion of the esophagus near the GE junction. These mucosal glands are sometimes called **esophageal cardiac glands** because of their resemblance to the cardiac glands of the stomach. The muscularis mucosa consists of a smooth muscle layer.

   b. Submucosa: The submucosa of the esophagus consists of dense, irregular connective tissue, submucosal glands, blood vessels, diffuse lymphatic tissue, and the submucosal (Meissner) nerve plexus. It contains **esophageal submucosal glands** that are found throughout the esophagus but concentrated more in the proximal portion of the esophagus.

   c. Muscularis externa: The muscularis externa of the esophagus consists of both skeletal muscle and smooth muscle, sphincters at specific locations, and the myenteric (Auerbach) plexus. The muscularis externa in the **upper 5%** portion of the esophagus consists of skeletal muscle only. The muscularis externa in the **middle 45%** portion of the esophagus consists of both skeletal muscle and smooth muscle interwoven together. The muscularis externa in the **distal 50%** portion of the esophagus consists of smooth muscle only. In this distal 50% portion, the muscularis externa consists of two distinct layers of smooth muscle called the **inner circular layer** and **outer longitudinal layer**.

   d. Adventitia (serosa): The adventitia consists of dense, irregular connective tissue that blends in with the connective tissue of the body wall. Short segments of the thoracic or abdominal esophagus may be associated with a serosa derived from either the pleura or the peritoneum.

   e. Gastroesophageal junction: The mucosal lining of the cardiac portion of the stomach **extends about 2 cm into the esophagus** so that the distal 2 cm of the esophagus is lined by a **simple columnar epithelium**. The junction where nonkeratinized stratified squamous epithelium changes to simple columnar epithelium (or the mucosal GE junction) can be seen macroscopically as a **zigzag line** (called the **Z-line**).

> **Barrett esophagus** is defined as the replacement of esophageal-stratified squamous epithelium with metaplastic "intestinalized" simple columnar epithelium with goblet cells extending **at least 3 cm** into the esophagus. This metaplastic invasion is most commonly caused by GERD. The clinical importance of this metaplastic invasion is that virtually all lower esophageal adenocarcinomas occur as a sequela.

3. **Stomach embryology:** A fusiform dilation forms in the foregut that gives rise to the **primitive stomach** (Fig. 4.25). The dorsal part of the primitive stomach grows faster than the ventral part, resulting in the greater curvature and lesser curvature, respectively. The primitive stomach undergoes a **90° clockwise rotation** around its longitudinal axis. As a result of the 90° clockwise rotation, four major events occur: (1) the dorsal mesentery is carried to the left side and eventually forms the **greater omentum**, (2) the ventral mesentery is carried to the right side and eventually forms the lesser omentum, (3) the **right vagus nerve (CN X)** becomes positioned on the dorsal surface of the stomach (as the posterior vagal trunk), and (4) the **left vagus nerve (CN X)** becomes positioned on the ventral surface of the stomach (as the anterior vagal trunk).

4. **Stomach anatomy:** The stomach is the proximal portion of the GI track in the abdominal cavity, mainly occupying the upper left quadrant (Fig. 4.26). It can be divided into four parts: **cardia, fundus, body,** and **pyloric region**. The cardiac region, or cardia, surrounds the GE junction at the cardial orifice, while the fundus extends superolaterally to the left, just inferior to the left hemidiaphragm. The body of the stomach represents the majority of surface area, before narrowing into the pyloric region, which marks the transition between the stomach and proximal small intestine—the duodenum. The pyloric region is made up of an **antrum** (chamber) and a **pyloris**, which contains the thick, muscular **pyloric sphincter**. This sphincter controls transport of stomach contents into the duodenum. The stomach has well-defined anterior and posterior surfaces and two distinct borders. The right-situated superior border—the **lesser curvature**—is short and concave. The left-situated inferior border—the **greater curvature**—is longer and convex. The lesser and greater curvatures have attachments to the lesser omentum and greater omentum, respectively. These peritoneal attachments make the stomach entirely **intraperitoneal**.

   a. **Blood supply:** The lesser curvature and body are supplied by the left and right gastric arteries and veins, while the greater curvature and body are supplied by the left and right gastro-omental arteries and veins. The fundus receives short and posterior gastric arteries and veins from the splenic artery and vein, respectively.

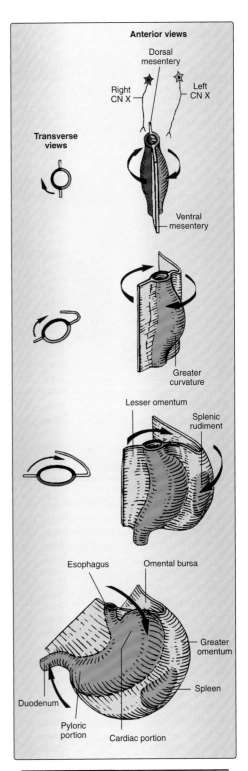

Figure 4.25
Embryologic formation of the stomach.

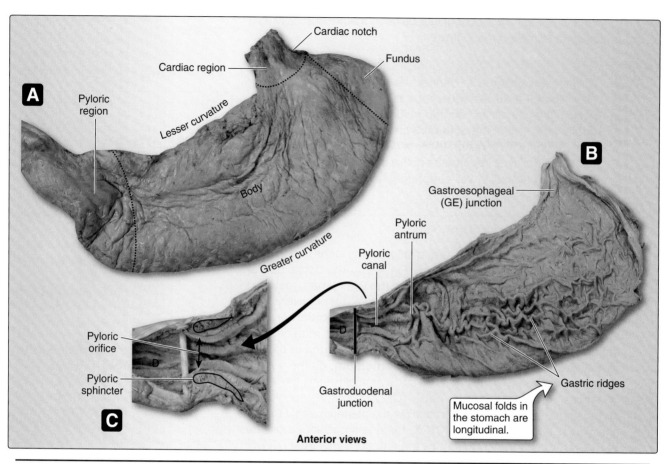

Figure 4.26
Stomach. A, External features and regions. B, Internal features and regions. C, Pyloric sphincter and orifice. D = duodenum.

Clinical Application 4.8: Gastroesophageal Reflux Disease

Gastroesophageal reflux disease (GERD) is described as the symptoms or mucosal damage produced by the abnormal reflux of gastric contents through the lower esophageal sphincter (LES) into the esophagus. The pathologic findings of GERD include hyperemia (engorgement of blood), superficial erosions and ulcers which appear as vertical linear streaks, and hydropic changes in the stratified squamous epithelium along with increased lymphocytes, eosinophils, and neutrophils. The clinical features of GERD include heartburn (pyrosis), which may worsen when bending or lying down; regurgitation; and dysphagia (difficulty in swallowing). The most dreaded cause of dysphagia is esophageal cancer (e.g., either adenocarcinoma arising from Barrett metaplasia or squamous cell carcinoma).

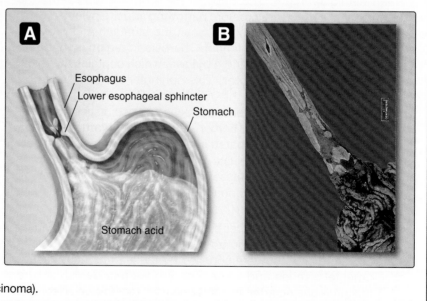

A, Coronal view of gastroesophageal junction showing reflux of acid. B, Gross specimen showing multiple linear continuous and noncontinuous erosions and ulcers in the esophagus.

b. **Innervation:** The stomach receives parasympathetic and sympathetic innervation from vagal trunks and greater splanchnic nerves, respectively.

c. **Lymphatics:** Lymph from the stomach is initially drained through gastric, gastro-omental, pyloric, and pancreaticoduodenal lymph nodes. Efferents from these nodes drain into celiac nodes.

5. **Stomach histology:** The wall of the stomach consists of four histologic layers, namely, the **mucosa**, **submucosa**, **muscularis externa**, and **serosa** (Fig. 4.27). The inner luminal surface of the stomach contains longitudinal ridges of mucosa and submucosa called **rugae** and is dotted with millions of openings called **gastric pits**, or **foveolae**.

a. **Mucosa:** The mucosa of the stomach consists of an **epithelium**, a **lamina propria**, and a **muscularis mucosa**. The epithelium consists of **surface mucous cells** that line both the stomach lumen and the gastric pits. The surface mucous cells secrete **mucus and** mucus and HCO_3^- to protect the stomach from the acid pH and hydrolytic enzymes contained in the gastric juice. The lamina propria consists of loose connective tissue, blood vessels, and diffuse lymphatic tissue. Within the lamina propria, **mucosal glands** are found that begin at the gastric pit and end at the muscularis mucosa. The muscularis mucosa consists of a smooth muscle layer.

[1] **Mucosal glands:** The epithelium of the stomach mucosa invaginates to form mucosal glands. The cellular composition of the mucosal glands changes depending on the gross anatomical region of the stomach. In the cardia region, **cardiac glands** are present and consist of **mucus-secreting cells** only. The cardiac glands probably aid in protecting the esophagus from the acidic chyme. In the pyloric region, **pyloric glands** are present and consist of **mucus-secreting cells** and **gastrin-producing cells (G cells)**. The pyloric glands probably aid in protecting the duodenum from the acidic chyme. In the fundus and body regions, gastric glands are present and consist of the following cell types.

(a) **Stem cells:** The stem cell demonstrates a high rate of mitosis. They migrate upward to replace surface mucous cells every 4–7 days and downward to replace other cell types.

(b) **Mucous neck cells:** The mucous neck cell secretes a neutral mucus.

(c) **Parietal cells:** The parietal cell contains **carbonic anhydrase** that generates H⁺, an **H⁺-K⁺ ATPase** that transports H⁺ out of the cell and a **Cl⁻ ion channel** that transports Cl⁻ out of the cell. This produces **gastric HCl**, which aids in the digestion of food, converts pepsinogen (inactive) to pepsin (active), and provides a defense mechanism by killing ingested microorganisms. The parietal cell releases HCO_3^- into the bloodstream, causing a rise in the pH called the **alkaline tide**. The parietal cell also releases **intrinsic factor** that complexes

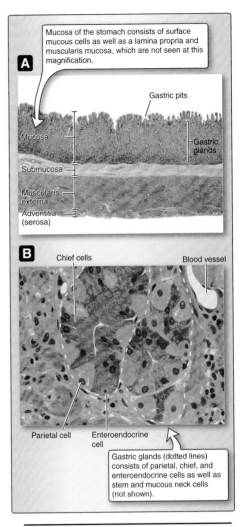

A Mucosa of the stomach consists of surface mucous cells as well as a lamina propria and muscularis mucosa, which are not seen at this magnification.

Gastric pits

Mucosa

Gastric glands

Submucosa

Muscularis externa

Adventitia (serosa)

B Chief cells

Blood vessel

Parietal cell

Enteroendocrine cell

Gastric glands (dotted lines) consists of parietal, chief, and enteroendocrine cells as well as stem and mucous neck cells (not shown).

Figure 4.27
Stomach histology. A, Stomach.
B, Lower portion of two gastric glands

Clinical Application 4.9: Hiatal Hernia

A hiatal hernia occurs when a portion of the stomach herniates through the esophageal hiatus in the diaphragm. This type of herniation is different from a congenital diaphragmatic hernia in that it is thought to be caused by a weakening in the diaphragm muscle that supports the esophageal hiatus and is most often seen in middle-aged patients. Hiatal hernias most often fall into two main categories—sliding or paraesophageal. In a sliding hiatal hernia, the Z-line that marks the mucosal transition between the esophagus and stomach slides superiorly with the herniation of stomach (cardia). In a paraesophageal hiatal hernia, the normal anatomical location of the Z-line is maintained, and the portion of stomach (fundus) and associated peritoneum protrudes through the hiatus, just anterior to the esophagus.

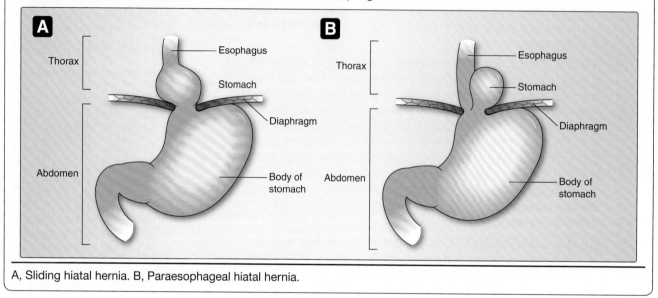

A, Sliding hiatal hernia. B, Paraesophageal hiatal hernia.

with vitamin B_{12} and promotes **vitamin B_{12} absorption** in the terminal ileum.

- (d) **Chief cells:** The chief cell secretes **pepsinogen**, which is converted to **pepsin** upon contact with gastric HCl (acid pH) and **lipase**.

- (e) **Enteroendocrine cells:** The enteroendocrine cell in the stomach secretes **gastrin**, **ghrelin**, **vasoactive intestinal polypeptide**, **somatostatin**, **serotonin**, and **histamine**.

b. **Submucosa:** The submucosa of the stomach consists of dense, irregular connective tissue, blood vessels, diffuse lymphatic tissue, and the submucosal (Meissner) nerve plexus. The submucosa and mucosa are thrown into a number of longitudinal ridges called **rugae**. The rugae give the lumen of the stomach a highly irregular surface.

c. **Muscularis externa:** The muscularis externa of the stomach consists of randomly oriented smooth muscle, blood vessels, and the myenteric (Auerbach) nerve plexus.

d. **Adventitia (serosa):** The adventitia of the stomach consists of dense, irregular connective tissue that blends in with the connective tissue of the body wall. The stomach is suspended by a mesentery (i.e., intraperitoneal), so that the adventitia is covered by a layer of simple squamous epithelium called **mesothelium** and is then referred to as a **serosa**.

6. **Liver embryology:** The endodermal lining of the foregut forms an outgrowth called the **hepatic diverticulum**, which grows into the surrounding mesoderm related to the **septum transversum** (Fig. 4.28). The mesoderm of the septum transversum is involved in the formation of the **diaphragm**, which explains the intimate gross anatomical relationship between the liver and diaphragm. Cords of hepatoblasts called **hepatic cords** from the hepatic diverticulum grow into the mesoderm of the septum transversum. The hepatic cords arrange themselves around the **vitelline veins** and **umbilical veins**, which course through the septum transversum and form the **hepatic sinusoids**. Due to the tremendous growth of the liver, it bulges into the abdominal cavity, which stretches the septum transversum to form the **ventral mesentery**. The **left umbilical vein** lies in the inferior, free border of an extension of ventral mesentery—**falciform ligament**—and eventually regresses after birth to form the **ligamentum teres**. The ventral mesentery also gives rise to the lesser omentum.

7. **Liver anatomy:** The liver is a solid organ that occupies much of the right upper quadrant, sitting just inferior to the right hemidiaphragm (Fig. 4.29). Depending on size, shape, and pathology, it is protected at least partially by the right lower thoracic rib cage. It has a smooth, convex **diaphragmatic surface** (anterosuperior) and a concave **visceral surface** (posteroinferior), which have fissures and fossae to accommodate associated structures. These surfaces are separated by the definitive **inferior margin**, or inferior border, of the liver. The liver is primarily described as intraperitoneal, although a **bare area** on the posterior diaphragmatic surface lacks peritoneal covering. This area is bound by the **right** and **left coronary ligaments**.

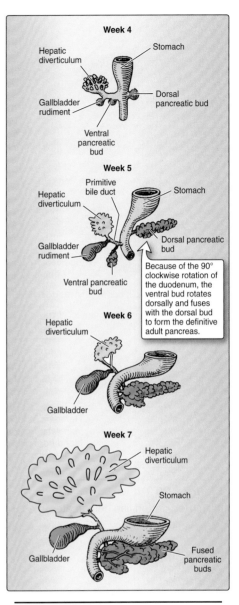

Figure 4.28
Embryologic formation of the liver, gallbladder, and pancreas.

> Because of the liver's relationship with the diaphragm and thoracic cage, its position changes with respiration—elevating with full expiration (diaphragm is domed) and depressing with full inspiration (diaphragm is flattened). The mobility of the liver during respiration can aid in palpation of the inferior margin to assess liver size and position. Assessment of the inferior margin is important in screening for various pathologies, such as hepatitis and metastatic carcinoma, which can cause liver enlargement (hepatomegaly). When the liver is enlarged or engorged, the inferior margin may be easily palpated as it extends well beyond the inferior border of the ribs.

   a. **Lobes:** Anatomically, the liver is divided into four lobes: **right**, **left**, **quadrate**, and **caudate**. On the diaphragmatic surface of the liver, right and left lobes are divided by the falciform ligament, and its superior extension the left and right coronary ligaments. The visceral surface of the liver is characterized

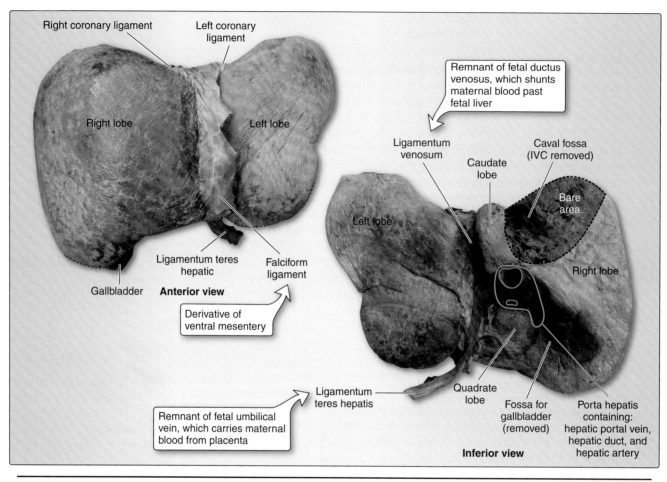

Figure 4.29
Liver. Red dotted line demarcates inferior margin. IVC, inferior vena cava.

by multiple impressions, fossae, and fissures. Impression from the IVC and gallbladder form **caval** and **gallbladder fossae**, respectively, and separate the liver into functional right and left lobes. The **porta hepatis**—where vessels and ducts enter/exit the liver—is located centrally on the visceral surface and is flanked on the left by fissures formed by the **ligamentum teres** (anterior fissure) and the **ligamentum venosum** (posterior fissure), which represent the obliterated ductus venosus (see Fetal Circulation, Chapter 5). The **caudate lobe** is located between the caval fossa and posterior fissure, while the **quadrate lobe** lies between the gallbladder fossa and anterior fissure.

b. **Blood supply:** The liver is supplied by **right** and **left hepatic arteries** (from proper hepatic artery) and receives venous blood for processing from the **hepatic portal vein**. Filtered blood is transported from the liver to the IVC via short, multiple **hepatic** veins.

c. **Innervation:** The liver receives parasympathetic and sympathetic innervation from the vagal trunks and hepatic plexus (derived from celiac plexus), respectively.

d. **Lymphatics:** The liver has superficial and deep lymphatics that contribute a significant amount of lymph to the thoracic duct. Direction of lymph flow is driven by location, where superior posterior portions of the liver drain superiorly to **phrenic** or **posterior mediastinal lymph nodes** in the thoracic cavity, while anterior inferior portions drain inferiorly to **hepatic lymph nodes**. Efferent vessels from hepatic lymph nodes carry lymph to preaortic celiac nodes.

8. **Liver histology:** The classic liver lobule consists of radially arranged connecting plates of **hepatocytes** separated by vascular channels called **sinusoids** (Fig. 4.30). The classic liver lobule is roughly hexagon shaped with a **central vein** at its center and six **portal triads** at each corner of the hexagon. Along the six sides of the classic liver lobule, small branches of portal triad components can be found.

a. **Central vein:** The central vein receives blood from the hepatic sinusoids. The central veins empty into hepatic veins, which then empty into the IVC.

b. **Portal triad:** A portal triad located at each corner of the hexagon-shaped classic liver lobule contains the following (Fig. 4.31).

[1] **Hepatic arteriole:** The hepatic arteriole is a terminal branch of the right or left hepatic artery. It carries oxygen-rich blood and contributes 20% of the blood delivered to the hepatic sinusoids. Small branches of the hepatic arteriole run along all six sides of the classic liver lobule. The blood flows from the periphery to the center of a classic liver lobule (i.e., centripetal flow).

[2] **Portal venule:** The portal venule is a terminal branch of the portal vein. It carries nutrient-rich blood and contributes 80% of the blood delivered to the hepatic sinusoids. Small branches of the portal venule run along all six sides of the classic liver lobule. The blood flows from the periphery to the center of a classic liver lobule (i.e., centripetal flow).

[3] **Interlobular bile ductule:** Bile follows this route: bile canaliculus → canal of Hering → interlobular bile ductule along the sides of the classic liver lobule → interlobular bile ductule at the corners of the classic liver lobule → right and left hepatic ducts → common hepatic duct joined by the cystic duct → bile duct. Small branches of the interlobular bile ductule run along all six sides of the classic liver lobule. Bile flows from the center to the periphery of a classic liver lobule (i.e., centrifugal flow).

[4] **Lymphatic vessel:** Lymph follows this route: space of Disse → lymphatic vessel along the sides of the classic liver lobule → lymphatic vessel at the corners of the classic liver lobule → lymphatic vessels that parallel the portal vein → thoracic duct. Small branches of the lymphatic vessels run along all six sides of the classic liver lobule. Lymph flows from the center to the periphery of a classic liver lobule (i.e., centrifugal flow).

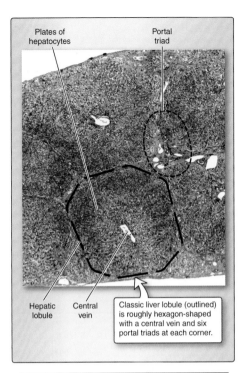

Plates of hepatocytes | Portal triad

Hepatic lobule | Central vein | Classic liver lobule (outlined) is roughly hexagon-shaped with a central vein and six portal triads at each corner.

Figure 4.30
Liver histology (live lobule).

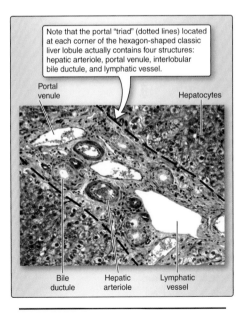

Note that the portal "triad" (dotted lines) located at each corner of the hexagon-shaped classic liver lobule actually contains four structures: hepatic arteriole, portal venule, interlobular bile ductule, and lymphatic vessel.

Portal venule | Hepatocytes

Bile ductule | Hepatic arteriole | Lymphatic vessel

Figure 4.31
Portal triad.

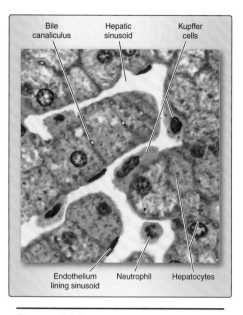

Bile canaliculus   Hepatic sinusoid   Kupffer cells

Endothelium lining sinusoid   Neutrophil   Hepatocytes

Figure 4.32
Hepatocytes.

c. **Hepatocytes:** The hepatocyte is a polygon-shaped cell with a round-shaped and centrally located nucleus (Fig. 4.32). It is binucleated and contains rough endoplasmic reticulum, polyribosomes, a Golgi complex, smooth endoplasmic reticulum, mitochondria, lysosomes, peroxisomes, lipid, iron, lipofuscin, and glycogen. The hepatocyte cell membrane contains **glucose transporter 2** and the **insulin receptor**. The hepatocytes are organized as radially arranged connecting plates and have surfaces that abut with the **perisinusoidal space of Disse** and the **hepatic sinusoids**, as well as neighboring hepatocytes. At these surfaces, the hepatocyte cell membranes form a **bile canaliculus** that is sealed by a zonula occludens (tight junction). Hepatocyte functions are described in Table 4.4.

d. **Kupffer cells:** The Kupffer cell is a macrophage derived from circulating monocytes. It forms part of the lining of the hepatic sinusoids along with the endothelium (see Fig. 4.32). The Kupffer cell may phagocytize damaged or senile RBCs missed by the splenic macrophages. The Kupffer cell secretes the following pro-inflammatory cytokines.

[1] **Tumor necrosis factor-α:** Tumor necrosis factor-α causes a slowdown in bile flow called cholestasis.

[2] **Interleukin-6:** Interleukin-6 causes synthesis of acute-phase proteins by hepatocytes.

[3] **Transforming growth factor-β:** Transforming growth factor-β causes synthesis of type I collagen by hepatic stellate cells.

e. **Hepatic stellate cells (Ito cells):** The hepatic stellate cell is located in the perisinusoidal space of Disse and contains numerous lipid droplets, which store **vitamin A** in the form of **retinyl esters**. The hepatic stellate cell secretes the following substances.

[1] **Retinol:** Bound to **retinol-binding protein**, retinol travels to the retina where it is converted to **rhodopsin**.

[2] **Type III collagen:** This is secreted into the perisinusoidal space of Disse as part of the normal stroma of the liver.

[3] **Type I collagen:** Along with laminin and proteoglycans, type I collagen is secreted during inflammation.

Table 4.4: Hepatocyte Functions

• Lymph production	• Metabolism of drugs
• Uptake and release of immunoglobulin A	• Metabolism of ethanol
• Storage of iron	• Synthesis of bile salts
• Storage of vitamin A	• Production of bile
• Carbohydrate metabolism, which includes glycogen synthesis, glycogen degradation, monosaccharide metabolism, and gluconeogenesis	• Production of bilirubin
• Protein and amino acid metabolism, which includes synthesis of plasma proteins, ammonia metabolism, synthesis of nonessential amino acids	• Secretion of angiotensinogen
• Lipid metabolism, which includes 25-hydroxylation of vitamin D, β-oxidation of fatty acids, synthesis of fatty acids, production of ketone bodies, synthesis of cholesterol, synthesis of lipoproteins	• Secretion of α$_1$-antitrypsin (or serpin peptidase inhibitor A1), which is encoded by the *SERPINA1* gene on chromosome 14q32.1

In liver cirrhosis, increased deposition of type I collagen in the perisinusoidal space of Disse narrows the diameter of the sinusoid, thereby causing **portal hypertension**.

f. **Space of Disse:** The perisinusoidal space of Disse lies between the hepatocyte and the sinusoidal endothelium and is the site of exchange between the hepatocyte and the blood. The hepatic sinusoid is a discontinuous capillary that consists of an endothelium surrounded by a discontinuous basal lamina. The endothelial cells contain fenestrae and are joined by a fascia occludens that create wide gaps between the endothelial cells.

g. **Biliary tree:** The biliary tree carries **bile** produced by the hepatocytes to the gallbladder and finally to the small intestine. The biliary tree follows this route: bile canaliculus → canal of Hering → interlobular bile ductule along the sides of the classic liver lobule → interlobular bile ductule at the corners of the classic liver lobule → right and left hepatic ducts → common hepatic duct joined by the cystic duct → bile duct. The entire biliary tree is lined by cells called **cholangiocytes**, except for the bile canaliculus (Fig. 4.33).

[1] **Bile canaliculus:** The zonula occludens (tight junction) surrounding the bile canaliculus are relatively "leaky" that allows passage of H_2O and Na^+ into the bile canaliculus. The hepatocyte surface extends numerous **microvilli** into the bile canaliculus.

[2] **Canal of Hering:** The bile canaliculus transitions into the canal of Hering located at the very periphery of the classic liver lobule (see Fig. 4.33A). The canal of Hering is lined by both hepatocytes and cholangiocytes and is a niche for **hepatic stem cells**.

[3] **Interlobular bile ductule along the sides:** The canal of Hering transitions into a small interlobular bile ductule located in the loose connective tissue along the sides of the classic liver lobule (see Fig. 4.33B). It is lined by low cuboidal cholangiocytes.

[4] **Interlobular bile ductule at the corners:** The small interlobular bile ductule along the sides of the classic liver lobule transitions into a larger interlobular bile ductule located in the loose connective tissue at the corners of the classic liver lobule (see Fig. 4.33C). It is lined by cuboidal cholangiocytes.

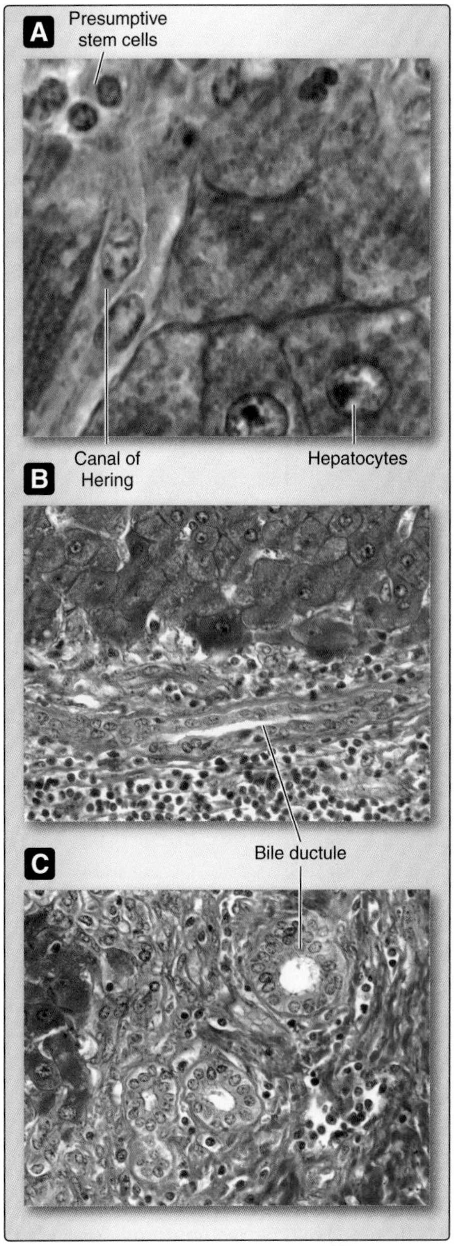

Figure 4.33
Biliary tree. A, Canal of Hering. B, Bile ductule along the sides. C, Bile ductule at the corners

Clinical Application 4.10: Primary Biliary Cirrhosis

Primary biliary cirrhosis is an autoimmune disease characterized by a CD8⁺ cytotoxic T-cell–mediated attack on intrahepatic bile ductules, the exact cause of which is unknown. The T-cell–mediated attack seems to require both a genetic susceptibility and an environmental triggering factor (e.g., bacteria, virus, or a toxin). **Molecular mimicry** has been speculated to initiate the T-cell–mediated attack. Molecular mimicry occurs when foreign antigens stimulating an immune response have enough similarity to "self" proteins that the immune response "spills over" to attack normal tissues.

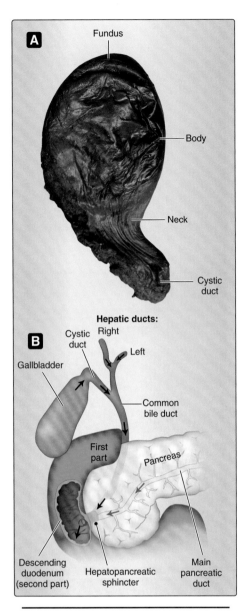

Figure 4.34
Gallbladder. A, Gross anatomy. B, Schematic showing relationship with duodenum and pancreas. Arrows indicate direction of bile flow toward Sphincter of Oddi and into duodenum.

9. **Gallbladder embryology:** The connection between the hepatic diverticulum and the foregut narrows to form the **primitive bile duct** (see Fig. 4.28). An outgrowth from the primitive bile duct gives rise to the **gallbladder rudiment** and **cystic duct**. The cystic duct divides the primitive bile duct into the **common hepatic duct** and the definitive **common bile duct**.

10. **Gallbladder anatomy:** The gallbladder is a small reservoir located in the gallbladder fossa on the inferior surface of the right lobe of the liver (Fig. 4.34). It functions to store bile that is produced in the liver. It is described as having a fundus, body, and neck, from which the cystic duct extends to meet the common hepatic duct to form the common bile duct. The common bile duct transports bile to the descending part of the duodenum (second part) at the hepatopancreatic ampulla.

    a. **Blood supply:** The gallbladder is supplied by the **cystic artery**, which is typically a branch of the right hepatic artery. Venous drainage of the body and fundus occurs directly into the visceral surface of the liver into hepatic sinusoids by way of multiple, small **cystic veins**. Another set of cystic veins drains the neck and cystic duct through the hepatic portal vein.

    b. **Innervation:** The gallbladder receives parasympathetic and sympathetic innervation from vagus nerves and celiac plexus, respectively. The gallbladder also receives general somatic afferent innervation from the right phrenic nerve (C_3–C_5), which may account for the referred pain experienced in gallbladder pathology.

    c. **Lymphatics:** Lymphatic drainage is through cystic lymph nodes located around the neck, which then drain through hepatic lymph nodes, before sending efferent vessels to celiac lymph nodes.

11. **Gallbladder histology:** The wall of the gallbladder consists of three histologic layers, namely, the: **mucosa**, **muscularis externa**, and **adventitia** (Fig. 4.35). A submucosa is absent in the gallbladder.

    a. **Mucosa:** The mucosa of the gallbladder consists of an **epithelium** and a **lamina propria**. There is no muscularis mucosa in the gallbladder. Numerous mucosal folds project into the lumen of the gallbladder and flatten out as the gallbladder is distended by bile. The mucosa may also penetrate deep into the muscularis externa to form **Rokitansky–Aschoff sinuses**, which are early signs of pathologic changes within the mucosa. The epithelium consists of **simple columnar epithelial cells**. The apical region of the epithelial cells is characterized by numerous, short **microvilli**. The lateral region of the epithelial cells is characterized by juxtaluminal **zonula occludens (tight junctions)**, **complex interdigitations**, and a **Na⁺-K⁺ ATPase**. The apical, lateral, and basal regions of the epithelial cells are characterized by **aquaporin (AQ)** water **channels (AQP1** and **AQP8)** that participate in rapid passive movement of water. The epithelial cells **secrete mucus**, which is added to the bile (called **white bile**). The lamina propria consists of loose connective tissue and blood vessels but no lymphatic vessels. The lamina propria generally has a large number of lymphocytes and plasma cells and may also contain **mucus glands**.

b. **Muscularis externa:** The muscularis externa of the gallbladder consists of randomly arranged smooth muscle cells, collagen fibers, and elastic fibers.

c. **Adventitia/serosa:** The adventitia consists of a thick layer of connective tissue found in the area where the gallbladder attaches to the liver surface and contains an extensive network of lymphatic vessels. The serosa consists of a thick layer of connective tissue covered by mesothelium of the peritoneum found in the area that is not attached to the liver surface.

12. **Pancreatic embryology:** The **ventral pancreatic bud** and the **dorsal pancreatic bud** are direct outgrowths of foregut endoderm (see Fig. 4.28). Within both pancreatic buds, endodermal tubules surrounded by mesoderm branch repeatedly to form acinar cells and ducts (i.e., the exocrine pancreas). In addition, isolated clumps of endodermal cells separate from the tubules and accumulate within the mesoderm to form **islet cells** (i.e., the endocrine pancreas). Because of the 90° clockwise rotation of the duodenum, the ventral bud rotates dorsally and fuses with the dorsal bud to form the definitive adult pancreas. The ventral bud forms the **uncinate process** and a **portion of the head of the pancreas**. The dorsal bud forms the **remaining portion of the head**, **body**, and **tail of the pancreas**. The main pancreatic duct is formed by the anastomosis of the **distal two thirds of the dorsal pancreatic duct** (the proximal one third regresses) and the **entire ventral pancreatic duct** (48% incidence). The main pancreatic duct and common bile duct form a single opening (at the **hepatopancreatic ampulla of Vater**) into the posteromedial wall of the duodenum at the tip of a major papillae (**hepatopancreatic papillae**).

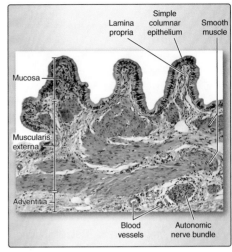

Figure 4.35
Gallbladder histology.

Clinical Application 4.11: Gallstones

Cholelithiasis is characterized by the presence or formation of gallstones either in the gallbladder (called **cholecystolithiasis**) or common bile duct (called **choledocholithiasis**).

Gallstones form when bile salts and lecithin are overwhelmed by cholesterol. Most stones consist of **cholesterol (major component)**, **bilirubin**, and **calcium**. The three main types of gallstones are:

Cholesterol stones. These stones are yellow to tan, round or faceted, smooth, and single or multiple. These stones are composed mainly of cholesterol.

Black pigment stones. These stones are black, irregular, glassy upon cross section, and <1 cm in diameter. They are composed mainly of calcium bilirubinate, bilirubin polymers, other calcium salts, and mucin.

Brown pigment stones. These stones are brown, spongy, and laminated. They are composed mainly of calcium bilirubinate, cholesterol, and calcium soaps of fatty acids.

A, Cholesterol gallstones. B, Brown pigment gallstones. C, Black pigment gallstones.

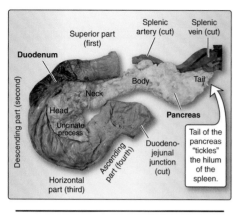

Figure 4.36
Duodenum and pancreas. Relationship of duodenal and pancreatic parts shown. Spleen not shown. Discoloration of duodenum between first and second part due to proximity to gallbladder in cadaver.

13. **Pancreatic anatomy:** The pancreas is both an endocrine and digestive organ. It is divided into four parts: **head**, **neck**, **body**, and **tail** and traverses the abdomen primarily in a retroperitoneal position (Fig. 4.36, also see Fig. 4.34). The pancreatic head is nestled in the C-shape configuration of the duodenum, and an inferior extension of the head—the **uncinate process**—extends posterior to the superior mesenteric vasculature. The organ narrows at the neck before extending across the posterior abdominal wall, posterior to the stomach. The tail is the only part of the pancreas that is intraperitoneal, as it enters the **splenorenal ligament** at the hilum of the spleen. The **main pancreatic duct** spans the length of the organ, from the tail to the head, before descending to join the common bile duct at the **hepatopancreatic ampulla**. A series of sphincters associated with these ducts controls the flow of pancreatic fluids and bile into the descending part of the duodenum (second part) at the **major duodenal papilla**. An **accessory pancreatic duct** may also be present and share connections with the main pancreatic duct, while also emptying contents into a separate opening in the duodenum, called the **minor duodenal papilla**.

    a. **Blood supply:** The pancreas is one of the few abdominal organs that receives arterial supply from branches of the celiac trunk and SMA. The head of the pancreas is well vascularized by anterior

Clinical Application 4.12: Pancreatitis

Pancreatitis is the clinical manifestation of inflammation of the pancreas. Acute pancreatitis is characterized by a sudden onset of epigastric pain that is often exacerbated when the patient is supine. The primary cause of pancreatitis is obstruction of the hepatopancreatic ampulla from a gallstone. Additionally, the main pancreatic duct can lose patency with swelling of the pancreatic head. Retrograde flow of pancreatic products and bile may also occur as a result of the blockage. Imaging is often needed to confirm the cause and guide treatment. On computed tomography, the pancreas typically looks enlarged with poorly defined margins due to edema. Chronic alcohol abuse is the most common cause of chronic pancreatitis.

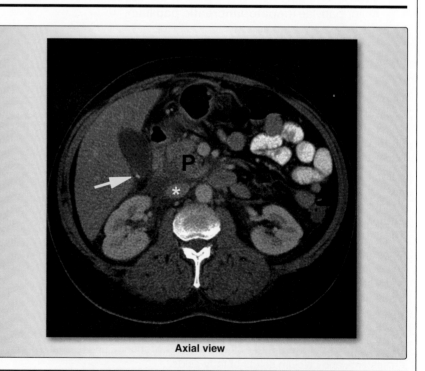

Axial view

CT images showing inflammation and fluid surrounding the pancreatic head (P) and the descending duodenum (*; second part) with fluid in the retroperitoneal space just anterior and lateral to the inferior vena cava (IVC). Arrow shows gallstone, which is primary cause of patient's pancreatitis. CT = computed tomography.

and posterior superior pancreaticoduodenal arteries (from the gastroduodenal artery and celiac trunk) and anterior and posterior inferior pancreaticoduodenal arteries (from the SMA). Dorsal and greater pancreatic arteries branch from the splenic artery as it courses along the posterior superior surface of the body of the pancreas to reach the spleen. Pancreatic veins drain into the splenic and superior mesenteric veins to drain the organ.

b. **Innervation:** The pancreas receives parasympathetic and sympathetic innervation from vagus nerves and thoracic splanchnic nerves (greater and lesser), respectively. Because the pancreas receives blood supply from branches of both the celiac trunk and SMA, pre- and postganglionic fibers from the associated plexuses travel along the vasculature to reach the pancreas.

c. **Lymphatics:** Lymph from the pancreas is primarily drained through **pancreaticosplenic lymph nodes**, which drain into hepatic lymph nodes before sending efferent vessels to either the preaortic celiac or superior mesenteric nodes.

14. **Pancreatic histology:** The pancreas can be subdivided histologically and functionally into the **exocrine pancreas** and the **endocrine pancreas**.

a. **Exocrine pancreas:** The exocrine pancreas is a compound tubuloacinar serous gland, which consists of **pancreatic acini** and a network of **pancreatic ducts** (Fig. 4.37). The functional unit of the exocrine pancreas is the **pancreatic acinus**.

[1] **Pancreatic acinus:** The pancreatic acinus consists of a number of pancreatic **acinar cells** that are arranged in grape-like structures connected to a network of pancreatic ducts. The pancreatic acinar cell secretes the following digestive enzymes: **trypsinogen, chymotrypsinogen, proelastase, procarboxypeptidase A, procarboxypeptidase B, pancreatic lipase, colipase, cholesterol ester hydrolase, phospholipase A$_2$, ribonuclease, deoxyribonuclease**, and **pancreatic amylase**. Several of the digestive enzymes are capable of damaging the pancreas and are, therefore, secreted in an inactive form (called a **proenzyme**). The proenzymes are activated in the duodenum by **enterokinase** located in the glycocalyx of enterocytes, which converts trypsinogen (inactive proenzyme) to trypsin (active enzyme). Trypsin then converts all other inactive proenzymes to their active form.

[2] **Pancreatic duct system:** The network of pancreatic ducts carries "pancreatic juice," which contains digestive enzymes, anions (Cl$^-$, HCO$_3^-$), and cations (Na$^+$, K$^+$) to the small intestine. The network of pancreatic ducts follows this route: intercalated ducts → intralobular ducts → interlobular ducts → and the main pancreatic duct (duct of Wirsung), which joins the bile duct at the hepatoduodenal ampulla (ampulla of Vater). The entire network of pancreatic ducts is lined by **duct epithelium**. The duct epithelium produces and releases anions (Cl$^-$, HCO$_3^-$) into the pancreatic juice using various transporter proteins ("pumps") and ion-channel proteins. The cations (Na$^+$, K$^+$) present in the juice follow the Cl$^-$ movement.

(a) **Intercalated duct:** The **intercalated duct** begins with the **centroacinar cells** that are located within the acinus.

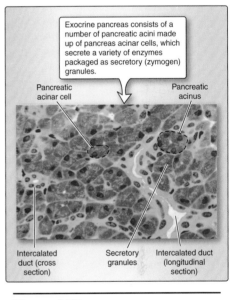

Exocrine pancreas consists of a number of pancreatic acini made up of pancreas acinar cells, which secrete a variety of enzymes packaged as secretory (zymogen) granules.

Pancreatic acinar cell

Pancreatic acinus

Intercalated duct (cross section)

Secretory granules

Intercalated duct (longitudinal section)

Figure 4.37
Exocrine pancreas histology.

It is lined by a simple squamous or simple low cuboidal epithelium. It transitions into an intralobular duct.

(b) **Intralobular duct:** The **intralobular duct** is lined by a simple cuboidal epithelium. It transitions into an interlobular duct that is located within the connective tissue septae from the capsule.

(c) **Interlobular duct:** The **interlobular duct** is lined by a simple columnar epithelium. A large interlobular duct is lined by a pseudostratified, stratified cuboidal, or stratified columnar epithelium. They empty into the main pancreatic duct (duct of Wirsung).

(d) **Main pancreatic duct (duct of Wirsung):** This duct is lined by a pseudostratified, stratified cuboidal or stratified columnar epithelium and is located within the connective tissue septae from the capsule.

b. **Endocrine pancreas:** The endocrine pancreas consists of the **islets of Langerhans** comprised of a number of cell types, including the α **cell**, β **cell**, and δ **cell** (Fig. 4.38). The functional unit of the endocrine pancreas is the islet of Langerhans, which comprise ~2% of the entire pancreas. The estimated 1–3 million islets of Langerhans are scattered through the exocrine pancreas with most located within the tail of the pancreas.

[1] α **Cell:** The α cell (20% of the total islet cells) secretes **glucagon** (29 amino acids, 3.5 kDa). Glucagon binds to the **glucagon receptor**, which is a G-protein–linked receptor present primarily on hepatocytes and adipocytes. The α cells produce ~30%–40% of the total glucagon within the blood. The enteroendocrine cells within the GI tract produce the remaining glucagon (called **enteroglucagon**). Glucagon is involved in **glucose homeostasis**.

[2] β **Cell:** The β cell (75% of the total islet cells) secretes **insulin** (51 amino acids, 6 kDa). Insulin binds to the **insulin receptor**, which is a receptor tyrosine kinase present primarily on hepatocytes, adipocytes, and skeletal muscle cells. Insulin is involved in **glucose homeostasis**.

[3] δ **Cell:** The δ cell (5% of total islet cells) secretes **somatostatin** (14 amino acids, 1.6kDa). Somatostatin binds to the **somatostatin receptor**, which is a G-protein–linked receptor. Somatostatin probably inhibits hormone secretion from nearby α cells and β cells in a paracrine manner.

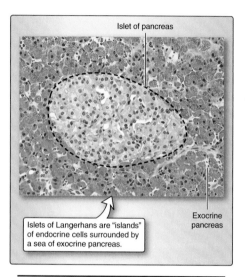

Islet of pancreas

Islets of Langerhans are "islands" of endocrine cells surrounded by a sea of exocrine pancreas.

Exocrine pancreas

Figure 4.38
Endocrine pancreas histology.

Clinical Application 4.13: Diabetes

Type 1 diabetes is marked by **autoantibodies** and an **insulitis reaction** that results in the destruction of pancreatic β cells. Type 1 diabetes is a **multifactorial inherited disease** and shows an association with human leukocyte antigen (HLA) complex loci named HLA-DR3 and HLA-DR4 located on the p arm of chromosome 6 (p6). The clinical features of type I diabetes include hyperglycemia, ketoacidosis, and exogenous insulin dependence. Long-term clinical effects of type I diabetes include neuropathy, retinopathy leading to blindness, and nephropathy leading to kidney failure.

Type 2 diabetes is marked by **insulin resistance of peripheral tissues** and **abnormal β cell function** and is often **associated with obesity**. Type 2 diabetes is a **multifactorial inherited disease** often detected during routine screening by detection of hyperglycemia or by patient complaining of polyuria.

The embryologic formation of the **spleen** does not form as part of the primitive gut tube but is located within the abdominal cavity. The spleen develops from **mesoderm** associated with the **dorsal mesentery of the stomach**. Due to the 90° clockwise rotation of the stomach, the dorsal mesentery of the stomach establishes in the adult a mesenteric connection with both the kidney (called the **splenorenal ligament**) and the stomach (called the **gastrosplenic ligament**).

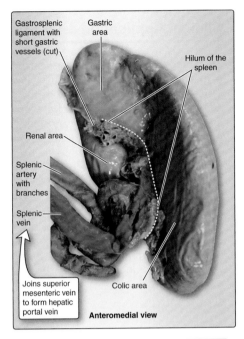

Figure 4.39
Spleen.

15. **Splenic anatomy:** The spleen is a hematopoietic organ that plays an important role in immunity. It is located in the left upper quadrant, between the 9th and 11th intercostal space, posteriorly and has anatomical relationships medially (visceral surface) with the stomach, left kidney, tail of the pancreas, and left (splenic) flexure of the large intestine. The outer convex surface of the spleen is the diaphragmatic surface, which fits just inferior to the left hemidiaphragm. The gastrosplenic and splenorenal ligaments connect the spleen to the stomach and left kidney, respectively, making it an intraperitoneal structure (Fig. 4.39). These mesenteries transmit the splenic, short gastric, and left gastro-omental vessels; lymphatic vessels; and autonomic nerve fibers. The phrenicocolic ligament extends from the diaphragm to the left (splenic) colic flexure, thus creating a shelf-like structure on which the spleen rests.

a. **Blood supply:** The spleen is supplied by the splenic artery, a main branch of the celiac trunk, which branches in to multiple vessels at the hilum of the spleen. The splenic vein carries venous blood from the spleen to the hepatic portal vein. Splenic circulation is further detailed below.

b. **Innervation:** The spleen receives parasympathetic and sympathetic innervation from vagal trunks and celiac plexus (greater splanchnic nerve), respectively.

c. **Lymphatics:** Lymph from the spleen leaves the nodes in the hilum to drain through the pancreaticosplenic lymph nodes along the course of the splenic vein as it travels posterior to the pancreas.

16. **Splenic histology:** The spleen is surrounded by a connective tissue **capsule** that projects **trabeculae**, which blends into a **reticulum** (i.e., fine connective tissue framework) and the connective tissue at the **hilus**. The spleen is divided histologically into the **white pulp** and **red pulp** each of which have different functions (Fig. 4.40). The **marginal zone** is an ill-defined zone located between the white pulp and red pulp.

a. **White pulp:** The white pulp of the spleen immunologically monitors the blood, unlike the lymph nodes which immunologically monitor the lymph. The white pulp is where B lymphocytes and T lymphocytes interact to form a large number of **plasma cells**

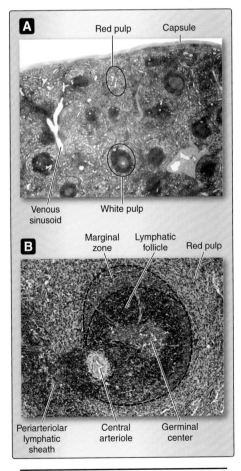

Figure 4.40
Splenic histology (A and B).

Clinical Application 4.14: Splenomegaly

Splenomegaly, or enlarged spleen, can occur by a number of mechanisms, although most cases involve some type of hepatic pathology. Additionally, hematologic pathology and infection can contribute to splenic engorgement. While splenic size and shape can vary significantly between patients, the organ should not be easily palpated in the normal population. A palpable spleen—below the left costal margin—likely indicates the presence of splenomegaly in which the spleen is enlarged ≥40% of its original size. A massively enlarged spleen may cross the midline into the right abdominal quadrants and extend inferiorly into the pelvis. Palpation and percussion maneuvers are used to assess splenic size and position, and imaging (ultrasound, computed tomography, plain film) may be used to confirm and establish baseline measurements.

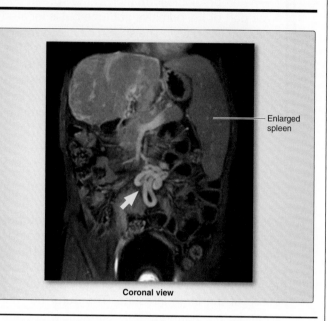

Enlarged spleen

Coronal view

T1-weighted 3D SPGR post-contrast images of 6-year-old boy showing an enlarged spleen and multiple collateral venous structures (arrow head) in the mid-abdomen secondary to portal hypertension.

that migrate to the red pulp and produce immunoglobulins. The white pulp of the spleen contains a number of cell types.

[1] Mature B lymphocytes: These are organized into **lymphatic follicles** that are closely associated with the **central arteriole**. The mature B lymphocytes may be organized into either **primary lymphatic follicles** (without a germinal center) or **secondary lymphatic follicles** (with germinal centers). Germinal centers are evidence that activated B lymphocytes have begun their transformation into plasma cells.

[2] Mature T lymphocytes: The mature T lymphocytes are organized into a sheath around a central arteriole called the **periarteriolar lymphatic sheath** (**PALS**).

[3] Fibroblasts: The fibroblast secretes **type III collagen** that forms the splenic reticulum.

b. Marginal zone: This is the site where the **immune response is initiated** and where **lymphocytes exit the bloodstream** to repopulate the spleen. The marginal zone of the spleen also contains fibroblasts as well as two other cell types.

[1] Macrophage: The macrophage has both a phagocytic and antigen-presenting function.

[2] Antigen-presenting cells: The **antigen-presenting cell** (**APC**) internalizes antigen either by **phagocytosis** or by **receptor-mediated endocytosis** and then displays a fragment of the antigen complex to the major histocompatibility complex

(MHC) II on its cell surface. A T lymphocyte recognizes and interacts with the antigen fragment–MHC II complex. Subsequently, the APC produces a **costimulatory signal** that activates the T lymphocyte.

c. **Red pulp:** The red pulp removes senescent, damaged, or genetically altered (e.g., sickle cell disease) red blood cells (RBCs) and particulate matter from the blood circulation through the action of macrophages. The red pulp also stores platelets and is the site of immunoglobulin production released from plasma cells. It is organized into **splenic cords** that are separated by **splenic venous sinusoids**.

[1] **Splenic cords:** The splenic cords consist of B and T lymphocytes, other white blood cells (leukocytes), macrophages, plasma cells, RBCs, platelets, and fibroblasts. Basically, the splenic cords consist of all blood elements that may have extravasated out of the bloodstream due to the open circulation in the spleen.

[2] **Splenic venous sinusoids:** The splenic venous sinusoids are lined by specialized endothelial cells that are long, narrow, and have wide gaps between their lateral margins with connecting rings of basement lamina for support. This microanatomy resembles the metal hoops (i.e., basal lamina) that support the wooden staves (i.e., specialized endothelial cells) of a barrel. These endothelial cells provide an effective **filter** between the splenic cords and lumen of the sinusoids. Defective RBCs, dead leukocytes, senescent platelets, and particulate matter are phagocytized by macrophages as they try to negotiate their passage through the filter.

d. **Splenic microcirculation:** The spleen has a unique blood supply that is directly related to the functions of the white pulp and red pulp. The **splenic artery** enters the spleen via the hilus and gives off arterial branches within trabeculae called **trabecular arteries** (Fig. 4.41). The trabecular arteries leave the trabeculae and enter the parenchyma as **central arterioles**. The central arterioles immediately become ensheathed by T lymphocytes called the **periarteriolar lymphatic sheath (PALS)**. The central arterioles branch into **radial arterioles**, which enter the marginal zone, and **penicillar arterioles**, which enter the red pulp. The penicillar arterioles become capillaries some of which are surrounded by macrophages and are then called **sheathed capillaries**. The sheathed capillaries become **terminal capillaries**.

[1] **Closed circulation:** The terminal capillaries may terminate by connecting directly to the **venous sinusoids** so that the blood is always enclosed by an endothelium. This is called the **closed circulation**.

[2] **Open circulation:** The terminal capillaries may also terminate as open-ended capillaries that extravasate blood into the splenic cords. The blood must reenter the vasculature by passing through the unique endothelium of the venous sinusoids. This is called the **open circulation**.

The venous sinusoids coalesce and empty into **trabecular veins** and finally the **splenic vein** at the hilus.

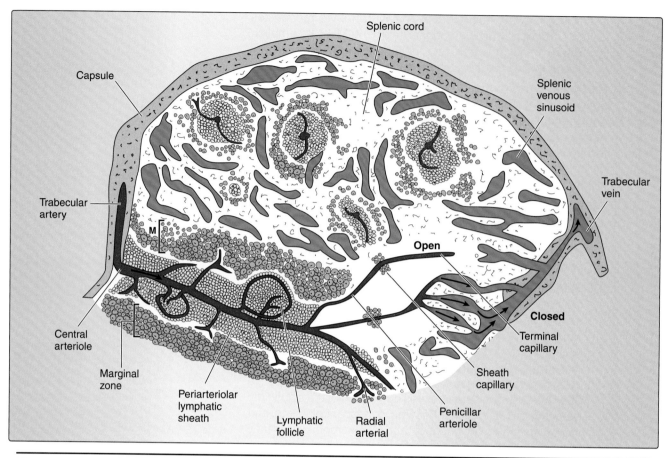

Figure 4.41
Splenic microcirculation, M = marginal zone.

C. Midgut derivatives

The derivatives of the midgut include the **lower part of the duodenum**, **jejunum** and **ileum** (small intestine), **appendix**, **ascending colon**, and the **proximal two thirds of the transverse colon**. The derivatives of the midgut receive their blood supply from the **superior mesenteric artery**.

1. **Duodenal embryology:** Although the duodenum develops as both a foregut and midgut derivative, it is described in its entirety in this section. The upper portion of the duodenum develops from the caudalmost portion of the foregut. The lower portion of the duodenum develops from the cranialmost portion of the midgut. The accepted junction of the upper and lower duodenum is a line drawn just distal to the opening of the bile duct (see Figs. 4.22 and 4.28).

2. **Duodenal anatomy:** The duodenum is the most proximal and shortest (~1 foot in length) segment of the small intestine and is characterized by its C-shaped structure (see Fig. 4.36). Compared to the jejunum and ileum, the duodenum has a wider luminal diameter along its short course.

   a. **Parts:** It spans between the pyloric sphincter of the stomach to the jejunum and is divided into four different parts.

      [1] **First part:** The **superior** section runs horizontally to the right from the pylorus and is the only section that is intraperitoneal with its connection to the hepatoduodenal ligament.

[2] **Second part:** The **descending** section runs vertically and to the right of the pancreatic head, which sits in the concavity of the second part.

[3] **Third part:** The **horizontal** section runs inferior to the pancreatic head and uncinate process before traveling superiorly and transitioning into the fourth part.

[4] **Fourth part:** The **ascending** section is continuous with the jejunum at the **duodenojejunal junction** and is supported at this junction by the **suspensory muscle of the duodenum** (ligament of Treitz).

b. **Blood supply:** Like the pancreas, the duodenum is also supplied by branches of the celiac trunk (gastroduodenal, supraduodenal, and superior pancreaticoduodenal arteries) and SMA (inferior pancreaticoduodenal artery). Veins of the same name form tributaries that drain into the superior mesenteric or splenic veins, or directly into the hepatic portal vein.

c. **Innervation:** The duodenum receives parasympathetic and sympathetic innervation from vagus nerves and celiac (greater splanchnic nerve) and superior mesenteric (lesser splanchnic nerve) ganglia/plexuses, respectively.

d. **Lymphatics:** Duodenal lymphatics are divided into anterior and posterior systems. The anterior lymphatic vessels drain first into the pyloric lymph nodes before sending efferents to the celiac nodes. The posterior lymphatic vessels drain into the superior mesenteric lymph nodes before sending efferents to the celiac nodes as well.

3. **Embryologic formation of midgut distal to duodenum:** The midgut forms a U-shaped loop (**midgut loop**) that herniates through the primitive umbilical ring into the extraembryonic coelom (i.e., a **physiologic umbilical herniation** occurs) beginning at week 6 (see Fig. 4.22). The midgut loop consists of a **cranial limb** and a **caudal limb**. The cranial limb forms the **jejunum** and **upper part of the ileum**. The caudal limb forms the **cecal diverticulum** from which the **cecum** and **appendix** develop. The rest of the caudal limb forms the **lower part of the ileum**, **ascending colon**, and **proximal two thirds of the transverse colon**. The midgut loop rotates a total of **270° counterclockwise** around the **superior mesenteric artery** as it returns to the abdominal cavity, thus reducing the physiologic herniation around week 11.

4. **Small intestinal anatomy:** Collectively, the **jejunum** and **ileum** make up the majority of the small intestine length and surface area (Fig. 4.42). The jejunum begins at the duodenojejunal junction (~L3 level) and occupies a portion of the left upper quadrant. The ileum is the third and most distal portion of the small intestine, occupying a portion of the right lower quadrant and ending at the **iliocecal junction**, where it empties into the **cecum**. Both portions are intraperitoneal and mobile, as they are suspended in the fan-shaped **mesentery of the small intestine**.

a. **Blood supply:** The jejunum and ileum receive blood from **intestinal branches** of the SMA (Fig. 4.43). These branches course through the mesentery of the small intestine and form intricate arrangements of **arterial arcades** before giving off small, straight arteries—**vasa recta**—to the visceral walls. The pattern of arterial arcades and length of the vasa recta differ

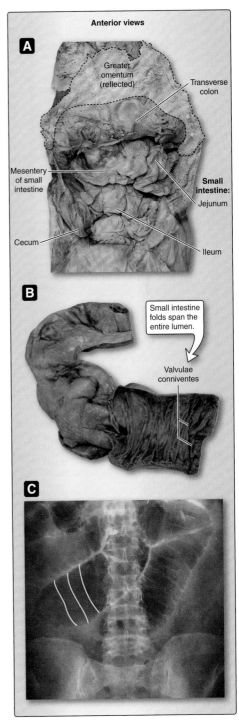

Figure 4.42

Small intestine. A, In situ. B, Gross specimen showing external and internal surfaces. C, Plain-film showing pattern of small intestinal folds (valvulae conniventes) as yellow lines.

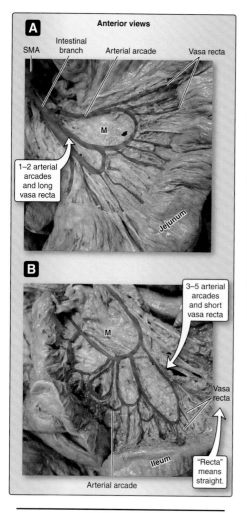

Figure 4.43
Arterial arrangement in small intestine. A, Jejunum. B, Ileum. M = mesentery of small intestine, SMA = superior mesenteric artery.

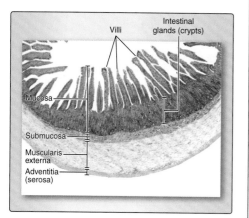

Figure 4.44
Small intestine histology.

Clinical Application 4.15: Omphalocele

An **omphalocele** occurs when abdominal contents herniate through the umbilical ring and persists outside the body, covered variably by a translucent peritoneal membrane sac (a light gray, shiny sac) protruding from the base of the umbilical cord. Large omphaloceles may contain stomach, liver, and intestines. Small omphaloceles contain only intestines. Omphaloceles are usually associated with other congenital anomalies

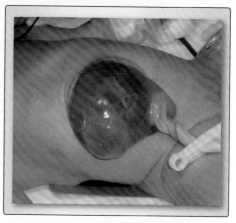

(e.g., trisomy 13, trisomy 18, or Beckwith–Wiedemann syndrome) and with increased levels of α-**fetoprotein**.

in both portions. The jejunum has one to two arterial arcades and long vasa recta, whereas the ileum has three to five arterial arcades and short vasa recta. Venous drainage occurs through tributaries of the superior mesenteric vein.

b. Innervation: The jejunum and ileum receive parasympathetic and sympathetic innervation from vagus nerves and thoracic splanchnic nerves by way of the celiac and superior mesenteric ganglia/plexuses, respectively.

Clinical Application 4.16: Ileal Diverticulum

An **ileal diverticulum (Meckel diverticulum)** occurs when a remnant of the vitelline duct persists, thereby forming an outpouching located on the antimesenteric border of the ileum. The outpouching may connect to the umbilicus via a fibrous cord or fistula (which may leak meconium). An ileal diverticulum is usually located about 30 cm proximal to the ileocecal valve in infants and varies in length from 2 to 15

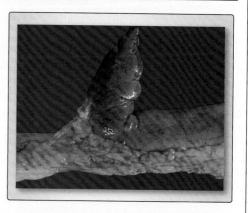

cm. Heterotopic gastric mucosa may be present, which leads to ulceration, perforation, or GI bleeding, especially if a large number of parietal cells are present. An ileal diverticulum is associated clinically with symptoms resembling appendicitis and bright red or dark red stools (i.e., bloody).

Ileal diverticulum arising from antimesenteric portion of ileum.

c. **Lymphatics:** Lymph nodes and vessels are located throughout the mesentery of the small intestine. Nodes within the mesentery—from closest to viscera to closest to the SMA—include **juxtaintestinal**, **mesenteric**, and **central nodes**. Lymph flows through these nodes sequentially before sending efferents to the superior mesenteric nodes.

5. **Small intestinal histology:** The wall of the small intestine consists of four histologic layers, namely, the **mucosa, submucosa, muscularis externa**, and **serosa** (Fig. 4.44). The inner luminal surface of the small intestine contains semilunar folds of mucosa and submucosa called **plica circulares (valves of Kerckring)**, is dotted with millions of openings where the intestinal glands open to the surface, and has finger-like projections of epithelium and lamina propria called **villi**.

a. **Mucosa:** The mucosa of the small intestine consists of an **epithelium**, a **lamina propria**, and a **muscularis mucosa**. The epithelium consists of **enterocytes** and **goblet cells** that cover the intestinal villi (Fig. 4.45). The lamina propria consists of loose connective tissue, blood vessels, lacteals (specialized lymphatic vessels), and diffuse lymphatic tissue. Within the lamina propria, **mucosal glands** are found that begin at the base of the villi and end at the muscularis mucosa. The muscularis mucosa consists of a smooth muscle layer.

[1] **Enterocytes:** The apical region of the enterocyte is characterized by **microvilli** that are coated by filamentous glycoproteins called the **glycocalyx**. The glycocalyx contains important enzymes necessary for digestion, including maltase, α-dextrinase, sucrase, lactase, trehalase, aminopeptidases, and enterokinase. The lateral region of the enterocyte is characterized by juxtaluminal **zonula occludens (tight junctions)** and **Na$^+$-K$^+$ ATPase**. The enterocyte synthesizes the enzymes of the glycocalyx. It also absorbs carbohydrates, protein, lipids, vitamins, Ca^{2+}, Fe^{2+}, Na^+, Cl^-, K^+, HCO_3^-, and H_2O from the intestinal lumen and secretes Na^+, Cl^-, HCO_3^-, and H_2O into the intestinal lumen.

[2] **Goblet cells:** The goblet cell secretes **mucus**.

[3] **Mucosal glands:** The epithelium of the small intestine mucosa invaginates to form mucosal glands called the **intestinal glands (crypts of Lieberkühn)**. The intestinal glands are simple, tubular glands that begin at the base of the villi and end at the muscularis mucosa. The intestinal glands of the small intestine consist of **LGR5$^+$ stem cells**, **Paneth cells**, and **enteroendocrine cells** (Fig. 4.46).

(a) **LGR5$^+$ stem cells:** Leucine-rich repeat-containing G-protein–coupled receptor 5 (LGR5$^+$) cells reside at the base of the intestinal glands in close association with CD24$^+$ Paneth cells. The LGR5$^+$ stem cells produce rapidly proliferating transit amplifying (**TA**) **cells** located in the lower portion of the intestinal gland. The TA cells differentiate into enterocytes, goblet cells, Paneth cells, and enteroendocrine cells and migrate up and down the intestinal gland–villus axis.

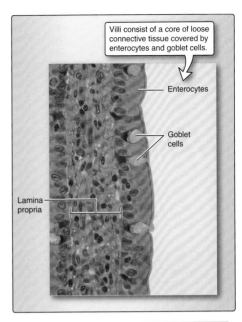

Figure 4.45
Villus histology.

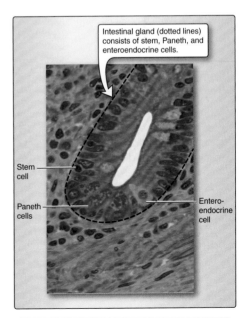

Figure 4.46
Intestinal crypt histology.

(b) **Paneth cells:** The Paneth cell secretes **lysozyme, tumor necrosis factor-α, and defensins (cryptidins).**

(c) **Enteroendocrine cells:** The enteroendocrine cell in the small intestine secretes **cholecystokinin, secretin, gastric-inhibitory peptide, glucagon-like peptide, and peptide YY.**

b. **Submucosa:** The submucosa of the small intestine consists of dense, irregular connective tissue; blood vessels; diffuse lymphatic tissue; and the submucosal (Meissner) nerve plexus. The submucosa and mucosa are thrown into a number of semilunar folds called the **plica circulares (valves of Kerckring).** The duodenum has prominent glands in the submucosa called **duodenal submucosal glands (Brunner glands),** which secrete an alkaline mucus to neutralize the acidic chyme.

c. **Muscularis externa:** The muscularis externa of the small intestine consists of an inner circular layer of smooth muscle, an outer longitudinal layer of smooth muscle, blood vessels, and the myenteric (Auerbach) nerve plexus.

d. **Adventitia (serosa):** The adventitia of the small intestine consists of dense, irregular connective tissue that blends in with the connective tissue of the body wall. Most of the small intestine is suspended by a mesentery (i.e., intraperitoneal), so that the adventitia is covered by a layer of simple squamous epithelium called **mesothelium** and is then referred to as a **serosa.**

6. **Appendicular anatomy:** The appendix is a thin, worm-like, blind diverticulum that extends from the cecum of the large intestine (Fig. 4.47). It is suspended by the **mesoappendix** and can assume a variety of positions in relation to the cecum, although it is typically found in the **retrocecal position.** Appendicular position can dictate symptoms associated with appendix pathology.

a. **Blood supply:** The appendix receives blood from the **appendicular artery,** a branch of the ileocolic artery (SMA). The appendicular artery travels through the mesoappendix to reach the

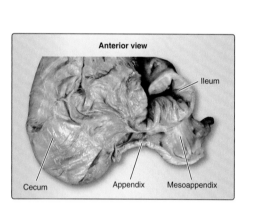

Figure 4.47
Appendix anatomy. At ileocecal junction.

Clinical Application 4.17: Crohn Disease

Crohn disease (CR) is a chronic inflammatory bowel disease that usually appears in teenagers and young adults. CR most commonly affects the **ileum** and the **ascending right colon.** The etiology of CR is unknown, although epidemiologic studies have indicated a **strong genetic predisposition,** and immunologic studies have indicated a role of **cytotoxic T cells** in the damage to the intestinal wall. Pathologic findings include transmural nodular lymphoid aggregates, noncaseating epithelioid granulomas, neutrophil infiltration of the intestinal glands that ultimately destroys the glands leading to ulcers, and coalescence of the ulcers into **long, serpentine ulcers (linear ulcers)** oriented along the long axis of the bowel. Additionally, a classic feature of CR is the clear demarcation between diseased bowel segments located directly next to uninvolved normal bowel and a **cobblestone appearance** that can be seen grossly and radiographically.

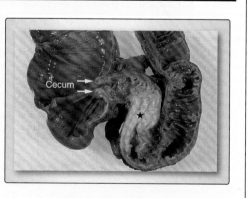

Opened specimen at ileocecal junction. Arrows show ileocecal valve, which is very stenotic. Terminal ileum lumen is almost completely occluded due to disease process (black star).

organ. Venous blood is drained by the vein of the same name into the superior mesenteric vein tributaries.

b. **Innervation:** Parasympathetic and sympathetic innervation of the appendix comes from the vagal and thoracic splanchnic contributions to the superior mesenteric plexus, respectively.

> Visceral pain fibers (GVA) from the appendix travel with the sympathetic fibers back to the T_{10} spinal cord segment. With this in mind, it makes sense that referred pain would be localized around the umbilicus, which represents the area of the T_{10} dermatome.

c. **Lymphatics:** Lymph nodes in the mesoappendix receive lymph from the appendix before draining through ileocolic nodes, which send efferents to the superior mesenteric lymph nodes.

7. **Appendicular histology:** The wall of the appendix consists of four histologic layers, namely, the **mucosa**, **submucosa**, **muscularis externa**, and **serosa** (Fig. 4.48).

a. **Mucosa:** The mucosa of the appendix consists of an **epithelium**, a **lamina propria**, and a **muscularis mucosa**. The epithelium consists of **enterocytes** and **goblet cells** that line the lumen of the appendix. The epithelium forms intestinal glands (crypts of Lieberkühn) that extend to the muscularis mucosa, although the

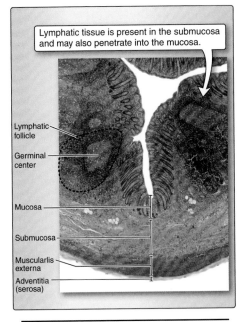

Figure 4.48
Appendix histology.

Clinical Application 4.18: Appendicitis

Appendicitis is the acute inflammation of the appendix caused by blockage of the organ's small lumen by fecal concretion (older patients) or by lymphoid hyperplasia (younger patients). Luminal obstruction causes distention and may lead to rupture. The pattern of referred visceral pain associated with appendicitis begins in the periumbilical region (dull in nature) and migrates to the lower right quadrant. Nausea, vomiting, and fever are often present as well. Irritation of the parietal peritoneum adjacent to the appendix often causes severe pain, which presents with rebound tenderness and guarding (see Clinical Application 4.4). Pressure over the McBurney point (midpoint along the line from the right anterior superior iliac spine to the umbilicus)

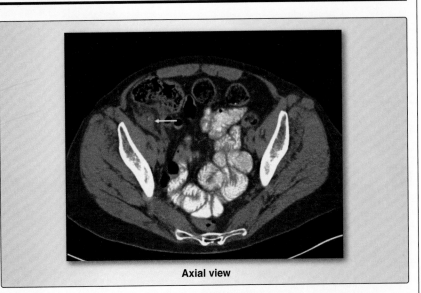

Axial view

produces this point tenderness. Imaging can be used (computed tomography) to assess severity and guide subsequent treatment (surgical vs. nonsurgical). Ultrasound is used to assess pathology in children and pregnant women. If surgery is indicated, the laparoscopic approach is preferred over the open approach, as it reduces risk of infection, decreases pain, and has a shorter recovery time.

CT image showing inflamed appendix (arrow) measuring 14 cm.

muscularis mucosa is often inconspicuous due to the infiltration of lymphocytes.

b. **Submucosa:** The submucosa of the appendix consists of dense, irregular connective tissue; blood vessels; abundant lymphatic tissue organized into lymphatic follicles with germinal centers that may extend into the mucosa; and the submucosal (Meissner) nerve plexus.

c. **Muscularis externa:** The muscularis externa of the appendix consists of an inner circular layer of smooth muscle and outer longitudinal layer of smooth muscle, blood vessels, and the myenteric (Auerbach) nerve plexus.

d. **Adventitia (serosa):** The adventitia of the appendix consists of dense, irregular connective tissue that blends in with the connective tissue of the body wall. The appendix is suspended by a mesentery (i.e., intraperitoneal), so that the adventitia is covered by a layer of simple squamous epithelium called **mesothelium** and is then referred to as a **serosa**.

8. **Large intestinal (midgut derivatives) anatomy:** Collectively, the large intestine comprises the cecum, appendix, ascending colon, transverse colon, descending colon, sigmoid colon, rectum, and anal canal (Fig. 4.49). These structures form a peripheral "frame"

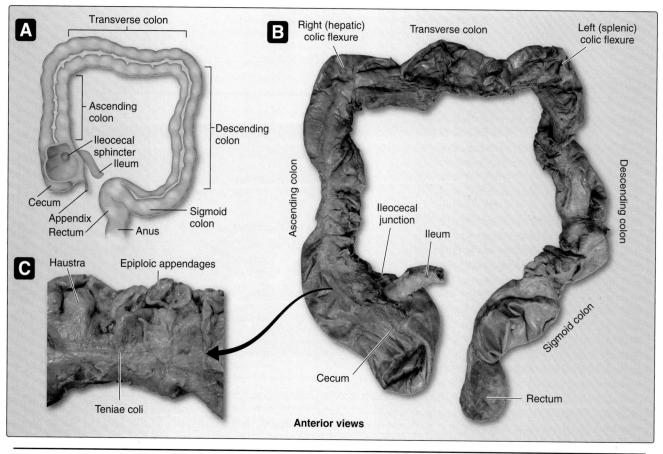

Figure 4.49
Large intestine. A, Schematic. B, Gross specimen. C, External characteristic features of large intestine.

around the centrally located small intestine. General, distinguishing features of the large intestine include **omental (epiploic) appendices**, a set of three longitudinal bands called **teniae coli**, and sac-like structures called **haustra** (Fig. 4.50). Anatomy of the midgut derivatives of the large intestine is detailed in this section.

a. **Cecum:** The cecum can be described as the "cul-du-sac" of the large intestines. This blind pouch represents the first portion of the large intestine at the ileocecal junction and is located in the lower right quadrant. It is intraperitoneal and continuous superiorly with the ascending colon.

b. **Ascending colon:** At the junction of the cecum and **ascending colon** is a luminal narrowing. Although initially an intraperitoneal structure during development, the ascending colon is eventually pushed posteriorly along the right posterior abdominal wall so that it is no longer suspended in mesentery and is thus described as **secondarily retroperitoneal**. The **right paracolic gutter** lies between the lateral border of the ascending colon and the neighboring abdominal wall musculature.

c. **Transverse colon:** At the superior end of the ascending colon, an acute angulation occurs inferior to the right lobe of the liver. This change in direction marks the **right (hepatic) colic flexure** and transition to the **transverse colon**. The transverse colon courses from the right upper quadrant to the left upper quadrant in a fairly horizontal position. This large intraperitoneal structure is the most mobile of the large intestine as it is suspended by the broad **transverse mesocolon** and also has connections to the greater omentum. At its distal end is another acute angulation, the **left (splenic) colic flexure** that marks the transition from transverse to descending colon. The phrenicocolic ligament connects the left colic flexure to the diaphragm, thus creating a splenic shelf.

d. **Blood supply:** The midgut derivatives of the large intestine are supplied by branches of the SMA. Specifically, the ileocolic artery supplies the cecum, right colic artery supplies the ascending colon, and middle colic artery supplies the proximal two thirds of the transverse colon. Marginal arteries along the concavities of the colic flexures represent anastomoses between the right and left colic arteries with the middle colic artery. These important anastomoses endure collateral blood flow to the large intestine in the event of an occlusion. Veins of the same name drain into the superior mesenteric vein.

e. **Innervation:** The midgut derivative of the large intestine receives parasympathetic and sympathetic innervation from the vagal and thoracic splanchnic contributions to the superior mesenteric plexus, respectively.

f. **Lymphatics:** Peripheral lymph nodes associated with the cecum (ileocolic), ascending colon (epicolic/paracolic → intermediate right colic), and transverse colon (epicolic/paracolic → intermediate middle colic) send efferents to superior mesenteric lymph nodes.

9. **Large intestinal histology:** The wall of the large intestine consists of four histologic layers, namely, the **mucosa**, **submucosa**, **muscularis externa**, and **serosa** (Fig. 4.51). The inner luminal surface

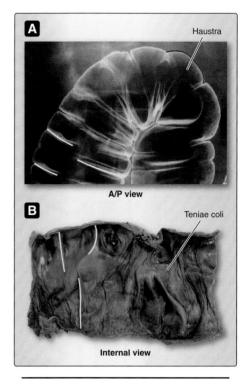

Figure 4.50
Large intestine folds. A, Plain-film image at (hepatic) flexure. B, Internal structures. Yellow lines show pattern of haustral folds throughout large intestine. Red line outlines haustra. A/P = anterior/posterior.

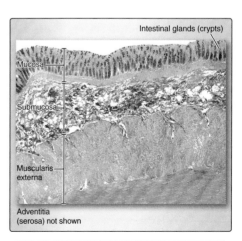

Figure 4.51
Large intestine histology.

of the large intestine is smooth (i.e., no longitudinal folds, no rugae, plicae circulares, or villi are present). The inner luminal surface is dotted with millions of openings where intestinal glands open to the surface.

a. Mucosa: The mucosa of the large intestine consists of an **epithelium**, a **lamina propria**, and a **muscularis mucosa**. The epithelium consists of **enterocytes** and **goblet cells** that line the lumen of the large intestine. The apical region of the enterocyte is characterized by **microvilli**. The lateral region of the enterocyte is characterized by juxtaluminal **zonula occludens (tight junctions)** and **Na$^+$-K$^+$ ATPase**. The enterocyte absorbs Na$^+$, Cl$^-$, K$^+$, and H$_2$O from the intestinal lumen and secretes Cl$^-$, K$^+$, and HCO$_3^-$ into the intestinal lumen. The goblet cell secretes **mucus**. The lamina propria consists of loose connective tissue, blood vessels, and diffuse lymphatic tissue. Within the lamina propria, **mucosal glands** are found that begin at the surface and end at the muscularis mucosa. The muscularis mucosa consists of a smooth muscle layer.

b. Mucosal glands: The epithelium of the large intestine mucosa invaginates to form mucosal glands called **intestinal glands (crypts of Lieberkühn)**. The intestinal glands are simple, tubular glands that begin at the surface and end at the muscularis mucosa (Fig. 4.52). The intestinal glands of the large intestine consist of **LGR5$^+$ stem cells**, **goblet cells**, and **enteroendocrine cells**.

> **[1] LGR5$^+$ stem cells:** These reside at the base of the intestinal glands and produce rapidly proliferating **TA (Transit-Amplifying) cells**. The TA cells differentiate into enterocytes, goblet cells, and enteroendocrine cells and migrate up and down the intestinal gland axis.
>
> **[2] Goblet cells:** The goblet cell secretes **mucus**.
>
> **[3] Enteroendocrine cells:** In the large intestine, these secrete **vasoactive polypeptide**, **somatostatin**, **serotonin**, **glucagon-like polypeptide**, and **peptide YY**.

c. Submucosa: The submucosa of the large intestine consists of dense, irregular connective tissue; blood vessels; diffuse lymphatic tissue; and the submucosal (Meissner) nerve plexus.

d. Muscularis externa: The muscularis externa of the large intestine consists of an inner circular layer of smooth muscle, **teniae coli** (mesocolic, omental, and free tenia), blood vessels, and the myenteric (Auerbach) nerve plexus. In the rectum, the inner circular smooth muscle of the muscularis externa, the submucosa, and the mucosa are thrown into three permanent **transverse rectal folds** (called **Houston valves**), which probably support the fecal mass.

e. Adventitia (serosa): The adventitia of the large intestine consists of dense, irregular connective tissue that blends in with the connective tissue of the body wall. Some portions of the large intestine are suspended by a mesentery (i.e., intraperitoneal), so that the adventitia is covered by **mesothelium** and then referred to as a **serosa**. The serosa also contains fatty tags called **appendices epiploicae**.

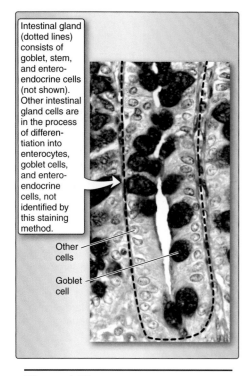

Intestinal gland (dotted lines) consists of goblet, stem, and enteroendocrine cells (not shown). Other intestinal gland cells are in the process of differentiation into enterocytes, goblet cells, and enteroendocrine cells, not identified by this staining method.

Other cells

Goblet cell

Figure 4.52
Intestinal gland (crypt) histology.

Clinical Application 4.19: Ulcerative Colitis

Ulcerative colitis (UC) is an idiopathic inflammatory bowel disease that usually appears in teenagers and young adults. UC always involves the **rectum** and may extend proximally for varying distances into the **descending colon**. The etiology of UC is unknown. Pathologic findings include raw, red, and granular mucosal surface; continuous inflammation (i.e., no "skip areas" as in Crohn disease); a diffuse, chronic inflammatory infiltration in the lamina propria; damage to the intestinal glands (crypts); inflammatory pseudopolyps; areas of friable, bloody residual mucosa; "collar-button" ulcers; and "lead-pipe" appearance in the chronic state.

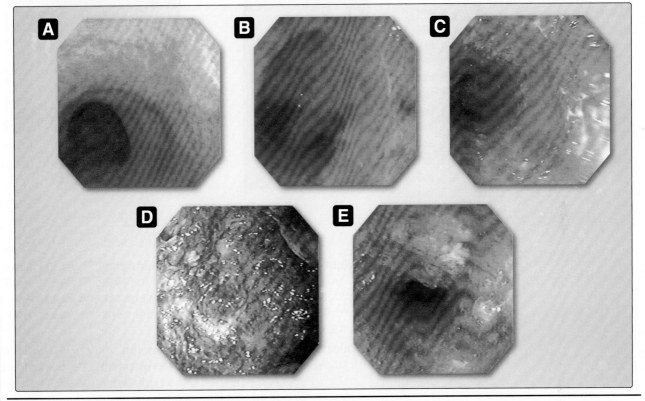

Colonoscopic changes in ulcerative colitis. A, Loss of vessel pattern. B, Contact bleeding present. C, Granular changes. D, Ulcerated mucosa showing florid changes. E, Colonic stricture.

D. Hindgut derivatives

The derivatives of the hindgut include the **distal third of the transverse colon**, **descending colon**, **sigmoid colon**, **rectum**, and **upper anal canal**. The derivatives of the hindgut receive their blood supply from the **inferior mesenteric artery**.

1. **Hindgut embryology:** The cranial portion of the hindgut develops into the distal third of the transverse colon, descending colon, and sigmoid colon (see Fig. 4.22). The caudal portion of the hindgut is an endoderm-lined pouch called the **cloaca**, which contacts the surface ectoderm of the **proctodeum** to form the **cloacal membrane**. The cloaca is partitioned by the **urorectal septum** into the **rectum/upper anal canal** and the **urogenital sinus**. The cloacal membrane is partitioned by the urorectal septum into the **anal membrane** and **urogenital membrane**. The urorectal septum fuses with the cloacal membrane at the future site of the gross anatomical **perineal body**. See Chapter 5 for mroe details on anal canal development.

Clinical Application 4.20: Colonic Aganglionosis

Colonic aganglionosis (Hirschsprung disease) is caused by the arrest of the caudal migration of neural crest cells. The hallmark is the absence of ganglionic cells in the myenteric and submucosal plexuses (most commonly in the sigmoid colon and rectum), resulting in a narrow segment of colon (i.e., colon fails to relax). The most characteristic functional finding is the failure of internal anal sphincter to relax following rectal distention (i.e., abnormal rectoanal reflex). Colonic aganglionosis is associated clinically with a distended abdomen, inability to pass meconium, gushing of fecal material on a rectal digital exam, and a loss of peristalsis in the colon segment distal to the normal innervated colon.

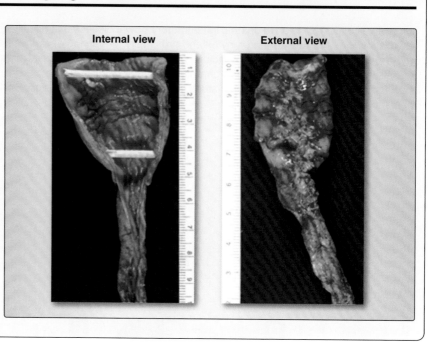

Internal view   External view

2. **Hindgut derivatives anatomy (up to anal canal):** The distal third of the transverse colon marks the start of the hindgut (see Fig. 4.49). This area also marks an important transition of neurovascular supply. At the left (splenic) colic flexure, the transverse colon ends, and the **descending colon** begins.

   a. **Descending colon and sigmoid colon:** Although initially an intraperitoneal structure during development, the descending colon is eventually pushed posteriorly along the left posterior abdominal wall so that it is no longer suspended in mesentery and is thus described as **secondarily retroperitoneal**. The **left paracolic gutter** lies between the lateral border of the descending colon and the neighboring abdominal wall musculature. At its distal end—in the left iliac fossa—the descending colon is continuous with the **sigmoid colon**. The sigmoid colon is characterized by its S-shape appearance and typically extends inferiorly to ~3 vertebral level, where it transitions into the rectum. The sigmoid is suspended in a **sigmoid mesocolon**, making it an intraperitoneal structure.

   b. **Rectum and anal canal:** The transition from sigmoid colon to **rectum** occurs in the pelvis, which makes the upper third of the rectum retroperitoneal (only covered laterally and anteriorly) and the lower two thirds, subperitoneal. Although classified as a part of the large intestine, the rectum lacks teniae coli and omental appendices. The **anal canal** is continuous with the rectum and is discussed in detail in Chapter 5.

   c. **Blood supply:** Hindgut derivatives of the large intestine are supplied by branches of the inferior mesenteric artery. Specifically, the left colic artery supplies the descending colon, sigmoid arteries supply the sigmoid colon, and the superior rectal artery supplies the upper rectum. Marginal arteries along the concavities of the colic flexures represent anastomoses between the right and left colic arteries with the middle colic artery. These important anastomoses ensure collateral blood flow to the large intestine in the event of an occlusion. Veins of the same name drain into the inferior mesenteric vein.

   d. **Innervation:** The distal third of the transverse colon marks an important transition in autonomic innervation. Parasympathetic innervation including and distal to this region is supplied by pelvic splanchnic nerves (S_2–S_4), which travel superiorly through the inferior hypogastric plexus → hypogastric nerve → superior hypogastric plexus to reach the rectum, sigmoid colon descending colon, and distal third of the transverse colon. Sympathetic innervation is provided by upper lumbar splanchnic nerves (L_1–L_2) associated with the inferior mesenteric ganglion and plexus. Postganglionic fibers travel out to the viscera on the arterial network.

   e. **Lymphatics:** Peripheral lymph nodes associated with the descending and sigmoid colon (epicolic/paracolic) drain into intermediate left colic nodes, which then send efferents to inferior mesenteric lymph nodes.

VII. POSTERIOR ABDOMINAL WALL

The posterior abdominal wall comprises structures that lie posterior to the parietal peritoneum in the abdominal cavity (Fig. 4.53). This region is bound posteriorly by lumbar vertebrae (L1–L5) and intervertebral discs; superiorly by portions of the muscular diaphragm; posterolaterally by psoas major, quadratus lumborum, iliacus, and transversus abdominus; and anteriorly and inferiorly by posterior parietal peritoneum. In addition to the structures that bind this region, it contains the kidneys, suprarenal glands, ureters, abdominal aorta and branches, IVC and tributaries, sympathetic trunks, lymph nodes, lumbar plexus branches, and variable amounts of fat.

A. Viscera

Viscera contained in the posterior abdominal wall region include the right and left kidneys, ureters, and suprarenal glands. These structures are discussed in detail in Chapter 5.

B. Muscles

The muscles that support the posterior abdominal wall act on both the spine and the lower limbs (thighs). Some of these muscles also contribute to the formation of the anterolateral abdominal wall. **Endoabdominal fascia** lies between the muscles and posterior parietal peritoneum, which is continuous laterally with the transversalis fascia of the anterolateral abdominal wall (Fig. 4.54).

   1. **Psoas major:** This muscle originates on lumbar vertebrae transverse processes, bodies (T12 as well), and associated intervertebral discs and inserts with the iliacus onto the lesser trochanter of the femur. This muscle is a powerful flexor of the thigh and spine and

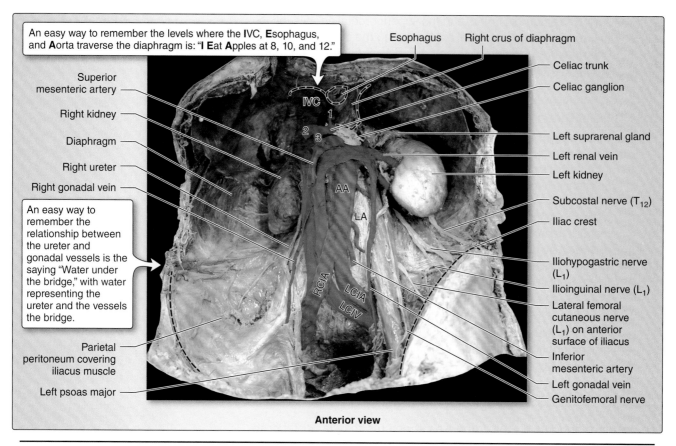

An easy way to remember the levels where the **I**VC, **E**sophagus, and **A**orta traverse the diaphragm is: "**I E**at **A**pples at 8, 10, and 12."

Superior mesenteric artery

Right kidney

Diaphragm

Right ureter

Right gonadal vein

An easy way to remember the relationship between the ureter and gonadal vessels is the saying "Water under the bridge," with water representing the ureter and the vessels the bridge.

Parietal peritoneum covering iliacus muscle

Left psoas major

Esophagus   Right crus of diaphragm

Celiac trunk

Celiac ganglion

Left suprarenal gland

Left renal vein

Left kidney

Subcostal nerve (T$_{12}$)

Iliac crest

Iliohypogastric nerve (L$_1$)

Ilioinguinal nerve (L$_1$)

Lateral femoral cutaneous nerve (L$_1$) on anterior surface of iliacus

Inferior mesenteric artery

Left gonadal vein

Genitofemoral nerve

Anterior view

Figure 4.53

Posterior abdominal wall structure. Gastrointestinal viscera and peritoneum removed to reveal posterior abdominal wall structures. 1 = left gastric artery, 2 = common hepatic artery, 3 = splenic artery, AA = abdominal aorta, IVC = inferior vena cava, LA = lumbar artery, LCIA = left common iliac artery, LCIV = left common iliac vein, RCIA = right common iliac artery.

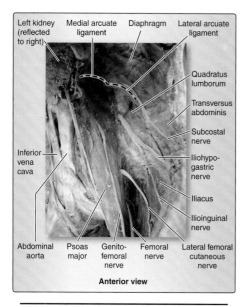

Left kidney (reflected to right)   Medial arcuate ligament   Diaphragm   Lateral arcuate ligament

Quadratus lumborum

Transversus abdominis

Subcostal nerve

Inferior vena cava

Iliohypo-gastric nerve

Iliacus

Ilioinguinal nerve

Abdominal aorta   Psoas major   Genito-femoral nerve   Femoral nerve   Lateral femoral cutaneous nerve

Anterior view

Figure 4.54

Posterior abdominal wall muscles and nerves. Left posterior abdominal wall with left kidney reflected to reveal musculature and nerves.

also laterally flexes the lumbar spine. It is innervated by anterior rami of L$_1$–L$_3$. The superior portion of psoas fascia thickens to form the **medial arcuate ligament**.

2. **Quadratus lumborum:** This muscle originates from lumbar transverse processes and the lower border of rib 12, medially, and inserts onto the iliac crest and iliolumbar ligaments. It extends and laterally flexes the lumbar spine and stabilizes the 12th rib during inspiration. It receives innervation from anterior rami of T$_{12}$ and L$_1$–L$_4$. The superior portion of quadratus lumborum fascia (anterior layer of **thoracolumbar fascia**) thickens to form the **lateral arcuate ligament**.

3. **Iliacus:** This muscle originates from the iliac fossa and inserts with psoas major onto the lesser trochanter of the femur. It flexes the thigh and stabilizes the hip joint and is innervated in the pelvis by the femoral nerve.

4. **Transversus abdominis:** The deepest of the flat lateral abdominal wall muscles, transversus abdominis originates posteriorly and is located internally, just lateral to quadratus lumborum and inferior to the posterior diaphragm. See II.A.1.c. for more details.

5. **Diaphragm:** The diaphragm separates the thoracic and abdominal cavities and functions in respiration. Centrally, the diaphragm is characterized by an aponeurotic **central tendon**. Along its periphery,

the diaphragm becomes more muscular. The muscular arrangement and attachments of the lumbar portion of the diaphragm create a series of hiatuses to permit passage of vessels and viscera between thoracic and abdominal cavities.

a. **Attachments:** The muscular portion of the diaphragm is attached along the inner boundary of the thoracic outlet (sternal and costal portions) and on the first through third lumbar vertebrae (lumbar portion). Posteriorly, the lumbar portion divides around the vertebral bodies, forming two extensions of muscle—**right** and **left crura** (crus means "leg"; see Fig. 4.20). These crura serve to anchor the diaphragm posteriorly. In the midline, the left and right crura are joined by the **median arcuate ligament**, a fibrous structure that completes the opening for the aorta.

b. **Hiatuses:** The diaphragm has three main hiatuses to allow for the **IVC**, **esophagus**, and **descending aorta** to pass between the thoracic and abdominal cavities. Each passageway occurs at a specific vertebral level.

[1] **T8, caval opening (for IVC):** Located in the central tendon region, terminal branches of the right phrenic nerve and lymphatic vessels also pass through this opening.

[2] **T10, esophageal hiatus:** This opening is located in the right crus of the diaphragm. Hiatal fibers constrict the esophagus during contraction of the diaphragm, acting as a sphincter. It also transmits vagal trunks, esophageal vessels (left gastric branches), and lymphatic vessels.

[3] **T12, aortic hiatus:** This opening is located between the left and right crura of the diaphragm, and diaphragm movement does not interfere with blood flow through the aorta. The aponeurotic arch between right and left crura—median arcuate ligament—caps the aorta in the midline.

An easy way to remember the order of openings in the diaphragm and the main structures that pass through them is to use the phrase: **I E**at **A**pples at **8**, **10**, and **12**. In this mnemonic phrase, "I" stands for IVC, "E" stands for esophagus, and "A" stands for aorta.

c. **Neurovascular and lymphatic supply:** The inferior (abdominal) surface of the diaphragm receives blood supply from the **inferior phrenic vessels** and innervation from **phrenic nerves** (C_3–C_5) and **intercostal nerves** (laterally). Lymph from the inferior surface of the diaphragm drains into **phrenic**, **anterior diaphragmatic**, and **lumbar lymph nodes**.

C. Blood supply

As shown in Figures 4.16 and 4.18, blood supply to the posterior abdominal wall is achieved through paired branches of the abdominal aorta (inferior phrenic, lumbar, and subcostal arteries) and tributaries of the IVC and azygos system (posterior intercostal and lumbar veins).

D. Innervation

Innervation of the posterior abdominal wall musculature is described above. Visceral innervation of the kidneys, suprarenal glands, and ureters is described in detail in Chapter 5. Autonomic plexuses associated with the aorta are also found in the posterior abdominal wall region, some extending to viscera in this region as well. Branches of the lumbar plexus, along with the subcostal nerve (T_{12}), course along posterior abdominal wall musculature to provide motor and sensory innervation to abdominal wall and lower limb structures (see Fig. 4.54).

1. **Subcostal (T_{12}):** This branch travels anterior to the transversus abdominis before piercing the muscle to run between it and the internal oblique to innervate the external oblique and overlying anterolateral abdominal wall skin.

2. **Iliohypogastric (L_1):** This branch travels anterior to the quadratus lumborum, then between the transversus abdominis and internal oblique to innervate muscles and skin of the anterolateral abdominal wall. It may arise from a common trunk with ilioinguinal nerve.

3. **Ilioinguinal (L_1):** This branch travels anterior to quadratus lumborum, then between the transversus abdominis and internal oblique to innervate muscles and skin of the anterolateral abdominal wall. It may arise from a common trunk with iliohypogastric nerve. The ilioinguinal nerve travels through portions of the inguinal canal to reach the inferior portion of this region.

4. **Lateral femoral cutaneous (L_2–L_3):** This branch travels anterior to iliacus, then deep to the inguinal ligament just medial to the anterior superior iliac spine to innervate skin on the superolateral thigh.

5. **Femoral (L_2–L_4):** This branch travels deep to psoas major before exiting laterally, passing deep to the inguinal ligament to enter the femoral triangle. The femoral nerve provides motor and sensory innervation to anterior thigh and medial leg/foot structures. (See Chapter 6 for more details.)

6. **Genitofemoral (L_1–L_2):** This branch travels on the anterior surface of psoas major and splits distally into a genital branch and femoral branch, which innervate structures of the perineum and anterior thigh, respectively.

7. **Obturator (L_2–L_4):** This branch travels deep to psoas major before exiting medially, traveling through a small opening in the obturator fascia to reach and innervate structures in the medial thigh. (See Chapter 6 for more details.)

E. Lymphatics

Lymphatic structures are intimately related to the abdominal aorta (see Fig. 4.20). These centrally located nodes and vessels collect lymph from peripheral viscera and the posterior abdominal wall structures. Specifically, lymph from the posterior abdominal wall drains initially into **right** and **left lumbar lymph nodes** before sending efferents superiorly to form **lumbar lymphatic trunks** (right and left). These trunks, along with intestinal lymphatic trunks, join at the abdominal confluence, where a small dilated sac—**cisterna chyli**—is located. Lymph then passes superiorly into the thoracic duct.

VIII. IMAGING

Interpretation of abdominal imaging requires a thorough approach. A solid understanding of the abdominal anatomy and spatial relationships is very important and useful in both plain film and computed tomography (CT) interpretation.

A. Radiology

Although a variety of radiologic approaches is possible, here we use the BBC approach, which stands for **B**owel (and other organs), **B**ones, and **C**alcifications (and artifacts). Adopting a stepwise approach to interpreting radiographic images minimizes errors and maximizes the effectiveness of a treatment plan.

1. **Bowel and other organs:** Typically, the small bowel lies more centrally, with the large bowel framing it around the periphery (Fig. 4.55). You should look for mucosal fold patterns in both the small and large bowels. The small bowel folds—valvulae conniventes (plicae circularis)—span the full width of the bowel, while large bowel folds—haustral folds (plicae semilunaris)—do not completely traverse the large bowel. Normal gas patterns should also be present and outline these features. For other organs, proceed in the following order.

    a. **Lungs:** Check lung bases for pathology.

    b. **Liver:** Assess size of this large right upper quadrant organ.

    c. **Gallbladder:** This organ is difficult to see on x-ray.

    d. **Stomach:** This left upper quadrant/midline organ may contain variable amounts of air (gastric bubble).

    e. **Psoas muscles:** These are located in the lumbar region. Look for demarcation on the lateral edge (psoas fat plane).

    f. **Kidney: The** right kidney is often more visible than the left.

    g. **Spleen:** This left upper quadrant organ lies superior to the left kidney. Look for enlargement.

    h. **Bladder:** The variable size of this organ depends on fullness (in pelvis vs. suprapubic region).

2. **Bones:** Use bones for important landmarks. Also look for pathology, proceeding from the ribs → lumbar vertebrae, → sacrum → coccyx → pelvis → and finally to the proximal femurs.

3. **Calcifications and artifacts:** Various high-density areas of calcification can be visualized on an abdominal x-ray. Some examples are calcified gallstones; renal stones; pancreatic, vascular, and costochondral calcifications; and contrast. Artifacts may include surgical clips, jewelry (umbilicus), intrauterine device, and other objects. (Can you spot any of these in Fig. 4.55?)

B. Abdominal computed tomography radiology

A solid understanding of the spatial arrangement of structures in the abdomen is essential for diagnostic and interventional radiology. A systematic approach to interpreting abdominal CT images involves identifying abdominal wall layers, peritoneal spaces/structures, normal fat planes, and solid organ location and features. Working from superficial to deep allows

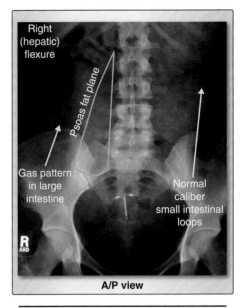

Figure 4.55
Plain-film radiology of the abdomen. Image shows normal bowel-gas patterns. Note dark appearance of air (gas) in large and small intestines. A/P = anterior/posterior.

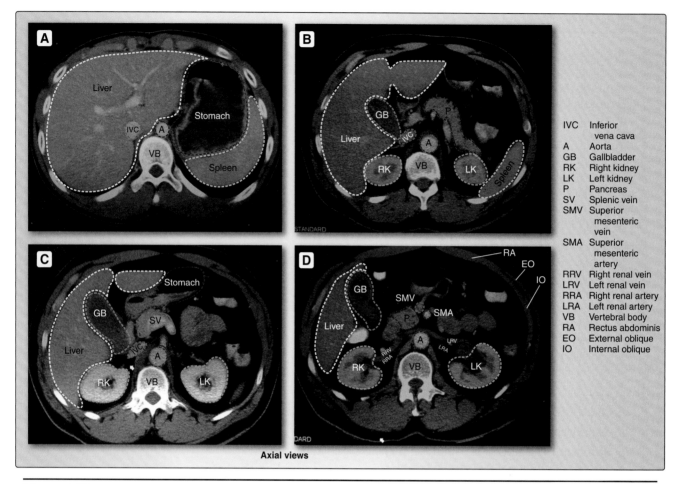

Axial views

Figure 4.56
CT Radiology of the abdomen. CT scans organized from superior to inferior (A–D). CT = computed tomography.

for a thorough interpretation, wherein abnormal anatomy and pathology can be identified properly. Recall that when viewing axial CT images, the patient's feet are coming out of the plane of the image and the head is into the plane. This makes the right side of the image the left side of the patient. With this in mind, organizing viscera into abdominal quadrants can help to determine position in the stacked images.

Chapter Summary

Anterolateral Abdominal Wall

- The anterolateral abdominal wall is characterized laterally by the **external** and **internal oblique** and **transversus abdominis** and anteriorly by the **rectus abdominis**.
- Aponeuroses of the lateral flat muscles are arranged to form the rectus sheath.
- The **inguinal canal** transmits the spermatic cord in males and round ligament of the uterus in females.
- Direct inguinal hernias occur medial to the **inferior epigastric vessels**, while indirect inguinal hernias occur lateral.
- The umbilicus lies at the T10 dermatome.
- As the **testis** descends through the inguinal canal, it pulls layers of the anterolateral abdominal wall with it, forming coverings of the spermatic cord and testis.

Peritoneal Cavity

- The **peritoneal cavity** is the space between the **parietal** and **visceral peritoneum** in the abdominal cavity.
- Abdominal viscera that is suspended in peritoneum is **intraperitoneal**. Viscera that is only covered on one side is **retroperitoneal**.
- The **greater omentum** is the omental apron of the abdominal cavity that hangs down from the greater curvature of the stomach.
- The **lesser omentum** has attachments on the stomach, liver, and duodenum and forms the anterior boundary of the **lesser omental bursa** (sac).

Abdominal Vasculature and Lymphatics

- The **abdominal aorta** extends from the aortic hiatus (T12) to the bifurcation (L4).
- Three unpaired vessels—**celiac trunk** and **superior** and **inferior mesenteric arteries**—supply the gastrointestinal (GI) viscera and serve as the main blood supply to the foregut, midgut, and hindgut, respectively.
- Unpaired aortic branches serve the body wall, kidneys, suprarenal glands, and ureter.
- The **portal venous system** drains blood from GI viscera and filters it to the liver before returning it to the inferior vena cava (IVC).
- Anastomoses between the portal and caval systems allow for collateral blood flow. Main anastomoses occur in the esophagus, paraumbilical region, and anal canal. Varicosities at these locations occur in the event of **portal hypertension**.
- Peripheral collections of lymph nodes send efferents centrally to para-aortic and preaortic nodes before draining into lymph trunks and cisterna chyli.

Abdominal Innervation

- Abdominal viscera receive autonomic innervation through a series of **ganglia** and **plexuses** associated with abdominal vasculature.
- **Sympathetic innervation** occurs through **thoracic and lumbar splanchnic nerves** (preganglionic) that synapse on preaortic ganglia.
- **Parasympathetic innervation** occurs through the **vagus nerve** and **pelvic splanchnic nerves** (preganglionic) to synapse in or near the visceral walls.
- Sympathetic innervation decreases peristalsis and gland secretion, increases vasoconstriction, and closes sphincters. Parasympathetic innervation drives the opposite reactions.
- **General visceral afferent** fibers primarily follow the pathway of the sympathetic preganglionic fibers back to their origin. This relationship may underlie the concept of referred visceral pain.

Digestive Tract Embryology

- The primitive gut tube extends from the **oropharyngeal membrane** cranially to the **cloacal membrane** caudally.
- The primitive gut tube is divided into the **foregut, midgut**, and **hindgut**.
- Foregut derivatives include the **esophagus, stomach, liver, gallbladder/extrahepatic bile ducts, pancreas**, and the **upper part of the duodenum**. They receive their blood supply from the **celiac trunk**.

Chapter Summary (*continued*)

- Midgut derivatives include the **lower part of the duodenum, jejunum, ileum, appendix, ascending colon,** and the **proximal two thirds of the transverse colon.** They receive their blood supply from the **superior mesenteric artery.**

- Hindgut derivatives include the **distal third of the transverse colon, descending colon, sigmoid colon, rectum,** and **upper anal canal.** They receive their blood supply from the **inferior mesenteric artery.**

- The cloaca is partitioned by the **urorectal septum** into the **rectum/upper anal canal** and the **urogenital sinus.**

- The urorectal septum fuses with the cloacal membrane at the future site of the gross anatomical **perineal body.**

Esophagus

- The distal esophagus travels through the diaphragm at T10 level before transitioning into the stomach at the **gastro-esophageal (GE) junction.**

- The esophagus wall consists of four histologic layers: mucosa, submucosa, muscularis externa, and adventitia (or serosa).

- The mucosa consists of an epithelium, a lamina propria, and a muscularis mucosa. The epithelium is a nonkeratinized stratified squamous epithelium, except for the distal 2 cm at the GE junction, which is lined by simple columnar epithelium.

- **Gastroesophageal reflux disease (GERD)** is described as the symptoms or mucosal damage produced by the abnormal reflux of gastric contents through the lower esophageal sphincter (LES) into the esophagus.

- **Barrett esophagus** is defined as the replacement of esophageal stratified squamous epithelium with metaplastic "intestinalized" simple columnar epithelium with goblet cells extending at least 3 cm into the esophagus.

Stomach

- The stomach lies in the upper left quadrant and is made up of four parts: **cardia, fundus, body,** and **pylorus.**

- The **gastroduodenal junction** is the region between the pylorus and the first part of the duodenum. The **pyloric sphincter** controls transport of stomach contents into the duodenum.

- Gastric and gastro-omental vessels supply the majority of the stomach.

- The stomach wall consists of four histologic layers: mucosa, submucosa, muscularis externa, and serosa.

- The mucosa consists of an epithelium, a lamina propria, and a muscularis mucosa. The epithelium consists of surface mucous cells that line both the stomach lumen and the gastric pits. The surface mucous cells secrete mucus and HCO_3^-.

- In the fundus and body regions, gastric glands are present and consist of stem, mucous neck, parietal, chief, and enteroendocrine cells.

- The parietal cell contains **carbonic anhydrase,** which generates H^+, an **H^+-K^+ ATPase** that transports H^+ out of the cell, and a **Cl^- ion channel** that transports Cl^- out of the cell.

- The chief cell secretes **pepsinogen,** which is converted to **pepsin** upon contact with gastric HCl (acid pH) and **lipase.**

Liver

- The **liver** is located in the upper right quadrant and has four anatomical lobes—**right, left, quadrate,** and **caudate.**

- The liver is intraperitoneal, except for the **bare area** on the posterior superior surface, which is framed by the coronary ligaments.

- The classic liver lobule is roughly hexagonal with a central vein at its center and six portal triads at each corner.

- The **portal triad** contains a hepatic arteriole, portal venule, interlobular bile ductule, and a lymphatic vessel.

- The **hepatocyte** contains rough endoplasmic reticulum (rER), polyribosomes, a Golgi complex, smooth endoplasmic reticulum (sER), mitochondria, lysosomes, peroxisomes, lipid, iron, lipofuscin, and glycogen.

- The Kupffer cell is a macrophage and secretes tumor necrosis factor-α (TNF-α), interleukin-6 (IL-6), and transforming growth factor-β (TGF-β).

- The hepatic stellate cell secretes retinol bound to retinol-binding protein, type III collagen, and type I collagen during inflammation.

- The biliary tree follows this route: bile canaliculus → canal of Hering → interlobular bile ductule along the sides of the classic liver lobule → interlobular bile ductule at the corners of the classic liver lobule → right and left hepatic ducts → common hepatic duct joined by the cystic duct → bile duct.

Chapter Summary (*continued*)

- The cell membranes of adjacent hepatocytes form a bile canaliculus that is sealed by a zonula occludens (tight junction).
- The canal of Hering is located at the very periphery of the classic liver lobule and may be a niche for hepatic stem cells used in the regeneration the liver.

Gallbladder

- The **gallbladder** is a small bile reservoir located in the gallbladder fossa of the liver, in the upper right quadrant.
- The **cystic duct** joins the **common hepatic duct** to form the **common bile duct**.
- The gallbladder wall consists of three histologic layers: mucosa, muscularis externa, and adventitia. A submucosa is absent in the gallbladder.
- The mucosa consists of an **epithelium** and a **lamina propria**. There is no muscularis mucosa in the gallbladder.
- The epithelium consists of **simple columnar epithelial cells**. The apical region of the epithelial cells is characterized by numerous, short **microvilli**. The lateral region of the epithelial cells is characterized by juxtaluminal **zonula occludens** (**tight junctions**), **complex interdigitations**, and a **Na^+-K^+ ATPase**. The apical, lateral, and basal regions are characterized by **aquaporin water channels** (**AQP1** and **AQP8**) that participate in rapid passive movement of water.
- **Gallstones** form when bile salts and lecithin are overwhelmed by cholesterol. The three main types are cholesterol, black pigment, and brown pigment stones.

Pancreas

- The **pancreas** has four main parts—**head**, **neck**, **body**, and **tail**—and extends from the second part of the duodenum to the hilum of the spleen.
- The pancreas receives arterial supply from branches of the celiac trunk and superior mesenteric arteries, allowing for important collateral flow.
- The **main pancreatic duct** joins the common bile duct at the **hepatopancreatic ampulla** of the second part of the duodenum.
- The functional unit of the **exocrine pancreas** is the **pancreatic acinus**, which consists of a number of pancreatic acinar cells arranged in grapelike structures connected to a network of pancreatic ducts.
- The network of pancreatic ducts follows this route: intercalated ducts → intralobular ducts → interlobular ducts → and the main pancreatic duct (duct of Wirsung), which joins the bile duct at the hepatoduodenal ampulla (ampulla of Vater).
- The functional unit of the endocrine pancreas is the islet of Langerhan, which comprises α, β, and δ cells.
- α Cells secrete glucagon (29 amino acids, 3.5 kDa). β Cells secrete insulin (51 amino acids, 6 kDa). δ Cells secrete somatostatin (14 amino acids, 1.6 kDa).

Spleen

- Embryologic formation of the spleen is from **mesoderm**, not directly from the primitive gut tube.
- The **spleen** is an intraperitoneal structure located in the upper left quadrant and has visceral relationships with the stomach, pancreas, kidney, and large intestine.
- The spleen is divided histologically into **white** and **red pulp**, each with different functions. The **marginal zone** is an ill-defined zone located between the white and red pulp.
- The white pulp contains **mature B** and **T lymphocytes** and **fibroblasts**. The mature B lymphocytes are organized into **lymphatic follicles** that are closely associated with the **central arteriole**. The mature T lymphocytes are organized into a **periarteriolar lymphatic sheath** (**PALS**) around a central arteriole.
- The marginal zone is where the **immune response is initiated** and where **lymphocytes exit the bloodstream** to repopulate the spleen.
- The red pulp is organized into **splenic cords**, which are separated by **splenic venous sinusoids**.

Small Intestine

- The **small intestine** comprises a short **duodenum**, **jejunum**, and **ileum**. The latter two sections sit centrally in the abdominal cavity, often framed by the large intestine.
- The duodenum has four parts—**superior**, **descending**, **horizontal**, and **ascending**.

Chapter Summary (*continued*)

- The duodenum receives blood supply from branches of the celiac trunk and superior mesenteric arteries to allow for important collateral flow.
- The jejunum and ileum receive blood supply from superior mesenteric intestinal branches. These sections have specific arterial arrangements of multiple **arterial arcades** and **vasa recta**. The jejunum has 1–2 arcades with long vasa recta, while the ileum has 3–5 arcades and short vasa recta.
- The small intestine wall consists of four histologic layers: mucosa, submucosa, muscularis externa, and serosa.
- The mucosa consists of an epithelium, a lamina propria, and a muscularis mucosa. The epithelium consists of enterocytes and goblet cells that cover the intestinal villi.
- Enterocytes synthesize the enzymes of the glycocalyx and absorb carbohydrates, protein, lipids, vitamins, Ca^{2+}, Fe^{2+}, Na^+, Cl^-, K^+, HCO_3^-, and H_2O from the intestinal lumen. They secrete Na^+, Cl^-, HCO_3^-, and H_2O into the intestinal lumen. Goblet cells secrete mucus.
- Intestinal glands (or crypts of Lieberkühn) consist of $LGR5^+$ stem cells, Paneth cells, and enteroendocrine cells.
- Paneth cells secrete lysozyme, TNF-α, and defensins (cryptidins).

Appendix

- The **appendix** is a wormlike diverticulum that is attached to the cecum and suspended in a **mesoappendix**.
- Pain associated with **appendicitis** often begins in the periumbilical region and migrates to the lower right quadrant.
- The appendix wall consists of four histologic layers: mucosa, submucosa, muscularis externa, and serosa.
- The mucosa consists of an epithelium, a lamina propria, and a muscularis mucosa. The epithelium consists of enterocytes and goblet cells.
- The submucosa is characterized by abundant lymphatic tissue organized into lymphatic follicles with germinal centers that may extend into the mucosa.

Large Intestine

- The **large intestine** frames the more centrally located small intestine and consists of the **cecum**, **appendix**, **ascending colon**, **transverse colon**, **descending colon**, **sigmoid colon**, **rectum**, and **anal canal**.
- Three distinguishing features of the large intestine include **omental appendices**, **teniae coli**, and **haustra**.
- **Right** and **left colic flexures** mark the transition from ascending colon to transverse colon and transverse colon to descending colon, respectively.
- Blood supply to the large intestine arises from both **superior** and **inferior mesenteric arteries**.
- The left (splenic) colic flexure marks the transition of parasympathetic innervation from **vagus nerves** to **pelvic splanchnic nerves**.
- The large intestine wall consists of four histologic layers: mucosa, submucosa, muscularis externa, and adventitia (or serosa).
- The mucosa consists of an epithelium, a lamina propria, and a muscularis mucosa. The epithelium consists of enterocytes and goblet cells that line the lumen of the large intestine.
- Enterocytes absorb Na^+, Cl^-, K^+, and H_2O from the intestinal lumen and secrete Cl^-, K^+, and HCO_3^- into the lumen. Goblet cells secrete mucus.
- The intestinal glands consist of $LGR5^+$ stem cells, goblet cells, and enteroendocrine cells.

Posterior Abdominal Wall

- The posterior abdominal wall is supported by **lumbar vertebrae; intervertebral discs**; and a collection of muscles, including **psoas major, quadratus lumborum, transversus abdominis, diaphragm, and iliacus.**
- The abdominal aorta, IVC, kidneys, suprarenal glands, and ureters are all associated with the posterior abdominal wall.
- Nerves from the lumbar plexus, as well as the subcostal nerve, run along the surfaces of the muscles in the region.
- The muscular arrangement of the diaphragm posteriorly allows for the passage of the **IVC**, **esophagus**, and **aorta** between the thoracic and abdominal cavities at T8, T10, and T12 levels, respectively.

Study Questions:

Choose the ONE correct answer.

4.1 A 4-day-old boy has not defecated since coming home from the hospital even though his feeding pattern has been normal without any excessive vomiting. Rectal examination reveals a normal anus, anal canal, and rectum. However, a large fecal mass is found in the colon, and a large release of flatus and feces follows the rectal examination. Which of the following conditions would be suspected?

A. Imperforate anus

B. Anal agenesis

C. Anorectal agenesis

D. Rectal atresia

E. Colonic aganglionosis

Correct answer = E. This baby suffers from colonic aganglionosis, or Hirschsprung disease, which results in the retention of fecal material, causing the normal colon to enlarge. The retention of fecal material results from a lack of peristalsis in the narrow segment of colon distal to the enlarged colon. A biopsy of the narrow segment of colon would reveal the absence of parasympathetic ganglion cells in the myenteric plexus caused by failure of neural crest migration.

4.2 A 21-year-old man suffered a knife wound 2 inches left to the umbilicus, extending through the anterior abdominal wall layers to the rectus abdominis muscle. Which of the following layers is still completely intact?

A. Scarpa's fascia

B. Camper's fascia

C. Internal oblique aponeurosis

D. Transversus abdominis aponeurosis

E. External oblique aponeurosis

Correct answer = D. At the level described in this scenario, the anterior rectus sheath covers is comprised of external and internal oblique aponeuroses. The posterior rectus sheath is comprised of the internal oblique and transversus abdominis aponeuroses. In this scenario, the knife does not extend through the rectus abdominis muscle. Therefore, the transversus abdominis aponeuroses is still intact.

4.3 A 55-year-old female patient with a history of alcohol abuse is being seen in the emergency department for suspected pancreatitis. Ultrasound images reveal a gallstone obstructing the common bile duct. Excision through which of the following structures would be necessary to reach the common bile duct?

A. Transverse mesocolon

B. Hepatoduodenal ligament

C. Coronary ligament

D. Hepatogastric ligament

E. Greater omentum

Correct answer = B. The common bile duct, along with the hepatic portal vein and proper hepatic artery (portal triad), travels within the hepatoduodenal ligament.

4.4 A 25-year-old female is seen by a gastroenterologist for irritable bowel syndrome (IBS). Her primary complaints include abdominal distention, pain, and increased gastrointestinal (GI) motility. With every meal, she experiences bloating and diarrhea. Pharmacotherapy will target the motor nerves that increase GI motility. Which of the following nerves is involved in increasing peristalsis in the portion of the GI track located in the lower left quadrant?

A. Greater splanchnic

B. Vagus

C. Pelvic splanchnic

D. Lumbar splanchnic

E. Iliohypogastric

Correct answer = C. Parasympathetic nerves are responsible for increasing peristalsis in the GI tract. Portions of the GI tract in the lower left quadrant are distal to the transition to pelvic splanchnic nerves, which are parasympathetic nerves from S_2–S_4.

4.5 A 32-year-old pregnant female patient is being seen for sudden-onset right-sided abdominal pain, nausea, and discolored urine. The patient is in her second trimester and has a history of kidney stones. Ultrasonography detects two small stone in the renal pelvis. Pain produced by the kidney stones is referred back through which of the following autonomic nerve pathways?

A. Greater splanchnic
B. Lumbar splanchnic
C. Lesser splanchnic
D. Pelvic splanchnic
E. Vagus

Correct answer = C. Afferent pain fibers from viscera travel back to the sympathetic preganglionic origin. Lesser and least splanchnic nerves originate from T_{10}–T_{11} and T_{12}, respectively, and distribute through plexuses associated with the kidneys. Therefore, the best answer is C. Referred pain from the kidney maps back to T_{10}–T_{12} dermatome regions.

4.6 A 31-year-old male patient is admitted to the emergency department after suffering multiple injuries in a motor vehicle collision. He is found to have a lacerated liver, and the surgical team is consulted and prepped for emergency surgery to repair the organ. Surgeons found that the liver was lacerated anteriorly between the gallbladder and round ligament (ligamentum teres hepatis). Which of the following liver structures is located in the region of the laceration?

A. Bare area
B. Left lobe
C. Caudate lobe
D. Ductus venosus
E. Quadrate lobe

Correct answer = E. The quadrate lobe is located between the gallbladder and round ligament of the liver.

4.7 A 10-year-old male is admitted for complications with Crohn disease. Imaging reveals a diseased section of the distal ileum, approximately 2 inches in length, and the medical team determines that it must be surgically removed to improve the patient's symptoms. Vessels must be ligated prior to surgical excision of the bowel. Which of the following best describes the organization of arterial vessels in the ileum?

A. Intestinal branches give rise to 1–2 arterial arcades and long vasa recta.
B. Intestinal branches give rise to 3–5 arterial arcades and long vasa recta.
C. Intestinal branches give rise to 3–5 arterial arcades and short vasa recta.
D. Intestinal branches give rise to 1–2 arterial arcades and short vasa recta.
E. Ileocolic branches give rise to 3–5 arterial arcades and long vasa recta.

Correct answer = C. Intestinal branches from the superior mesenteric artery travel through the mesentery of the small intestine to reach the viscera. Prior to supplying the ileum, these branches form intricate arrangements of 3–5 arterial arcades and short vasa recta. The jejunum has 1–2 arterial arcades and long vasa recta.

4.27 A retroperitoneal mass in the lower right quadrant is putting pressure on a portion of the gastrointestinal tract, causing digestive issues and discomfort. Which of the following structures may be affected by the pressure of the mass?

   A. Sigmoid colon
   B. Rectum
   C. Jejunum
   D. Duodenum
   E. Cecum

Correct answer = E. The cecum is the only structure in the list that is located in the lower right quadrant. Even though it is an intraperitoneal structure, a large retroperitoneal mass can still extend anteriorly and create pressure on adjacent structures.

5 Pelvis and Perineum

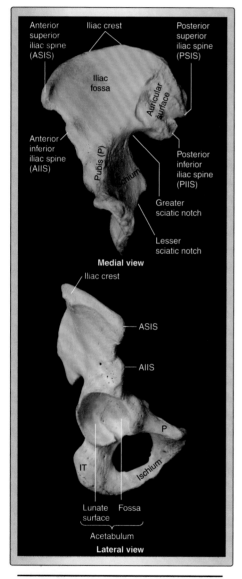

Anterior superior iliac spine (ASIS)

Iliac crest

Posterior superior iliac spine (PSIS)

Iliac fossa

Auricular surface

Anterior inferior iliac spine (AIIS)

Pubis (P)

Ischium

Posterior inferior iliac spine (PIIS)

Greater sciatic notch

Lesser sciatic notch

Medial view

Iliac crest

ASIS

AIIS

P

IT

Ischium

Lunate surface   Fossa

Acetabulum

Lateral view

Figure 5.1
Osteology of the hip bone.

I. OVERVIEW

The pelvis is defined as the area and contents contained within the framework of the bony pelvis. Pelvic structures are located between parietal peritoneum of the abdomen and the skin of the perineum. Organs of the genitourinary and distal gastrointestinal (GI) systems make up pelvic viscera.

II. PELVIC OSTEOLOGY

Unlike the shoulder girdle/complex, the bones of the pelvic girdle form a continuous bony ring that provides for visceral protection and muscle attachment, allows for limited movements, and distributes weight from the vertebral column to the lower limbs.

A. Bony pelvis

The bony pelvis is made up of right and left os coxae anterolaterally and the unpaired sacrum and coccyx posteriorly (Fig. 5.1). (Refer to Chapters 2 and 6 for additional details on the sacrum and coccyx.)

1. **Os coxae (hip bones):** Each os coxae is formed by fusion of three bones—ischium, ilium, and pubis. Each bone contributes to the formation of the acetabulum and has important bony landmarks that serve as tendon and ligament attachment sites (Fig. 5.2).

   a. **Ilium:** The superior lateral portion of the hip is characterized by an anterior concave **iliac fossa** and a posterior gluteal surface. The superior border of the ilium forms the **iliac crest**, which terminates anteriorly and posteriorly in projections called **anterior superior** and **posterior superior iliac spines**, respectively. Paired anterior and posterior inferior iliac spines lie inferior to their superior counterparts. The medial auricular surface of the ilium articulates with the sacrum posteriorly. The most inferior posterior portion forms the greater sciatic notch.

   b. **Ischium:** The posteroinferior portion of the hip is characterized by a large, rough projection of bone, the **ischial tuberosity**, which serves as an attachment site for hamstring musculature and the sacrotuberous ligament. The **ischial spine** projects from the superior ischium and is the attachment site for the sacrospinous ligament, superior gemellus, and pelvic floor musculature. **Ischial rami** (superior and inferior) contribute anteriorly to the formation of the **obturator foramen**.

c. **Pubis:** The anterior portion of the hip is characterized by a central body and superior and inferior **pubic rami**, which collectively contribute to the formation of the obturator foramen. The right and left pubic bones articulate anteriorly at the **pubic symphysis**. Additional important bony landmarks include the **pubic tubercle** and **pectin pubis**.

> The anterior superior iliac spines and pubic tubercles align in the frontal plane when the pelvis is in anatomical position.

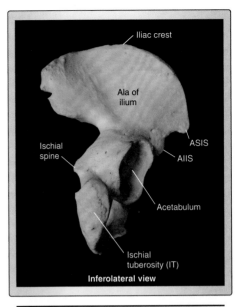

Inferolateral view

Figure 5.1
(*continued*)

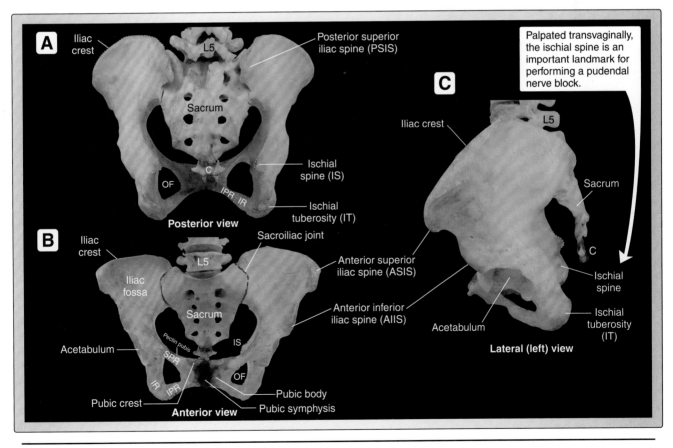

Figure 5.2
Articulated pelvis. C = coccyx, IPR = inferior pubic ramus, IR = ischial ramus, OF = obturator foramen, SPR = superior pubic ramus.

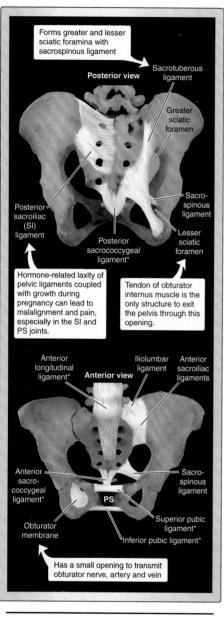

Figure 5.3
Pelvic ligaments. (Most ligaments are bilateral but illustrated unilaterally here for simplicity.) PS = pubic symphysis; * = unpaired ligaments.

Clinical Application 5.1: Pelvic Fractures

Pelvic fractures most often occur as a result of trauma and can be categorized as pelvic ring fractures (anteroposterior forces), acetabular fractures (lateral forces), or avulsion injuries (muscular forces). Due to the bony construction and arrangement of the pelvic (ring) girdle, traumatic pelvic ring fractures are multiple. This is akin to being unable to break a lifesaver candy in one spot—based on the forces on and design of the lifesaver, a second break will occur. Acetabular fractures are classified by the area affected and can extend into other areas of the os coxae. Avulsion injuries most often involve young athletes and target anterior superior and inferior iliac spines and ischial tuberosities as a result of quick, forceful contraction of the muscles attached at these sites. These injuries are often unilateral and isolated. In contrast to pelvic ring fractures, fragility fractures of the pelvis, which often occur in the geriatric, osteoporotic population, can occur in isolation. In trauma patients with pelvic fractures, assessment of pelvic viscera and vasculature integrity is of utmost importance. Once stable, these patients are often managed by a surgical team consisting of trauma and orthopedic surgeons and vascular specialists, such as interventional radiologists.

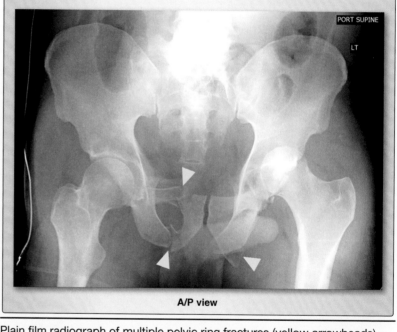

Plain film radiograph of multiple pelvic ring fractures (yellow arrowheads) and left posterior hip dislocation in a male patient. A/P = anterior/posterior.

B. Articulations

Joints of the pelvis provide stability, protection, and controlled mobility. As shown in Figure 5.3, strong ligaments support these joints and, if stretched or injured, can produce pain through ma-lalignment. Joints of the pelvis include the following.

1. **Lumbosacral:** Articulation of L5 and S1 includes synovial joints between articular processes and a symphysis joint between the L5/S1 intervertebral disc. **Iliolumbar ligaments** (anterior and posterior) support this joint by limiting axial rotation of L5 on S1.

2. **Sacroiliac (SI):** Articulations between the right and left auricular surfaces of os coxae and sacrum (right and left SI joints) transmit body weight to the os coxae and the lower limbs and are supported by SI (anterior and posterior) and interosseous ligaments. Secondary support ligaments include the sacrotuberous and sacrospinous ligaments.

   a. **Greater and lesser sciatic notches:** Sacrotuberous and sacrospinous ligaments anchor the sacrum to the ischial tuberosity and ischial spine, respectively. The arrangement of these ligaments turns greater and lesser sciatic notches into greater and lesser sciatic foramina, which serve as passageways for structures to exit and enter the pelvis.

3. **Pubic symphysis:** This articulation between the right and left pubic bodies is connected through an interpubic fibrocartilage disc and supported by superior and inferior pubic ligaments.

4. **Sacrococcygeal:** This symphysis articulation between the distal sacrum and coccyx contains a small disc and is supported by sacrococcygeal ligaments.

C. Regions of articulated pelvis

The articulated pelvis can be divided at the level of the **pelvic brim** into a superior **greater (false) pelvis** and an inferior **lesser (true) pelvis** (Fig. 5.4). The greater pelvis represents the area superior to the pelvic brim that houses abdominal viscera. The lesser pelvis represents the area inferior to the pelvic brim that houses pelvic viscera. The pelvic brim also serves at the boundary for the pelvic inlet (superior pelvic aperture). The pelvic outlet (inferior pelvic aperture) is bound by the coccyx, sacrotuberous ligament, ischial tuberosities, ischiopubic rami, and pubic symphysis.

Male and female pelvises are different in size and shape, which, in turn, dictates function. A female pelvis has a wider **pubic arch**, broad sacrum with less anterior concavity, and everted ischial tuberosities. This structural arrangement creates a wide and shallow pelvis—compared to the narrow, deep male pelvis—which is designed for childbirth.

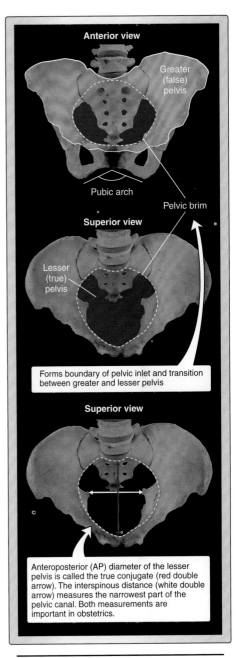

Anterior view

Greater (false) pelvis

Pubic arch

Pelvic brim

Superior view

Lesser (true) pelvis

Forms boundary of pelvic inlet and transition between greater and lesser pelvis

Superior view

Anteroposterior (AP) diameter of the lesser pelvis is called the true conjugate (red double arrow). The interspinous distance (white double arrow) measures the narrowest part of the pelvic canal. Both measurements are important in obstetrics.

Figure 5.4
Pelvic regions and boundaries.

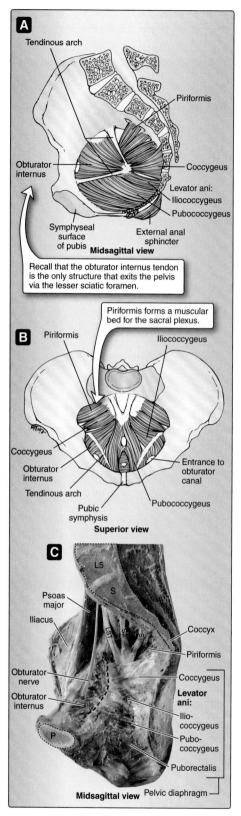

Figure 5.5
Pelvic floor muscles. A and B. Pelvic musculature with organs removed. C. Cadaveric specimen with pelvic viscera and vasculature removed. Dashed black line represents tendinous arch. A = anal canal site, LST = lumbosacral trunk, P = pubic symphysis, S = sacrum, U = urethra site, V = vagina site.

III. PELVIC MUSCLES AND FASCIA

Muscles of the pelvic wall assist in supporting pelvic viscera by partially closing off the pelvic outlet (Fig. 5.5). These muscles include obturator internus, piriformis, coccygeus, and levator ani, with the latter two forming the **pelvic diaphragm**. Obturator internus and piriformis externally rotate the thigh and are detailed in Chapter 6. Pelvic fascia provides additional support and protection to pelvic viscera. In this chapter, the muscles of the pelvic diaphragm and pelvic fascia are discussed.

A. Pelvic diaphragm

Coccygeus and **levator ani** collectively form the pelvic diaphragm, which serves as the floor of the pelvic cavity. This hammock-like muscular diaphragm is reinforced by pelvic fascia and interrupted in the anterior midline at the **urogenital hiatus**. The urogenital hiatus allows for the passage of the urethra and vagina in females and the intermediate (membranous) urethra in males. Pelvic diaphragm muscles are innervated by the **nerve to levator ani and coccygeus** (S_3–S_4).

1. **Coccygeus:** Located inferior to the piriformis internally, coccygeus originates from the ischial spine and inserts onto the sacrum and coccyx. It functions to raise the pelvic floor by flexing the coccyx anteriorly.

2. **Levator ani:** Levator ani is made up of three muscles, which collectively form the majority of the pelvic diaphragm. Together, these muscles raise the pelvic floor, which increases intra-abdominal pressure during urination, defecation, vomiting, and parturition.

   a. **Pubococcygeus:** Originating anteriorly on the pubis and inserting onto the coccyx, pubococcygeus can be further differentiated by its anterior fibers that form a supportive sling around the vagina (pubovaginalis) or prostate (puboprostaticus). These fibers insert directly into, and further strengthen, the **perineal body**.

   b. **Puborectalis:** Located inferomedially to pubococcygeus and also originating from the pubis, this muscle forms a U-shaped sling (rectal sling) at the level of the anorectal junction. In addition to supporting the pelvic floor, it functions to pull the anorectal junction anteriorly to support fecal mass. Relaxation of puborectalis allows for fecal mass to pass into the anal canal for defecation.

   c. **Iliococcygeus:** Iliococcygeus originates from the ischial spine and **tendinous arch** and inserts into the coccyx.

B. Pelvic fascia

Pelvic fascia is a connective tissue matrix that fills or lines spaces around viscera and between the parietal peritoneum of the abdominal cavity and the muscular walls and floor of the pelvic cavity. It is described as having **visceral** and **parietal** (membranous) components, which are separated by **endopelvic fascia**.

1. **Visceral pelvic fascia:** This layer lines the pelvic viscera and is continuous with parietal fascia where the organs pass through the pelvic hiatuses—urogenital and rectal.

2. **Parietal pelvic fascia:** This layer lines the muscles of the pelvic walls and floor internally. Selective areas are thicker than others, such as the obturator fascia and tendinous arch of levator ani.

3. **Endopelvic fascia:** Endopelvic fascia occupies spaces around pelvic viscera (Fig. 5.6). Described as either loose areolar connective tissue or dense fibrous tissue—often referred to as ligaments—this fascia functions to support and protect pelvic viscera, while allowing for distension of viscera. Two of the most prominent ligaments formed by endopelvic fascia are the paired **transverse cervical (cardinal)** and **uterosacral ligaments** in the female pelvis. Additional supportive structures include the **lateral ligaments of the bladder** and **rectum**.

   a. **Transverse cervical (cardinal) ligament:** Located at the broad ligament base, these ligaments support the cervix by connecting it to the pelvic walls laterally and transmit uterine arteries and veins.

   b. **Uterosacral:** These ligaments help to maintain the position of the uterus by connecting the cervix to the sacrum.

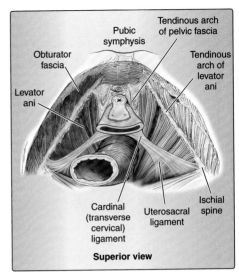

Figure 5.6
Pelvic fascia.

Clinical Application 5.2: Pelvic Organ Prolapse

Pelvic organ prolapse (POP) in females is described as herniation of the bladder (cystocele), rectum (rectocele), or uterus (uterine prolapse) to the level of the vaginal walls or inferior. In cystocele and rectocele, anterior and posterior vaginal segments are herniated along with the viscera, respectively. Enterocele involves herniation of intestines through the wall of the vagina. Uterine prolapse involves the herniation of the uterus into the lower vagina and, potentially, beyond the vaginal orifice in the vestibule. POP often occurs due to loss or weakening of pelvic floor muscle and ligamentous support and has significant negative impact on quality of life. Bowel, urinary, and sexual dysfunction are indications for treatment, which often includes conservative methods such as pelvic floor physical therapy and the use of a pessary, or surgical methods such as reconstruction, organ removal, or surgical-mesh implantation.

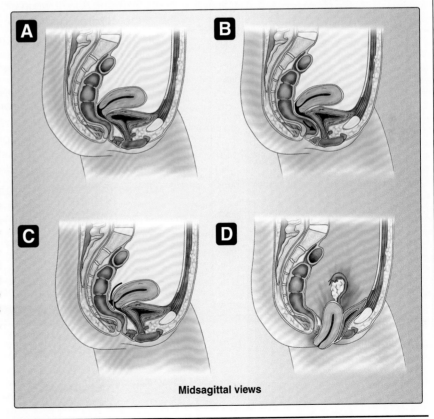

A, Cystocele. B, Rectocele. C, Enterocele. D, Uterine prolapse.

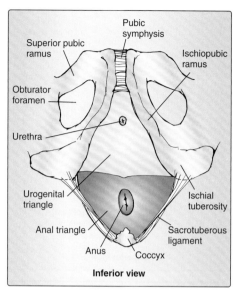

Figure 5.7
Perineum. Urogenital and anal triangle
boundaries.

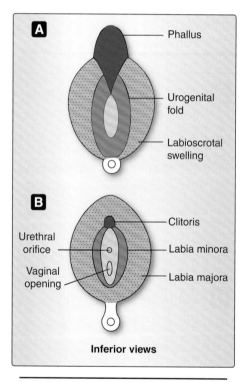

Figure 5.8
A and B, Female external genitalia
embryology.

IV. PERINEUM

The perineum represents the region inferior to the pelvic diaphragm
and is associated with male and female external genitalia and the anus
(Fig. 5.7). It is a diamond-shaped area that is further divided into an
anterior **urogenital triangle** and a posterior **anal triangle**. The triangles
share a common boundary represented by an imaginary line drawn
between the right and left ischial tuberosities. Here, the development
and anatomy of the female and male perineum is presented. The remaining structures of the female and male reproductive systems are
presented with pelvic viscera.

A. Urogenital triangle

Bound by the ischiopubic rami, pubic symphysis, and an imaginary
line drawn through the ischial tuberosities, the urogenital triangle is
described as having superficial and deep perineal spaces (pouches).
Homologous female and male structures are organized into either
the superficial or deep space.

1. **External genitalia development:** Starting in week 5, a proliferation
   of **mesoderm** around the cloacal membrane causes the overlying
   ectoderm to rise up so that three structures are visible externally:
   the **phallus**, **urogenital folds**, and **labioscrotal swellings**. These
   primordia continue to develop and differentiate into homologous
   structures in both sexes.

   a. **Female:** As shown in Figure 5.8, the phallus in the female forms
      the **clitoris** (**glans clitoris**, **corpora cavernosa clitoris**, and
      vestibular bulbs). The urogenital folds in the female form the
      labia minora. The labioscrotal swellings in the female form the
      labia majora and **mons pubis**.

   b. **Male:** As shown in Figure 5.9, the phallus in the male forms the
      penis (**glans penis**, **corpora cavernosa penis**, and **corpus
      spongiosum penis**). The urogenital folds in the male fuse in the
      midline and form the **ventral aspect of the penis** and **penile
      raphe**. The labioscrotal swellings in the male fuse in the midline
      and form the **scrotum** and **scrotal raphe**.

2. **Urogenital triangle anatomy:** Differentiation of male and female
   primordial structures in the urogenital triangle results in fusion
   of bilateral structures in the male and maintenance of bilateral
   structures with a midline cleft—vestibule—in the female. Table 5.1

Table 5.1: Homologous Perineal Structures

Primordial Structure	Female Homologue	Male Homologue
Phallus	Clitoris	Penis
Urogenital folds	Labia minora	Ventral aspect of penis Penile raphe
Labioscrotal swellings	Labia majora Mons pubis	Scrotum Scrotal raphe
	Paraurethral gland	Prostate gland
	Greater vestibular glands	Bulbourethral (Cowper) glands

lists homologous perineal structures in the adult female and male. Structures in the male and female urogenital triangle are described as being in the **superficial perineal pouch** or space, as they are suspended from a broad sheet of fascia—**perineal membrane**. The perineal membrane spans the width of the urogenital triangle, serving as the superior and inferior boundaries of the superficial and deep perineal pouches, respectively. Erectile tissues in both the female and male external genitals are cavernous by design, allowing for vasocongestion during sexual arousal and erection. Surrounding musculature contracts to maintain erection by limiting venous drainage.

> The deep perineal pouch contains the neurovascular bundles supplying clitoris/penis, external urethral sphincter and urethra (both sexes), bulbourethral glands and deep transverse perineal muscle (males only), and an unnamed transverse smooth muscle in females. This space lies between the perineal membrane and the fascia of the inferior surface of the pelvic diaphragm. There is no anatomical communication between the deep pouch and these adjacent structures.

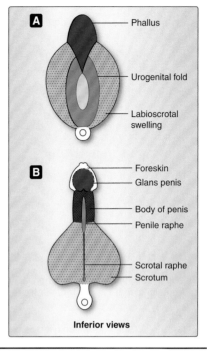

Figure 5.9
A and B, Male genitalia embryology.

a. **Female:** Structures of the female urogenital triangle include bilateral **labia majora** and **minora**, a midline superior **mons pubis**, **clitoris**, and **vestibule of the vagina**. Female external genitalia collectively make up the **vulva** (Fig. 5.10).

 [1] **Labia majora:** Labia majora are hair-covered longitudinal folds with varying degrees of fat on either side of the vestibule.

 [2] **Labia minora:** Labia minora are hairless, thin longitudinal folds found medial and deep to labia majora, and also frame the vestibule. Anteriorly, the labia minora contribute skin to form the prepuce and frenulum of the clitoris.

 [3] **Clitoris:** The clitoris is nestled between the prepuce and frenulum and consists of a body and glans, which are formed by specialized erectile tissue. Proximally, the body is formed by bilateral **corpora cavernosa** and a **commissure of the bulbs**. Distally, the commissure of the bulbs expands to form the **glans clitoris**. Posteriorly, the corpora cavernosa and commissure of the bulbs expand to form the **crura of the clitoris** and the **vestibular bulbs**, respectively.

 [4] **Vestibule:** The **vestibule of the vagina** is located between the labia minora and contains the external urethral orifice and the vaginal opening. Paraurethral, greater vestibular, and lesser vestibular glands open into this space.

 [5] **Female perineal muscles:** Female **perineal muscles** include **ischiocavernosus** and **bulbospongiosus**, which cover the crura of the clitoris and vestibular bulbs, respectively (Fig. 5.11). These muscles function to keep blood in the erectile tissues and maintain clitoral erection. Bulbospongiosus

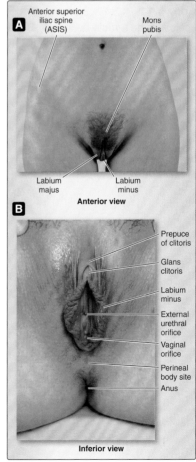

Figure 5.10
External female genitalia. A, Anatomical position. B, Supine with labia majora spread apart to reveal deeper structures.

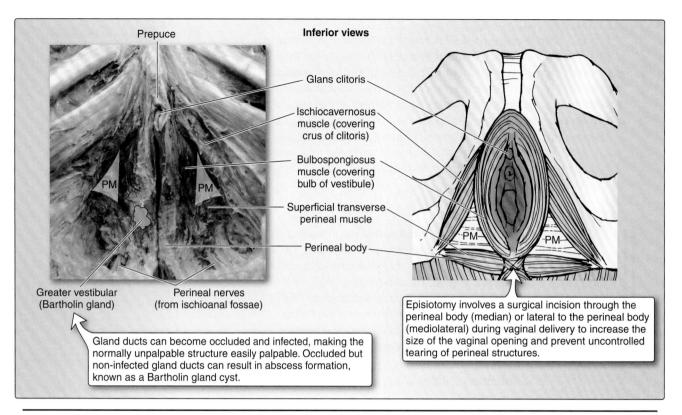

Figure 5.11
Muscles of the female perineum. Cadaveric (left; adductors intact) and schematic (right; adductors removed) representation of female urogenital triangle structures. PM = perineal membrane.

also compresses the greater vestibular gland and attaches at the **perineal body**, thereby strengthening the structure. **Superficial transverse perineal** muscles course across the posterior border of the urogenital triangle, also inserting into and supporting the perineal body.

b. Male: Structures of the male urogenital triangle include the **scrotum** and **penis** (Fig. 5.12). A major distinction in the male urogenital triangle is the lack of a midline cleft, as is seen in the female. During development, male structures fuse along the midline, which is evident by a scrotal and penile raphe.

[1] Scrotum: The scrotum is a hair-covered outpouching of the anterior abdominal wall and is, therefore, made up of cutaneous and fascial layers. The **superficial perineal fascia** is deep to the skin and is the perineal continuation of the superficial fascia of the abdomen. Within the fascia lays a layer of smooth muscle—**dartos muscle**—which functions primarily when the scrotum is exposed to cold temperatures. The scrotum contains a portion of the spermatic cord and the testes (see Fig. 4.8).

[2] Penis: The penis is rooted at its base and extends distally as into a hairless mobile body (shaft). It is formed by paired **corpora cavernosa** and an unpaired **corpus spongiosum**. These cylinders of erectile tissue have a sponge-like appearance on cross section, which is interrupted centrally by the deep arteries of the penis and the spongy urethra in the corpora cavernosa and corpus spongiosum, respectively. Paired corpora cavernosa in the penile shaft separate into right and left **crura**, which anchor the penis to the ischiopubic rami. The corpus spongiosum expands proximally into the **bulb of the penis** (base), which anchors the penis to the perineal membrane. It expands distally into the **glans penis**, which is covered by a double layer of skin, the **prepuce** (foreskin) in an uncircumcised individual. The penis is supported by facial layers, including the **tunica albuginea** around each cylinder and the **deep fascia of the penis** around all three cylinders. Neurovascular bundles travel between fascial layers. A thin layer of loose areolar tissue (superficial perineal fascia) separates the deep fascia from the overlying skin.

[3] **Male perineal muscles:** This group of muscles includes **ischiocavernosus** and **bulbospongiosus**, which cover the crura and bulb of the penis, respectively (Fig. 5.13). These muscles function to keep blood in the erectile tissues and maintain clitoral erection. Bulbospongiosus also compresses the bulb of the penis to expel urine and ejaculate and attaches at the **perineal body**, thereby strengthening the structure. **Superficial transverse perineal** muscles course across the posterior border of the urogenital triangle, also inserting into and supporting the perineal body.

c. **Perineal vasculature:** Genital structures of the perineum rely on adequate blood supply for erectile tissue engorgement (Fig. 5.14). Coordination between vasculature and perineal musculature is necessary during clitoral/penile erection and remission.

[1] **Arterial supply:** The **internal pudendal artery** is the primary arterial supply to the male and female perineum. A branch of the internal iliac (anterior division), the internal pudendal artery courses through the greater and lesser sciatic foramina, travels through the **pudendal canal**, and gives off inferior rectal arteries in the ischioanal fossa. It continues as the **perineal artery** and gives off branches to the labia/scrotum and bulb of the vestibule/penis before terminating into **deep** and **dorsal arteries of the clitoris/penis**.

[2] **Venous drainage:** Venous drainage occurs partially through branches of **internal and external pudendal veins**. Venous blood in the corpora cavernosa is drained through the deep dorsal vein of the clitoris/penis, which is a tributary of the **vesicle/prostatic venous plexus**.

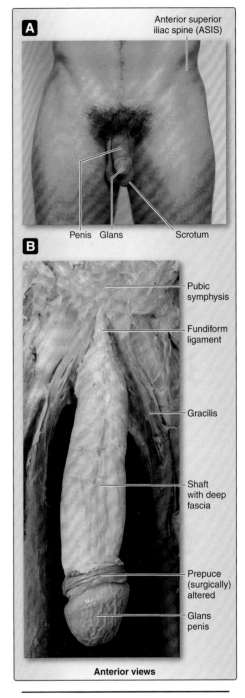

Figure 5.12
Penis and scrotum. A, Surface anatomy. B, Cadaveric specimen with scrotum and testes removed. Skin removed from shaft, but not glans.

The deep arteries of the clitoris/penis give off helicine arteries within the respective cavernous bodies. At rest (remission), these arteries are coiled and relaxed. With sexual arousal, helicine arteries dilate and straighten to allow increased arterial blood flow into the cavernous spaces, thereby producing erection of the penis in males and clitoral tumescence (swelling) in females. This process is under parasympathetic control.

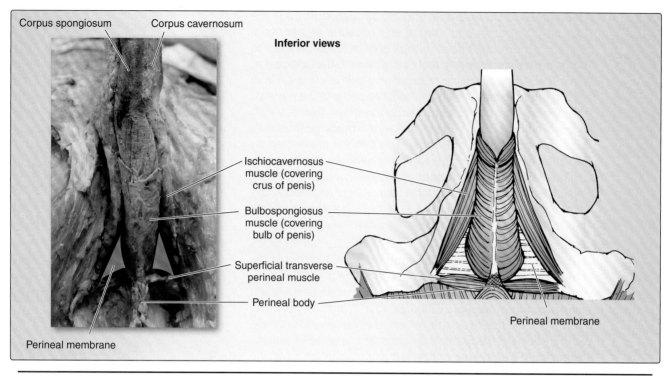

Figure 5.13
Muscles of the male perineum. Cadaveric (left; adductors intact) and schematic (right; adductors removed) representation of male urogenital triangle structures.

d. Lymphatics: Lymphatic drainage of perineal structures occurs through either **superficial inguinal** or **internal iliac lymph nodes**. Table 5.2 lists the lymphatic drainage of the pelvis and perineum.

e. Innervation: The perineum is rich with innervation, as it is a highly sensitive area. While primary innervation is provided through the **pudendal nerve** (somatic), reproductive function of perineal structures also requires autonomic control (see Fig. 5.14).

[1] Somatic innervation: Somatic innervation to the perineum occurs through the **pudendal nerve** (S_2–S_4). Like the internal pudendal vessels, the pudendal nerve exits the pelvis through the greater sciatic foramen and reenters the perineum through the lesser sciatic foramen. After giving off **inferior rectal nerves** in the ischioanal fossa, the nerve continues as the perineal nerve, which then divides into **superficial** and **deep branches**. Superficial branches supply the scrotum/posterior vulva. Deep branches innervate the muscles of the perineum and receive sensory input from erectile tissue of the vestibular bulb/bulbospongiosum. The deep branches continue as the **dorsal nerve of the clitoris/penis** and travel through the deep perineal pouch along the ischiopubic ramus to emerge on the dorsal surface of the clitoris/penis and provide sensory innervation. Additional sensory innervation

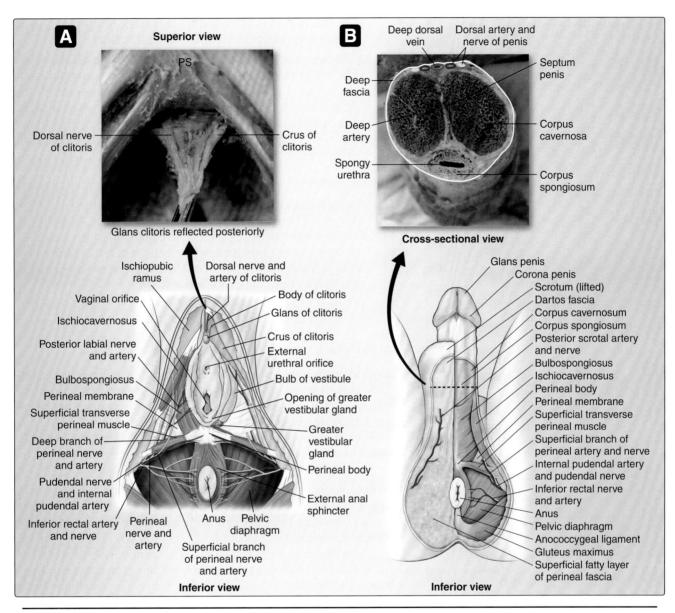

Figure 5.14
Neurovascular supply of perineum. A, Female. B, Male. PS = pubic symphysis.

Table 5.2: Perineal Lymphatics

Superficial Inguinal Nodes	Deep Inguinal Nodes	External Iliac Nodes	Internal Iliac Nodes	Lumbar Nodes
Vulva and perineal skin	Spongy urethra (male)	Ductus deferens	Cavernous bodies (proximal part)	Testes
Inferior vagina	Glans clitoris/penis	Seminal vesical	Deep perineal pouch	Ovaries
Scrotum		Superior vagina	Female urethra	
Skin of penis		Uterine body	Intermediate urethra (male)	
Inferior anal canal		Cervix	Superior vagina	
Uterus (around round ligament)		Superior urinary bladder	Prostate	
			Superior anal canal	
			Urinary bladder	

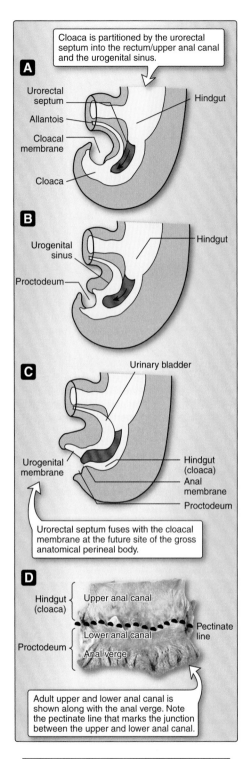

Cloaca is partitioned by the urorectal septum into the rectum/upper anal canal and the urogenital sinus.

A

Urorectal septum

Allantois

Cloacal membrane

Cloaca

Hindgut

B

Urogenital sinus

Proctodeum

Hindgut

C

Urinary bladder

Urogenital membrane

Hindgut (cloaca)

Anal membrane

Proctodeum

Urorectal septum fuses with the cloacal membrane at the future site of the gross anatomical perineal body.

D

Hindgut (cloaca)

Upper anal canal

Lower anal canal

Pectinate line

Proctodeum

Anal verge

Adult upper and lower anal canal is shown along with the anal verge. Note the pectinate line that marks the junction between the upper and lower anal canal.

Figure 5.15
A–D, Embryologic formation of the anal canal, A-C Embryologic formation of the anal canal. A, week 4, B, week 6, C, week 8, D, Photograph of adult anal canal.

to this region is provided by branches of the ilioinguinal, genitofemoral, and posterior femoral cutaneous nerves.

[2] Autonomic innervation: Autonomic sympathetic fibers primarily distribute with branches of the pudendal nerve (see Figs. 5.22 and 5.23). **Pelvic splanchnic nerves** (S_2–S_4) contribute to the vesicle/prostatic plexuses, which give rise to cavernous nerves. These parasympathetic fibers distribute to microvasculature of erectile bodies (clitoris/penis) and are responsible for engorgement/erection of the clitoris/penis.

> Erection is under parasympathetic control, while emission (delivery of semen) is under sympathetic control. An easy way to remember this is "*P*oint and *S*hoot," in which *p*oint (erection) represents *p*arasympathetic and *s*hoot (emission) represents *s*ympathetic. Male ejaculation involves additional coordination of somatic motor fibers to the bulbospongiosus muscle.

B. Anal triangle

Bound by the sacrotuberous ligaments bilaterally, coccyx posteriorly, and an imaginary line drawn through the ischial tuberosities, the anal triangle houses the centrally located anal canal and anus, bound by fat-laden ischioanal fossae bilaterally (see Fig. 5.7). As the distal end of the GI tract terminates in this region, development of the anal canal is detailed here before describing anatomy in the anal triangle.

1. **Embryologic formation of the anal canal:** As shown in Figure 5.15, the **upper anal canal** develops from the **hindgut**. The **lower anal canal** develops from the **proctodeum**, which is an invagination of surface ectoderm caused by a proliferation of mesoderm surrounding the anal membrane. The dual components (hindgut and proctodeum) involved in the embryologic formation of the entire anal canal determine the gross anatomy of this area, which becomes important when considering the clinical characteristics of hemorrhoids and metastasis of anorectal tumors. The junction between the upper and lower anal canals is indicated by the **pectinate line** in the adult, which also marks the site of the former **anal membrane**.

2. **Anal canal anatomy:** The anal canal makes up the distal 2 inches of the GI tract. It is continuous with the rectum at the anorectal junction and extends to the anus. The upper anal canal is characterized by longitudinal mucosal ridges called **anal columns**, which are connected inferiorly by **anal valves**. The inferior border of the valves forms the **pectinate line** and demarcates upper from lower anal canals and, in turn, a transition of neurovascular and lymphatic supply (Fig. 5.16).

  a. **Muscles:** The anal canal is supported by both smooth and skeletal sphincters. The **internal (involuntary) anal sphincter** surrounds the upper anal canal and extends inferiorly to lie medial to the external (voluntary) anal sphincter. The **external anal sphincter** has three parts—deep, superficial, and subcutaneous—and contributes to the formation of the perineal body.

Clinical Application 5.3: Hemorrhoids

Hemorrhoids are the physical presentation of varicosities in the venous plexus of the anal canal. Recall that important portacaval anastomoses in this region are vulnerable to injury with disease processes such as portal hypertension. In the anal canal, hemorrhoids are classified as either internal or external, based on their origin superior or inferior to the pectinate line, respectively. Internal hemorrhoids are varicosities of superior rectal veins. The mucosa in this region does not have pain receptors, so these hemorrhoids are painless. External hemorrhoids are varicosities of inferior rectal veins. The skin in this region does possess pain receptors, making this type of hemorrhoid painful for the patient.

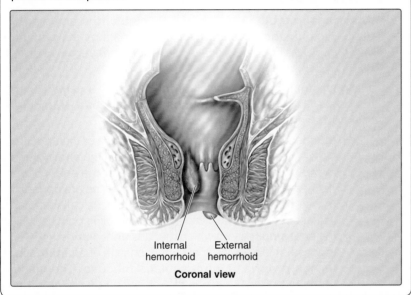

Internal hemorrhoid | External hemorrhoid
Coronal view

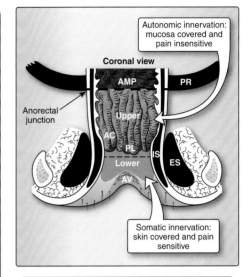

Figure 5.16
Schematic of anal canal. AC = anal column, AMP = ampulla of rectum, AV = anal verge, ES = external anal sphincter, IS = internal anal sphincter, PL = pectinate line, PR = puborectalis muscle.

b. **Blood supply:** As shown in Figure 5.17, superior to the pectinate line, the upper anal canal is supplied by the **superior rectal artery** from inferior mesenteric artery (abdominal aorta). Venous drainage occurs through the **rectal plexus** into superior rectal vein of the portal system. Inferior to the pectinate line, the lower anal canal is supplied by the **inferior rectal arteries** from internal pudendal artery (internal iliac). Venous drainage occurs through inferior rectal veins, ultimately draining into the caval system. The anal canal is an important site for portacaval anastomoses.

c. **Innervation:** Superior to the pectinate line, the upper anal canal structures receive *autonomic* fibers through the **rectal plexus**, which is continuous with the **inferior hypogastric plexus** (see Figs. 5.22 and 5.23). Inferior to the pectinate line, the lower anal canal structures receive *somatic* innervation from the **inferior rectal nerves**, branches of the pudendal nerve. Fecal continence involves the coordination of both internal and external anal sphincters and the puborectalis muscle. Sympathetic stimulation causes tonic contraction of internal anal sphincter, while parasympathetic stimulation causes relaxation.

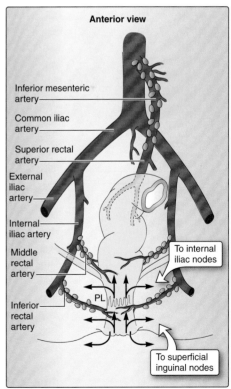

Figure 5.17
Anal canal arterial supply and lymphatics. PL = pectinate line.

> Afferent fibers in the anal canal mediate different sensations based on their relationship to the pectinate line—again tracing back to embryologic origin. The upper anal canal is primarily sensitive to stretch, while afferents in the inferior anal canal transmit pain, touch and temperature sensations.

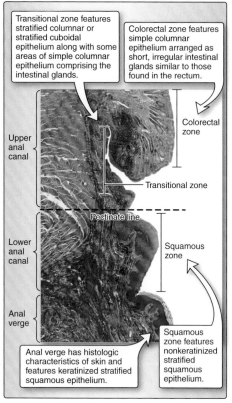

Figure 5.18
Anal canal histology.

d. **Lymphatics:** Upper anal canal structures drain to internal iliac nodes, while lower anal structures drain to superficial inguinal nodes (see Fig. 5.17).

3. **Anal canal histology:** As previously stated, the anal canal is divided into the **upper** and **lower anal canals** by the **pectinate line** (Fig. 5.18). The anal canal ends at the **anal verge** where the perianal skin begins.

a. **Upper anal canal:** The wall of the upper anal canal consists of four histologic layers: **mucosa**, **submucosa**, **muscularis externa**, and **adventitia**.

[1] **Mucosa:** The mucosa and the submucosa of the upper anal canal extend into longitudinal folds called the **anal columns** (or **columns of Morgagni**). The base of the anal columns defines the pectinate line. The anal columns are connected at their bases by transverse folds of mucosa called the **anal valves**. Behind the anal valves are small, blind pouches called the **anal sinuses** into which mucous **anal glands** open. The mucosa of the upper anal canal consists of an **epithelium**, **lamina propria**, and **muscularis mucosa**. The mucosa of the upper anal canal is characterized by the **colorectal zone** and the **transitional zone** as defined by the type of epithelium present. The lamina propria consists of loose connective tissue, blood vessels, and diffuse lymphatic tissue. The muscularis mucosa consists of a smooth muscle layer that may not be prominent.

(a) **Colorectal zone:** Immediately distal to the rectum, the colorectal zone features **simple columnar epithelium** arranged as short, irregular intestinal glands similar to those found in the rectum.

(b) **Transitional zone:** The transitional zone features a transition from simple columnar epithelium to **stratified columnar epithelium** or **stratified cuboidal epithelium**, along with some areas of simple columnar epithelium comprising the intestinal glands.

[2] **Submucosa:** The submucosa of the upper anal canal consists of dense, irregular connective tissue; blood vessels, in particular the **superior hemorrhoidal venous plexus**; anal glands that open into the anus sinuses; diffuse lymphatic tissue; and the submucosal (Meissner) nerve plexus. The mucosa and the submucosa of the upper anal canal extend into **anal columns**.

[3] **Muscularis externa:** The muscularis externa of the upper anal canal consists of an inner circular layer of smooth

muscle that thickens to form the **internal anal sphincter**, an outer longitudinal layer of smooth muscle (may not be prominent), and the myenteric (Auerbach) nerve plexus.

    [4] Adventitia: The adventitia of the upper anal canal consists of dense, irregular connective tissue that blends in with the connective tissue of the body wall.

b. Lower anal canal: The wall of the lower anal canal also consists of mucosa, submucosa, muscularis externa, and adventitia.

    [1] Mucosa: The mucosa of the lower anal canal consists of an **epithelium**, **lamina propria**, and **muscularis mucosa**. The mucosa of the lower anal canal is characterized by a **squamous zone** as defined by the type of epithelium present. Located immediately distal to the pectinate line, the squamous zone features **nonkeratinized stratified squamous epithelium**. The lamina propria consists of loose connective tissue, blood vessels, and diffuse lymphatic tissue. The muscularis mucosa consists of a smooth muscle layer, which may not be prominent.

    [2] Submucosa: The submucosa of the lower anal canal consists of dense, irregular connective tissue; blood vessels, in particular the **inferior hemorrhoidal venous plexus**; diffuse lymphatic tissue; and the submucosal (Meissner) nerve plexus.

    [3] Muscularis externa: The muscularis externa of the lower anal canal consists of an inner circular layer of smooth muscle that thickens to form the **internal anal sphincter**, an outer layer of skeletal muscle called the **external anal sphincter**, and the myenteric (Auerbach) nerve plexus.

    [4] Adventitia: The adventitia of the upper anal canal consists of dense, irregular connective tissue that blends in with the connective tissue of the body wall.

c. Anal verge: The anal verge has the histologic characteristics of skin (not the GI tract), which consists of the **epidermis** and **dermis**. The epidermis of the anal verge features **keratinized stratified squamous epithelium**. The dermis consists of dense, irregular connective tissue, blood vessels, lymphatics, myelinated and unmyelinated axons, sensory receptors, hair follicles with sebaceous glands, and circumanal glands (apocrine sweat glands).

4. Ischioanal fossae: Ischioanal fossae are wedge-shaped, fat-laden spaces located on either side of the anal canal (Fig. 5.19).

a. Boundaries: Each space is bound by the **levator ani muscles** and anal canal medially, **obturator internus** muscle and ischial tuberosity laterally, and skin and fascia of the anal region at the base.

b. Contents: The fossae primarily contain adipose, which allows for distension during passage of fecal matter and provides further support to the anal canal. The **internal pudendal artery and vein**, along with the **pudendal nerve**, enter the ischioanal fossa by way of the lesser sciatic foramen. In each fossa, this neurovascular bundle travels deep to the obturator internus fascia, although the pudendal canal, and gives off branches to the inferior anal and perineal structures.

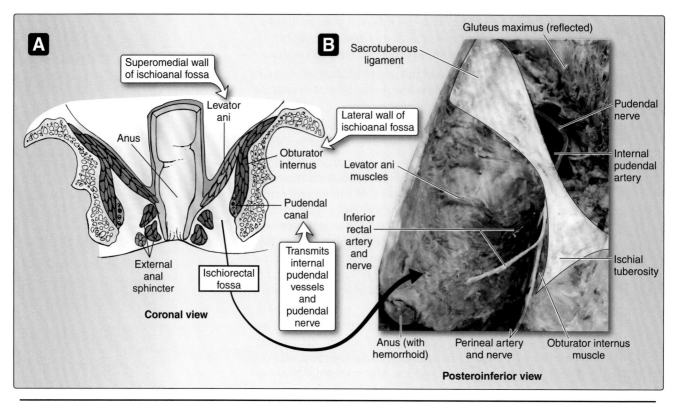

Figure 5.19
Ischioanal fossa. A, Schematic showing boundaries of ischioanal fossa. B, Cadaveric specimen with neuromuscular bundle released from pudendal canal.

Clinical Application 5.4: Ischioanal Fossa Abscess

Abscesses within the perianal and perirectal regions can extend through the external anal sphincter into the ischioanal fossa. This common infection may arise due to a blocked anal crypt gland. To avoid the spread of infection to adjacent structures, abscesses in this region should be surgically drained and packed if necessary. Anorectal fistulas may develop as a result of a long-standing abscess. Males are more likely to develop an abscess and fistula in this region, compared to females.

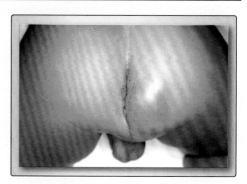

Ischioanal fossa abscess.

V. PELVIC VASCULATURE

At the aortic bifurcation, right and left **common iliac arteries** course laterally before terminating as **internal** and **external iliac arteries** bilaterally (Figs. 5.20 and 5.21). The external iliac arteries continue toward the anterior thigh. The internal iliac arteries course medially, divide into posterior and anterior divisions, and serve as the main blood supply to pelvic and perineal structures. Venous drainage of pelvic and perineal structures occurs through tributaries of the iliac system, which then drain into the caval circulation. External and internal iliac veins unite to form common iliac veins, which merge to form the inferior vena cava at approximately the L4–L5 level.

A. Internal iliac posterior division

Three branches arise from the posterior division of the internal iliac artery. These branches primarily supply gluteal and pelvic wall structures.

1. **Iliolumbar:** This artery provides muscular branches to iliacus, psoas major, and quadratus lumborum muscles.

2. **Lateral sacral:** This branch can present as paired arteries and courses interiorly along the sacrum to enter an anterior sacral foramen.

3. **Superior gluteal:** The largest of the three posterior division branches, this artery typically passes between the lumbosacral trunk (L_4–L_5) and S_1 to exit the pelvis through the greater sciatic foramen. It enters the gluteal region superior to the piriformis and supplies gluteus maximus, minimus, and medius and tensor fasciae latae.

B. Internal iliac anterior division

Multiple branches arise from the anterior division, which supply thigh, perineal, gluteal, and pelvic structures.

1. **Obturator:** This artery exits the pelvis through a small opening in the obturator membrane to enter the medial thigh and gives off a small acetabular branch to the head of the femur.

2. **Umbilical:** The distal end of this artery becomes obliterated after birth to form the medial umbilical ligament, and its proximal end gives off the artery to ductus deferens and multiple superior vesical branches to the bladder.

3. **Uterine:** This artery passes along the side of uterus to the broad ligament base, where it is crossed inferiorly by the ureter and supplies the uterus, fallopian tubes, and upper vagina.

   a. **Vaginal:** Commonly a branch of the uterine artery, this artery supplies the vaginal wall.

> The intimate relationship between the uterine artery and ureter at the base of the broad ligament is very important clinically. Great care must be taken to identify the ureter before ligating the uterine artery to avoid unnecessary injury.

4. **Inferior vesical:** A homologue to the vaginal artery in females, this artery supplies the bladder, seminal glands, and prostate.

5. **Middle rectal:** This artery may share a common stem with the internal pudendal or inferior vesicle and contributes to collateral blood flow to the rectum.

6. **Internal pudendal:** This artery often shares a common stem with the inferior gluteal artery. It exits the pelvis through the greater

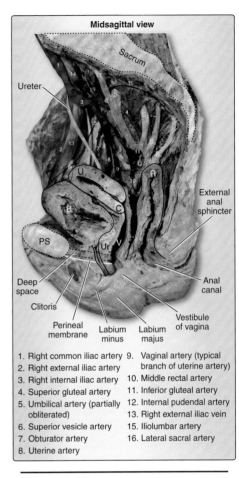

Midsagittal view

1. Right common iliac artery
2. Right external iliac artery
3. Right internal iliac artery
4. Superior gluteal artery
5. Umbilical artery (partially obliterated)
6. Superior vesicle artery
7. Obturator artery
8. Uterine artery
9. Vaginal artery (typical branch of uterine artery)
10. Middle rectal artery
11. Inferior gluteal artery
12. Internal pudendal artery
13. Right external iliac vein
15. Iliolumbar artery
16. Lateral sacral artery

Figure 5.20
Female pelvic vasculature and of vagina sacral plexus. Parietal peritoneum removed. B = bladder, C = cervix, LT = lumbosacral trunk, PS = pubic symphysis, R = rectum, U = uterus, Ur = urethra, V = vagina.

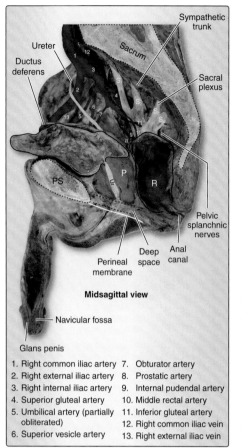

Midsagittal view

1. Right common iliac artery
2. Right external iliac artery
3. Right internal iliac artery
4. Superior gluteal artery
5. Umbilical artery (partially obliterated)
6. Superior vesicle artery
7. Obturator artery
8. Prostatic artery
9. Internal pudendal artery
10. Middle rectal artery
11. Inferior gluteal artery
12. Right common iliac vein
13. Right external iliac vein

Figure 5.21
Male pelvic vasculature and sacral plexus. Parietal peritoneum removed. B = bladder, P = prostate gland, PS = pubic symphysis, R = rectum, Ur = urethra.

sciatic foramen, then enters the ischioanal fossa through the lesser sciatic foramen. It gives off inferior gluteal branches before supplying structures of the perineum.

7. **Inferior gluteal:** This artery exits the pelvis through the greater sciatic foramen and enters the gluteal region inferior to piriformis. It supplies the gluteus maximus primarily.

C. Venous drainage

A series of pelvis venous plexuses surround pelvic viscera within the true (lesser) pelvis. These plexuses primarily drain into tributaries of internal iliac veins, although portacaval anastomoses are present in the rectum. Venous drainage from the gonads (testes and ovaries) terminates in the caval system by way of gonadal veins (testicular and ovarian). Right and left gonadal veins drain into the inferior vena cava and left renal vein, respectively (see Fig. 4.18).

VI. INNERVATION

Innervation of pelvic and perineal structures can be divided into somatic and autonomic origin. Pelvic floor and perineal musculature and skin receive somatic innervation, while pelvic viscera receive autonomic innervation.

A. Somatic innervation

Muscle and skin of the pelvic floor (diaphragm), pelvic wall, and perineum receive somatic innervation that arises from the **sacral plexus** (Figs. 5.22 and 5.23; see also Fig. 6.11) The sacral plexus is made up of anterior rami from S_1–S_4 and receives contributions from lumbar spinal nerves by way of the **lumbosacral trunk** (L_4–L_5).

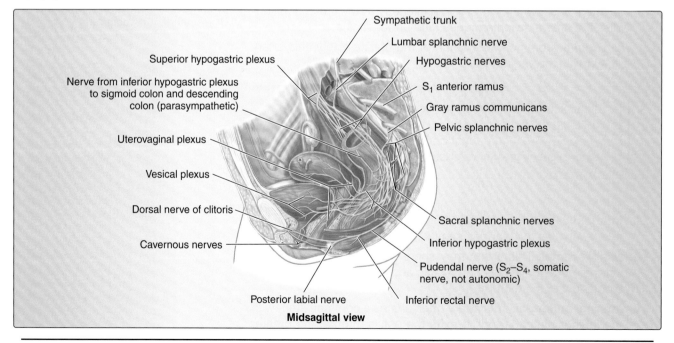

Midsagittal view

Figure 5.22
Female pelvic autonomic innervation.

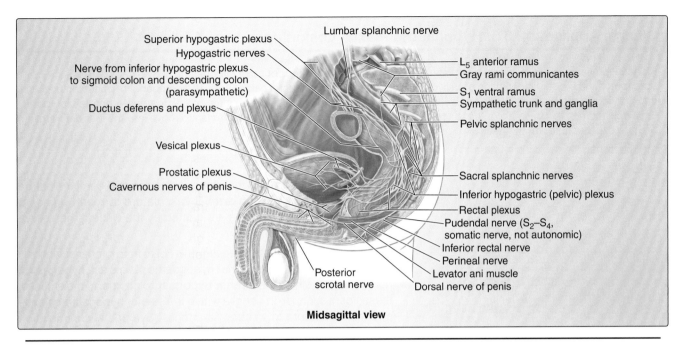

Figure 5.23
Male pelvic autonomic innervation.

Two important branches in this region are the **pudendal nerve** and the **nerves to levator ani** and **coccygeus**.

1. **Pudendal nerve:** The pudendal nerve arises from S_2–S_4 anterior rami. It provides motor and sensory innervation to structures of the perineum, including genital sensation and voluntary motor control of external anal and urethral sphincters (see Figs. 5.19B, 5.22, and 5.23). Branches of the pudendal nerve include **inferior rectal** and **perineal nerves**.

> Pudendal nerve blocks are commonly administered to reduce perineal pain experienced during childbirth. This process involves transvaginal palpation of the ischial spine and injection of anesthesia at the spine where the pudendal nerve crosses the sacrospinous ligament.

2. **Nerves to levator ani and coccygeus:** These nerves arise from S_3–S_4 anterior rami. They provide motor innervation to the pelvic (diaphragm) floor musculature. Additional details about contributions to the lower limb from the sacral plexus can be found in Chapter 6.

B. Autonomic innervation

Pelvic viscera and perineal vasculature are controlled by parasympathetic and sympathetic autonomic plexuses (see Figs. 5.22 and 5.23). Primarily, preganglionic parasympathetic and sympathetic fibers merge to form the **inferior hypogastric plexus**, which is

Clinical Application 5.5: Hypogastric Plexus Lesioning

Planned (presacral neurectomy) and unplanned (surgical disruption) interruption of hypogastric nerves and plexuses affects both motor and sensory innervation of pelvic viscera. For example, presacral neurectomy of the superior hypogastric plexus can alleviate menstrual pain, while accidental lesion of the hypogastric plexus can interrupt sympathetic coordination during ejaculation. In this case, the internal urethral sphincter does not close, allowing semen to move into the bladder, rather than be expelled through the penis.

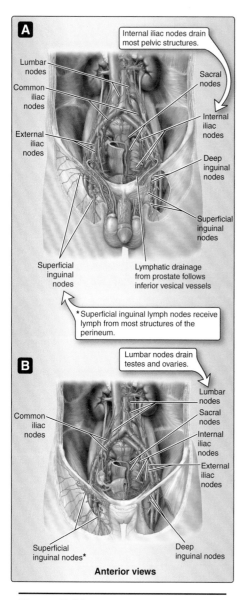

Figure 5.24
Pelvis and perineum lymphatics.
A, Male. B, Female.

located bilaterally around the rectum, bladder, and cervix/prostate and extends distally along arterial vasculature to reach adjacent viscera. Subsidiary plexuses are named by the viscera they serve (e.g., prostatic plexus).

1. **Sympathetic:** Sympathetic preganglionic fibers from lumbar splanchnic nerves travel through the **superior hypogastric plexus** and **hypogastric nerves** before joining the **inferior hypogastric plexus**. In most cases, these fibers synapse in ganglia within the inferior hypogastric plexus and then distribute to viscera via arteries. Sympathetic stimulation drives closure of sphincters, ejaculation, and orgasm. This includes coordinated closure of internal urethral sphincter during ejaculation, to prevent retrograde flow of semen into the bladder. Sympathetic afferent fibers mediate sensation from the uterine fundus and body and superior surface of the bladder. Sympathetic fibers will also join sacral and coccygeal spinal nerves by way of the gray rami communicantes of the sacral sympathetic trunks. These fibers distribute to posterior and anterior rami in this region.

2. **Parasympathetic:** Parasympathetic preganglionic fibers from **pelvic splanchnic nerves** (S_2–S_4) exit the spinal nerves to join the inferior hypogastric plexus. These fibers generally synapse on postganglionic neurons in visceral walls. Parasympathetic stimulation drives opening of sphincters, bladder emptying, erection, and sexual excitation. Aside from the uterine fundus and body and superior bladder, autonomic afferent fibers mediate sensation from pelvic viscera. Therefore, pain sensation from viscera typically travels back to the origin of pelvic splanchnic nerves (S_2–S_4).

VII. LYMPHATICS

In general, the lymphatic organization in the pelvis and perineum is best remembered by following the vasculature (Fig. 5.24). Three main groups of lymph nodes drain structures in this region—**inguinal nodes**, **iliac nodes**, and **para-aortic (lumbar) nodes**. Smaller collections of nodes are present within the pelvis, including sacral and pararectal. Note that lymph flow can vary in this region or flow into more than one set of nodes, but the information presented here represents general flow patterns (see Table 5.2).

A. Inguinal nodes

Organized into **superficial** and **deep inguinal** groups, these nodes are arranged along the inguinal ligament. The superficial inguinal nodes drain the majority of the perineum, including the scrotum in males and the anal canal inferior to the pectinate line. A small amount of lymph from the uterus in the region of the round ligament drains through the superficial lymph nodes as well. The spongy urethra in males, glans penis, and clitoris typically drain into deep inguinal nodes.

B. Iliac nodes

Organized into **external**, **internal**, and **common iliac** groups, these nodes are arranged along arteries of the same name. The internal iliac nodes drain selective deep structures of the perineum, anal canal superior to the pectinate line, and pelvic viscera (urinary bladder fundus, cervix, superior vagina, prostate, seminal glands, prostatic, and intermediate urethra in males and the entire urethra in females). External iliac nodes drain most of the uterine body, ductus deferens, and superior urinary bladder.

C. Para-aortic (lumbar) nodes

Detailed in Chapter 4, these nodes are arranged along the abdominal aorta. Importantly, lymph from both the testes and ovaries—which developed in the abdomen—drain into these nodes.

VIII. PELVIC SPACES

Parietal peritoneum from the abdominal cavity extends into the pelvic cavity and covers portions of pelvic viscera (Fig. 5.25). This draping effect creates a series of **peritoneal** and **subperitoneal recesses**. The subperitoneal recesses are filled with endopelvic fascia that creates supportive septa between viscera.

A. Peritoneal recesses

These intraperitoneal spaces are typically filled with small intestinal loops and normal peritoneal fluids.

1. **Rectovesical pouch:** In the male, this is the space between the bladder and rectum.
2. **Vesicouterine pouch:** In the female, this is the space between the bladder and uterus.
3. **Rectouterine pouch:** In the female, this is the space between the uterus and rectum. The inferior limit of this space is located adjacent to the posterior fornix of the vagina.

The rectouterine pouch (clinically named the pouch of Douglas) is a common site for sampling in the female due to its anatomical relationship to the posterior fornix of the vagina. Peritoneal fluids or cells are collected by passing a needle through the posterior fornix and into the rectouterine pouch. Additionally, a culdoscope can be inserted through an incision in the posterior fornix to assess and drain abscesses in the region.

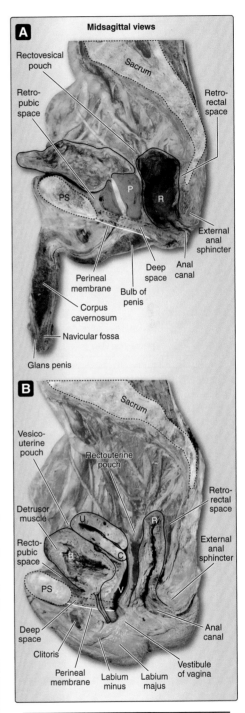

Figure 5.25
Pelvic spaces. Yellow area represents parietal peritoneum draping over pelvic viscera. A, Male. B, Female. B = bladder, C = cervix, P = prostate, PS = pubic symphysis, R = rectum, U = uterus, V = vagina.

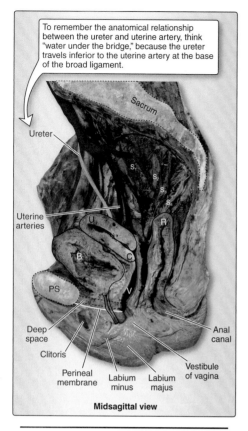

To remember the anatomical relationship between the ureter and uterine artery, think "water under the bridge," because the ureter travels inferior to the uterine artery at the base of the broad ligament.

Figure 5.26
Female pelvic viscera. B = bladder, C = cervix, PS = pubic symphysis, R = rectum, U = uterus, V = vagina.

B. Subperitoneal recesses

These spaces or septa lie inferior to the parietal peritoneum and are filled with endopelvic fascia. They are continuous with the retroperitoneal space in the abdominal cavity.

1. **Retropubic space:** Known clinically as the space of Retzius, it is located just posterior to the pubic symphysis and anterior to the bladder.

2. **Retrorectal space:** This space is located anterior to the sacrum (presacral) and posterior to the rectum.

3. **Rectovesical septum:** Found only in males, this septum is found between the bladder and rectum and extends from the rectovesical pouch to the perineum.

4. **Rectovaginal septum:** Found only in females, this septum is found between the vagina and rectum and extends from the rectouterine pouch to the perineum.

IX. PELVIC VISCERA

Pelvic viscera represent portions of the urinary, reproductive, and digestive systems. Pelvic viscera are protected and supported by the bony limits of the pelvis and the muscular and fascial confines of the pelvic walls and floor. The order of structures from anterior to posterior in the female is bladder, uterus/vagina, and rectum (Fig. 5.26). For males, it is bladder/prostate and rectum (Fig. 5.27). Important relationships exist between pelvic vasculature and viscera.

Development of each of these systems will be detailed, followed by gross anatomy and histology.

A. Urinary system

The urinary system consists of the **kidneys**, **ureters**, **urinary bladder**, and **urethra**. Although the kidneys and proximal ureters are located in the abdomen, they will be included in this section, as will the suprarenal gland, for completeness.

1. **Kidney and ureter development:** The **intermediate mesoderm** forms a longitudinal elevation along the dorsal body wall called the **urogenital ridge**. A portion of the urogenital ridge forms the **nephrogenic cord**, which gives rise to the urinary system. The nephrogenic cord develops into the **pronephros**, the **mesonephros**, and the **metanephros** (Fig. 5.28).

   a. **Pronephros:** At the start of week 4, the pronephros develops by the differentiation of **mesoderm** within the nephrogenic cord to form **pronephric tubules** and the **pronephric duct**. The pronephros is the cranialmost nephric structure and is a transitory structure that regresses completely by week 5. The pronephros is not functional in humans.

   b. **Mesonephros:** At the end of week 4, the mesonephros develops by the differentiation of **mesoderm** within the nephrogenic cord to form **mesonephric tubules** and the **mesonephric duct** (**Wolffian duct**). The mesonephros is the middle nephric structure and is a partially transitory structure. Most of the mesonephric tubules regress, but the mesonephric duct persists and opens into the urogenital sinus. The mesonephros is functional for a short period.

c. **Metanephros:** At the start of week 5, the metanephros develops from an outgrowth of the mesonephric duct, the **ureteric bud**, and from a condensation of mesoderm within the nephrogenic cord, the **metanephric mesoderm**. The metanephros is the caudalmost nephric structure. The metanephros is functional in the fetus at about week 10. It develops into the **definitive adult kidney**. The fetal kidney is divided into lobes, in contrast to the definitive adult kidney, which has a smooth contour.

[1] **Ureteric bud:** The ureteric bud initially penetrates the metanephric mesoderm and then undergoes repeated branching to eventually form the **ureter, renal pelvis, major calyx, minor calyx,** and **collecting duct (CD)**. At the tip of each branch of the ureteric bud, the metanephric mesoderm aggregates as a cap called **cap mesoderm**. The cap mesoderm plays an inductive role in the formation of the **metanephric vesicles**, which later give rise to primitive **S-shaped renal tubules**. The S-shaped renal tubules differentiate into the **connecting tubule, distal convoluted tubule (DCT), loop of Henle, proximal convoluted tubule (PCT)**, and the **Bowman capsule**. The surrounding metanephric mesoderm forms tufts of capillaries called **glomeruli** that protrude into the Bowman capsule. Nephron formation is complete at birth, but functional maturation of nephrons continues throughout infancy.

d. **Relative ascent of the kidneys:** The fetal metanephros is located at vertebral level S1–S2, whereas the definitive adult kidney is located at vertebral level T12–L3. The change in location results from a disproportionate growth of the embryo caudal to the metanephros. During the relative ascent, the kidney rotates 90°, which causes the hilum, which initially faces ventrally, to finally face medially.

e. **Kidney blood supply:** During the relative ascent of the kidneys, the kidneys receive their blood supply from arteries at progressively higher levels until the definitive renal arteries develop at L2. Some of the arteries that form during the ascent may persist as end arteries and are called supernumerary arteries. Therefore, any damage to supernumerary arteries (e.g., ligation during surgery) will result in necrosis of kidney parenchyma.

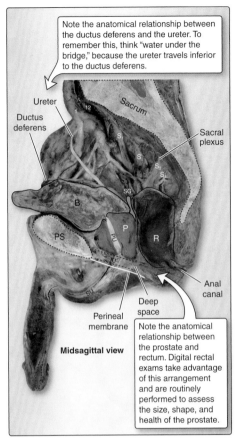

Note the anatomical relationship between the ductus deferens and the ureter. To remember this, think "water under the bridge," because the ureter travels inferior to the ductus deferens.

Note the anatomical relationship between the prostate and rectum. Digital rectal exams take advantage of this arrangement and are routinely performed to assess the size, shape, and health of the prostate.

Figure 5.27
Male pelvic viscera. B = bladder, IU = intermediate urethra, P = prostate gland, PS = pubic symphysis, PU = prostatic urethra, R = rectum, SG = seminal gland, SU = spongy urethra.

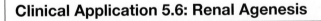

Clinical Application 5.6: Renal Agenesis

Renal agenesis occurs when the ureteric bud fails to develop, thereby eliminating the induction of metanephric vesicles and nephron formation. **Unilateral renal agenesis** is relatively common (more common in males). Therefore, a physician should never assume a patient has two kidneys. Unilateral renal agenesis is asymptomatic and compatible with life because the remaining kidney hypertrophies. **Bilateral renal agenesis** is relatively uncommon. Bilateral renal agenesis causes oligohydramnios, which is a lack of amniotic fluid. Oligohydramnios causes compression of the fetus and results in **Potter syndrome** (i.e., deformed limbs, wrinkly skin, and abnormal facial appearance). Potter syndrome infants are usually stillborn or die shortly after birth.

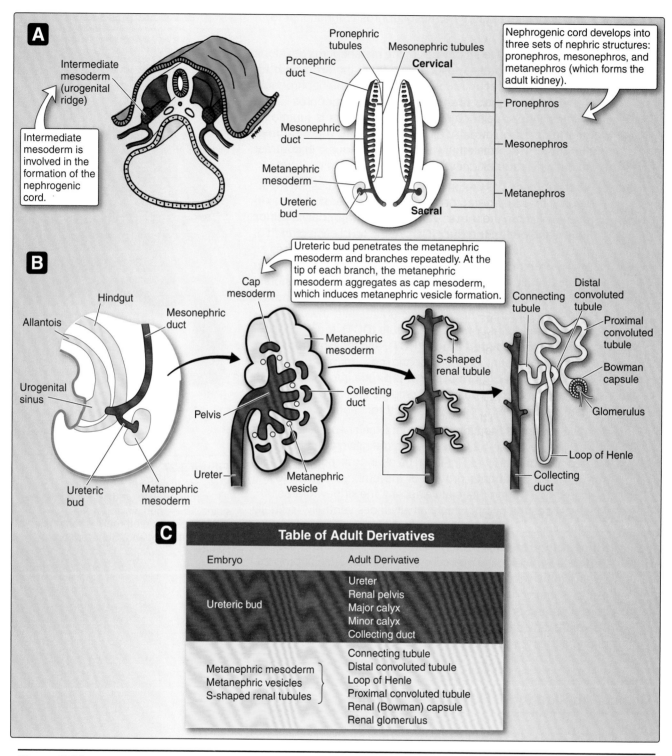

Figure 5.28
Kidney embryology. A, Early embryology. B, Week 6, week 8, week 12, adult C, Table of Adult Derivatives.

2. **Kidney and ureter anatomy:** The kidney is a bean-shaped organs located against the posterior abdominal wall bilaterally between T12–L3 vertebral levels (see Fig. 4.53). The right kidney is positioned more inferiorly than the left—due to the presence of the liver (Fig. 5.29). Each kidney (right and left) is surrounded by a **perirenal fat capsule** and **renal fascia**. A fibrous capsule lies deep to the perirenal fat. Renal vessels exit and enter the organ at the concave **renal hilum**, which is found within the **renal sinus**—a fat-filled space that also houses the renal pelvic and calices. In general, the kidney is comprised of an outer **cortex**, an inner **medulla**, and a **collecting system**.

a. **Cortex and medulla:** A coronal slice through the kidney would reveal two-toned parenchyma—the lighter cortex and darker medulla (Fig. 5.30). **Renal pyramids** and **columns** alternate within the kidney substance. The apex of each pyramid is called a **renal papilla**.

b. **Collecting system:** At the gross anatomical level, the collecting system consists of **minor calyces**, major **calyces**, the **renal pelvis**, and the **ureter**. The ureter exits the hilum of the kidney posteriorly to the renal vessels and travels into the pelvis to terminate in the posterior wall of the bladder.

c. **Vasculature: Renal arteries** and **veins** supply the kidney. Renal veins drain into the inferior vena cava and are positioned anteriorly to renal arteries, which are branches of the abdominal aorta. The **arteries to the ureters** are typically branches of renal arteries, gonadal arteries, and the abdominal aorta.

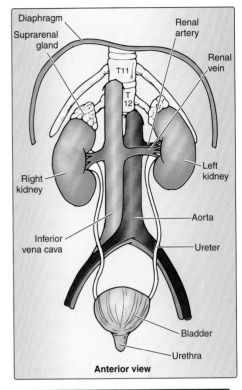

Anterior view

Figure 5.29
Urinary system.

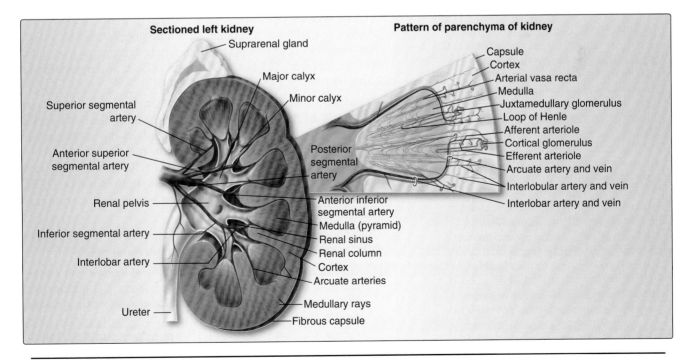

Figure 5.30
Kidney gross and microanatomy.

d. **Innervation:** Kidneys receive autonomic innervation through the **renal nerve plexus** associated with the least splanchnic and vagus nerves (see Fig. 4.21). Along their course in the abdomen and pelvis, the ureters receive fibers from the renal, intermesenteric, superior hypogastric, and inferior hypogastric plexuses.

> Even though ureters extend into the pelvis, visceral pain from the outflow duct follows the sympathetic fibers back to T11–L1 levels.

e. **Lymphatics:** Lymph from the kidneys follows the renal veins and drains into lumbar lymph nodes (see Fig. 4.20). The ureter drains into nodes along its course, including lumbar and iliac (common, external, internal) nodes.

3. **Urinary system histology:** The kidney comprises the outer **cortex**, an inner **medulla**, and a **collecting system** (Fig. 5.31). At a microscopic level, additional structural differences are revealed. The intricate CD system is found throughout and connects the cortex and medulla.

a. **Renal cortex:** The renal cortex lies under the connective tissue capsule of the kidney and also extends between the renal pyramids as the **renal columns of Bertin**. The renal cortex may be divided into the **cortical labyrinth** and the **medullary rays**. The cortical labyrinth consists of renal corpuscles (renal glomeruli plus the glomerular [Bowman] capsule), proximal (PCT) and distal convoluted tubules (DCT), interlobular arteries, afferent and efferent arterioles, and a peritubular capillary bed. The medullary rays consist predominately of proximal and distal straight tubules (PST and DST), cortical CDs, and a peritubular capillary bed.

b. **Renal medulla:** The renal medulla is composed of **5–11 renal pyramids of Malpighi** whose tips terminate as **5–11 renal papillae**. The base of a renal pyramid abuts the renal cortex, whereas the tip of a renal pyramid (renal papilla) abuts a minor calyx. The renal medulla consists of PSTs, descending and ascending thin limbs (DTL and ATL) of the loop of Henle, DSTs, medullary collecting ducts (CDs), vasa recta, and a peritubular capillary bed.

c. **Collecting system:** The collecting system of the kidney includes **CDs**, **minor** and **major calyces**, and the **renal pelvis**.

[1] **Collecting ducts:** CDs located in the cortex are called **cortical collecting ducts**. As the cortical CDs travel into the medulla, they are called **medullary collecting ducts**. As the medullary CDs travel toward the renal papillae, they merge into larger CDs called the **papillary ducts of Bellini**. The papillary ducts of Bellini open onto the surface of the renal papillae at the **area cribrosa**. The CDs are lined by a simple cuboidal epithelium that transitions into a simple

---

Clinical Application 5.7: Nephrolithiasis

Nephrolithiasis, commonly known as kidney or ureteral stones, is most often of the calcium variety, but can also comprise uric acid, magnesium ammonium phosphate, and cystine stones. Although some patients are asymptomatic, the primary complaint of pain often develops when the stone shifts from the renal pelvis into the ureter. Stones in the ureter can cause obstruction and proximal distention of the pelvis, which is thought to be the main cause of pain. Referred pain is often dictated by site of obstruction, so that unilateral flank pain is associated with proximal ureter or renal pelvis obstruction, and distal ureter obstruction pain may spread to the perineum. Patients may also experience hematuria (blood in urine). Conservative management includes pushing fluids, controlling pain, and waiting for the stone to pass. Shock-wave lithotripsy is used when stones are too large (>4 mm diameter) to pass spontaneously.

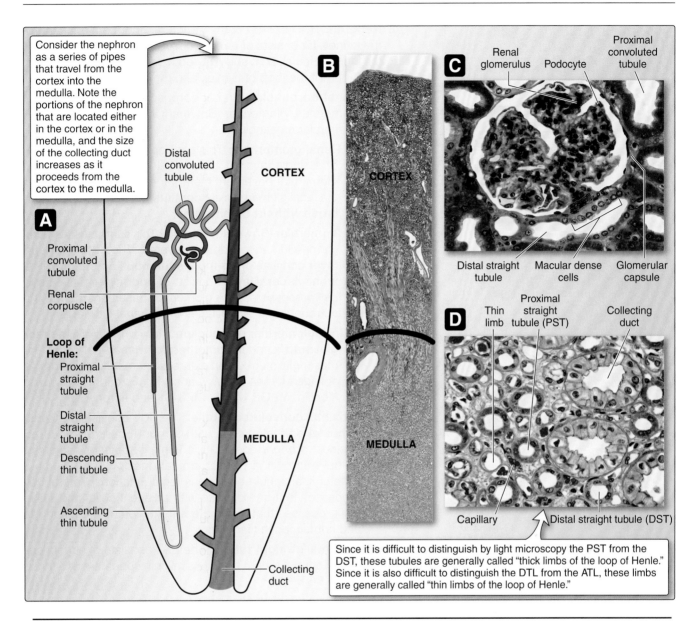

Figure 5.31
Histology of urinary system. A, Nephron. B, Kidney. C, Cortex. D, Medulla.

columnar epithelium as the CDs increase in size toward the renal papillae. The epithelium is composed of two cell types: **intercalated (types A** and **B)** and **principal**.

[2] **Minor calyces:** The 5–11 minor calyces are cup-shaped structures that abut the 5–11 renal papillae. They consist of a transitional epithelium, a lamina propria rich in collagen and elastic fibers, and a smooth muscle layer.

[3] **Major calyces:** The 2–3 major calyces are continuous with the minor calyces and have the same composition.

[4] **Renal pelvis:** The renal pelvis is continuous with the major calyces and has the same composition.

d. **Nephron:** The nephron is the structural and functional unit of the kidney. It consists of a **renal corpuscle, PCT, PST** (part of the loop of Henle), **DTL** and **ATL** (both part of the loop of Henle), **DST** (part of the loop of Henle), and the **DCT**.

[1] **Renal corpuscle:** A renal corpuscle consists of a renal glomerulus, glomerular (Bowman) capsule, and the intraglomerular mesangium.

(a) **Renal glomerulus:** This capillary bed (or tuft) consists of a single layer of endothelial cells surrounded by a glomerular basement membrane. The capillaries within the renal glomerulus are **continuous, fenestrated capillaries without diaphragms.**

(b) **Glomerular (Bowman) capsule:** This surrounds the renal glomerulus and is double layered. The **outer parietal layer** consists of a **simple squamous epithelium.** The **inner visceral layer** consists of **podocytes** that extend cell processes to the glomerular basement membrane surrounding the capillaries of the renal glomerulus.

(c) **Intraglomerular mesangium:** This consists of a **mesangial matrix** and **intraglomerular mesangial cells.** The mesangial matrix is an extracellular matrix and contains collagen (types III, IV, V, and VI), microfibrillar proteins (fibrillin, MAGP, MP78, MP340), and fibronectin.

[2] **Proximal convoluted tubule:** The PCT consists of simple cuboidal epithelial cells with a round, centrally located nucleus, a *bright* eosinophilic (pink) cytoplasm, a distinct apical microvillus border, apical endocytotic vesicles, juxtaluminal zonula occludens (tight junctions), lateral cell processes that interdigitate with adjacent cells, and basal cell processes that associate with numerous mitochondria and contain actin filaments.

[3] **Proximal straight tubule:** The PST consists of simple cuboidal epithelial cells that are similar in appearance to those of the PCT.

[4] **Descending thin limb:** The DTL consists of simple squamous epithelial cells with deep juxtaluminal zonula occludens (tight junctions) and a few microvilli. It does not have lateral cell processes.

[5] **Ascending thin limb:** The ATL consists of simple squamous epithelial cells with shallow juxtaluminal zonula occludens (tight junctions) and extensive lateral cell processes.

[6] **Distal straight tubule:** The DST consists of simple cuboidal epithelial cells with a round, centrally located nucleus, a *pale* eosinophilic (pink) cytoplasm, juxtaluminal zonula occludens (tight junctions), lateral cell processes that interdigitate with adjacent cells, and basal cell processes that associate with numerous mitochondria and contain actin filaments. It does not possess an apical microvillus border. The DST contains specialized cells called **macula densa (MD) cells** in the region of the afferent and efferent arterioles.

[7] **Distal convoluted tubule:** The DCT is composed like the DST apart from containing MD cells.

e. **Collecting ducts:** CDs consists of either a simple cuboidal or simple columnar epithelium depending on size. CDs are found in both the renal cortex and renal medulla. They are composed of three cell types: **types A** and **B intercalated** and **principal cells**.

[1] **Type A intercalated cell:** These are found predominately in *cortical CDs* and gradually *decrease* in number in the medullary CDs until they are completely absent in the largest papillary ducts. They have a round and basally located nucleus, distinctive apical microfolds, juxtaluminal zonula occludens (tight junctions), apical endocytotic vesicles, numerous mitochondria, and an **H+ ATPase** located on the apical membrane. The type A intercalated cell does not possess lateral cell processes or basal cell processes.

[2] **Type B intercalated cell:** These are similar in appearance to type A intercalated cells but differ in physiologic function.

[3] **Principal cell:** These are found in *both* cortical CDs and medullary CDs. They have a round and basally located nucleus, a few apical microvilli, a single primary cilium, juxtaluminal zonula occludens (tight junctions), basal processes that associate with numerous mitochondria, and **AQ2** aquaporin water channels that are regulated by **antidiuretic hormone**. Principal cells do not have lateral cell processes that interdigitate with adjacent cells.

f. **Glomerular filtration barrier:** Urine formation begins with filtration, which occurs where the renal glomerulus and the glomerular (Bowman) capsule interact to form the glomerular filtration barrier (GFB). Filtration is the bulk flow of fluid from the glomerular capillaries into the urinary (Bowman) space to form tubular fluid. The GFB comprises the **glomerular capillary endothelium**, **glomerular basement membrane**, and **slit diaphragms** (Fig. 5.32).

[1] **Glomerular capillary endothelium:** This is a continuous, fenestrated (without diaphragms) endothelium.

[2] **Glomerular basement membrane:** This **300–350-nm thick basement membrane** is synthesized jointly by the glomerular capillary endothelium and podocytes.

[3] **Slit diaphragms:** These are found between neighboring **podocytes** (Fig. 5.33). The podocyte has a voluminous cell body that bulges into the urinary (Bowman) space and makes up the visceral layer of the glomerular (Bowman) capsule. It gives rise to **primary** and **secondary foot processes** and **pedicels**, which make contact with the GBM. The pedicels from neighboring podocytes regularly interdigitate with one another, thereby forming elongated 25-nm wide spaces called the **filtration slits** that are bridged by **slit diaphragms**.

g. **Juxtaglomerular complex:** The juxtaglomerular (JG) complex is a specialized structure located where the DST of the nephron makes contact with the vascular pole of the glomerulus (i.e., where the afferent and efferent arterioles are located). The JG complex regulates arterial blood pressure in a slow, long-term, hormonal manner through the **renin–angiotensin II mechanism**. Its components include **MD** and **JG cells** (Fig. 5.34).

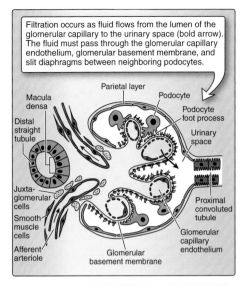

Figure 5.32
Renal corpuscle and related structure histology

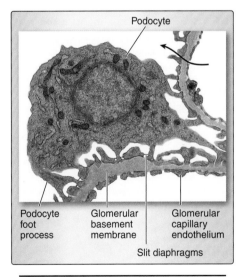

Figure 5.33
Glomerular filtration barrier histology. Arrow indicates fluid flow from the capillary lumen to the urinary space.

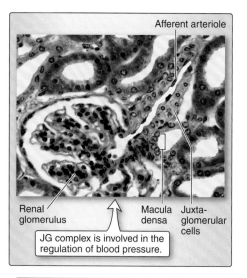

Figure 5.34
Juxtaglomerular (JG) complex histology.

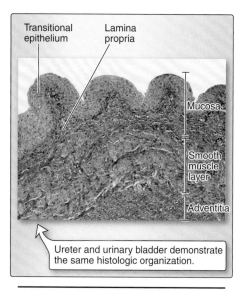

Figure 5.35
Ureter histology.

[1] **Macula densa:** This modified epithelial cell lines the DST and is columnar-shaped with a round nucleus. The nuclei of adjacent MD cells are crowded together and may appear to be superimposed on each other. The MD cell monitors changes in Na+ levels in the DST fluid and stimulates the release of renin from JG cells.

[2] **Juxtaglomerular cell:** This modified smooth muscle cell is located in the tunica media of the afferent arteriole and early portion of the efferent arteriole. It is cuboidal-shaped with a round nucleus and has numerous cell processes, gap junctions that communicate with neighboring cells, and distinct granules that contain **renin** (a proteolytic enzyme). The JG cell secretes renin, monitors changes in blood pressure, and is innervated by postganglionic sympathetic nerves.

4. **Ureter histology:** The ureter is organized into a **mucosa, smooth muscle layer**, and an **adventitia** (Fig. 5.35).

   a. **Mucosa:** The mucosa of the ureter consists of a **transitional epithelium** and a **lamina propria**. The transitional epithelium is a stratified epithelium, whereby the cells in the surface layer undergo a transition in shape from dome shaped to flat. The lamina propria of the ureter is a dense, irregular connective tissue.

   b. **Smooth muscle:** The smooth muscle layer of the ureter consists of two layers of helically arranged single-unit smooth muscle cells.

   c. **Adventitia:** The adventitia of the ureter consists of dense, irregular connective tissue and retroperitoneal adipose tissue.

5. **Urinary bladder development:** The urinary bladder is formed from the upper portion of the urogenital sinus, which is continuous with the allantois (Fig. 5.36). The allantois becomes a fibrous cord called the **urachus** (or **median umbilical ligament** in the adult). The lower ends of the mesonephric ducts become incorporated into the posterior wall of the bladder to form the **trigone of the bladder**. The mesonephric ducts eventually open just below the neck of the bladder. The transitional epithelium lining the urinary bladder is derived from endoderm because of its etiology from the urogenital sinus and gut tube.

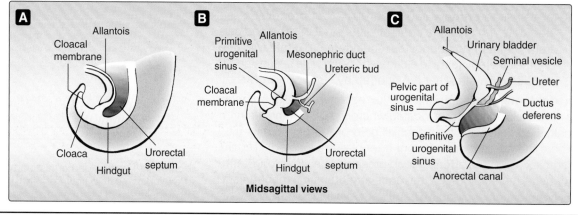

Figure 5.36
Urinary bladder development. A, Formation and partitioning by urorectal septum. B, Formation of urogenital sinus and anorectal canal. C, Development of urinary bladder from urogenital sinus.

6. **Urinary bladder and urethra anatomy:** The urinary bladder and urethra are continuous and represent the inferior pelvic portion of the urinary system.

a. **Urinary bladder:** The urinary bladder is a muscular reservoir for urine positioned posterior to the pubic symphysis (Fig. 5.37). It has an **apex**, **fundus**, **body**, and **neck**. The **detrusor muscle** constitutes most of the bladder wall and contributes to the formation of the **internal urethral sphincter**, which is more prominent in males. Along the internal, posterior surface of the bladder is an inverted triangular region called the **trigone**. The **ureteric orifices** mark the two superior corners of the trigone (triangle base), and the apex sits at the **internal urethral orifice**.

b. **Urethra:** In both females and males, the **urethra** begins at the internal urethral orifice, just inferior to the neck of the bladder.

[1] **Female urethra:** The female urethra is short and travels posterior and inferior to the pubic symphysis, through the deep perineal pouch, and ends in the vestibule of the vagina at the external urethral orifice (see Fig. 5.36). The posterior wall of the female urethra is anatomically related to the anterior wall of the vagina. Multiple **paraurethral glands** (also called lesser vestibular glands and Skene glands) are present alongside the urethra and empty through a common duct bilaterally near the external urethral orifice. These glands are thought to aid in lubricating the vestibule.

[2] **Male urethra:** The male urethra is long and divided into three parts based on adjacent anatomy—**prostatic**, **intermediate** (membranous), and **spongy** parts—which pass through the prostate, deep pouch, and corpus spongiosum, respectively (Fig. 5.38).

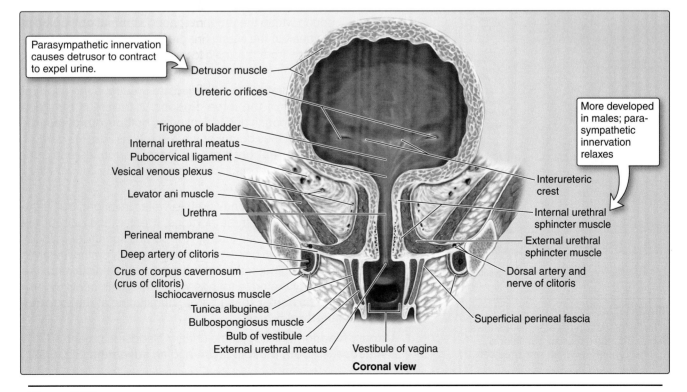

Figure 5.37
Urinary bladder and urethra (female).

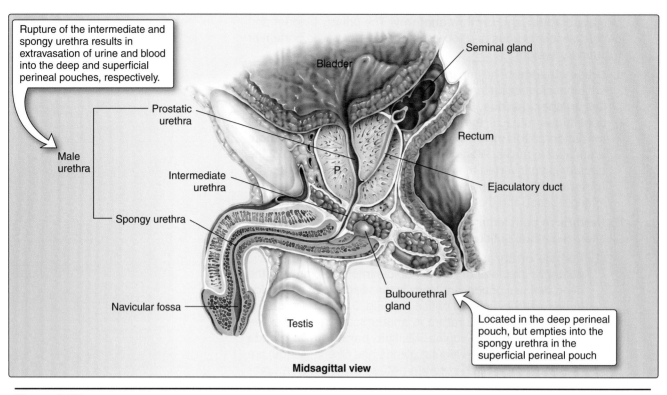

Rupture of the intermediate and spongy urethra results in extravasation of urine and blood into the deep and superficial perineal pouches, respectively.

Seminal gland

Bladder

Prostatic urethra

Rectum

Male urethra

Intermediate urethra

Ejaculatory duct

Spongy urethra

P

Navicular fossa

Bulbourethral gland

Testis

Located in the deep perineal pouch, but empties into the spongy urethra in the superficial perineal pouch

Midsagittal view

Figure 5.38
Male urethra. P = prostate.

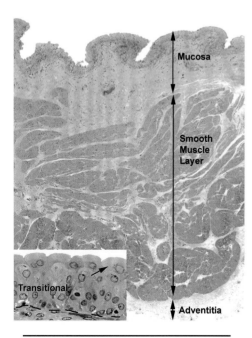

Mucosa

Smooth Muscle Layer

Transitional

Adventitia

Figure 5.39
Urinary bladder histology. Inset shows higher magnification of transitional epithelium, arrow=dome-shaped cell.

(a) **Prostatic:** The prostatic urethra has a midline **urethral crest**, flanked by grooves called **prostatic sinuses**. Multiple **prostatic ducts** open into the sinuses. Paired **ejaculatory ducts** open onto the surface of the urethra crest on either side of the **prostatic utricle**—a small blind pouch within the mound-shaped **seminal colliculus** at the peak of the crest. The prostatic urethra receives secretions from the vas deferens (sperm), seminal glands, and prostate to form semen.

(b) **Intermediate:** The intermediate urethra is the shortest in length of the three portions. It traverses the deep perineal pouch and is flanked by **bulbourethral glands**, although they do not empty secretions into this portion. The **external urethral sphincter** surrounds and supports the intermediate urethra and allows for voluntary control of urine flow.

(c) **Spongy:** The spongy urethra varies in length, but is the longest of the three portions. It enters the bulb of the penis and travels through the corpus spongiosum (body of penis). The proximal end of the spongy urethra receives paired bulbourethral gland ducts. At the distal end, the spongy urethra expands within the glans penis to form the **navicular fossa** before terminating at the **external urethral orifice**.

7. **Urinary bladder histology:** The urinary bladder is organized into a **mucosa**, **smooth muscle layer**, and an **adventitia** (Fig. 5.39).

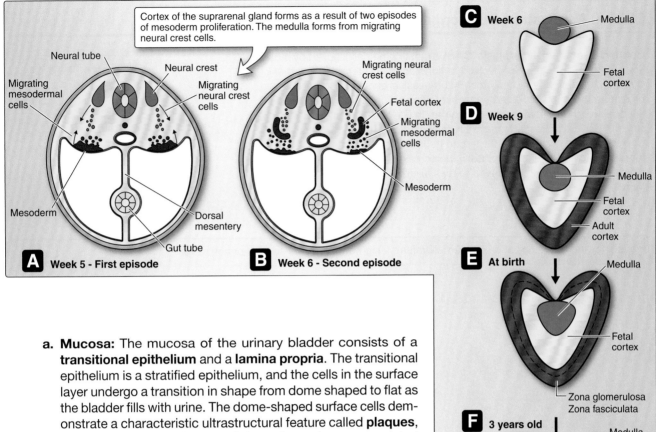

Cortex of the suprarenal gland forms as a result of two episodes of mesoderm proliferation. The medulla forms from migrating neural crest cells.

a. **Mucosa:** The mucosa of the urinary bladder consists of a **transitional epithelium** and a **lamina propria**. The transitional epithelium is a stratified epithelium, and the cells in the surface layer undergo a transition in shape from dome shaped to flat as the bladder fills with urine. The dome-shaped surface cells demonstrate a characteristic ultrastructural feature called **plaques**, which are thick, focal areas of the cell membrane associated with actin filaments. The lamina propria of the urinary bladder is a dense, irregular connective tissue.

b. **Smooth muscle:** The smooth muscle layer of the urinary bladder consists of a complex meshwork of single-unit smooth muscle cells (called the **detrusor muscle**). In the male, the detrusor muscle forms a complete collar around the neck of the bladder called the **internal urethral sphincter** and extends longitudinally into the prostatic urethra. In the female, the detrusor muscle does not form a significant sphincter around the neck of the bladder but does extend longitudinally into the urethra.

c. **Adventitia:** The adventitia of the urinary bladder consists of dense, irregular connective tissue.

8. **Suprarenal gland development:** The suprarenal gland consists of a cortex and medulla each of which have a separate embryologic origin (Fig. 5.40).

a. **Suprarenal cortex:** The cortex forms as a result of two episodes of mesoderm proliferation that occur near the root of the dorsal mesentery. During week 5, the first episode begins as mesoderm proliferates, migrates deep into the underlying mesoderm, and forms the inner fetal cortex. During week 6, the second episode begins as mesoderm proliferates, migrates deep into the underlying mesoderm, and forms the outer adult cortex. During the fetal period and at birth, the suprarenal glands are very large due to the size of the fetal

Figure 5.40
A–F, Suprarenal gland embryology.

Clinical Application 5.8: Congenital Adrenal Hyperplasia

Congenital adrenal hyperplasia (CAH) is most commonly caused by mutations in genes for enzymes involved in adrenocortical steroid biosynthesis. **CYP21A2 deficiency** is an autosomal-recessive genetic disorder caused by a mutation in the *CYP21A2* gene located on chromosome 6p21.3, which encodes for the **21-hydroxylase enzyme**. In CYP21A2 deficiency, conversion of 17-hydroxyprogesterone to 11-deoxycortisol is defective, and virtually no synthesis of cortisol or aldosterone happens, so that intermediates are funneled into androgen biosynthesis, thereby elevating androgen levels. The elevated levels of androgens lead to masculinization of a female fetus (i.e., female pseudointersexuality).

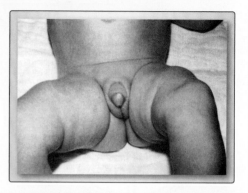

Image showing masculinization of a female infant, a sign of congenital adrenal hyperplasia.

cortex. The suprarenal glands become smaller as the fetal cortex involutes rapidly during the first 2 weeks after birth and continues to involute during the first year of life. The **zona glomerulosa (ZG) and zona fasciculata (ZF)** of the adult cortex are present at birth, but the **zona reticularis (ZR)** is not formed until 3 years of age.

b. **Suprarenal medulla:** The medulla forms when neural crest cells migrate from an area around the neural tube and aggregate at the medial aspect of the fetal cortex. The neural crest cells eventually become surrounded by the fetal and adult cortex. The neural crest cells differentiate into **chromaffin cells**, which stain yellow-brown with chromium salts.

9. **Suprarenal gland anatomy:** Although found in the abdominal cavity, the **suprarenal** (adrenal) **glands** are detailed here because of their relationship with the kidneys (Fig. 5.41). Both right and left suprarenal glands sit on the superomedial surface of the right and left kidneys, respectively. The right suprarenal gland is pyramidal, while the left is more crescent shaped. Both glands are encased with the kidney in the perirenal fat capsule, and they are also attached to the respective crura of the diaphragm.

a. **Blood supply:** Suprarenal glands are supplied by a series of **suprarenal arteries** (superior, middle, inferior) and drained by a **right** or **left suprarenal vein**. Superior, middle, and inferior suprarenal arteries arise from the inferior phrenic, abdominal aorta, and renal arteries, respectively. Right suprarenal vein drains into the inferior vena cava, while the left drains into the left renal vein.

b. **Innervation:** Suprarenal glands are unique in that the medulla receives preganglionic sympathetic fibers from the celiac plexus (continuation of greater splanchnic nerve). These axons synapse directly onto chromaffin cells in the suprarenal medulla.

c. **Lymphatics:** Suprarenal lymph drains into lumbar lymph nodes.

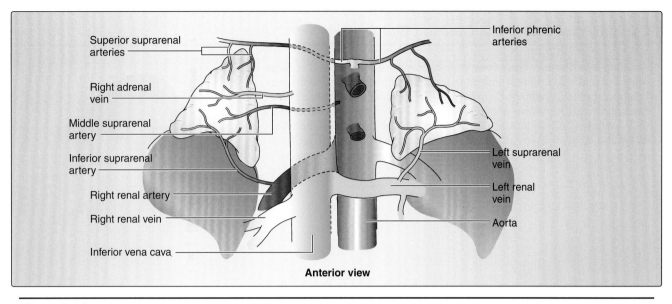

Figure 5.41
Suprarenal glands.

10. **Suprarenal gland histology:** The suprarenal gland consists of two embryologic distinct components: **suprarenal cortex** and **suprarenal medulla** (Fig. 5.42).

a. **Suprarenal cortex:** The suprarenal cortex is divided into three zones: **ZG**, **ZF**, and **ZR**.

[1] **Zona glomerulosa:** The ZG constitutes 15% of cortical volume. ZG cells are arranged in oval-shaped clusters or curved columns that are continuous with the ZF. They are small, pyramidal cells with round, centrally located nucleus. They contain rough endoplasmic reticulum (RER), polyribosomes, prominent smooth endoplasmic reticulum (SER), mitochondria with tubular cristae, and lipid droplets. The ZG cell synthesizes and secretes **aldosterone** (steroid hormone).

[2] **Zona fasciculata:** The ZF constitutes 78% of cortical volume. ZF cells are arranged in vertical cords and are large, polyhedral cells with a round, centrally located nucleus. They contain RER, polyribosomes, prominent SER, mitochondria with tubular cristae, numerous conspicuous lipid droplets, and lysosomes. The ZF cell synthesizes and secretes **cortisol** (steroid hormone).

[3] **Zona reticularis:** The ZR constitutes 7% of cortical volume. ZR cells are arranged in an anastomosing network of cords. They are small, round cells with a round, centrally located nucleus. They contain RER, polyribosomes, prominent SER, mitochondria with tubular cristae, numerous lipid droplets, and lipofuscin pigment. The ZR cell synthesizes and secretes **dehydroepiandrosterone** and **androstenedione**.

b. **Suprarenal medulla:** The suprarenal medulla contains **chromaffin cells**, which are **modified postganglionic sympathetic**

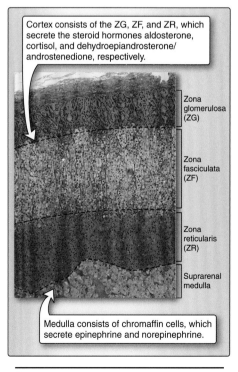

Cortex consists of the ZG, ZF, and ZR, which secrete the steroid hormones aldosterone, cortisol, and dehydroepiandrosterone/androstenedione, respectively.

Zona glomerulosa (ZG)

Zona fasciculata (ZF)

Zona reticularis (ZR)

Suprarenal medulla

Medulla consists of chromaffin cells, which secrete epinephrine and norepinephrine.

Figure 5.42
Suprarenal gland histology.

Clinical Application 5.9: Cushing Syndrome

Cushing syndrome is most commonly caused by administration of **large doses of steroids** for the treatment of a primary condition (i.e., iatrogenic). If not iatrogenic, elevated levels of cortisol may be caused by either an **adrenocorticotropic hormone–secreting adenoma** within the adenohypophysis (75% of cases, strictly termed **Cushing disease**) or a **suprarenal cortical adenoma** (25% of cases). Clinical features include mild hypertension, impaired glucose tolerance, acne, hirsutism, oligomenorrhea, impotence and loss of libido (men), osteoporosis with back pain and buffalo hump, central obesity, moon facies, and purple skin striae (bruise easily).

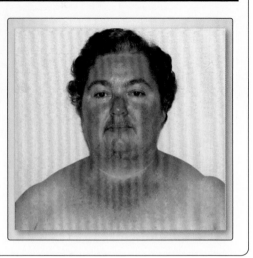

neurons. Preganglionic sympathetic axons (via splanchnic nerves) synapse on chromaffin cells and upon stimulation cause chromaffin cells to secrete the catecholamines **epinephrine** and **norepinephrine**. Chromaffin cells are derived from neural crest cells and are of two types: **epinephrine containing** and **norepinephrine containing**.

[1] Epinephrine-containing cell: These contain RER, polyribosomes, a Golgi complex, mitochondria, and small secretory granules with a low-to-moderate spherical electron-dense core and a minimal electron-lucent halo. The epinephrine-containing cell secretes **epinephrine**, and all of the circulating epinephrine in the blood is derived from the suprarenal medulla.

[2] Norepinephrine-containing cell: These contain RER, polyribosomes, a Golgi complex, mitochondria, and large secretory granules with a highly electron-dense spherical core and a conspicuous electron-lucent halo. The norepinephrine-containing cell secretes **norepinephrine**. The majority of the circulating norepinephrine in the blood is derived from the postganglionic sympathetic neurons and the brain, with the secretion from the suprarenal medulla contributing only a minor portion.

B. Reproductive system

The female and male reproductive systems arise from common embryologic origin but differentiate over the course of fetal development into homologous structures with distinct physiologic functions. The distal portion of the urinary tract—the urethra—is integrated into the male reproductive system as it serves as a conduit for sperm delivery, in addition to urine excretion. In the female, the urethra is functionally separate, but anatomically related to the reproductive system. These relationships explain why the two systems are commonly combined and described as urogenital systems. While urethra anatomy is detailed in the urinary system section, it is also mentioned here briefly for completeness.

1. **Reproductive system development:** The intermediate mesoderm forms a longitudinal elevation along the dorsal body wall called the **urogenital ridge**. A portion of the urogenital ridge forms the **gonadal ridge**, which gives rise to the **gonads** of the reproductive system. The embryologic formation of the male and female reproductive systems has a common ancestry, which is highlighted by the term **indifferent embryo** (Fig. 5.43). In addition, due to the complexity involved in gender determination, the embryo may be considered to have four assignments: **genotype**, **gonotype**, **phenotype**, and **neurotype**. If the genotype, gonotype, phenotype, and neurotype do not align in a congruous manner, a condition of **intersexuality** exists.

   a. **Genotype: Genotype** depends on whether the chromosome composition is 46, XY (male) or 46, XX (female).

   b. **Gonotype: Gonotype** depends on whether the indifferent gonad develops into a testes (male) or ovary (female).

   c. **Phenotype: Phenotype** depends on whether the external genitalia (and genital ducts) can be unambiguously identified as male (e.g., penis, scrotum) or female (e.g., clitoris, vagina).

   d. **Neurotype: Neurotype** depends on whether the brain has been sexualized as either masculine or feminine.

Figure 5.43
Reproductive system development.

Clinical Application 5.10: Intersexuality

Male intersexuality (MI) occurs when an individual has only testicular tissue histologically and various stages of stunted development of the male external genitalia. These individuals have a **46, XY genotype**. MI is most often observed clinically in association with a condition in which the fetus produces a **lack of androgens** (and **Müllerian inhibitory factor**). This is caused most commonly by mutations in genes for androgen steroid biosynthesis (e.g., **5a-reductase 2 deficiency** or **17b-hydroxysteroid dehydrogenase**). The reduced levels of androgens lead to the **feminization of a male fetus**.

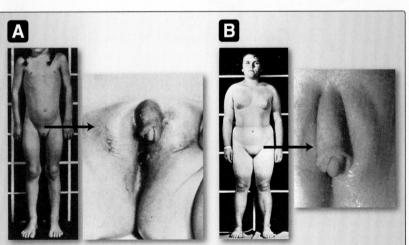

Female intersexuality (FI) occurs when an individual has only ovarian tissue histologically and masculinization of the female external genitalia. These individuals have a **46, XX genotype**. FI is most often observed clinically in association with a condition in which the fetus produces an **excess of androgens** (e.g., **congenital adrenal hyperplasia [CAH]**). CAH is caused most commonly by mutations in genes for enzymes involved in adrenocortical steroid biosynthesis (e.g., **21-hydroxylase deficiency**, **11b-hydroxylase deficiency**). **21-Hydroxylase deficiency** (current terminology is **CYP21A2 deficiency**) accounts for 90% of all cases of CAH. The elevated levels of androgens lead to **masculinization of a female fetus**.

A, Male intersexuality. B, Female intersexuality.

e. **Indifferent embryo: At fertilization**, the genotype of the embryo (46, XY or 46, XX) is established (see Fig. 5.43). **During weeks 1–6**, the embryo remains in an indifferent stage called the indifferent embryo. This means that genetically male embryos and genetically female embryos are visibly indistinguishable (e.g., by a sonogram). **During week 7**, the indifferent embryo begins differentiation along either a male or female pathway. **By week 12**, male or female characteristics of the external genitalia can be recognized. **By week 20**, the differentiation of male or female characteristics is complete.

2. **Female reproductive system development:** The components of the indifferent embryo that are remodeled to form the adult female reproductive system include the **gonads** (**ovaries**), **genital ducts**, and **primordia of external genitalia** (Fig. 5.44). The sequence of remodeling begins with the gonads, then the genital ducts, and finally the primordia of the external genitalia, which has already been discussed in the perineum.

a. **XX gonad:** The coelomic epithelium associated with the gonadal ridge forms **somatic support cells** within the XX gonad. The somatic support cells do not express the **SRY gene** located on

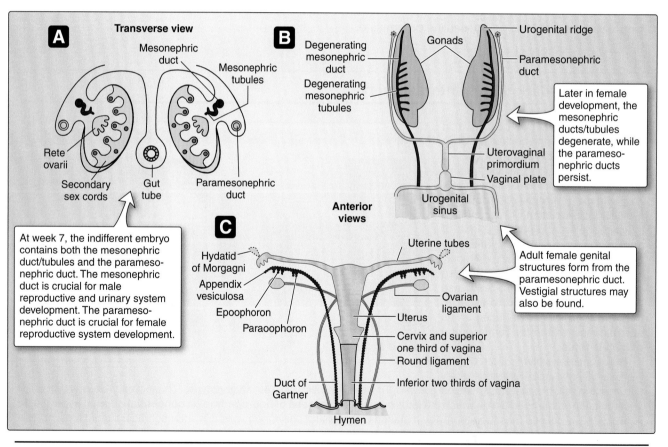

Figure 5.44
Female reproductive system embryology. A, Week 12 XX gonad. B, XX gonad and genital duct. C, Primordia of external genitalia.

chromosome Yp11.3, which encodes for the **sex-determining region Y protein (Sry protein)** because no Y chromosome is present. In the absence of the Sry protein, somatic support cells within the XX gonad differentiate into **follicular cells**. In the absence of Sry protein, Müllerian inhibitory factor (MIF), and testosterone, the XX gonad forms the **ovary**, and the indifferent embryo will be directed toward female characteristics. During week 7, **primary sex cords** develop from the gonadal ridge and incorporate primordial germ cells (XX genotype), which migrate into the XX gonad from the wall of the yolk sac. The primary sex cords extend into the medulla of the XX gonad and develop into the **rete ovarii**, which eventually degenerates. Later, **secondary sex cords** develop and incorporate primordial germ cells as a thin **tunica albuginea** forms. The secondary sex cords break apart and form isolated cell clusters called **primordial follicles**. A primordial follicle consists of a **primary oocyte** surrounded by a **single layer of follicular cells**.

b. **Female genital ducts:** The indifferent embryo—no matter whether it possesses a XY genotype or XX genotype—contains both the **mesonephric (Wolffian) ducts/tubules** and the **paramesonephric (Müllerian) ducts**.

   [1] **Mesonephric:** The mesonephric (Wolffian) ducts/tubules in the female **degenerate**.

   [2] **Paramesonephric:** The cranial portion of the paramesonephric (Müllerian) ducts in the female form the uterine tubes. The caudal portion of the paramesonephric (Müllerian) ducts in the female fuse in the midline to form the **uterovaginal primordium**. The uterovaginal primordium later develops into the **uterus**, **cervix**, and **superior third of the vagina**. The caudal portion of the paramesonephric (Müllerian) ducts in the female projects into the dorsal wall of the cloaca and induces the formation of the **sinovaginal bulbs**. These fuse to form the solid **vaginal plate**, which later canalizes and develops into the **inferior third of the vagina**.

> Vestigial remnants of the mesonephric duct (called the **appendix vesiculosa** and **Garner duct**) may be found in the female. Vestigial remnants of mesonephric tubules (called the **epoophoron** and **paroophoron**) may be found in the female. Vestigial remnants of the paramesonephric duct (called the **hydatid of Morgagni**) may be found in the adult female.

3. **Female reproductive system anatomy:** The female reproductive system includes the **uterine tubes**, **ovaries**, **uterus**, **cervix**, and **vagina** (Fig. 5.45). These structures are adjacent or continuous with one another and are generally positioned between the bladder and rectum.

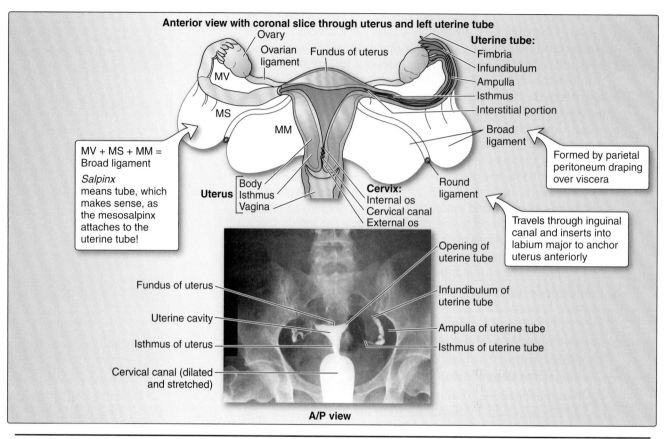

Figure 5.45
Female reproductive organs. A, Uterus, ovaries, uterine tubes, cervix, and upper vagina. B, Hysterosalpingograph.
A/P = anterior/posterior, MM = mesometrium, MS = mesosalpinx, MV = mesovarium.

a. **Uterine tubes:** The uterine tube is divided into four regions: **infundibulum**, **ampulla**, **isthmus**, and the **intramural segment**.

[1] **Infundibulum:** The **infundibulum** is the flared open end of the uterine tube next to the ovary. The **fimbriae** are delicate, finger-like projections that extend from the infundibulum toward the ovary.

[2] **Ampulla:** The **ampulla** is the longest segment of the uterine tube and has the largest diameter. This region is where **fertilization** typically occurs.

Tubal ligation is one form of female sterilization, which involves surgical cutting, clipping, or blocking the uterine tubes to prevent pregnancy.

[3] **Isthmus:** The **isthmus** is the narrow segment of the uterine tube between the ampulla and uterus.

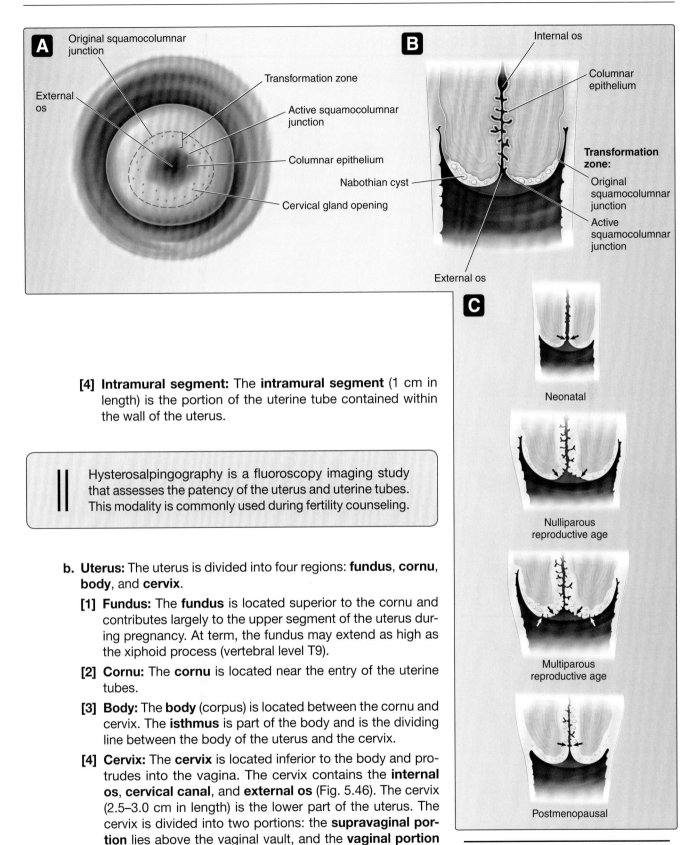

[4] Intramural segment: The **intramural segment** (1 cm in length) is the portion of the uterine tube contained within the wall of the uterus.

Hysterosalpingography is a fluoroscopy imaging study that assesses the patency of the uterus and uterine tubes. This modality is commonly used during fertility counseling.

b. **Uterus:** The uterus is divided into four regions: **fundus, cornu, body,** and **cervix.**

   [1] Fundus: The **fundus** is located superior to the cornu and contributes largely to the upper segment of the uterus during pregnancy. At term, the fundus may extend as high as the xiphoid process (vertebral level T9).

   [2] Cornu: The **cornu** is located near the entry of the uterine tubes.

   [3] Body: The **body** (corpus) is located between the cornu and cervix. The **isthmus** is part of the body and is the dividing line between the body of the uterus and the cervix.

   [4] Cervix: The **cervix** is located inferior to the body and protrudes into the vagina. The cervix contains the **internal os, cervical canal,** and **external os** (Fig. 5.46). The cervix (2.5–3.0 cm in length) is the lower part of the uterus. The cervix is divided into two portions: the **supravaginal portion** lies above the vaginal vault, and the **vaginal portion** protrudes into the vagina. The junction between the cervix and the body of the uterus is at the **internal os.**

Figure 5.46
Cervix.

Clinical Application 5.11: Ectopic Pregnancy

Ectopic pregnancies occur outside the uterus. The vast majority (96%) of ectopic pregnancies occur in the uterine tube, although they can also occur in the cervix, intramural segment, abdomen, or ovary. Vaginal bleeding, often accompanied by abdominal/pelvic pain, is the most common manifestations of an ectopic pregnancy. In addition to a pregnancy test to measure human chorionic gonadotropin, transvaginal ultrasound is used to assess the location of an ectopic pregnancy.

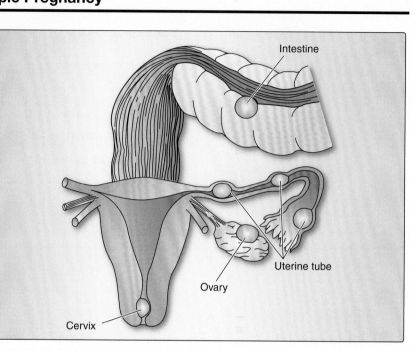

Intestine

Uterine tube

Ovary

Cervix

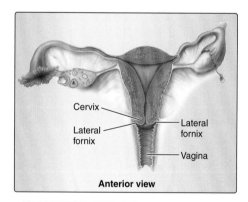

Cervix

Lateral fornix

Lateral fornix

Vagina

Anterior view

Figure 5.47
Vagina.

c. **Vagina:** The vagina spans between the cervix and vestibule of the vagina and is positioned posterior to the bladder/urethra and anterior to the rectum (Fig. 5.47). As the vaginal portion of the cervix extends into the superior vagina, a circumferential recess is created. Continuous zones of the recess are called the **anterior fornix**, **posterior fornix**, and **lateral fornix**.

d. **Connective tissue support:** In addition to the pelvic floor muscles and endopelvic fascia extensions, the uterus, uterine tubes, and ovaries are supported by a series of connective tissue "ligaments" (Fig. 5.48).

Clinical Application 5.12: Uterine Leiomyomas

Uterine leiomyomas (fibroids) are benign tumors that develop from myometrium smooth muscle cells and typically affect females of reproductive age. Symptoms include pelvic pain, pressure, reproductive dysfunction, and uterine bleeding. Fibroids can be located in the uterine wall (intramural myomas), just deep to endometrium (submucosal myomas), at the serosal surface

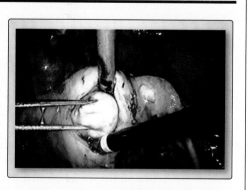

of uterus (subserosal myomas) or in the cervix (cervical myomas). Pelvic ultrasound is used to assess uterine fibroids location and characteristics.

Clinical Application 5.13: Cervical Carcinoma

High-risk human papillomavirus (HPV) plays a major role in the development of cervical neoplasia. Squamous cell carcinoma and adenocarcinoma are two major histologic types of cervical cancer. HPV is a sexually transmitted disease, so patient sexual history is an important risk factor in the transmission and subsequent development of cervical cancer in females. Cervical cancer can begin in the cervix and invade adjacent structures, such as the uterus, vagina, and rectum, by direct extension. Metastasis through the lymphatic system can occur through pelvic or para-aortic lymph nodes first, before spreading. Hematogenous dissemination most commonly occurs to the lungs, bone, and liver.

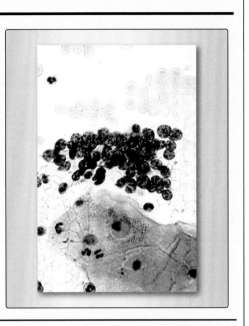

Cervical smear showing small-cell carcinoma cells demonstrating classic cytomorphology with salt-pepper chromatin.

Clinical Application 5.14: Hysterectomy

Hysterectomy is the surgical removal of the uterus. It can be performed transvaginally or through the anterior abdominal wall. Of importance is the proximity of the ureter to the uterine artery, which must be ligated to remove the uterus. The ureter needs to be identified prior to ligation to minimize the risk of injury. Removal of the uterus can be partial (subtotal, leaves cervix), total (removes cervix and uterus) or radical (includes removal of superior vagina). The procedure is indicated for endometriosis, uterine fibroids, abnormal bleeding, carcinoma, and chronic pelvic pain.

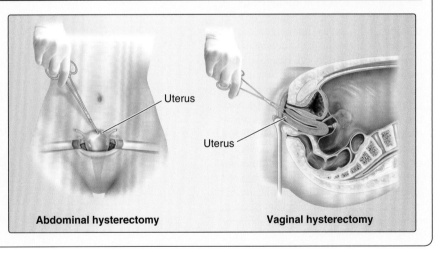

Abdominal hysterectomy   **Vaginal hysterectomy**

[1] **Broad ligament:** Uterus position is maintained by the broad ligament, which has three parts: **mesometrium** (attached along uterine body), **mesovarium** (attached to ovary), and **mesosalpinx** (attached to uterine tube). Although not a true ligament, this double layer of peritoneum drapes over the uterus, extends along the sides of the uterine body, and attaches to the pelvic walls.

[2] **Suspensory ligament of the ovary:** Continuous with the broad ligament, the suspensory ligament of the ovary is formed by the double layer of peritoneum draped over the ovarian

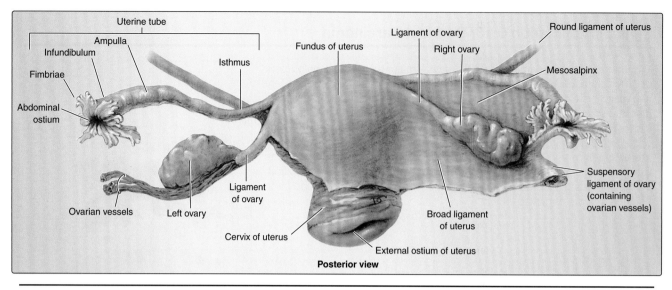

Figure 5.48
Female reproductive visceral support.

Clinical Application 5.15: Anesthesia During Childbirth

Pain associated with childbirth is often treated with regional anesthesia, which includes a pudendal block, a caudal epidural block, and a spinal block. A pudendal block is administered around the site of the ischial spine and targets the somatic afferents to the perineum and inferior vagina. Pudendal blocks do not eliminate the pain associated with uterine contractions. A caudal epidural block is administered into the epidural space of the sacral canal to target spinal nerve roots of S_2–S_4. This anesthetizes the perineum and inferior vagina (pudendal afferents) as well as the superior vagina and cervix. Pain from uterine contractions is still present, as is lower limb motor and sensory function. A spinal block is administered directly superior or inferior to the L4 spinous process to avoid injury of spinal cord, which ends at L2 level in adults. Anesthetic agent is delivered into the subarachnoid space, which anesthetizes structures from at least the waist down, including the lower limbs. With a spinal block, the patient does not feel pain associated with labor and delivery.

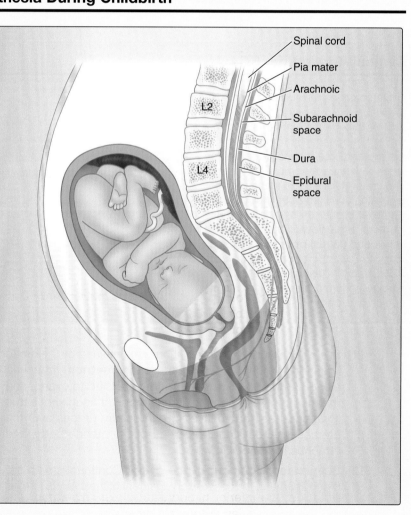

Green = spinal block, Yellow = caudal epidural, Blue = pudendal nerve block.

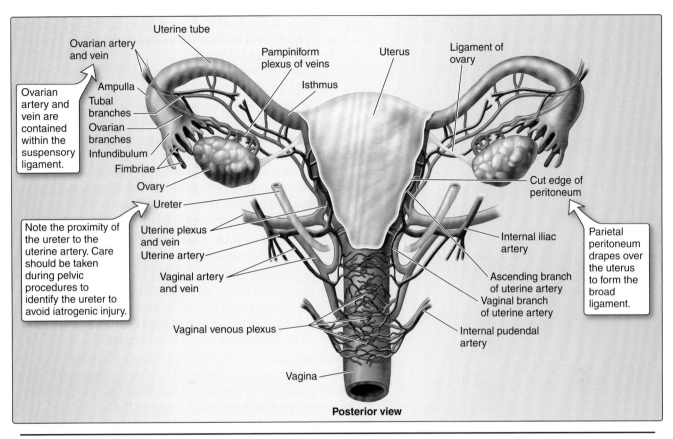

Figure 5.49
Vascular supply to female reproductive viscera.

artery and vein that course into the pelvis from the abdomen. It supports the position of the ovary and uterine tubes.

[3] **Round ligament of the uterus:** The round ligament in the female represents the distal end of the gubernaculum, which helped guide the ovary into the pelvis from the abdomen. It extends anterolaterally from the uterus, travels through the inguinal canal, and inserts into the labia majora bilaterally. This ligament helps to maintain the anteverted position of the uterus.

[4] **Ligament of the ovary:** This ligament represents the proximal end of the gubernaculum and attaches the ovary to the uterus at the uterotubal junction.

e. **Vasculature:** The uterus is supplied by the **uterine arteries**, with contributions from branches of the **ovarian arteries** after supplying the ovaries (Fig. 5.49). Both of these arteries supply portions of the uterine tubes as well. The superior vagina is supplied by **vaginal arteries**, while internal pudendal artery branches serve the inferior vagina. Venous drainage occurs by way of the uterine venous plexus, which drains into the uterine veins, tributaries of the iliac veins.

f. **Innervation:** The **uterovaginal nerve plexus**, which is a subsidiary of the inferior hypogastric plexus by way of the pelvic plexus, provides autonomic innervation to the uterus and superior vagina (see Fig. 5.22). The inferior vagina receives somatic innervation from branches of the pudendal nerve. Visceral sympathetic afferent fibers carrying pain from the uterine body and fundus travel back to inferior thoracic/superior lumbar ganglia. Visceral afferents from the cervix and vagina follow the parasympathetic motor outflow back to the level of pelvic splanchnics (S_2–S_4).

g. **Lymphatics:** Structures of the female reproductive viscera have multiple lymph drainage patterns (see Fig. 5.24 and Table 5.2). Superior structures such as the uterine fundus and superior body may drain into lumbar nodes, while the area adjacent to the round ligament drains through superficial inguinal nodes. Inferior uterine body and cervix drain into external and internal iliac nodes, respectively. Lymphatic drainage of the ovaries follows ovarian vessels back into the abdomen to drain through lumbar nodes.

4. **Female reproductive system histology:** This includes the ovary, uterine tube, uterus (menstrual cycle), cervix, and vagina.

a. **Ovary:** The ovary is an almond-shaped structure located posterior to the broad ligament (Fig. 5.50). The ovary is covered by a simple cuboidal epithelium called the **serosal epithelium** with a subjacent connective tissue layer called the **tunica albuginea**. The ovary is divided into a **medulla** and **cortex**.

[1] **Ovarian medulla:** The ovarian medulla lies deep to the cortex and contains connective tissue, occasional smooth muscle cells, and numerous tortuous arteries (and veins) from which small branches radiate to the cortex.

[2] **Ovarian cortex:** The ovarian cortex contains **primordial, primary, secondary preantral, secondary antral, selectable, selected preovulatory,** and **Graafian follicles**. It consists of highly cellular connective tissue stroma and occasional smooth muscle cells.

(a) **Primordial follicle (resting stage):** Primordial follicle makes up a pool of resting follicles that constitute the **ovarian reserve** and undergo a spontaneous initiation to form growing follicles. The primordial follicle is characterized by its size (~0.35 mm in diameter) and a single layer of squamous granulosa cells. The primordial follicle consists of three cell types: **primary oocyte, granulosa cells,** and **fibroblasts**.

(b) **Primary follicle (first stage):** A large primary follicle is the first stage in ovarian follicle growth. The large primary follicle is characterized by its size (~0.35–0.1 mm in diameter) and a single layer of ~600 cuboidal granulosa cells. Like the primordial follicle, this follicle consists of **primary oocyte, granulosa cells,** and **fibroblasts**.

(c) **Secondary preantral follicle (second stage):** The secondary preantral follicle is characterized by its size (~0.1–0.2 mm in diameter) and two or more layers of ~2,100 cuboidal granulosa cells that surround the primary oocyte. The secondary preantral follicle consists of three cell types: **primary oocyte, granulosa cells,** and **thecal cells** (i.e., **thecal interna** and **externa**).

(d) **Secondary antral follicle (third stage):** The secondary antral follicle is characterized by its size (~0.20–2.0 mm

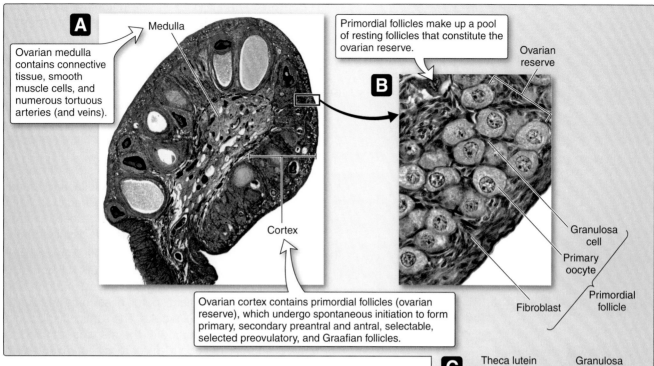

Ovarian medulla contains connective tissue, smooth muscle cells, and numerous tortuous arteries (and veins).

A Medulla

Cortex

Primordial follicles make up a pool of resting follicles that constitute the ovarian reserve.

B

Ovarian reserve

Granulosa cell

Primary oocyte

Primordial follicle

Fibroblast

Ovarian cortex contains primordial follicles (ovarian reserve), which undergo spontaneous initiation to form primary, secondary preantral and antral, selectable, selected preovulatory, and Graafian follicles.

in diameter), multiple layers of ~7,600–176,000 cuboidal granulosa cells, and a crescent-shaped, fluid-filled cavity called the **antrum**. Like the secondary preantral follicle, this follicle consists of **primary oocyte**, **granulosa cells**, and **thecal cells**.

(e) **Selectable follicle (fourth stage):** The selectable follicle is characterized by its size (~2–5 mm in diameter), multiple layers of ~933,000 cuboidal granulosa cells, the presence of an antrum, and the development of follicle-stimulating hormone (FSH) sensitivity. At the beginning of each menstrual cycle, a cohort of 3–11 selectable follicles is present in the ovary, from which normally only one follicle will be selected to continue ovarian growth toward the Graafian follicle and ovulation. The selectable follicle consists of the same three cell types as the secondary preantral and antral follicles.

(f) **Selected preovulatory follicle (fifth stage):** The selected preovulatory follicle is characterized by its size (~5–18 mm in diameter), multiple layers of ~340,000 cuboidal granulosa cells, the presence of an antrum, and the development of **FSH** and **luteinizing hormone (LH) sensitivity**. The selected preovulatory follicle is the largest healthy follicle out of the cohort of 3–11 selectable follicles: it grows at a faster rate, accumulates large amounts of fluid within the antrum, contains detectable levels of FSH, and has a higher estradiol concentration. It also consists of a **primary oocyte**, **granulosa cells**, and **thecal cells**. The granulosa cells express **FSH** and **LH receptors**, and theca interna cells express **LH**

C Theca lutein cells   Granulosa lutein cells

After ovulation of a secondary oocyte from a Graafian follicle, the granulosa cells of the Graafian follicle become highly infolded and consist of granulosa lutein cells and theca lutein cells.

Figure 5.50
Ovarian histology. A, Ovary. B, Primordial follicle. C, Corpus luteum.

receptors. The LH causes the theca interna cells to produce **androstenedione**, which is then transported to the granulosa cells, where it is converted to estradiol. The theca externa layer remains a highly cellular connective tissue stroma.

(g) **Graafian follicle (sixth stage):** The Graafian follicle is characterized by its size (~25 mm in diameter), multiple layers of ~59,000,000 cuboidal granulosa cells, the presence of an antrum, FSH and LH sensitivity, and the presence of a secondary oocyte arrested in metaphase of meiosis II. The Graafian follicle consists of three cell types: **secondary oocyte**, **granulosa cells**, and **thecal cells**. Androstenedione is converted to estradiol as in the fifth stage of ovarian follicle growth, and the theca externa layer remains a highly cellular connective tissue stroma.

(h) **Corpus luteum:** The corpus luteum is a temporary endocrine gland whose formation is **LH dependent**. If fertilization occurs, the corpus luteum enlarges and becomes the predominant source of steroids needed to sustain pregnancy for ~**8 weeks**. Thereafter, the placenta becomes the major source of the steroids required. If fertilization does not occur, the corpus luteum regresses and forms a **corpus albicans**. The corpus luteum consists of **granulosa lutein** and **theca lutein cells**.

(i) **Granulosa lutein cell:** This is a large (30 μm in diameter) cell with a round nucleus located toward the center of the corpus luteum. It contains predominately

Clinical Application 5.16: Ovarian Germ Cell Tumors

Ovarian germ cell tumors (OGCTs) develop from ovarian primordial germ cells and can be malignant or benign. Different types of OGCTs include teratomas (most common, typically benign), dysgerminomas, yolk sac tumors (cancerous), mixed germ cell tumors, and other rare germ cell carcinomas. OGCTs are capable of and often produce hormones, including human chorionic gonadotropin, which can mimic pregnancy. Associated signs and symptoms include abdominal enlargement due to tumor growth or abdominal fluid collection, abdominal pain, abnormal vaginal bleeding, and other signs of pregnancy due to tumor hormone production. Surgery is indicated for removal and histologic assessment. Depending on type, OGCTs can contain mature ectodermal, mesodermal, and ectodermal tissues, such as hair, skin, muscle, and teeth.

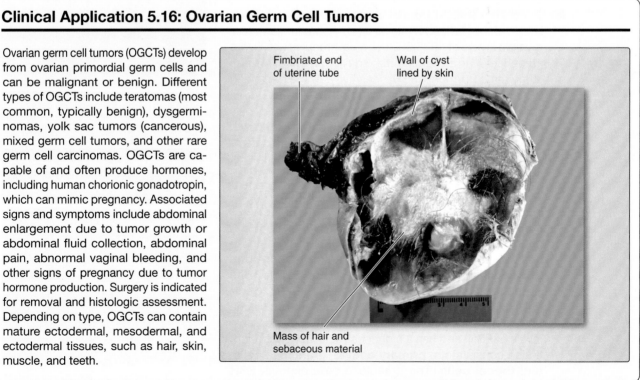

Fimbriated end of uterine tube

Wall of cyst lined by skin

Mass of hair and sebaceous material

SER, mitochondria with tubular crista, lipid droplets, and lipochrome pigment and secretes **progesterone** and **estradiol**.

    (ii) Theca lutein cell: This is a small (15 μm in diameter) cell with a round nucleus located toward the periphery of the corpus luteum. It also contains predominately SER, mitochondria with tubular crista, lipid droplets, and lipochrome pigment but secretes **progesterone** and **androstenedione**.

b. Uterine tube: The uterine tube is organized into a **mucosa**, **muscularis layer**, and a **serosa**.

    [1] Mucosa: The mucosa of the uterine tube consists of a **simple columnar epithelium** and a **lamina propria**. The simple columnar epithelium consists of **ciliated cells** and **secretory (peg) cells**. The ciliated cells have cilia that beat toward the uterus. The secretory (Peg) cells secrete a nutrient-rich medium for the nourishment of the sperm and preimplantation embryo. The lamina propria consists of loose connective tissue.

    [2] Muscularis: The muscularis layer consists of smooth muscle oriented in an inner circular layer and an outer longitudinal layer.

    [3] Serosa: The serosa consists of a simple squamous epithelium (**mesothelium**) and a thin layer of loose connective tissue.

c. Uterus: As shown in Figure 5.51, the uterus is organized into in an **endometrium (mucosa)**, **myometrium (muscularis layer)**, and **perimetrium (serosa)**.

    [1] Endometrium: The endometrium of the uterus consists of a **simple columnar epithelium** and an **endometrial stroma (lamina propria)**. The simple columnar epithelium invaginates

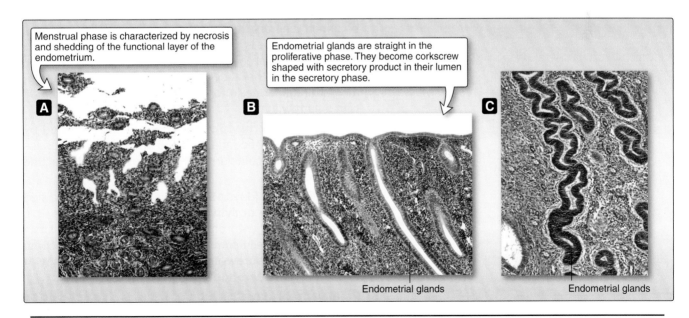

Menstrual phase is characterized by necrosis and shedding of the functional layer of the endometrium.

Endometrial glands are straight in the proliferative phase. They become corkscrew shaped with secretory product in their lumen in the secretory phase.

Endometrial glands

Endometrial glands

Figure 5.51
Uterine histology. A, Menstrual phase. B, Proliferative phase. C, Secretory phase.

into the underlying endometrial stroma (lamina propria) to form **endometrial glands**, which consist of mainly secretory cells. The endometrium can be divided into a **functional layer** and a **basal layer**. The **functional layer** undergoes cyclic changes each month as part of the menstrual cycle and is sloughed off each month during menses. The **basal layer** is responsible for the regeneration of the functional layer each month during the menstrual cycle. The basal layer is never sloughed off.

[2] **Myometrium:** The myometrium consists of smooth muscle oriented in **inner, middle, and outer layers**. The inner and outer layers of smooth muscle are arranged along the long axis of the uterus proper. The middle layer of smooth muscle is arranged in a spiral manner. The middle layer of smooth muscle contains the **stratum vasculare**, which is highly vascular and is the source of the endometrial blood supply.

[3] **Perimetrium:** The perimetrium consists of **mesothelium** and a layer of connective tissue.

d. **Menstrual cycle:** The menstrual cycle is a series of five phases that repeats ideally every 28 days: **menstrual, proliferative (follicular), ovulatory, secretory (luteal),** and **premenstrual phases**.

[1] **Menstrual (days 1–4):** This phase is characterized by the **necrosis and shedding** of the functional layer of the endometrium. Spiral arterioles constrict episodically for a few days and finally constrict permanently, resulting in ischemia that leads to necrosis of endometrial glands and stroma. The spiral arterioles subsequently dilate and rupture, resulting in hemorrhage that sheds the necrotic endometrial glands and stroma.

[2] **Proliferative/follicular (days 4–15):** This phase is characterized by the **regeneration** of the functional layer of the endometrium from the devastating effects of the menstrual phase. This phase is controlled by **estrogen** secreted by the granulosa cells of the selected preovulatory and Graafian follicles. The epithelial cells in the basal layer of the endometrium regenerate to form **straight endometrial glands** with a narrow lumen.

[3] **Ovulatory (days 14–16):** This phase is characterized by **ovulation** of the secondary oocyte arrested in metaphase of meiosis II that coincides with **peak levels of LH** (i.e., the **LH surge**).

[4] **Secretory/luteal (days 15–25):** This phase is characterized by the **secretory activity** of the endometrial glands. It is controlled by **progesterone** secreted by the granulosa lutein cells of the corpus luteum. The endometrial glands become modified to **corkscrew-shaped endometrial glands with glycogen-rich secretion product** within their lumen.

[5] **Premenstrual (days 25–28):** This phase is characterized by **ischemia** due to reduced blood flow to the endometrium. It is controlled by the **reduction in estrogen and progesterone** as the corpus luteum involutes. As the endometrial

glands begin to shrink, the spiral arterioles are compressed, thereby reducing blood flow and causing ischemic damage.

e. **Cervix:** The cervix is organized into a **mucosa** and a **stromal wall** (Fig. 5.52; see also Fig. 5.46).

[1] **Mucosa:** The mucosa of the cervix consists of a simple columnar epithelium or a nonkeratinized stratified squamous epithelium and a lamina propria.

(a) **Simple columnar epithelium:** This lines the supravaginal portion of the cervix and invaginates into the lamina propria to form **cervical glands**, which secrete **mucus**. The simple columnar epithelium and glands do not slough off during the menstrual cycle and are relatively unaffected by it. The nonkeratinized stratified squamous epithelium covers the vaginal portion of the cervix and is continuous with the vaginal epithelium.

(b) **Lamina propria:** This consists of a relatively thick layer of loose connective tissue.

[2] **Stromal wall:** The stromal wall of the cervix is predominately **dense, irregular connective tissue** with very little smooth muscle. This contrasts with the uterine wall, which is predominately smooth muscle. During pregnancy, the cervix becomes relatively rigid and undergoes little to no expansion. Before childbirth, the dense, irregular connective tissue undergoes extensive remodeling along with the removal of collagen fibers by macrophages. As a result, the cervix becomes pliable (**cervical effacement**).

f. **Vagina:** The vagina is organized into a **mucosa, submucosa, muscularis layer**, and **adventitia** (Fig. 5.53).

[1] **Mucosa:** This consists of a **nonkeratinized stratified squamous epithelium** that lines the lumen of the vagina and a **lamina propria**. The most superficial layer of the epithelium is continuously exfoliated during the menstrual cycle, but exfoliation increases during the late secretory phase and menstrual phase. The lamina propria consists of loose connective tissue with numerous elastic fibers, a rich network of blood vessels, and numerous lymphocytes and neutrophils that migrate into the epithelium.

[2] **Submucosa:** This consists of dense, irregular connective tissue, blood vessels, lymphatics, and some lymphatic follicles. The submucosa is not very prominent.

[3] **Muscularis:** This consists of an inner circular layer and an outer longitudinal layer of smooth muscle. These layers are often ill-defined bundles. The muscularis layer also contains numerous **elastic fibers** that contribute to the distensibility of the vagina during childbirth.

[4] **Adventitia:** The adventitia of the vagina consists of dense, irregular connective tissue with a rich network of **elastic fibers** that contribute to the distensibility of the vagina during childbirth.

5. **Male reproductive system development:** The components of the indifferent embryo that are remodeled to form the adult male

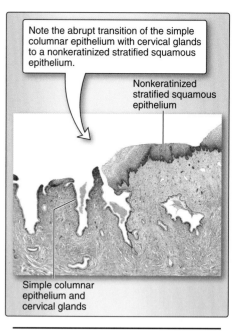

Note the abrupt transition of the simple columnar epithelium with cervical glands to a nonkeratinized stratified squamous epithelium.

Nonkeratinized stratified squamous epithelium

Simple columnar epithelium and cervical glands

Figure 5.52
Cervical histology.

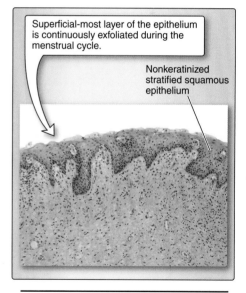

Superficial-most layer of the epithelium is continuously exfoliated during the menstrual cycle.

Nonkeratinized stratified squamous epithelium

Figure 5.53
Vaginal histology.

reproductive system include the **gonads**, **genital ducts**, and **primordia of external genitalia** (Fig. 5.54). The sequence of remodeling begins with the gonads, then the genital ducts, and finally the primordia of the external genitalia (see Perineum section).

a. **XY gonad:** The coelomic epithelium associated with the gonadal ridge forms **somatic support cells** within the XY gonad. The somatic support cells express the **_SRY_ gene** located on chromosome Yp11.3, which encodes for the Sry protein, a 220–amino acid transcription factor that contains a highly conserved DNA-binding region called a high-mobility group box. In response to the Sry protein, somatic support cells within the XY gonad differentiate into **Sertoli cells** that secrete **MIF**, which induces the degeneration of the paramesonephric (Müllerian) ducts. In response to signals from the Sertoli cells, mesenchymal cells within the XY gonad differentiate into **Leydig cells** that secrete **testosterone**. In the presence of Sry protein, MIF, and testosterone, the XY gonad forms the **testes**, and the indifferent embryo will be directed toward male characteristics. During week 7, **primary sex cords** develop from the gonadal ridge and incorporate primordial germ cells (XY genotype), which migrate into the XY gonad from the wall of the yolk sac. The primary sex cords extend into the medulla of the XY gonad and lose their connection with the surface epithelium as the thick **tunica**

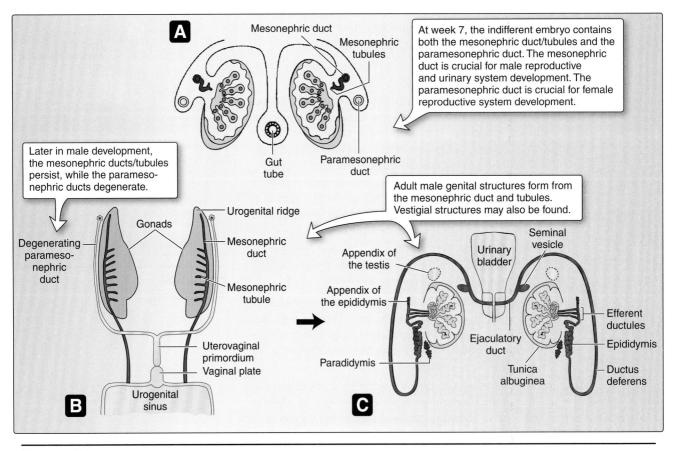

Figure 5.54
Male reproductive system embryology. A, Week 7 XY gonad. B, XY gonad and genital ducts.

albuginea develops and form the **secondary sex cords**. These, in turn, form the **seminiferous cords**, **tubuli recti**, and the **rete testes**. The seminiferous cords consist of **primordial germ cells** surrounded by **Sertoli cells** and **mesenchymal cells**.

b. **Male genital ducts:** The indifferent embryo—no matter whether it possesses an XY genotype or XX genotype—contains both **mesonephric (Wolffian) ducts/tubules** and **paramesonephric (Müllerian) ducts**.

   [1] **Mesonephric (Wolffian):** In the male, these ducts form the **epididymis**, **ductus deferens**, **seminal gland**, and the **ejaculatory duct**. The mesonephric tubules form the **efferent ductules** of the testes.

   [2] **Paramesonephric (Müllerian):** In the male, these ducts **degenerate** due to MIF secreted by the Sertoli cells.

> Vestigial remnants of the mesonephric duct (appendix epididymis), mesonephric tubules (paradidymis), and paramesonephric duct (appendix testis) may be found in the adult male.

c. **Testes descent:** Initially, the testes develop in the abdomen and descend during fetal development to their final location in the scrotum (Fig. 5.55). This significant change in position creates a scenario in which testicular vasculature and lymphatics are pulled with the testes but trace back to the abdomen, despite that they are housed within a superficial perineal structure. Understanding the pathway and associated structures that guide the descent will help in understanding the gross anatomy of the testes.

   [1] **Gubernaculum:** In week 7, a ligamentous cord called the **gubernaculum** forms and attaches distally in the fascia of the labioscrotal swellings. The proximal end of the gubernaculum attaches to the testis (gonad).

   [2] **Processus vaginalis:** Also during week 7, an invagination of peritoneum, the **processus vaginalis**, forms and extends inferiorly through the abdominal wall layers, ending in the labioscrotal folds. The processus vaginalis creates the pathway for testes descent that will become the **inguinal canal**. Recall that the inguinal canal is an oblique tunnel bound by layers of the lateral abdominal wall that has a deep and superficial ring.

   [3] **Descent:** Testes typically descend to the deep inguinal ring by the seventh month of development. Between months 7 and 8, the testes continue through the inguinal canal, passing posterior to the processus vaginalis. Along this pathway, selective layers of the abdominal wall are pulled through to become layers of the spermatic cord and testis (see Fig. 4.8). The testes pull the ductus deferens and testicular vessels

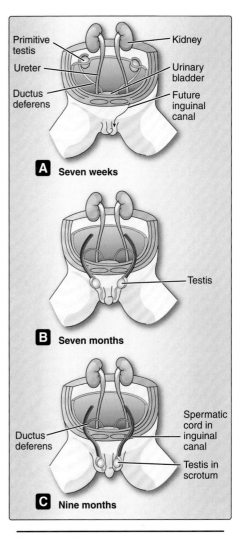

Figure 5.55
Testes descent.

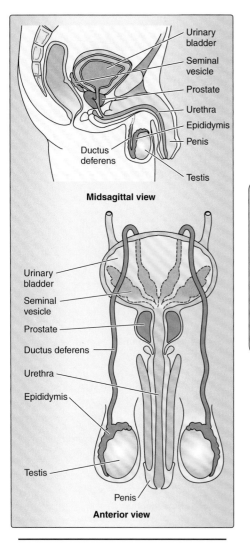

Figure 5.56
Male reproductive structures.

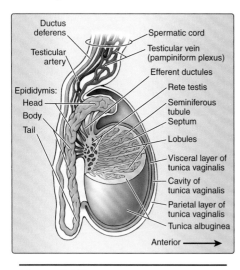

Figure 5.57
Testes and epididymis.

along with them, which assume a position superior and anterior to the ureters. During this descent, the gubernaculum functions as a guiding line, progressively shortening as the testes get closer to their final position in the scrotum. Eventually, the processus vaginalis is obliterated, leaving only a small remnant, the **tunica vaginalis**, in the scrotum, anterior to each testis. The gubernaculum remnant helps to anchor the testis within the scrotum.

Cryptorchidism occurs when the testes fail to descend from the abdomen into the scrotum. This condition occurs in up to 30% of premature males and 3%–4% in full-term males. Sterility is a common effect when the testes remain in the abdominal cavity, and these males are at higher risk of developing germ cell tumors. Testes can also assume ectopic locations after traveling through the inguinal canal, including in the thigh, contralateral side, posterior to penis, or superficial to external oblique aponeurosis.

6. **Male reproductive system anatomy:** The male reproductive system consists of paired **testis**, **epididymis**, **ductus (vas) deferens**, **seminal glands (vesicles)**, **prostate**, and **penis** (Fig. 5.56). These structures collectively function to produce and carry cells and fluids that constitute semen. The male urethra is integrated into this system but described with other urinary system structures. Penile structures are described in the perineum portion of this chapter.

   a. **Testis:** The testis (singular) is an ovoid structure that is surrounded by a thick connective tissue capsule called the **tunica albuginea** because of its whitish color (Fig. 5.57). Suspended in the scrotum, but anchored inferiorly by the gubernaculum remnant, the testis produces hormones and spermatozoa within a delicate, intricate system of tubules.

      [1] **Tunica vaginalis layers:** The cavity or space of the tunica vaginalis is found between visceral and parietal layers that line the testis and internal scrotum, respectively. The resulting cavity allows for movement of the testis within the scrotum.

   b. **Epididymis:** The epididymis is a highly coiled duct ~6 m in length that is divided into **head**, **body**, and **tail regions** (see Fig. 5.57). It is located posteriorly on the testis and is continuous with the ductus deferens.

   c. **Ductus (vas) deferens:** The ductus deferens connects the tail of the epididymis to the ejaculatory duct (Fig. 5.58). It is contained within the spermatic cord and travels through the inguinal canal, anterior and superior to the ureter. At the posterior midline of the urinary bladder, it expands into the ampulla of the ductus deferens before joining the seminal gland to form the ejaculatory duct.

Deferentectomy (vasectomy) is the most widely used form of male sterilization. This procedure involves surgical cutting or blocking the ductus deferens to prevent the transport of sperm. This is typically an outpatient procedure that involves a small incision of the superior scrotum to access the ductus deferens.

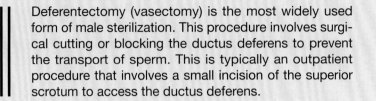

d. Seminal glands: Paired seminal glands sit posterior to the fundus of the urinary bladder, anterior to the rectum, and superior to the prostate (see Fig. 5.58). They produce an alkaline fluid that contributes to the formation of semen by way of the ejaculatory duct.

e. Prostate: Commonly referred to as the prostate gland, this walnut-sized structure is two thirds glandular and a third fibromuscular. The base of the prostate sits at the neck of the urinary bladder, while the apex is adjacent to the deep perineal pouch fascia (see Figs. 5.27 and 5.58). The first main part (prostatic) of the male urethra and ejaculatory ducts travels through the substance of the prostate. It is surrounded by a fibrous capsule that holds nervous and venous plexuses of the prostate.

f. Vasculature: Blood supply to male reproductive structures can arise/drain in the abdomen or within the pelvis (Fig. 5.59; see also Fig. 5.14). Veins in this region accompany arteries of the same name, unless otherwise noted.

Figure 5.58
Ductus deferens and seminal glands and prostate.

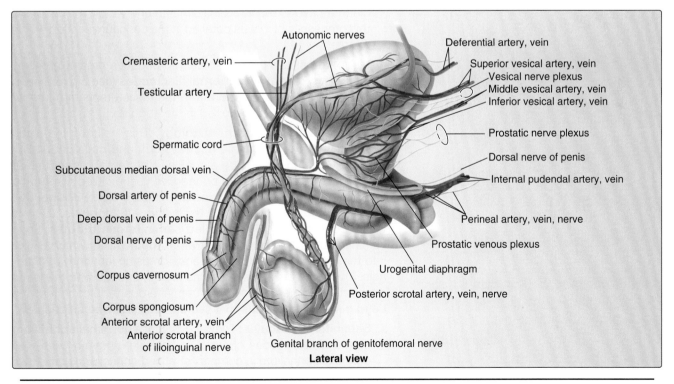

Figure 5.59
Neurovascular supply to male reproductive viscera.

[1] **Testicular arteries and veins:** Testicular arteries are direct branches of the abdominal aorta that supply the testes and epididymis. The pampiniform venous plexus drains these structures and converges to form right and left testicular veins, which ultimately drain into the inferior vena cava and left renal vein, respectively.

[2] **Deferential artery and vein:** Typically a branch and tributary of the superior vesical artery and vein, respectively, these supply and drain the ductus deferens.

[3] **Inferior vesical artery and vein:** A branch of the internal iliac artery and vein, respectively, these supply and drain the ductus deferens, seminal glands, and ejaculatory ducts.

[4] **Prostatic arteries and venous plexus:** Prostatic arteries can arise from several internal iliac branches, including the inferior vesical, middle rectal, and internal pudendal. These arteries supply the prostate. The prostatic venous plexus, which is continuous anteriorly and superiorly with the vesical venous plexus, drains the prostate into the internal iliac veins.

[5] **Dorsal artery and deep dorsal vein of penis:** The dorsal artery of the penis is a branch of the internal pudendal artery that travels along the dorsum of the penis.

g. **Innervation:** Sympathetic and parasympathetic fibers converge to form the **inferior hypogastric** and **pelvic plexuses** (prostatic nerve plexus), which innervate male reproductive structures (see Figs. 5.23 and 5.59). Structures involved in the transport and emission of semen (ductus deferens, ejaculatory ducts, seminal glands) have extensive sympathetic innervation that controls this process, which was detailed in the perineum section of this chapter.

h. **Lymphatics:** Lymph from male reproductive organs primarily drains into **external** or **internal iliac nodes** (see Fig. 5.24 and Table 5.2). However, lymph from the testis drains into lumbar lymph nodes, as it developed in the abdomen.

7. **Male reproductive system histology:** This includes the testis (seminiferous tubules, male duct system, and male accessory glands). Beneath the tunica albuginea, the testis is surrounded by a highly vascular layer of connective tissue called the **tunica vasculosa** (Fig. 5.60). The tunica albuginea projects **connective tissue septae** that divides the testis into ~**250 lobules**, each of which contains **1–4 highly coiled seminiferous tubules**. Each seminiferous tubule ends as a **straight tubule**, all of which empty into the **rete testis**, which is an anastomosing labyrinth of channels. The connective tissue septae are continuous with the loose connective tissue between the seminiferous tubules where the **Leydig (interstitial) cells** that secrete **testosterone** are located.

a. **Seminiferous tubules:** These consist of a **germinal epithelium** surrounded by loose connective tissue and myoid cells. The germinal epithelium (a complex stratified epithelium) comprises two basic cell types: **Sertoli** and **spermatogenic cells**.

[1] **Sertoli cell:** This tall, columnar cell has an oval or triangular, basally or centrally located nucleus with one or more deep

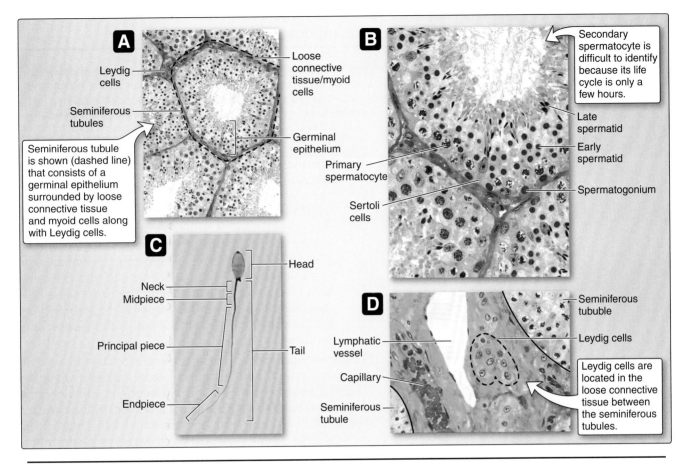

Figure 5.60
Testicular histology. A, Seminiferous tubules. B, Germinal epithelium. C, Spermatozoon. D, Leydig cells.

infoldings. It has unusually ruffled apical and lateral surfaces, as these surround the developing spermatogenic cells. The Sertoli cell extends the full thickness of the germinal epithelium and contains RER, polyribosomes, a Golgi complex, SER, mitochondria, annulate lamellae, lysosomes, vesicles, lipid droplets, glycogen, microtubules, a 7–9-nm filament sheath that surrounds the nucleus, and crystalloid inclusion bodies (of Charcot-Bottcher) that consist of 15-nm filament bundles.

(a) **Structure:** Sertoli cells are joined to each other by a **unique zonula occludens** (**tight junction**) associated with **SER** and **actin filaments**. This zonula occludens establishes two compartments within the germinal epithelium: **basal** and **luminal**. The basal compartment contains spermatogonia and early primary spermatocytes, and the luminal compartment contains more mature spermatocytes and spermatids. The zonula occludens also establishes the **blood–testis barrier**, which creates a pristine fluid environment for the more mature spermatocytes and spermatids and protects them (as well as genetically dissimilar cells) from the immune system.

(b) **Functions:** The Sertoli cell has these important functions: it provides mechanical and nutritional support for developing

Clinical Application 5.17: Testicular Teratocarcinoma

Testicular teratocarcinoma (TC) is a germ cell neoplasm. In its early histologic stages, a TC resembles a blastocyst with three primary germ layers and may be loosely referred to as a "male pregnancy." Later, the tumor comprises well-differentiated cells and structures from each of the three primary germ layers: colon glandular tissue (endoderm), cartilage (mesoderm), and squamous epithelium (ectoderm). TC is associated with **elevated human chorionic gonadotropin** and **α-fetoprotein levels**.

spermatogenic cells, phagocytizes excess cytoplasm discarded by spermatids, forms the blood–testes barrier, secretes **inhibin** that inhibits release of FSH from the adenohypophysis, secretes **MIF** during fetal development that inhibits development of the paramesonephric duct in a genotypic XY fetus, synthesizes **androgen-binding protein (ABP)** that binds testosterone so that the high levels necessary for spermatogenesis to occur are present in the seminiferous tubules, and it possesses **FSH receptors** (G-protein–linked receptors) so that FSH from the adenohypophysis stimulates spermatogenesis and synthesis of ABP.

[2] **Spermatogenic cells:** These "male germ cells" are transforming from type A spermatogonia → spermatozoa, a process called **spermatogenesis**. Spermatogenic cells migrate from the basal to the luminal compartment of the germinal epithelium as they undergo spermatogenesis. They consist of a number of cell types: **dark** and **pale type A spermatogonia**, **type B spermatogonium**, **primary** and **secondary spermatocytes**, **spermatid** (**early** and **late** stages), and **spermatozoon**.

(a) **Spermatozoon:** The spermatozoon undergoes **maturation in the epididymis** and **capacitation in the female reproductive tract** so that it is capable of delivering its (23,1N) complement of chromosomal material to the secondary oocyte. The spermatozoon consists of **head** and **tail regions**. The tail is further divided into a **neck**, **midpiece**, **principal piece**, and **endpiece**.

b. **Leydig cell:** This large, polygon-shaped cell has a round, centrally located nucleus and contains RER, polyribosomes, a Golgi complex, prominent SER, mitochondria with tubular cristae, lipid droplets, lysosomes, glycogen, lipofuscin pigment, and crystals of Reinke. The Leydig cell is located in the loose connective tissue between the seminiferous tubules. It possesses **LH receptors** so that LH from the adenohypophysis stimulates testosterone secretion.

[1] **Testosterone:** This steroid hormone secreted by Leydig cells plays a role in fetal development of the epididymis, ductus deferens, seminal gland, and ejaculatory duct (dihydrotestosterone is essential in the fetal development of the penis and scrotum [external genitalia] and prostate); spermatogenesis; function of the prostate, seminal gland, and bulbourethral glands; appearance of secondary sex characteristics; closure

of the epiphyseal growth plate; increase in muscle mass; lipid metabolism (testosterone supplementation increases high-density lipoprotein and decreases low-density lipoprotein); and stimulation of cartilage growth.

c. **Male duct system:** The spermatozoa travel from the seminiferous tubules → straight tubules → rete testis all of which are located inside the testis. The spermatozoa then travel from the efferent ductules → epididymis → ductus deferens → ejaculatory duct → urethra, all of which are located outside the testis.

[1] **Efferent ductules:** The ~20 efferent ductules consist of an epithelium, loose connective tissue, and a smooth muscle layer. The epithelium consists of alternating patches of ciliated simple columnar epithelium and unciliated simple cuboidal epithelium, giving the luminal surface an irregular or saw-toothed appearance.

[2] **Epididymis:** This is the site where spermatozoa maturation (i.e., develop motility) and short-term storage occurs (Fig. 5.61). It consists of an epithelium, loose connective tissue, and a smooth muscle layer. The epithelium consists of a pseudostratified columnar epithelium with tall, columnar **principal** and **basal cells (stem cells)**. The pseudostratified columnar epithelium gives the luminal surface a smooth appearance in contrast to the irregular appearance of the efferent ductules.

(a) **Principal cell functions:** This cell reabsorbs ~20% of the testicular fluid (efferent ductules reabsorb ~80%); phagocytizes degenerating spermatozoa or spermatid residual bodies not phagocytized by Sertoli cells; and secretes glycoproteins, sialic acid, and glycerophosphocholine, which aid in spermatozoa maturation.

[3] **Ductus (vas) deferens:** This consists of an epithelium, loose connective tissue, and a muscle layer. The epithelium consists of a pseudostratified columnar epithelium with tall, columnar **principal** and **basal cells (stem cells)**.

[4] **Ejaculatory duct:** This consists of an **epithelium** and the **fibromuscular stroma** of the prostate because the ejaculatory duct passes through the prostate. The epithelium consists of a **pseudostratified columnar epithelium**.

d. **Male accessory glands:** These include the seminal vesicle, bulbourethral, and prostate glands. Collectively, they produce secretions that contribute to the formation of semen or function to lubricate the male urethra.

[1] **Seminal vesicle:** This gland is organized into a **pseudostratified columnar epithelium**, **loose connective tissue**, a **muscle layer**, and a **capsule**. The epithelium consists of **secretory** and **basal (stem) cells**. The secretory cell secretes a pale yellow, viscous material called **seminal fluid** that contains **fructose** (the principal metabolic substrate for sperm), **other sugars**, **choline**, **proteins**, **amino acids**, **ascorbic acid**, **citric acid**, and **prostaglandins**. The seminal fluid accounts for 70% of the volume of the ejaculated semen.

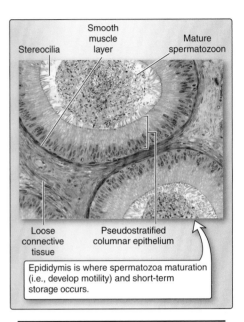

Epididymis is where spermatozoa maturation (i.e., develop motility) and short-term storage occurs.

Figure 5.61
Epididymis histology.

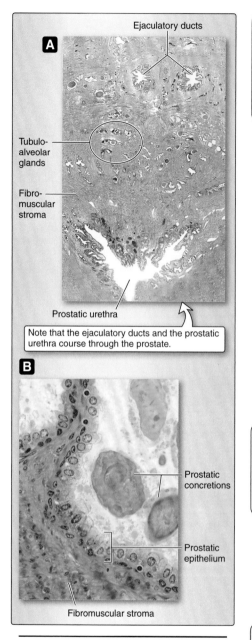

Ejaculatory ducts

Tubulo-
alveolar
glands

Fibro-
muscular
stroma

Prostatic urethra

Note that the ejaculatory ducts and the prostatic
urethra course through the prostate.

Prostatic
concretions

Prostatic
epithelium

Fibromuscular stroma

Figure 5.62
Prostate histology. A, Low magnification
showing ducts and urethra. B, High
magnification.

In forensic medicine, the presence of fructose (which is not produced elsewhere in the body) and choline crystals are used to determine the presence of semen. The characteristic pale yellow color of semen is due to the lipochrome pigment secreted by the epithelium.

[2] **Bulbourethral:** This gland is organized into a **simple cuboidal epithelium**, **loose connective tissue**, and a **capsule**. The epithelium produces a clear, mucus-like, slippery fluid, which contains galactose, galactosamine, galacturonic acid, sialic acid, and methylpentose. This fluid makes up a major portion of the preseminal fluid (pre-ejaculate) and probably serves to lubricate the spongy urethra.

[3] **Prostate:** This gland is organized into a **pseudostratified columnar epithelium**, **fibromuscular stroma**, and a **capsule** (Fig. 5.62). The epithelium consists of **secretory**, **neuroendocrine**, and **basal (stem) cells**. The secretory cell secretes a clear, slightly alkaline (pH 7.29) prostatic fluid that contains **citric acid**, **prostatic acid phosphatase**, **prostaglandins**, **fibrinolysin**, and **prostate-specific antigen (PSA)**. This fluid may precipitate or calcify within the lumen of the tubuloalveolar glands and form **prostatic concretions**, which increase with age.

PSA is a serine protease that liquefies semen after ejaculation. The PSA serum level serves as a diagnostic tool for prostatic carcinoma, although its usefulness has been questioned.

(a) **Neuroendocrine cell:** This cell secretes **serotonin**, **somatostatin**, **calcitonin**, and **bombesin**. It regulates the growth, differentiation, and secretory function of the prostate.

The neuroendocrine cell increases in number in high-grade and high-stage tumors, particularly in hormone-treated and hormone-refractory (androgen-independent) prostate cancer.

The prostate is partially made up of a collection of 30–50 compound tubuloalveolar glands that urologists/oncologists arrange in three concentric zones: **periurethral** (closest to prostatic urethra), **central**, and **peripheral** (farthest from prostatic urethra). The glands in the periurethral zone empty their secretions directly into the prostatic urethra. Those in the central and peripheral zones empty their secretions via excretory ducts into the prostatic urethra.

CHAPTER SUMMARY

Pelvic Osteology and Musculature

- The pelvic girdle is made up of the right and left hip bones (os coxae) and the sacrum.
- Os coxae are comprised of three fused bones—ilium, ischium, and pubis. All three bones fuse together at the acetabulum.
- Pelvic ligaments reinforce articulations between L5, the sacrum, and os coxae. Sacrotuberous and sacrospinous ligaments close off greater and lesser sciatic notches into greater and lesser sciatic foramina.
- The pelvic floor is formed by a series of fascia and muscles to support pelvic viscera. The pelvic diaphragm consists of levator ani and coccygeus muscles, which is interrupted in the midline for passage of the urogenital and anal structures.
- Weakening or tearing of pelvic floor structures may lead to pelvic organ prolapse.

Perineum

- The perineum is divided into anterior urogenital and posterior anal triangles.
- The phallus in the female forms the clitoris (glans clitoris, corpora cavernosa clitoris, and vestibular bulbs). The urogenital folds form the labia minora. The labioscrotal swellings form the labia majora and mons pubis.
- The phallus in the male forms the penis (i.e., glans penis, corpora cavernosa of the penis, and corpus spongiosum of the penis). The urogenital folds in the male fuse in the midline and form the ventral aspect of the penis and penile raphe. The labioscrotal swellings in the male fuse in the midline and form the scrotum and scrotal raphe.
- Female and male external genitalia occupy the urogenital triangle and are described as being in the superficial perineal space or pouch.
- The perineal membrane spans the area of the urogenital triangle and serves as a boundary between the superficial and deep perineal pouches.
- Branches of the internal pudendal artery and vein serve the perineum.
- Branches of the pudendal nerve provide somatic innervation to the perineum.
- Automonic innervation to the perineum primarily involves sexual function, where parasympathetic fibers control erection and sympathetic fibers control emission (male). Coordination of somatic structures is necessary for these functions as well.
- The lower anal canal develops from the proctoderm, which is an invagination of surface ectoderm caused by a proliferation of mesoderm surrounding the anal membrane.
- Innervation superior to pectinate line in anal canal is autonomic (rectal plexus), and inferior to pectinate line is somatic (inferior rectal nerves).
- Upper anal canal lymph drains into internal iliac nodes and lower anal canal into superficial inguinal nodes.
- Ischioanal fossa is a fat-laden space inferolateral to the pelvic diaphragm that transmits pudendal nerves and internal pudendal vessel branches.

Pelvic Vasculature and Innervation

- Branches of the internal iliac artery provide arterial blood to most pelvis and perineum structures.
- Autonomic innervation of pelvic viscera occurs through the inferior hypogastric plexus, which receives sympathetic fibers from hypogastric nerves and parasympathetic fibers from pelvic splanchnic nerves (S2–S4).
- Lymph from the pelvic drains into inguinal, iliac, or para-aortic (lumbar) nodes.

Pelvic Spaces

- Parietal peritoneum extends into the true pelvis and drapes over pelvic viscera, which creates clinically relevant spaces/pouches.
- Rectouterine pouch is found between the rectum and uterus in females and is easily accessed through the posterior fornix of the vagina. This procedure is performed to remove or sample fluid/pus/blood from this space.

Urinary System

- The urinary system consists of kidney, ureter, bladder, and urethra. This system is proximally located in the abdomen (kidney, proximal ureter) and distally located in the pelvis (distal ureter, urinary bladder, urethra).
- The nephrogenic cord develops into three sets of nephric structures: pronephros, mesonephros, and metanephros.

Chapter Summary (*continued*)

- The pronephros is the cranialmost nephric structure and is a transitory structure that regresses completely by week 5.

- The mesonephros is the middle nephric structure and is a partially transitory structure. Most of the mesonephric tubules regress, but the mesonephric duct persists and opens into the urogenital sinus.

- At the start of week 5, the metanephros develops from an outgrowth of the mesonephric duct (ureteric bud) and from a condensation of mesoderm within the nephrogenic cord (metanephric mesoderm).

- The kidneys undergo a relative ascent during embryologic development. The fetal metanephros is located at vertebral level S1–S2, whereas the definitive adult kidney is located at vertebral level T12–L3.

- Internally, the kidney is organized into a cortex and medulla. Renal pyramids drain into papillae, which drain into minor and major calyces. Major calyces drain into the renal pelvis and ureter.

- The urinary bladder is formed from the upper portion of the urogenital sinus. The lower ends of the mesonephric ducts become incorporated into the posterior wall of the bladder to form the trigone of the bladder.

- The cortical labyrinth consists of renal corpuscles (renal glomeruli plus the glomerular [Bowman] capsule), proximal and distal convoluted tubules, interlobular arteries, afferent and efferent arterioles, and a peritubular capillary bed.

- The renal medulla consists of proximal straight tubules, descending and ascending thin limbs of the loop of Henle, distal straight tubules (DSTs), medullary collecting ducts, vasa recta, and a peritubular capillary bed.

- The nephron consists of a renal corpuscle, proximal convoluted tubule, proximal straight tubule (part of the loop of Henle), descending and ascending thin limbs (parts of the loop of Henle), DST (part of the loop of Henle), and the distal convoluted tubule.

- The glomerular capsule is double layered and consists of an outer parietal layer (simple squamous epithelium) and an inner visceral layer (podocytes).

- The collecting duct is composed of three cell types: types A and B intercalated cells and principal cells.

- The components of the juxtaglomerular (JG) complex include the macula densa (MD) cell and the JG cell.

- The MD cell is a modified epithelial cell that lines the DST. It monitors changes in Na^+ levels in the DST fluid and stimulates the release of renin from JG cells.

- The JG cell is a modified smooth muscle cell that is located in the tunica media of the afferent arteriole and early portion of the efferent arteriole. It has distinct granules that contain renin (a proteolytic enzyme) and secretes renin, monitors changes in blood pressure, and is innervated by postganglionic sympathetic nerves.

- The ureter is organized into a mucosa, smooth muscle layer, and an adventitia. The mucosa consists of a transitional epithelium and a lamina propria.

- The urinary bladder is organized into a mucosa, smooth muscle layer, and an adventitia. The mucosa consists of a transitional epithelium and a lamina propria. The smooth muscle layer consists of a complex meshwork of single-unit smooth muscle cells (called the detrusor muscle).

- The female ureter is relatively short and empties into the vestibule of the vagina. The male ureter varies in length and is divided into three parts—prostatic, intermediate, and spongy.

- The endodermally lined spongy urethra meets the ectodermally lined navicular fossa to complete the length of the urethra in males.

Suprarenal Gland

- Right and left suprarenal glands are located superior to respective kidneys and encased in perirenal fat in the posterior abdominal wall.

- The suprarenal cortex forms as a result of two episodes of mesoderm proliferation that occur near the root of the dorsal mesentery.

- The first episode forms the inner fetal cortex, while the second episode forms the outer adult cortex.

- The suprarenal medulla forms from neural crest cells that eventually differentiate into chromaffin cells.

- Preganglionic sympathetic fibers synapse in the suprarenal medulla on chromaffin cells.

- The suprarenal cortex is divided into three zones: zona glomerulosa, zona fasciculata, and zona reticularis.

- The cells of the zona glomerulosa synthesize and secrete aldosterone (a steroid hormone).

Chapter Summary (*continued*)

- The cells of the zona fasciculata synthesize and secrete cortisol (a steroid hormone).
- The cells of the zona reticularis synthesize and secrete dehydroepiandrosterone and androstenedione.
- The suprarenal medulla contains chromaffin cells, which are modified postganglionic sympathetic neurons. The chromaffin cells synthesize and secrete the catecholamines epinephrine and norepinephrine.

Reproductive System

- A portion of the urogenital ridge forms the gonadal ridge that gives rise to the gonads of the reproductive system.

Female Reproductive System

- The female reproductive system contains the ovaries, uterine tubes, uterus, cervix, and vagina. These structures are collectively located posterior to the urinary bladder and anterior to the rectum.
- The ampulla of the uterine tube is the most common site for fertilization.
- The components of the indifferent embryo that are remodeled to form the adult female reproductive system include the gonads, genital ducts, and primordia of external genitalia.
- In the absence of Sry protein, Müllerian inhibitory factor (MIF), and testosterone, the XX gonad forms the ovary, and the indifferent embryo will be directed toward female characteristics.
- The mesonephric (Wolffian) ducts/tubules in the female degenerate.
- The cranial portion of the paramesonephric (Müllerian) ducts in the female form the uterine tubes.
- The caudal portion of the paramesonephric (Müllerian) ducts in the female fuse in the midline to form the uterovaginal primordium. The uterovaginal primordium later develops into the uterus, cervix, and superior third of the vagina.
- The caudal portion of the paramesonephric (Müllerian) ducts in the female projects into the dorsal wall of the cloaca and induces the formation of the sinovaginal bulbs. The sinovaginal bulbs fuse to form the solid vaginal plate, which later canalizes and develops into the inferior third of the vagina.
- Female reproductive viscera is supported by the cardinal, uterosacral, suspensory, round, and broad ligaments. The broad ligament is formed by parietal peritoneum and has three parts: mesosalpinx, mesovarium, and mesometrium.
- The uterine artery is a branch of the internal iliac artery and supplies the uterus, uterine tubes, and upper vagina. It comes in close proximity to the ureter at the base of the broad ligament, where it travels anterior and superior to the ureter. Understanding this relationship is important for surgical procedures to avoid unplanned damage to the ureter during uterine artery ligation and viscera removal.
- Visceral pain from the uterine fundus refers by way of sympathetic motor outflow.
- The ovarian cortex contains primordial, primary, secondary preantral, secondary antral, selectable, selected preovulatory, and Graafian follicles.
- Primordial follicles make up a pool of resting follicles that constitute the ovarian reserve. The primordial follicle is characterized by its size (~0.35 mm in diameter) and a single layer of squamous granulosa cells.
- The Graafian follicle is the sixth and final stage in ovarian follicle growth. It is characterized by its size (~25 mm in diameter), multiple layers of ~59,000,000 cuboidal granulosa cells, the presence of an antrum, follicle-stimulating hormone (FSH) and luteinizing hormone (LH) sensitivity, and the presence of a secondary oocyte arrested in metaphase of meiosis II.
- The corpus luteum is a temporary endocrine gland whose formation is LH dependent. The corpus luteum consists of granulosa lutein and theca lutein cells.
- The mucosa of the uterine tube consists of a simple columnar epithelium and a lamina propria. The simple columnar epithelium consists of ciliated cells and secretory (Peg) cells.
- The endometrium of the uterus consists of a simple columnar epithelium and an endometrial stroma (lamina propria). The simple columnar epithelium invaginates into the underlying endometrial stroma (lamina propria) to form endometrial glands, which consist of mainly secretory cells.
- The menstrual cycle is a series of five phases that repeats ideally every 28 days: menstrual, proliferative (follicular), ovulatory, secretory (luteal), and premenstrual phases.

Chapter Summary (*continued*)

- The mucosa of the cervix consists of a simple columnar epithelium or a nonkeratinized stratified squamous epithelium and a lamina propria. The simple columnar epithelium invaginates into the lamina propria to form cervical glands, which secrete mucus. The nonkeratinized stratified squamous epithelium covers the vaginal portion of the cervix and is continuous with the vaginal epithelium.

- The mucosa of the vagina consists of an epithelium and a lamina propria. The epithelium consists of nonkeratinized stratified squamous epithelium that lines the lumen of the vagina.

Male Reproductive System

- The male reproductive system consists of the penis, testis, ductus deferens, seminal gland, prostate, and accessory glands.

- The components of the indifferent embryo that are remodeled to form the adult male reproductive system include the gonads, genital ducts, and primordia of external genitalia.

- The somatic support cells express the *SRY* gene located on chromosome Yp11.3, which encodes for the sex-determining region Y protein (Sry protein).

- In the presence of Sry, MIF, and testosterone, the XY gonad forms the testes, and the indifferent embryo will be directed toward male characteristics.

- The mesonephric (Wolffian) ducts in the male form the epididymis, ductus deferens, seminal vesicle, and the ejaculatory. The paramesonephric (Müllerian) ducts in the male degenerate due to MIF secreted by the Sertoli cells.

- The phallus in the male forms the penis (i.e., glans penis, corpora cavernosa of the penis, and corpus spongiosum of the penis). The urogenital folds in the male fuse in the midline and form the ventral aspect of the penis and penile raphe. The labioscrotal swellings in the male fuse in the midline and form the scrotum and scrotal raphe.

- The testes develop in the abdomen and descend to the scrotum by way of the inguinal canal. The gubernaculum aids in this process and ultimately anchors the testis within the scrotum.

- The seminiferous tubules consist of a germinal epithelium, which is a complex stratified epithelium comprised of two basic cell types: Sertoli and spermatogenic cells.

- The Sertoli cells are joined to each other by a unique zonula occludens (tight junction) that establishes basal and luminal compartments.

- The Sertoli cell provides mechanical and nutritional support for developing spermatogenic cells, phagocytizes excess cytoplasm discarded by spermatids, forms the blood–testes barrier, secretes inhibin and MIF, synthesizes androgen-binding protein, and possesses FSH receptors.

- Spermatogenic cells are the "male germ cells" and consist of dark and pale type A spermatogonia, type B spermatogonium, primary and secondary spermatocytes, spermatid (early and late stages), and spermatozoon.

- The Leydig cell secretes testosterone and possesses LH receptors.

- The epididymis is where spermatozoa maturation (i.e., develops motility) and short-term storage occurs. The epididymis consists of an epithelium, loose connective tissue, and a smooth muscle layer. The epithelium consists of a pseudostratified columnar epithelium with tall, columnar principal and basal (stem) cells.

- The prostate is a glandular and fibromuscular structure that sits at the neck of the bladder and transmits the prostatic urethra in males.

- The prostate is organized into an epithelium, fibromuscular stroma, and a capsule. The epithelium consists of a pseudostratified columnar epithelium with secretory, neuroendocrine, and basal (stem) cells. The secretory cell secretes a clear, slightly alkaline (pH 7.29) prostatic fluid that contains citric acid, prostatic acid phosphatase, prostaglandins, fibrinolysin, and prostate-specific antigen.

Study Questions:

Choose the ONE correct answer.

5.1 A 32-year-old pregnant female patient is being seen for low back pain. She is 30 weeks' pregnant and complains of posterior and anterior pelvic pain, which has increased as her pregnancy has progressed. The source of pain is thought to be from relaxed ligaments in the pelvis, which is a common effect of the hormone relaxin. Which of the following affected ligaments helps to stabilize the joints that are primarily responsible for transmitting the weight of the body to the hip bones?

A. Lumbosacral
B. Superior pubic
C. Inferior (arcuate) pubic
D. Sacrococcygeal
E. Sacroiliac

Correct answer = E. The sacroiliac joints join the sacrum to the os coxae. They are responsible for stabilizing this joint and transferring the weight of the body laterally through the pelvis. These ligaments are prone to the effects of the hormone relaxin, which is released during pregnancy. In later stages of pregnancy, pelvic ligaments relax, and joints can become malaligned, causing pain and discomfort in the pelvis.

5.2 A 45-year-old male with an above-knee amputation presented with erectile dysfunction. It was discovered that his prosthesis was improperly fitted and placing constant pressure on his perineum at the ischial ramus. The genital structure that would most likely be damaged is the:

A. corpus spongiosum.
B. paraurethral gland.
C. vestibular bulb.
D. crus of the penis.
E. bulbourethral gland.

Correct answer = D. The crus of the penis attaches along the inferior border of the ischial ramus and extends medially and anteriorly to join the contralateral crus to form part of the body of the penis. In this case, the prosthesis was placing constant pressure on the crus and limiting sexual function.

5.3 A 73-year-old morbidly obese female patient is being seen for pelvic organ prolapse (POP). Her past medical history includes four natural childbirths of full-term babies, all weighing at least 8 lbs. She suffered perineal tearing in two of the deliveries, but did not receive surgical intervention. She is now experiencing prolapse of her uterus through her vagina. Which of the following structures separates the pelvic cavity from the perineum and is most likely damaged in this scenario?

A. Pelvic diaphragm
B. Pelvic brim
C. Perineal body
D. Perineal membrane
E. External urethral sphincter

Correct answer = A. While the perineal membrane and body support the perineum and pelvic viscera to an extent, the pelvic diaphragm is most often damaged or weakened in the case of severe POP.

5.4 A 36-year-old female presents with a pelvic abscess that needs to be drained. The abscess is covered in parietal peritoneum and located just posterior to the posterior uterine body. The abscess is most likely located in which of the following spaces/pouches?

A. Pararectal fossae
B. Retropubic space
C. Vesicouterine pouch
D. Rectouterine pouch
E. Rectovesical pouch

Correct answer = D. Parietal peritoneum drapes over surfaces of the pelvic viscera, which created spaces or pouches. The abscess described here is located posterior to the posterior uterine body, which means that it is within the rectouterine pouch. This pouch is located between the posterior uterus and anterior rectum.

5.5 In addition to surgically altering the uterine tube during a tubal ligation, which of the following is also affected?

A. Mesovarium
B. Round ligament of the uterus
C. Mesometrium
D. Mesosalpinx
E. Suspensory ligament of the ovary

> Correct answer: D. The mesosalpinx is the portion of the broad ligament that is attached to the uterine tube. Remember that "salpinx" means tube!

5.6 Which of the following visceral sexual functions would be affected with a lesion to the pelvic splanchnic nerves?

A. Closure of the urinary bladder neck prior to ejaculation
B. Delivery of sperm to the intermediate urethra
C. Sweating during the sexual response cycle
D. Engorgement of corpora cavernosa of the penis
E. Rhythmic downward contractions from the uterine fundus during orgasm

> Correct answer = D. Recall that pelvic splanchnic nerves arise from S2–S4 and are parasympathetic preganglionic fibers. Parasympathetic innervation during sexual function is primarily confined to the arousal/excitement and plateau phases. Therefore, engorgement of the corpora cavernosa of the penis would be under parasympathetic control.

5.7 During a total hysterectomy, the uterine artery must be ligated. Which of the following structures needs to be identified during this procedure due to its close proximity to the uterine artery?

A. Ureter
B. Round ligament of the uterus
C. Ovarian ligament
D. Uterine tube
E. Inferior vagina

> Correct answer = A. The ureter travels inferior to the uterine artery at the base of the broad ligament to reach the posterior bladder. This relationship must be identified prior to ligation of the uterine artery and removal of the uterus, as it creates a high-risk scenario for ureter damage.

5.8 A 57-year-old female patient is seen for peripheral vascular disease. Imaging reveals a mass compressing the right internal iliac artery. Which of the following structures would still receive adequate blood flow in this scenario?

A. Right ovary
B. Right vestibular bulb
C. Right crus of the clitoris
D. Right bladder wall
E. Right vaginal wall

> Correct answer = A. The right ovary would still be receiving adequate blood flow from the right ovarian artery, which is a direct branch of the abdominal aorta proximal to the site of compression.

Lower Limb

6

I. OVERVIEW

The lower limbs are designed for upright bipedal locomotion, maintenance of balance, and weight bearing through multiple articulations along the kinetic chain. These functions depend on lower limb strength in place of the increased range of motion in the upper limb.

Proximally, the pelvic girdle—composed of right and left hip bones and the sacrum—connects the lower limbs and trunk and transfers body weight distally. The lower limb can be divided into the following regions, from proximal to distal: gluteal, thigh, leg, ankle, and foot.

II. OSTEOLOGY

Bones of the lower limb (proximal to distal) include the **hip (os coxae)**, **femur**, **patella**, **tibia**, **fibula**, **tarsal bones**, **metatarsals**, and **phalanges**.

A. Hip

As shown in Figure 6.1, in the adult, each hip bone is formed by the fusion of three bones: **ilium**, **ischium**, and **pubis**. The **acetabulum**, which serves as the socket portion of the hip joint, is formed where all three bones intersect laterally. Right and left hip bones are joined posteriorly by the sacrum through the sacroiliac joint and anteriorly at the pubis symphysis—forming the ring-like pelvic girdle.

B. Femur

The femur (thigh bone) is the longest and heaviest bone in the body (Fig. 6.2). Proximally, the femur is characterized by a round **femoral head** (ball portion of the hip joint) and inferolaterally angled **neck**. The neck connects the head to the **shaft** of the femur adjacent to the **greater** and **lesser trochanters**—two bony prominences that serve as muscle and ligament attachment sites. The trochanters are connected

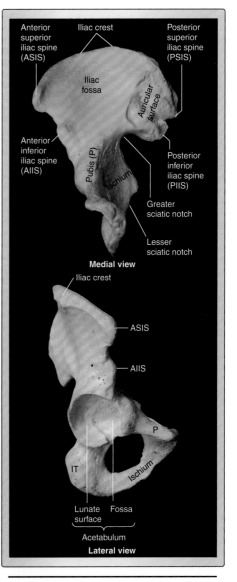

Figure 6.1
Osteology of the hip bone.

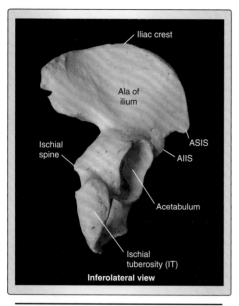

Figure 6.1
(*continued*)

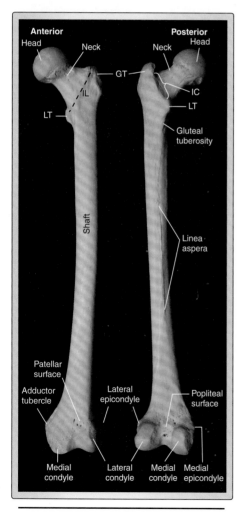

Figure 6.2
Osteology of the femur. GT = greater trochanter, IC = intertrochanteric crest, LT = lesser trochanter.

posteriorly by the **intertrochanteric crest** and anteriorly by the **intertrochanteric line**. The femoral shaft is primarily smooth, except for the raised ridge of bone posteriorly, the **linea aspera**. Distally, the femur has rounded **medial** and **lateral condyles** that articulate with the proximal tibia to form the knee joint. The condyles are separated by an intercondylar fossa posteriorly and inferiorly. **Medial** and **lateral epicondyles** extend superiorly from the condyles and serve as collateral ligament attachment sites. An **adductor tubercle** is located just superior to the **medial epicondyle** of the femur and serves as a tendon attachment site.

C. Patella

The **patella** (knee cap) is a triangular-shaped sesamoid bone that covers the anterior intercondylar surface of the femur and contributes to the kinetics of the knee joint.

D. Tibia

The tibia (shin bone) is the weight-bearing bone of the leg (Fig. 6.3). Proximally, it is characterized by flat, concave **lateral** and **medial tibial condyles** that articulate with the distal femur. Between the tibial condyles are the **intercondylar eminence** and **tubercles**, which serve as ligament attachment sites. Anteriorly, the **tibial tuberosity** is a palpable mass onto which the patellar ligament attaches. Posterolaterally, there is a concave facet where the fibular head articulates. The **shaft** of the tibia is marked by a lateral **interosseous border** and sharp anterior ridge that extends distally, where the bone tapers to articulate with the talus and distal fibula. The **medial malleolus** is the distalmost part of the tibia and frames the ankle joint medially.

E. Fibula

The fibula is a thin, non–weight-bearing bone in the leg that articulates laterally with the tibia. Proximally, it is characterized by an arrowhead-shaped head and narrow neck, which are easily palpated superficially (Fig. 6.4). The interosseous border lines the medial shaft. Distally, the fibula expands into the **lateral malleolus**, which frames the ankle joint laterally.

F. Tarsal bones

The tarsal bones include the **talus, calcaneus, cuboid, navicular,** and three **cuneiforms** (1–3), as shown in Figure 6.5. Of the seven tarsal bones, only the talus articulates with the tibia and fibula to form the ankle joint. Subtalar tarsal bones contribute to the shape and function of the foot. The **talus** is characterized by a dome-shaped **trochlea**, which is framed by the medial and lateral malleoli. The **calcaneus** (heel bone) articulates with the body of the talus inferiorly and with the cuboid anteriorly. It is the largest and strongest talar bone in the

Clinical Application 6.1: Femoral Fractures

Fractures of the femur are most common in the neck, but can also occur along the intertrochanteric line and ridge as well as midshaft. Owing to the proximity of the circumflex femoral arteries and the neck, care must be taken to identify any type of intracapsular bleed. Vascular injury in this region may lead to avascular necrosis of the femoral head.

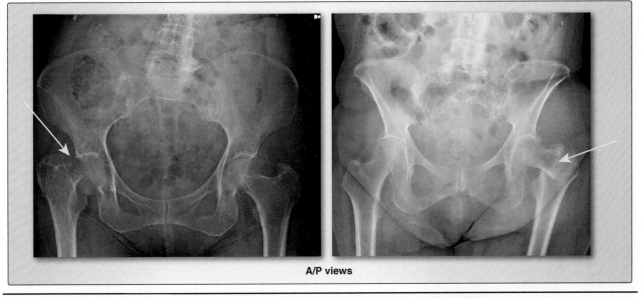

A/P views

Plain film radiographs of femoral fracture. Arrows indicate area of fracture. A/P, anterior/posterior.

Clinical Application 6.2: Tibial and Fibular Fractures

Tibial fractures occur most often between midshaft and distal tibia, commonly referred to as a "ski-boot" injury. Tibial fractures are the most common type of open fracture due to the superficial nature of the anterior tibial border. Fibular fractures are more often associated with severe inversion ankle sprains, in which the force is so great that the lateral ankle ligaments may cause an avulsion of the lateral malleolus or, if torn completely, the talus can translate laterally into the lateral malleolus, causing a fracture.

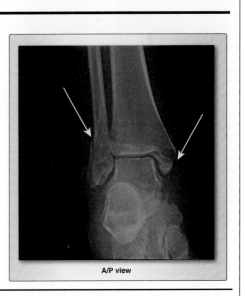

A/P view

Plain film radiographs of tibial and fibular fractures. Arrows indicate area of fracture. A/P = anterior/posterior.

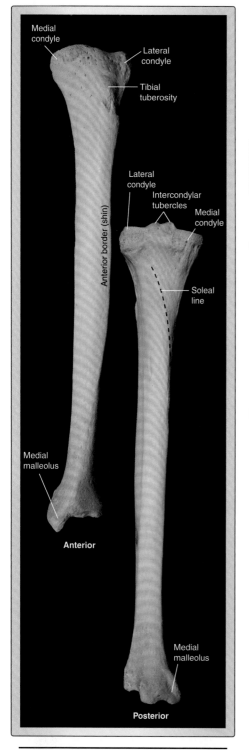

Figure 6.3
Osteology of the tibia

foot. The calcaneus has a shelf-like projection laterally, called the **sustentaculum tali**, which supports the talus, and a posteroinferior **calcaneal tuberosity**, which bears body weight in the hind foot. Medially, the boat-shaped **navicular** bone lies between the talus and three **cuneiforms**, while the **cuboid** lies laterally to complete the distal tarsal row.

> Common fractures of the foot bones include calcaneal (fall onto heel), talar (forced excessive dorsiflexion), and metatarsal fractures (long distance runners, ballet dancers).

G. Metatarsals and phalanges

Five **metatarsal** bones (1–5; medial to lateral) contribute to the forefoot and articulate with the distal row of tarsal bones (cuneiforms and cuboid). Each metatarsal has a proximal base, middle shaft, and distal head. The head of each metatarsal articulates with the base of the proximal **phalange**. The first digit (hallux; big toe) has two phalanges—proximal and distal—while the remaining four lateral digits have three—proximal, middle, and distal.

H. Surface anatomy

Several surface landmarks of the lower limb are important during physical examination (Fig. 6.6). Assessing symmetry of the kinetic chain, from the pelvis down to the feet, is essential when formulating a diagnosis. Symmetry and level of these landmarks can be assessed in sitting, standing, or supine positions to determine where along the kinetic chain an underlying deviation may be causing impairment.

1. **Bony landmarks:** In the pelvis, these include the **anterior** and **posterior superior iliac spines** (S2 level), **iliac crests** (L4 level), **pubic symphysis**, and **ischial tuberosities**. Femoral bony landmarks include the **greater trochanters** and **condyles**. Landmarks in the leg include the tibial tuberosity, fibular head, medial malleolus, and lateral malleolus. At the ankle, the talus can be palpated between the medial and lateral malleoli.

2. **Soft tissue landmarks:** These include the **gluteal**, **inguinal**, and **popliteal** creases.

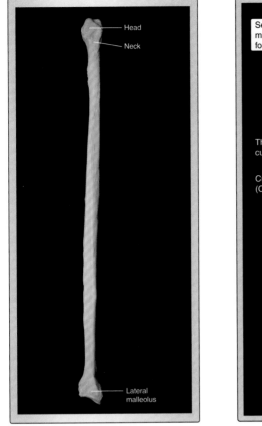

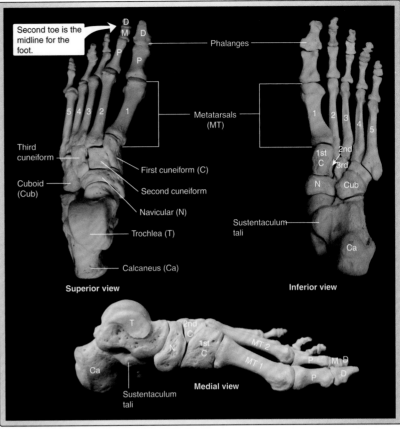

Figure 6.4
Osteology of the fibula.

Figure 6.5
Osteology of the foot. D = distal, M = middle, P = proximal.

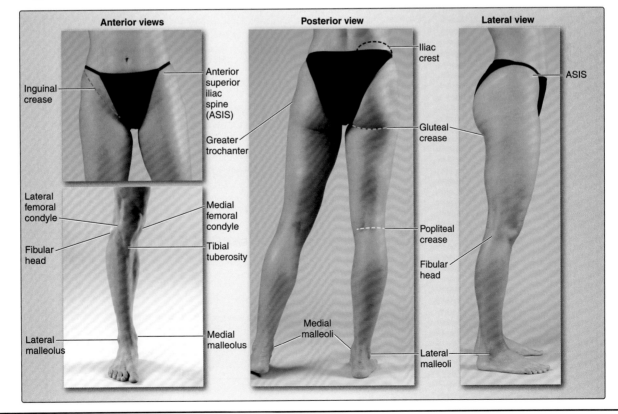

Figure 6.6
Surface anatomy of the lower limb.

III. FASCIA, VASCULATURE, LYMPHATICS, AND INNERVATION

Many structures in the lower limb can be described as either superficial or deep, including fascial layers, venous vessels, and lymphatic vessels and nodes. The following section describes the organization of these structures in addition to the arterial and nervous supply of the lower limb.

A. Superficial fascia

Deep to the skin of the lower limb lies a **superficial fascia** that contains varying amounts of loose connective and adipose tissues. Superficial veins, lymphatic vessels, and cutaneous nerves travel in this fascia, which is continuous with the superficial fascia of the abdomen.

B. Deep fascia

Deep to the superficial fascia is a thick, strong fascia that aids in venous blood return to the heart from the lower limbs by improving the efficiency of muscle contraction. The **deep fascia of the thigh** (**fascia lata**) and leg (**crural fascia**) are continuous with each other and collectively invest the lower limb muscle compartments (Fig. 6.7).

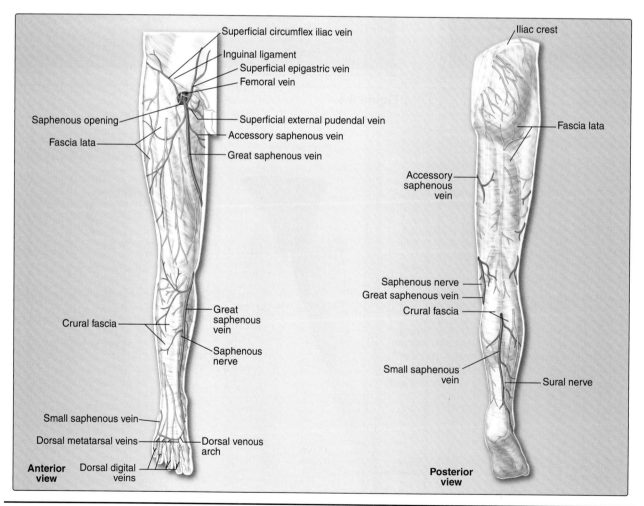

Figure 6.7
Deep fascia and superficial veins of the lower limb.

1. **Saphenous opening:** Proximally, the fascia lata is continuous with the deep fascia of the gluteal region, inguinal ligament, and membranous fascia of the abdomen (Scarpa fascia). There is an opening in the fascia lata over the femoral triangle region called the **saphenous opening**, which allows for the **great saphenous vein** to drain into the femoral vein.

2. **Iliotibial tract:** Laterally, the fascia lata thickens into a band of connective tissue called the **iliotibial tract** (or band), which runs from the ilium to the tibia. The gluteus maximus and tensor fasciae latae muscles use the iliotibial tract as a shared distal tendon.

3. **Fascial intermuscular septa:** These project internally to attach to bone and create the rigid compartments of the thigh (anterior, medial, posterior) and leg (anterior, lateral, posterior).

Clinical Application 6.3: Compartment Syndrome

Intermuscular septa from the deep fascia of the lower limb create tightly bound compartments. Increased pressure within a compartment can compromise the viability of the contained structures, causing an emergency medical situation. Swelling, pain, tightness, and absent distal leg pulses are all signs of compartment syndrome and should be addressed immediately to avoid permanent muscular, vascular, and nervous tissue damage. A fasciotomy—excising the fascia involved—is often performed to relieve pressure within the affected compartment.

C. Venous drainage

Venous drainage of the lower limb occurs through a superficial and deep venous network (Fig. 6.8). Superficial and perforating veins have valves to ensure—under normal conditions—unidirectional blood return.

1. **Superficial veins:** The **great saphenous vein** and **small saphenous vein** travel superiorly from the dorsum of the foot to drain into more proximal, deep veins—femoral and popliteal, respectively. Multiple, small tributary veins drain into these two main superficial veins. The great saphenous vein travels anterior to the medial malleolus, posterior to the medial femoral condyle, and then courses up the medial thigh before emptying into the femoral vein by way of the saphenous opening in the fascia lata. The small saphenous vein travels posterior to the lateral malleolus and courses up the posterior leg before piercing the crural fascia to empty into the popliteal vein in the popliteal fossa.

2. **Multiple perforating veins:** These pierce the deep fascia of the lower limb along the course of the superficial veins to connect superficial to deep veins.

3. **Deep veins:** In the lower limb, these travel with all major lower limb arteries and branches and typically carry the same name (see III.E). In the leg, a pair of veins often accompanies a single artery.

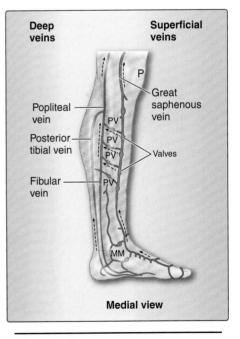

Figure 6.8
Venous drainage of the lower limb. Only deep and superficial veins of the leg are shown; deep veins of the thigh (not shown) correspond in course and name to lower limb arteries. Arrows indicate direction of blood flow. MM = medial malleolus, P = patella, PV = perforating vein.

Clinical Application 6.4: Venous System Considerations

Deep vein thrombosis (DVT): Formation of a thrombus (blood clot) within one or more deep veins of the leg presents with swelling, redness in the area, warmth, and pain with passive dorsiflexion and pressure on the calf (Homan sign). Common causes of DVTs include venous stasis and incompetence. Inflammation associated with DVTs is called *thrombophlebitis*. DVTs should be considered medical emergencies as an embolus can travel from the lower limb to the main pulmonary artery (pulmonary embolism) and may be fatal.

Varicose veins: When venous valves become incompetent, backflow of blood can occur from deep veins into the superficial venous system. Increased venous blood volume paired with increased pressure can cause superficial veins to become distended, tortuous, and often painful. Compression stockings and limiting prolonged standing can alleviate discomfort and swelling.

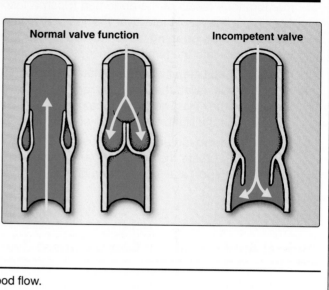

Varicose veins. Yellow arrows indicate direction of venous blood flow.

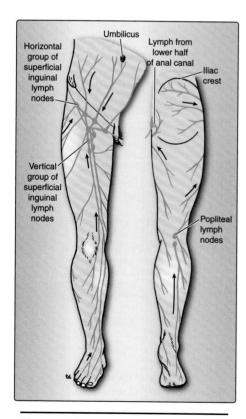

Figure 6.9
Lymphatics of the lower limb. Arrows indicate direction of lymph flow.

D. Lymphatics

Lymphatics of the lower limb are closely associated with the venous system (Fig. 6.9).

1. **Superficial:** Superficial lymphatic vessels travel with the saphenous vessels and drain into associated lymph nodes. Lymphatics that travel with the great saphenous vein drain into **superficial inguinal lymph nodes** (vertical group) first before draining into **external iliac nodes**. Those that travel with the small saphenous vein drain directly into the **popliteal nodes**.

2. **Deep:** Lymphatic vessels also travel with deep veins in the leg, which first drain into popliteal nodes, then into **deep inguinal nodes**, and **external** and **common iliac nodes**, and finally the **lumbar lymphatic trunks**.

E. Arterial supply

The lower limb receives arterial blood supply primarily from the **femoral artery** and its branches (Fig. 6.10). Additionally, the gluteal region is supplied by **superior** and **inferior gluteal arteries**, and the medial thigh by the **obturator artery**, which are all branches from the internal iliac artery system. The obturator artery also gives off a small acetabular branch to the head of the femur.

1. **Femoral artery:** After passing deep to the **inguinal ligament**, the **external iliac artery** is renamed as the **femoral artery**, which lies between the femoral nerve and vein in the **femoral triangle**. Within the femoral triangle, the femoral artery gives off three superficial branches (**superficial epigastric**, **superficial circumflex iliac**, and **superficial external pudendal**).

2. **Profunda femoris artery:** The main branch of the femoral artery is the **profunda femoris artery**, which travels between the pectineus

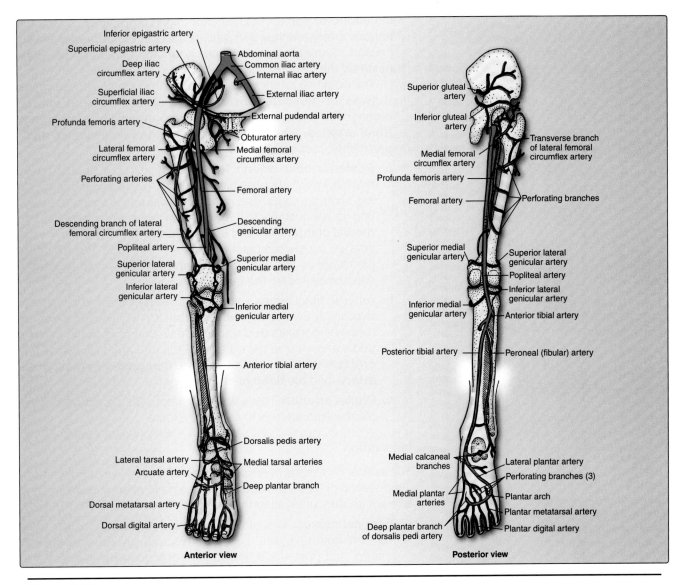

Figure 6.10
Arterial supply of the lower limb.

and adductor longus muscles to descend adjacent to the femur. Along its course, the profunda femoris artery gives off **lateral** and **medial femoral circumflex arteries** as well as three to four **perforating arteries**, which travel posteriorly to supply structures in the posterior thigh compartment.

   a. **Lateral femoral circumflex artery:** This artery has three main branches—ascending, transverse, and descending. The transverse branch anastomoses with the medial femoral circumflex artery, to supply the head and neck of the femur (intercapsular), while the descending branch supplies much of the lateral thigh and contributes to collateral blood supply to the knee.

   b. **Medial femoral circumflex artery:** This is the main artery to the hip joint.

3. **Popliteal artery:** After giving off superficial and deep branches, the femoral artery supplies adjacent structures as it travels inferiorly in

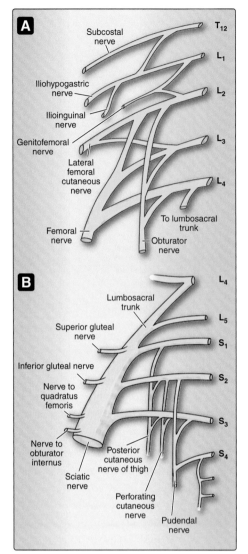

Figure 6.11
A, Lumbar plexus. B, Sacral plexus.

the **adductor canal** of the anterior thigh compartment. Once the femoral artery reaches and passes through the **adductor hiatus** (musculotendinous opening in the adductor magnus muscle), it is renamed the **popliteal artery**.

The popliteal artery is found deep in the popliteal fossa where it gives off **geniculate branches** to supply the knee joint. It crosses the knee joint and divides into **anterior** and **posterior tibial arteries**, which travel to anterior and posterior leg compartments, respectively.

a. Posterior tibial artery: This artery gives off a **fibular artery** branch, which supplies blood to both the posterior and lateral leg compartments. The posterior tibial artery courses distally and travels posterior to the medial malleolus where it divides into **medial plantar (MP)** and **lateral plantar (LP) arteries**. Plantar arteries supply the plantar surface of the foot. The LP artery continues as the **deep plantar arch artery**, which eventually anastomoses with the deep plantar artery.

b. Anterior tibial artery: This artery continues distally in the anterior leg compartment and crosses the ankle joint, at which point it is renamed **dorsalis pedis artery**. Main branches of the dorsalis pedis artery serve the dorsum of the foot and include the **lateral tarsal artery, arcuate artery, first posterior metatarsal artery**, and the **deep plantar artery**.

c. Digital arteries: These arise from both the arcuate and deep plantar arch arteries to supply the toes.

F. Innervation

The lumbar and sacral nerve plexuses—collectively referred to as the lumbosacral plexus—provide general somatic afferent (sensory) and efferent (motor) innervation to all lower limb structures (Fig. 6.11).

1. Terminal nerves: The lumbar and sacral plexuses contain anterior rami from L_1–L_4 and L_5, S_1–S_4, respectively. Rami divide into anterior and posterior divisions (pre- and postaxial, respectively) before forming terminal nerves. Although most terminal nerves are made up of anterior or posterior divisions, the sciatic nerve and posterior femoral cutaneous nerve have both anterior *and* posterior division components.

The five main terminal nerves (and their branches) of the lumbosacral plexus are:

- Femoral nerve, posterior divisions (L_2–L_4)
- Obturator nerve, anterior divisions (L_2–L_4)
- Superior gluteal nerve, posterior divisions (L_4–L_5, S_1)
- Inferior gluteal nerve, posterior divisions (L_5, S_1–S_2)
- Sciatic nerve, anterior and posterior divisions (L_4–L_5, S_1–S_3)
  - Common fibular nerve, posterior divisions (L_4–L_5, S_1–S_2)
    - Superficial fibular nerve
    - Deep fibular nerve
  - Tibial nerve, anterior divisions (L_4–L_5, S_1–S_3)
    - LP nerve
    - MP nerve

Cutaneous innervation (Fig. 6.12) of the lower limb is primarily relayed by branches of the main terminal nerves, as well as **lateral femoral cutaneous** (L_2–L_3), **genitofemoral** (L_1–L_2),

ilioinguinal (L_1), **posterior femoral cutaneous** (S_1–S_3), and **clunial** nerves (L_1–L_3; S_1–S_3).

2. **Nerves to lateral rotators:** The lumbosacral plexus also gives rise to smaller nerves that innervate the hip joint and muscles of the gluteal region. These include **nerve to quadratus femoris and inferior gemellus** (L_4–L_5, S_1), **nerve to piriformis** (S_1–S_2), and **nerve to obturator internus and superior gemellus** (L_5, S_1–S_2).

3. **Pelvic splanchnic nerves:** In addition, the sacral plexus gives rise to **pelvic splanchnic nerves** (S_2–S_4), which provide general visceral afferent (GVA) and general visceral efferent (GVE) parasympathetic innervation to structures in the pelvis and perineum (see Chapter 5 for more details). Postganglionic sympathetic fibers travel with terminal nerves to provide GVA and GVE innervation to lower limb vasculature and glands.

Clinical Application 6.5: Lumbosacral Nerve Lesions

Femoral nerve: Lesion of the femoral nerve as it enters the femoral triangle causes paralysis of the quadriceps femoris and loss of knee extension. Clinically, patients may compensate using momentum to achieve knee extension for heel strike and hyperextend ("lock") knee transitioning to midstance.

Superior gluteal: Lesion of the superior gluteal nerve is often due to trauma in the gluteal region and leads to paralysis of the gluteus medius and minimus and tensor fascia latae. A patient with gluteal medius and minimus paralysis presents with Trendelenburg gait, in which the pelvis drops on the contralateral side during ambulation.

Inferior gluteal: Lesion of the inferior gluteal nerve leads to paralysis of the gluteus maximus. Patients will have difficulty rising from a chair and ascending stairs. Patient will also lean the body trunk backward at heel strike.

Sciatic nerve: Lesion or compression of the sciatic nerve (as in piriformis syndrome) would cause almost complete loss of knee flexion and total loss of plantar flexion, dorsiflexion, eversion, inversion, and toe flexion and extension.

Common fibular nerve: This nerve has a very superficial course around the neck of the fibula. Crush injuries of the lateral leg can cause paralysis of anterior and lateral leg compartment muscles. A patient with this type of lesion would present with foot drop during ambulation and potentially compensate with high-steppage, circumduction, or waddling gait.

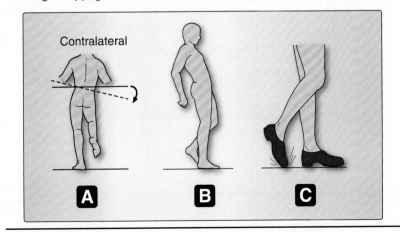

A, Positive Trendelenburg sign. B, Gluteus maximus paralysis. C, Foot drop due to common fibular nerve lesion.

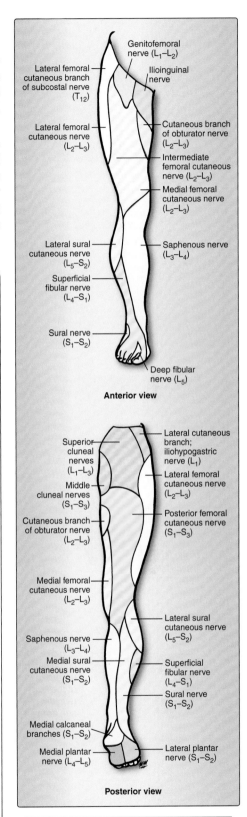

Figure 6.12
Cutaneous innervation maps for the lower limb.

IV. EMBRYOLOGY

At the end of week 4, the lower limb buds form pronounced protrusions from the lateral body wall at the L1–S2 levels (Fig. 6.13). In general, the lower limb bud consists of a core of mesoderm that is covered by ectoderm. Mesoderm from the lateral plate (**lateral plate mesoderm**) migrates into the lower limb bud and condenses in the center of the limb bud to eventually form the **skeletal component** (i.e., bone, ligaments, tendons, and dermis**)** of the lower limb. Mesoderm from the somites (**somitomeric mesoderm**) migrates into the lower limb bud and condenses into a posterior extensor condensation and an anterior flexor condensation to eventually form the **muscular component** of the lower limb.

> Limb development occurs over a 5-week period extending from week 4 to week 8. The upper limbs develop in advance of the lowers limbs. The upper limb bud appears first at day 24, whereas the lower limb bud appears second at day 28.

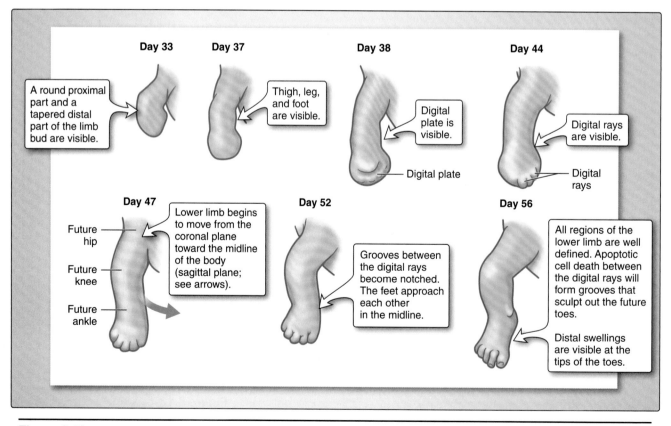

Figure 6.13

Embryologic development of the lower limb.

A. Special development zones

The lower limb bud displays two specialized areas called the **zone of polarizing activity (ZPA)** and the **apical ectodermal ridge (AER)** that play an important role in the development of the lower limb. The ZPA is a zone that consists of mesodermal cells located just beneath the AER along the caudal margin of the lower limb bud. The AER is a thickened ridge of ectoderm at the tip of the lower limb bud.

> Numerous genes are involved in limb development: *WNT3*, *WNT7a*, *SHH*, *LMBR1*, *GLI3*, *TBX3*, *TBX4*, *TBX5*, *PITX1*, *TP73L (P63)*, *DLX5*, *HOXD13*, *HOXA13*, *HOXD11*, *NIPBL*, *GDF5*, *ROR2*, *IHH*, *FGFR2*, and *EN1*. Mutations in any one of these genes will result in a congenital limb anomaly.

B. Development axes

The lower limb bud develops with respect to three axes. The **proximal–distal axis** runs from the hip to the toes. The **cranial–caudal axis** runs from the big toe to the little toe. The **posterior–anterior axis** runs from the dorsum of the foot to the sole of the foot.

C. Bone formation

The lateral plate mesoderm migrates into the lower limb bud and condenses in the center of the lower limb bud to eventually form the **skeletal component** of the lower limb. The lateral plate mesoderm forms the **ilium, ischium, pubis, femur, patella, tibia, fibula, tarsals, metatarsals,** and **phalanges**. All the bones of the lower limb undergo endochondral ossification.

D. Muscle formation

The lower limb bud site lies opposite somites L1–L5, S1, and S2. During week 5, mesoderm from these somites (myotomes) migrates into the limb bud and forms a **posterior extensor condensation** of mesoderm and an **anterior flexor condensation** of mesoderm. The mesoderm of these condensations differentiates into myoblasts. Then, the condensations split into anatomically recognizable muscles of the lower limb, although little is known about this process.

1. **Posterior extensor condensation of mesoderm:** In general, the posterior extensor condensation gives rise to the **extensor** and **abductor musculature** (Table 6.1).

2. **Anterior flexor condensation of mesoderm:** In general, the anterior flexor condensation gives rise to the **flexor** and **adductor musculature** (see Table 6.1).

E. Lumbosacral plexus formation

The axons within **anterior primary rami from L_2–L_5 and S_1–S_3** spinal nerves arrive at the base of the lower limb bud and mix in a specific pattern to form **posterior divisions** and **anterior divisions** of the lumbosacral plexus. At this point, axon migration pauses at the base of

Table 6.1: Posterior and Anterior Condensations of Mesoderm into Muscle

Posterior Extensor Condensation	Anterior Flexor Condensation
Gluteus maximus	Adductor longus
Gluteus medius	Adductor brevis
Gluteus minimus	Adductor magnus
Piriformis	Gracilis
Pectineus	Obturator externus
Iliacus	Obturator internus
Tensor fascia latae	Superior gemellus
Sartorius	Inferior gemellus
Rectus femoris	Quadratus femoris
Vastus lateralis	Semitendinosus
Vastus medialis	Semimembranosus
Vastus intermedius	Long head of biceps femoris
Short head of biceps femoris	Gastrocnemius
Tibialis anterior	Soleus
Extensor hallucis longus	Plantaris
Extensor digitorum longus	Popliteus
Peroneus tertius	Flexor hallucis longus
Peroneus longus	Flexor digitorum longus
Peroneus brevis	Tibialis posterior
Extensor digitorum brevis	Abductor hallucis
Extensor hallucis brevis	Flexor digitorum brevis
	Abductor digiti minimi
	Quadratus plantae
	Lumbricals
	Flexor hallucis brevis
	Adductor hallucis
	Flexor digiti minimi brevis
	Dorsal interosseus
	Plantar interosseus

the lower limb bud and then subsequently resumes so that axons are directed to either the posterior extensor condensation or the anterior flexor condensation. The direction that the axons take is controlled by the *homeobox gene Lim1* and its downstream target *ephrin type A receptor 4* (*EPHA4*), which allow axons to enter the posterior extensor condensation, but avoid the anterior flexor condensation.

1. **Posterior divisions:** These grow into the posterior extensor condensation of mesoderm.

   With further development of the limb musculature, the posterior divisions branch into the **superior gluteal nerve** (L_4, L_5, S_1), **inferior gluteal nerve** (L_5, S_1, S_2), **femoral nerve** (L_2–L_4), and **common fibular nerve** (L_4, L_5, S_1, S_2), thereby innervating all the muscles that form from the posterior extensor condensation.

2. **Anterior divisions:** These grow into the anterior flexor condensation of mesoderm. With further development of the limb musculature, the anterior divisions branch into the **tibial nerve** (L_4, L_5, S_1–S_3)

and **obturator nerve (L₂–L₄)**, thereby innervating all the muscles that form from the anterior flexor condensation.

F. Lower limb vasculature formation

The **umbilical artery** enters the lower limb bud as the **axis artery**, which ends in a **terminal plexus**. The terminal plexus participates in the formation of the **deep plantar arch**. The axis artery sprouts the **anterior tibial artery** (which continues as the **dorsalis pedis artery**) and the **posterior tibial artery** (which terminates as the **MP artery** and the **LP artery**).

1. **Axis artery:** While most of the axis artery regresses, the axis artery ultimately persists in the adult as the **inferior gluteal artery**, **sciatic artery** (accompanying the sciatic nerve), **proximal part of the popliteal artery**, and **distal part of the fibular artery**.

2. **External iliac artery:** The **external iliac artery** gives rise to the **femoral artery** of the lower limb, which constitutes a separate second arterial channel into the lower limb that connects to the axis artery. The femoral artery sprouts the **profunda femoris artery**.

G. Rotation and dermatome pattern

At week 4 (about 4 days after the upper limb buds appear), the lower limb buds appear as small bulges oriented in a **coronal plane** (Fig. 6.14). In week 6, the lower limb buds undergo a horizontal movement so that they are now oriented in a **sagittal plane**. During weeks 6–8, the lower limbs undergo a **90° medial rotation** such that the knee points anteriorly, the extensor compartment lies anterior, and the flexor compartment lies posterior. The 90° medial rotation of the lower limb bud alters the originally straight segmental pattern of innervation in the embryo; that is, the pattern of innervation becomes "twisted in a spiral" in the adult (Fig. 6.15).

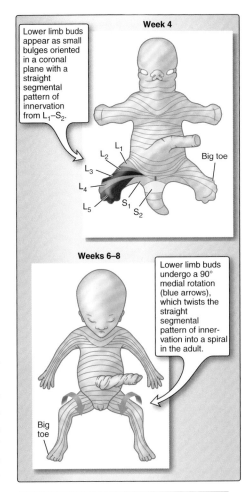

Figure 6.14
Rotation of the lower limb.

Clinical Application 6.6: Congenital Limb Anomalies

Congenital anomalies of the limbs fall into four general categories.

1. In reduction defects, a part of the limb is missing (meromelia) or the entire limb is missing (amelia).

2. In duplication defects, extra digits are present (polydactyly).

3. In dysplasia defects, fusion of digits occurs (syndactyly) or a disproportionate growth of the limb occurs.

4. In deformation defects, physical forces damage the developing limb (e.g., amniotic band syndrome).

‖ Numerous drugs (teratogens) cause limb anomalies: 5′-fluoro-2-deoxyuridine, acetazolamide, valproic acid, phenytoin, warfarin, thalidomide, alcohol, and cocaine.

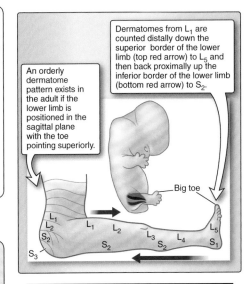

Figure 6.15
Dermatome pattern of the lower limb.

V. MUSCULATURE

The muscles of the lower limb are organized into specific compart-ments or regions: gluteal region; anterior, medial, and posterior thigh; and anterior, lateral, and posterior leg. The muscles in these com-partments commonly share similar neurovascular supply and overall function(s), with a few exceptions. Figure 6.16 shows the movements of the lower limb.

A. Gluteal region

The gluteal region is associated with the pelvis and hip joint posteriorly. Superficially, the gluteal region contains great amounts of subcutane-ous adipose tissue overlying a thick deep fascia that encompasses the underlying musculature. The deep fascia of the gluteal region is continuous with the fascia lata but separates the gluteal region from the posterior thigh. Musculature of the gluteal region is divided into two groups—superficial and deep.

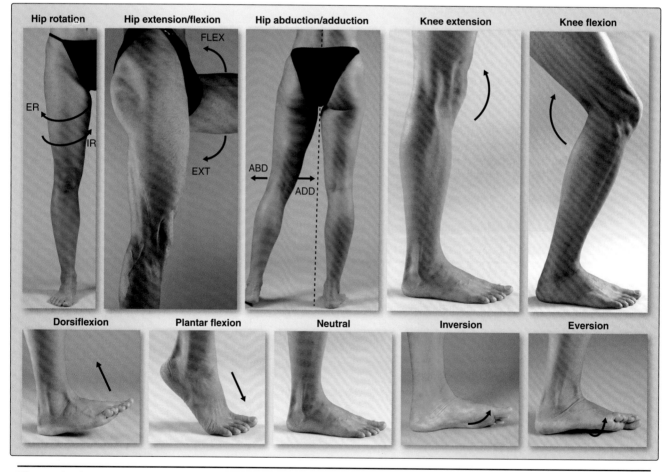

Figure 6.16

Movements of lower limb joints. ABD = abduction, ADD = adduction, ER = external rotation, EXT = extension, FLEX = flexion, IR = internal rotation.

1. **Superficial group:** The superficial group comprises three gluteal muscles—**gluteus maximus**, **medius**, and **minimus**—and **tensor fascia latae**.

   a. **Gluteus maximus:** This muscle is rhomboid-shaped and covers all other gluteal region muscles except for the superior fibers of gluteus medius along the posterior ilium (Fig. 6.17). Gluteus maximus is a powerful extensor of the femur and also assists in lateral rotation and adduction (inferior fibers) of the femur. It is innervated by the **inferior gluteal nerve** and supplied by both the **superior** and **inferior gluteal vessels**.

   b. **Gluteus medius and minimus:** These are fan-shaped muscles that abduct and medially rotate the femur (Fig. 6.18). Additionally, and very importantly, gluteus medius and minimus function together to maintain a level pelvis during the gait cycle. Both muscles are innervated and supplied by the **superior gluteal nerve** and vessels, respectively.

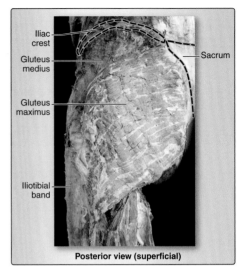

Figure 6.17
Superficial muscles of the gluteal region.

 Care must be taken when administering intragluteal injections. The superolateral quadrant of the gluteal region is the "safe zone" for intramuscular injections, as the sciatic nerve and large gluteal vessels are not at risk in this area.

   c. **Tensor fascia latae:** While included in this group, the **tensor fascia latae** is somewhat of a transitional muscle, as it is positioned between the gluteal region and the anterior thigh. It functions to abduct, flex, and medially rotate the femur and is innervated by the superior gluteal nerve. Along with gluteus maximus, tensor fascia latae attaches distally via the iliotibial band, and therefore, these muscles actively assist in stabilizing the knee joint as well.

2. **Deep musculature:** The deep group comprises a collection of small muscles that laterally rotate the femur and stabilize the hip joint (see Fig. 6.18). These muscles include **piriformis**, **superior gemellus**, **obturator internus**, **inferior gemellus**, and **quadratus femoris**. Each of these muscles is innervated by nerves of the same name that arise from the lumbosacral plexus (i.e., nerve to piriformis; nerve to superior gemellus and obturator internus; nerve to inferior gemellus and quadratus femoris). These five muscles collectively function to laterally rotate the femur and stabilize the head of the femur in the acetabulum.

   a. **Piriformis:** The pear-shaped **piriformis** is the most superior of the group and serves as a landmark structure in the gluteal region. Superior and inferior gluteal neurovascular bundles exit the pelvis superior and inferior to the piriformis, respectively. The **sciatic nerve** and **posterior femoral cutaneous nerve** also exit the pelvis inferior to the piriformis.

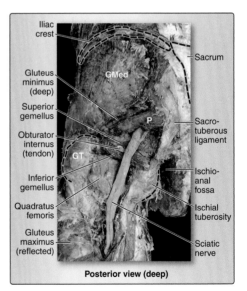

Figure 6.18
Deep muscles of the gluteal region. GMed = gluteus medius, GT = greater trochanter, P = piriformis.

Clinical Application 6.7: Piriformis Syndrome

Piriformis syndrome involves impingement of the sciatic nerve by the piriformis muscle. Under normal circumstances, the sciatic nerve exits the pelvis through the greater sciatic foramen inferior to the piriformis muscle. However, the sciatic nerve and its divisions may also travel superior to or through the piriformis muscle. Impingement of the sciatic nerve may result in downstream motor and sensory deficits as well as pain in the gluteal and posterior thigh regions.

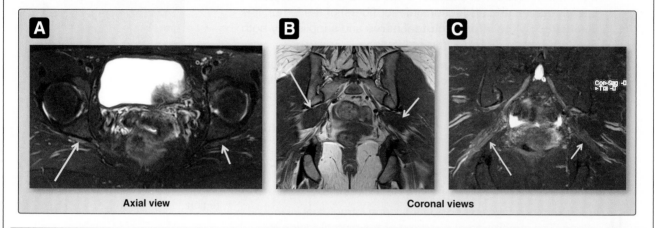

Axial view

Coronal views

Piriformis syndrome on magnetic resonance neurography in a 42-year-old woman with right buttock pain. Images show asymmetric increased signal of the right sciatic nerve (long arrows in A and C) and increased size (long arrow in C) relative to the normal left sciatic nerve (short arrows in A and C). Also note hypertrophy of the right piriformis (long arrow in B) relative to the normal left piriformis (short arrow in B).

    b. **Superior and inferior gemelli and obturator internus:** These muscles flank the tendon of the **obturator internus** as all three muscles insert on the greater trochanter.

    c. **Quadratus femoris:** This is the most inferior of the deep muscles, and it inserts on the intertrochanteric crest of the femur.

3. **Cutaneous innervation:** Cutaneous innervation of the gluteal region is mediated by cluneal nerves. From the iliac crest to the gluteal crease, dermatomes L_3–L_5 and S_1–S_5 are represented in the gluteal region (Fig. 6.19; also see Fig. 6.12).

B. Thigh

The thigh region spans between the hip and knee joints. The femur is the primary bone of the thigh, although muscles of this region also attach to the pelvis, tibia, and fibula and act at both the hip and knee joints. The fascia lata encases the thigh structures and gives rise to intermuscular septa, which divide this region into three main compartments—anterior, medial, and posterior. Each compartment has a main nerve and blood supply as well as muscles with common functions.

1. **Anterior thigh:** As shown in Figure 6.20, muscles of the anterior thigh include **quadriceps femoris**, **iliopsoas**, **sartorius**, and **pectineus**. In general, this group of muscles receives innervation from the femoral nerve (L_2–L_4) and functions to flex the hip and

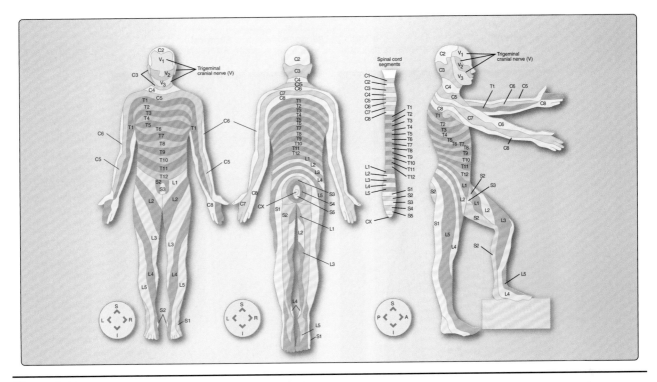

Figure 6.19
Dermatome maps. A = anterior, I = inferior, L = left, P = posterior, R = right, S = superior.

extend the knee. The femoral artery and its branches vascularize the anterior compartment.

a. **Quadriceps femoris:** This group of four muscles—**rectus femoris**, **vastus lateralis**, **vastus medialis**, and **vastus intermedius**—function together to extend the knee. All four muscles insert through a common **quadriceps tendon** on the tibial tuberosity.

b. **Iliopsoas:** The rectus femoris also crosses the hip joint and assists the **iliopsoas** with hip flexion. The iliopsoas is the primary flexor of the hip. In the anterior thigh, the iliopsoas represents the inferior portions of two muscles that originate in the posterior body wall and greater pelvis—**psoas major** and **iliacus**, respectively. As a result of its proximal attachments, the iliopsoas is also active during standing to assist in maintenance of posture and lumbar curvature.

c. **Sartorius (tailor's muscle):** This passes obliquely across the anterior thigh from lateral to medial, crossing both the hip and knee joints. It flexes, abducts, and externally rotates the hip and flexes the knee.

d. **Pectineus:** This is a transitional muscle, between the anterior and medial thigh compartments. It adducts, flexes, and medially rotates the hip.

e. **Femoral triangle:** The anterior thigh contains important neurovascular structures that travel from the pelvis to the lower limb. These structures are arranged within a proximal

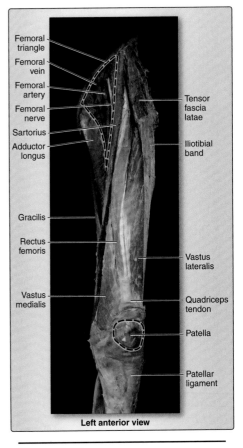

Left anterior view

Figure 6.20
Anterior thigh.

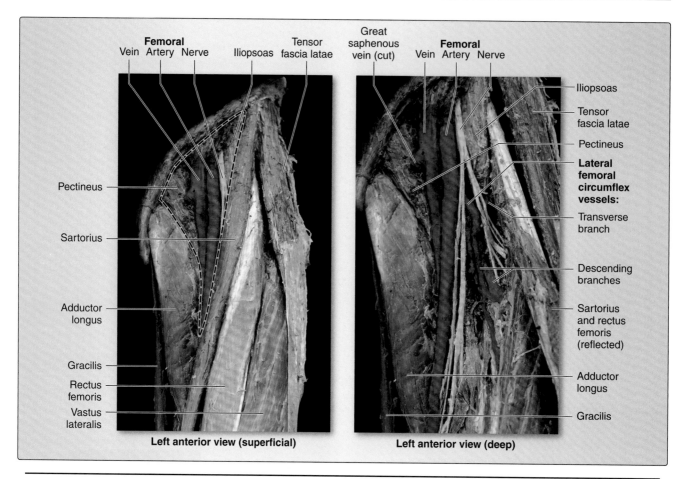

Figure 6.21
Femoral triangle.

space called the **femoral triangle** (Fig. 6.21). From lateral to medial, the triangle contains the femoral nerve, femoral artery, femoral vein, and lymphatics. The femoral artery, vein, and lymphatics are all contained in a funnel-shaped fascial covering called the **femoral sheath**, which is divided into lateral, intermediate, and medial compartments. The lateral compartment contains the femoral artery, intermediate the femoral vein, and medial compartment represents the **femoral canal**. The femoral canal contains varying amounts of loose connective tissue, fat, and lymphatics and communicates with the abdominal cavity. The boundaries of the femoral triangle are:

- Lateral: sartorius muscle
- Medial: adductor longus muscle
- Superior: inguinal ligament
- Floor: iliopsoas and pectineus muscles
- Roof: fascia lata

From lateral to medial, the contents of the femoral triangle spell out NAVEL, femoral **N**erve, femoral **A**rtery, femoral **V**ein, **E**mpty space (femoral canal), and **L**ymphatics

Clinical Application 6.8: Femoral Hernia

Femoral hernias are more common in females than males. This type of hernia involves protrusion of peritoneal contents (typically small bowel) through the femoral ring and into the medial compartment of the femoral sheath within the femoral triangle. Herniated small bowel can eventually exit the saphenous opening (hiatus) and present as a palpable mass in the proximal anterior thigh. Strangulation of herniated bowel and subsequent necrosis require immediate attention.

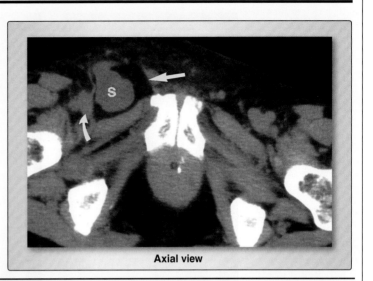

Axial view

Surgically proven femoral hernia in a patient with small bowel obstruction. The hernial sac (arrow) contains properitoneal fat and a loop of small bowel (S). The femoral vein (curved arrow) is displaced laterally.

    f. Adductor canal (Hunter canal): This begins at the apex of the femoral triangle, at which point the femoral artery and vein, saphenous nerve, and nerve to the vastus medialis travel deep to the sartorius muscle. The canal provides an intermuscular passageway for the femoral artery and vein as they travel toward the **adductor hiatus**, a musculotendinous opening in the adductor magnus muscle. The boundaries of the adductor canal are:

- Posteromedial: adductor longus and adductor magnus
- Anterior: sartorius
- Lateral: vastus medialis

    g. Cutaneous innervation: Cutaneous innervation of the anterior thigh is mediated by branches of the femoral (anterior branches) nerve, genitofemoral nerve, and lateral cutaneous nerve of the thigh. From the inguinal crease (hip crease) to the knee, dermatomes L_1–L_5 course lateral to medial across the anterior thigh (see Figs. 6.12 and 6.19).

2. Medial thigh: As shown in Figure 6.22, muscles of the medial thigh include **adductor longus**, **adductor brevis**, **adductor magnus**, **gracilis**, and **obturator externus**. Collectively, these muscles are innervated by the obturator nerve (L_2–L_4) and receive blood supply from the obturator artery—a branch of the internal iliac artery. In general, this group of muscles adducts the hip and plays a minor role in hip flexion.

    a. Adductors: The **adductor longus** is superficial to **adductor brevis**, and both arise from the pubis to insert along the medial femur. **Adductor magnus** is the largest muscle in the medial thigh and is made up of two parts—a horizontal adductor part, which is innervated by the obturator nerve, and a vertical hamstring part, which is innervated by the tibial division of the

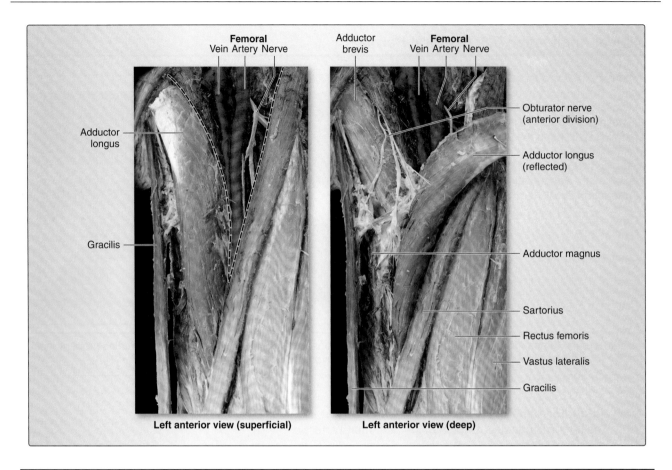

Femoral
Vein Artery Nerve

Adductor
brevis

Femoral
Vein Artery Nerve

Adductor
longus

Gracilis

Obturator nerve
(anterior division)

Adductor longus
(reflected)

Adductor magnus

Sartorius

Rectus femoris

Vastus lateralis

Gracilis

Left anterior view (superficial)   **Left anterior view (deep)**

Figure 6.22
Medial thigh.

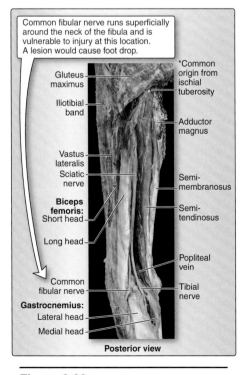

Common fibular nerve runs superficially
around the neck of the fibula and is
vulnerable to injury at this location.
A lesion would cause foot drop.

Gluteus
maximus

Iliotibial
band

Vastus
lateralis
Sciatic
nerve

**Biceps
femoris:**
Short head

Long head

Common
fibular nerve

Gastrocnemius:
Lateral head

Medial head

*Common
origin from
ischial
tuberosity

Adductor
magnus

Semi-
membranosus

Semi-
tendinosus

Popliteal
vein

Tibial
nerve

Posterior view

Figure 6.23
Posterior thigh.

sciatic nerve. The adductor portion of adductor magnus arises from the pubis and adducts the hip, whereas the hamstring portion arises from the ischial tuberosity and extends the hip (see V.B.3). The hamstring portion inserts medially on the adductor tubercle, which creates an opening in the tendon, previously described as the **adductor hiatus**.

b. Gracilis: This long, slender muscle crosses both the hip and knee joints and is most medial of the group. In addition to hip adduction, gracilis flexes the knee and medially rotates the hip.

c. Obturator externus: Located deep and superiorly in the medial compartment, obturator externus is not a hip adductor, but rather acts to externally rotate the hip, much like its counterpart obturator internus (see V.A).

d. Cutaneous innervation: Cutaneous innervation of the medial thigh is mediated by branches of the obturator, femoral (anterior branches), and ilioinguinal nerves. From the inguinal crease to the knee dermatomes, L_1–L_3 course lateral to medial to the medial thigh (see Figs. 6.12 and 6.19).

3. Posterior thigh: As shown in Figures 6.23 and 6.24, muscles of the posterior thigh include **semitendinosus**, **semimembranosus**, and

biceps femoris (short and long heads). Collectively, these muscles are innervated by divisions of the sciatic nerve (tibial or common fibular) and receive blood supply from the perforating branches of the profunda femoris artery. In general, this group of muscles extends the hip and flexes the knee.

a. **Semitendinosus, semimembranosus, and biceps femoris:** Semitendinosus, semimembranosus, and biceps femoris (long head) muscles originate from the ischial tuberosity, cross the hip and knee joints, and insert on either the tibia or the fibula. They extend the hip and flex the knee and are innervated by the tibial division (L_4–L_5, S_1–S_3) of the sciatic nerve. Biceps femoris (short head) is the exception, as it arises directly from the shaft of the femur and only crosses the knee joint to assist in knee flexion. It is innervated by the common fibular (L_4–L_5, S_1–S_2) division of the sciatic nerve. Semitendinosus and semimembranosus are located medially in the posterior thigh, whereas biceps femoris is located laterally. The hamstring portion of adductor magnus lies anterior to semitendinosus and semimembranosus and also assists in hip extension, but not knee flexion, as it does not cross the knee joint.

b. **Cutaneous innervation:** Cutaneous innervation of the posterior thigh is mediated by branches of the cluneal nerves and posterior and lateral cutaneous nerves of the thigh. From the gluteal crease to the knee, dermatomes L_1–L_2, L_5, and S_1–S_2 course inferiorly along the posterior thigh (see Figs. 6.12 and 6.19).

C. Leg

The leg represents the portion of the lower limb between the knee and ankle. The tibia and fibula make up the main bones of the leg and are positioned medial and lateral, respectively. The crural fascia encases the leg structures and gives rise to intermuscular septa, which divide this region into three main compartments—anterior, lateral, and posterior. Each compartment has a main nerve and blood supply, as well as muscles with common functions.

1. **Popliteal fossa:** The popliteal fossa is a diamond-shaped space located on the distal posterior thigh and proximal posterior leg that frames the posterior knee joint and surrounding structures (Fig. 6.25). The popliteal fossa is bound superiorly by the hamstring muscles and inferiorly by the medial and lateral heads of gastrocnemius. The floor is made up of the posterior surface of the femur, posterior knee capsule, and popliteus muscle fascia. The roof is made up of skin and underlying deep fascia (popliteal fascia).

   a. **Contents:** The popliteal fossa is an important space, as it contains all of the major neurovascular structures traveling to/from the leg and foot. The contents are:
   - Popliteal artery and vein and respective branches/tributaries
   - Tibial and common fibular nerves
     - Sural nerve branches
   - Lymph vessels and nodes (superficial and deep popliteal)
   - Fat
   - Small saphenous vein (where it drains into the popliteal vein)

   b. **Nerves:** The tibial nerve will continue inferiorly to innervate structures in the posterior compartment of the leg and plantar

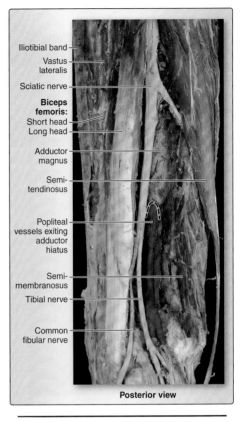

Posterior view

Figure 6.24
Posterior thigh and adductor hiatus (dotted line).

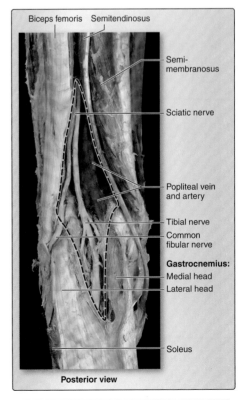

Posterior view

Figure 6.25
Popliteal fossa (dotted line).

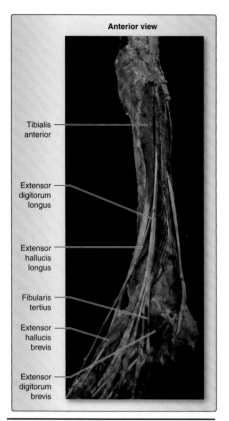

Figure 6.26
Anterior leg.

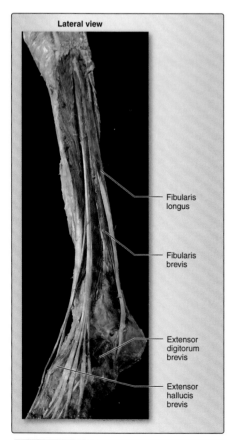

Figure 6.27
Lateral leg.

surface of the foot. The common fibular nerve will travel laterally to the level of the fibular head and split into deep and superficial fibular nerves to innervate structures in the anterior and lateral leg compartments, respectively.

2. **Anterior leg:** As shown in Figure 6.26, muscles of the anterior leg include **tibialis anterior**, **extensor digitorum**, **extensor hallucis longus**, and **fibularis tertius**. Muscles of the anterior leg span between the lateral tibial surface and the medial fibular surface, anterior to the interosseous membrane. Collectively, these muscles are innervated by the deep fibular nerve and receive blood supply from the anterior tibial artery. In general, this group of muscles dorsiflexes the ankle and extends the toes.

   a. **Tibialis anterior:** Tibialis anterior is the primary ankle dorsiflexor and constitutes most of the muscle bulk in the anterior compartment.

   b. **Extensors:** Extensor hallucis longus and extensor digitorum longus are positioned lateral to tibialis anterior and extend the hallux (first digit) and digits (second–fifth digits), respectively, as well as assist in ankle dorsiflexion.

   c. **Fibularis tertius:** Although sometimes absent, when present, this muscle is adjacent to extensor digitorum and functions to dorsiflex the ankle and evert the foot.

   d. **Fascia—extensor retinacula:** At the level of the distal anterior leg and ankle, extensor retinacula—superior and inferior—tack down the tendons of the anterior leg muscles to prevent bow-stringing during contraction and joint movement. These retinacula are thickenings of the crural fascia that surrounds the leg musculature.

   e. **Cutaneous innervation:** Cutaneous innervation of the anterior leg is mediated mainly by the saphenous nerve (femoral nerve branch) and partially by the lateral sural cutaneous nerve. From the knee to the ankle, dermatomes L_4–L_5 are represented in the anterior leg (see Figs. 6.12 and 6.19).

3. **Lateral leg**

   Muscles of the lateral leg include **fibularis longus** and **fibularis brevis** and originate from the fibula (Fig. 6.27). Collectively, these muscles are innervated by the superficial fibular nerve and receive blood supply from the fibular artery. In general, this group of muscles everts the foot and weakly plantarflexes the ankle.

   a. **Fibularis longus and brevis:** Fibularis longus sends its tendon across the plantar surface of the foot to insert medially. This attachment represents an active support of the transverse arch

---

Clinical Application 6.9: Tibialis Anterior Strain

Also known as "shin splints," strain of the tibialis anterior muscle in the inferior two thirds of the muscle along the anterior border of the tibia is typically caused by muscle microtrauma owing to overuse or poor running mechanics. Associated pain is often due to the tearing of tibial periosteum, inflammation, and swelling in the area.

of the foot. Fibularis brevis inserts laterally on the base of the fifth metatarsal.

b. **Fascia—fibular retinacula:** At the level of the distal lateral leg and ankle, fibular retinacula—superior and inferior—tack down the tendons of the lateral leg muscles to prevent bow-stringing during contraction and joint movement. These retinacula are thickenings of the crural fascia that surrounds the leg musculature.

c. **Cutaneous innervation:** Cutaneous innervation of the lateral leg is mediated by the lateral sural cutaneous nerve and superficial fibular nerve. The L_5 dermatome is represented along the lateral leg (see Figs. 6.12 and 6.19).

4. **Posterior leg:** Muscles of the posterior leg are arranged into superficial and deep groups and divided by the **transverse intermuscular septum**. Collectively, these muscles are innervated by the tibial nerve and receive blood supply from the posterior tibial and fibular arteries. In general, this group of muscles plantarflexes the ankle and flexes the toes.

a. **Superficial muscles: Gastrocnemius**, **soleus**, and **plantaris** share a common tendon—calcaneal ("Achilles") tendon that inserts on the calcaneus (Fig. 6.28). Muscles of the superficial posterior compartment represent the bulk of the "calf" muscle.

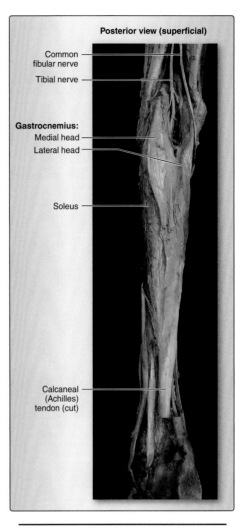

Posterior view (superficial)

Common fibular nerve
Tibial nerve
Gastrocnemius:
  Medial head
  Lateral head
Soleus
Calcaneal (Achilles) tendon (cut)

Figure 6.28
Superficial posterior leg.

Clinical Application 6.10: Ruptured Calcaneal Tendon

Rupture of the calcaneal (Achilles) tendon often follows chronic inflammation. A patient who suffers a complete rupture will describe the event as feeling like getting kicked in the back of the leg. Physical examination reveals a palpable gap in the distal posterior leg, no plantarflexion against resistance, and increased passive dorsiflexion. Surgical repair is often warranted, especially in athletes.

Ruptured calcaneal (Achilles) tendon. Sagittal T2–weighted magnetic resonance imaging of tendon rupture. Yellow arrows indicate area of injury.

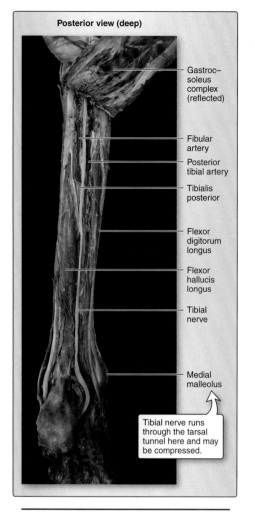

Posterior view (deep)

- Gastroc–soleus complex (reflected)
- Fibular artery
- Posterior tibial artery
- Tibialis posterior
- Flexor digitorum longus
- Flexor hallucis longus
- Tibial nerve
- Medial malleolus

Tibial nerve runs through the tarsal tunnel here and may be compressed.

Figure 6.29
Deep posterior leg.

[1] **Gastrocnemius:** The two-headed gastrocnemius is the most superficial and crosses both the knee and ankle. In addition to plantarflexing the ankle, the gastrocnemius flexes the knee.

[2] **Soleus:** Deep to the gastrocnemius is the fish-shaped soleus muscle, which only crosses the ankle joint and is, therefore, a powerful plantarflexor.

[3] **Plantaris:** When present, this muscle has a small muscle belly and long thin tendon, which limits its contribution to function.

b. **Deep muscles: Popliteus, tibialis posterior, flexor digitorum,** and **flexor hallucis longus** are the muscles of the deep posterior compartment and contribute to plantarflexion of the ankle as well as flexion of the toes (Fig. 6.29). From medial to lateral, flexor digitorum longus, tibialis posterior, and flexor hallucis longus arise from the posterior surface of the tibia, interosseous membrane, and fibula.

[1] **Tibialis posterior:** Similar to the fibularis longus, the tibialis posterior provides active support for the medial longitudinal arch of the foot during weight bearing.

[2] **Flexor hallucis longus:** This muscle is a powerful flexor of the hallux, which enables adequate "push off" during the gait cycle (preswing phase).

[3] **Flexor digitorum longus:** This muscle flexes digits two through five and assists in plantarflexion.

[4] **Popliteus:** The popliteus muscle lies in the proximal deep posterior leg and plays an important part in unlocking a fully extended knee joint. In an open-chain position (unfixed foot), popliteus internally rotates the tibia on the femur, while in a close-chain position (foot fixed as in during stance phase in gait cycle), the popliteus externally rotates the femur. Both of these actions unlock a fully extended knee.

c. **Tarsal tunnel:** Just prior to traveling posterior to the medial malleolus, the tendons of tibialis posterior and flexor digitorum longus cross (Fig. 6.30). Thus, the order of structures from anterior to posterior) traveling into the plantar foot is:
- *T*ibialis posterior
- Flexor *d*igitorum longus
- Posterior tibial *a*rtery/veins and tibial *n*erve
- Flexor *h*allucis longus

These structures are running through the tarsal tunnel and, just as in the upper limb's carpal tunnel, can become compressed. An easy way to remember the contents and order of structures in the tarsal tunnel is to use the phrase "**T**om, **D**ick, **AN**d, **H**arry," in which Tom represents **T**ibialis posterior, Dick represents flexor **D**igitorum longus, and Harry represents flexor **H**allucis longus. The "**AN**d" represents the posterior tibial **A**rtery and tibial **N**erve.

d. **Fascia—flexor retinaculum:** At this level, the posterior tibial artery and tibial nerve divide into **MP** and **LP arteries** and **nerves,**

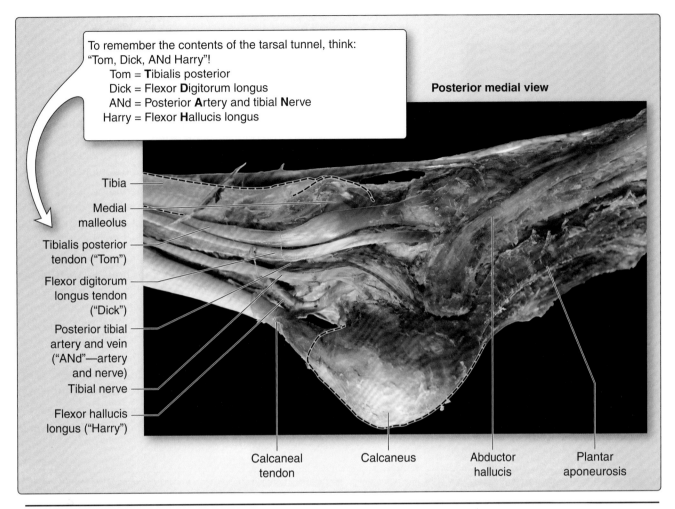

To remember the contents of the tarsal tunnel, think: "Tom, Dick, ANd Harry"!
- Tom = **T**ibialis posterior
- Dick = Flexor **D**igitorum longus
- ANd = Posterior **A**rtery and tibial **N**erve
- Harry = Flexor **H**allucis longus

Posterior medial view

Tibia

Medial malleolus

Tibialis posterior tendon ("Tom")

Flexor digitorum longus tendon ("Dick")

Posterior tibial artery and vein ("ANd"—artery and nerve)

Tibial nerve

Flexor hallucis longus ("Harry")

Calcaneal tendon

Calcaneus

Abductor hallucis

Plantar aponeurosis

Figure 6.30
Contents of the tarsal tunnel. Dotted line shows bony features.

respectively. A **flexor retinaculum** maintains the position of these structures posterior to the medial malleolus.

e. **Cutaneous innervation:** Cutaneous innervation of the posterior leg is mediated by the saphenous nerve (femoral nerve branch) and medial and lateral sural cutaneous nerves. From the knee to the ankle, dermatomes L_3 and S_1–S_2 are represented in the posterior leg (see Figs. 6.12 and 6.19).

D. Ankle and foot

The ankle represents the articulation between the distal tibia and fibula, with the talus as the leg transitions into the foot. The foot is made up of 7 tarsal bones, 5 metatarsal bones, and 14 phalanges (proximal, middle, distal) and serves as a weight-bearing structure, important for standing and gait (see Fig. 6.5). The foot has three parts—hindfoot (talus and calcaneus), midfoot (navicular, cuboid, and cuneiforms), and forefoot (metatarsals and phalanges)—which are functionally important when discussing load bearing and movement during the gait cycle. When describing structures of the foot, it is further divided into dorsum and plantar regions.

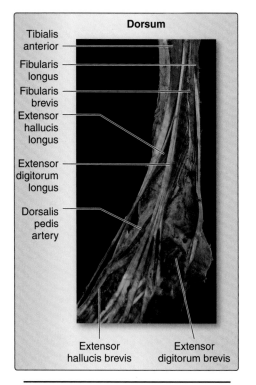

Figure 6.31
Dorsum of foot.

1. **Dorsum of foot:** The dorsum of the foot contains two muscles— **extensor hallucis brevis** and **extensor digitorum brevis** (Fig. 6.31). These muscles collectively extend the digits and arise from the calcaneus to insert onto the hallux and digits two through five, respectively. These muscles are innervated by the deep fibular nerve.

   a. **Vasculature:** The main arterial supply to the dorsum of the foot is **dorsalis pedis artery**, which is the continuation of the anterior tibial artery in the leg. The dorsalis pedis artery travels distally, gives off tarsal branches, and terminates into the arcuate and deep plantar arteries. The dorsal venous network drains the dorsum of the foot.

   b. **Cutaneous innervation:** Cutaneous innervation is mediated primarily by the superficial fibular nerve, while the deep fibular nerve supplies the skin between the first and second digits. Dermatomes L_5–L_4 and S_1 are represented on the dorsum of the foot (see Figs. 6.12 and 6.19).

2. **Plantar foot:** The plantar surface of the foot houses most of the intrinsic foot muscles (Fig. 6.32). These muscles function more as a collective unit to constantly modify movement and stability during ambulation. Innervation is generally provided by the LP and MP nerves (see Fig. 6.12). The plantar foot is further divided into four muscular layers, arranged superficial to deep.

   a. **First layer:** These muscles include **abductor hallucis** (MP), **flexor digitorum brevis** (MP), and **abductor digiti minimi** (LP).

   b. **Second layer:** These muscles include **quadratus plantae** (LP), lumbricals (MP/LP), and tendons of **flexor hallucis longus** and **flexor digitorum longus**.

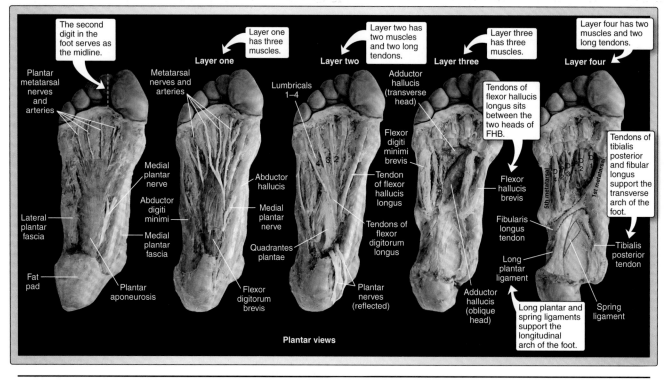

Figure 6.32
Layers of the foot. D = dorsal; P = plantar.

c. **Third layer:** These muscles include **flexor hallucis brevis** (MP), **adductor hallucis** (LP), and **flexor digiti minimi** (LP).

d. **Fourth layer:** These muscles include **plantar interossei** (LP), **dorsal interossei** (LP), and tendons of **fibularis longus** and **tibialis posterior**.

e. **Plantar aponeurosis:** The protective deep fascia of the foot covers the plantar surface and thickens centrally into the plantar aponeurosis. The plantar aponeurosis extends from the calcaneus to the metatarsal heads and sends intermuscular septa superiorly to further compartmentalize the plantar surface of the foot.

f. **Vasculature:** Plantar blood supply is achieved through **MP** and **LP arteries**, which are the main terminal branches of the posterior tibial artery.

g. **Cutaneous innervation:** Cutaneous innervation is mediated primarily by the **MP** and **LP nerves**. The heel receives cutaneous innervation by way of the **medial calcaneal branch** of the tibial nerve. Dermatomes L_5–L_4 and S_1–S_2 are represented on the plantar surface of the foot (see Figs. 6.12 and 6.19).

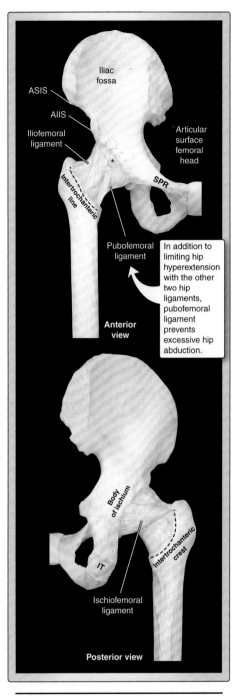

Figure 6.33
Hip joint and associated supporting structures. AIIS = anterior inferior iliac spine, ASIS = anterior superior iliac spine, IT = ischial tuberosity, SPR = superior pubic ramus.

Clinical Application 6.11: Plantar Fasciitis

Inflammation of the plantar aponeurosis presents with increased pain upon weight bearing first thing in the morning, focused pain upon palpation of the attachment to the calcaneus, and pain with passive hallux extension. Causes include running, improper footwear, and high-impact activities. Lifestyle modifications such as rest, stretching, and proper footwear are commonly recommended to decrease inflammation and pain. Cortisone injections and image-guided treatments may also provide relief.

VI. JOINTS AND LIGAMENTS

Joints of the lower limb include the hip joint, knee joint, tibiofibular joint, ankle joint, and foot joints. Joints of the pelvic girdle are discussed in Chapter 5.

A. Hip joint

The hip is a synovial, ball-and-socket joint that connects the pelvis to the lower limb (Figs. 6.33 and 6.34). The head of the femur (ball) and acetabulum (socket) articulate in a deep, protected configuration that still allows for movement in multiple planes. Movements at the joint include flexion, extension, abduction, adduction, medial rotation, lateral rotation, and circumduction. The hip joint is supported by ligamentous and capsular structures.

1. **Acetabulum:** Articular cartilage lines both the head of the femur and the lunate surface of the acetabulum. A fibrocartilagenous

Clinical Application 6.12: Hip Dislocation

Dislocation of the hip most commonly occurs in the posterior direction from severe trauma (motor vehicle accident; dashboard injury), in which the femur is forced posteriorly out of the acetabulum. The affected limb will present in a medially rotated and adducted position and appear shorter than the unaffected limb. If the circumflex femoral arteries are damaged, avascular necrosis of the femoral head may occur. The sciatic nerve may also be at risk of injury with a posterior dislocation. Anterior hip dislocations are less common. The affected limb would present in a laterally rotated and abducted position. Contents of the femoral triangle may be at risk with an anterior dislocation.

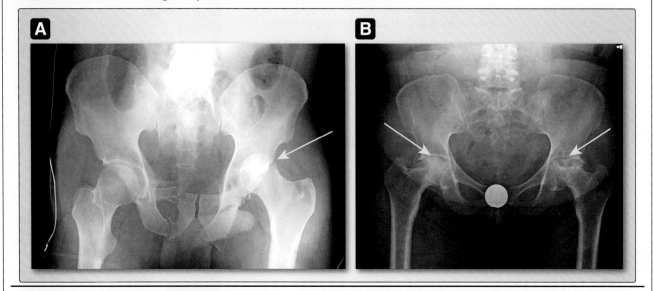

Plain film radiographs (arrows indicate region of injury/pathology). A, Posterior hip dislocation. Pelvic fractures are also present. B, Bilateral avascular necrosis of femoral heads. Note flattened and rough articular surface.

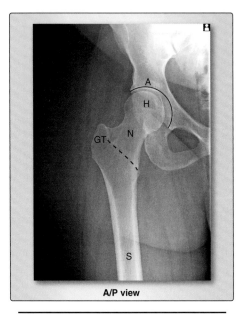

A/P view

Figure 6.34

Plain film radiograph of normal hip (dotted line—intertrochanteric line). A = acetabulum, A/P = anterior/posterior, GT = greater trochanter, H = head, N = neck, S = shaft.

acetabular labrum is attached along the rim of the acetabulum to further deepen the joint.

2. **Fibrous capsule:** The fibrous capsule of the hip extends from the bony rim of the acetabulum to portions of the femoral neck. Thickenings in the capsule represent hip ligaments.

3. **Ligaments:** The **iliofemoral ligament** lies anterior and superior and prevents hyperextension of the hip. The **pubofemoral ligament** lies inferior and prevents excessive abduction of the hip. The **ischiofemoral ligament** lies posterior and is the weakest of the three. Collectively, these ligaments assist the medial and lateral hip rotators in maintaining the position of the femoral head in the acetabulum to achieve stability. The ligament of the head of femur assists in the strength of the joint as well.

4. **Vasculature:** A small and often wanting branch from the obturator artery—artery to the head of the femur—travels through the ligament to supply this region. Medial and lateral circumflex femoral arteries give rise to retinacular arteries, which extend into the capsule and supply the hip joint.

5. **Articular innervation:** The joint receives innervation from branches of the femoral nerve, obturator nerve, superior gluteal nerve, and nerve to quadratus femoris.

6. **Bursae:** Three main synovial fluid-filled bursa sacs are associated with the hip and gluteal regions. The **trochanteric bursa** lies between the deep surface of gluteus maximus and greater trochanter. The **gluteofemoral bursa** lies between the proximal iliotibial band and the superior attachment of vastus lateralis. The **ischial bursa** lies between the inferior border of the gluteus maximus and ischial tuberosity.

B. Knee joint

The knee is a synovial, hinge joint that connects the thigh to the leg (Figs. 6.35 and 6.36). The distal femur articulates with both the proximal tibia and patella to allow for movement, primarily in the sagittal plane. Movements at the joint include flexion, extension, and very minimal terminal rotation. The knee joint is supported by ligamentous and capsular structures.

1. **Cartilage:** Articular hyaline cartilage lines both the femoral and tibial condyles and posterior patella. Crescent-shaped fibrocartilagenous plates called *menisci* (medial and lateral) are attached on the tibial

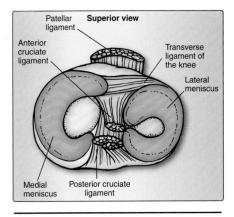

Figure 6.35
Knee joint.

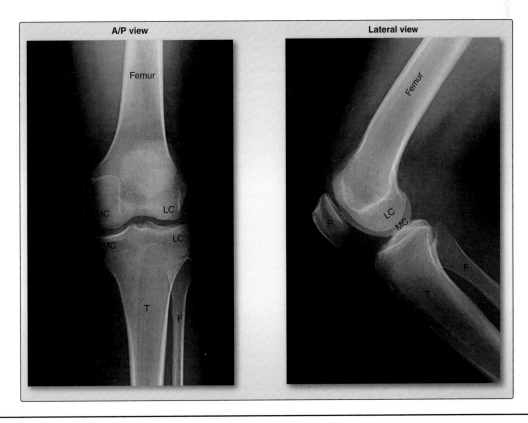

Figure 6.36
Plain film radiographs of normal knee joint. A/P = anterior/posterior, F = fibula, LC = lateral condyle, MC = medial condyle, P = patella, T = tibia.

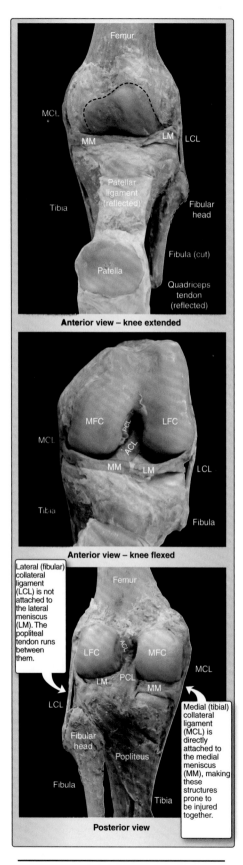

Anterior view – knee extended

Anterior view – knee flexed

Lateral (fibular) collateral ligament (LCL) is not attached to the lateral meniscus (LM). The popliteal tendon runs between them.

Medial (tibial) collateral ligament (MCL) is directly attached to the medial meniscus (MM), making these structures prone to be injured together.

Posterior view

Figure 6.37
Knee ligaments. ACL = anterior cruciate ligament, LFC = lateral femoral condyle, MFC = medial femoral condyle, PCL = posterior cruciate ligament.

articular surface to further deepen the joint surface and provide shock absorption.

2. **Fibrous capsule:** The fibrous capsule of the knee extends from the boundaries of the femoral and tibial articular surfaces and is inherently weak posteriorly. An inner synovial layer lines the surfaces of the joint that are void of articular cartilage.

3. **Ligaments:** Thickenings in the capsule represent the intrinsic knee ligaments (Fig. 6.37).

   a. **Medial (tibial) collateral ligament (MCL):** The MCL extends from the medial epicondyle of the femur to the medial condyle and superior surface of tibia. It tightens with valgus force and is attached to the medial meniscus.

   b. **Patellar ligament:** This ligament is a strong, thick extension of the quadriceps tendon. It attaches to the tibial tuberosity.

   c. **Arcuate popliteal ligament:** This ligament arises from the fibular head to support the posterior capsule.

   d. **Oblique popliteal ligament:** This ligament is an extension of the semimembranosus tendon and provides capsular support posteriorly.

   e. **Lateral (fibular) collateral ligament (LCL):** The cord-like LCL further supports the joint capsule but is considered extracapsular. It extends from the lateral epicondyle of the femur to the fibular head and is not directly attached to the lateral meniscus, as the popliteal tendon separates the two structures. The LCL tightens with a varus stress.

   f. **Anterior cruciate ligament (ACL) and posterior cruciate ligament (PCL):** These cross each other deep to the knee joint and limit the rotation at the knee. They lie outside the articular cavity, but within the capsule. The ACL runs from the anterior intercondylar region of the tibia to the posteromedial surface of the lateral femoral condyle. It limits anterior translation of the tibia on the femur (unfixed leg) and hyperextension of the knee. The PCL is the weaker of the two cruciates and runs from the posterior intercondylar region of the tibia to the anterolateral surface of the medial femoral condyle. It limits posterior translation of the tibia on the femur (unfixed leg) and hyperflexion of the knee.

4. **Vasculature:** The popliteal artery and vein give rise to geniculate vessels that extend into the capsule and supply the knee joint.

5. **Articular innervation:** The joint receives innervation from articular branches of the femoral, tibial, common fibular, and obturator nerves.

6. **Bursae:** Approximately a dozen bursae are associated with the knee region, but only four communicate directly with the articular cavity: The **suprapatellar bursa** lies deep to the quadriceps tendon, the **popliteus bursa** lies between the popliteus and lateral tibial condyle, the **anserine bursa** lies between the pes anserinus (gracilis, sartorius, and semitendinosus tendons) and MCL, and the **gastrocnemius bursa** lies deep to the medial head of the gastrocnemius.

Clinical Application 6.13: Knee Joint Injuries

Unhappy triad: The "unhappy triad" involves tearing of the anterior cruciate ligament (ACL), medial collateral ligament (MCL), and medial meniscus. The mechanism of injury often involves a posterolateral blow to a leg with foot planted, putting a rotary and valgus stress on the knee and tearing the ACL and MCL. The medial meniscus is often also affected because of its attachment to the MCL. A positive anterior drawer test would be present with an ACL tear. Reconstructive surgery often involves harvesting part of the semitendinosus tendon or using a cadaveric ligament.

Ligament rupture: Posterior cruciate ligament (PCL) rupture is less common than ACL rupture. PCL tears occur when a force is applied to a flexed knee at the tibial tuberosity, as in a dashboard injury. A positive posterior drawer test would be present.

Sagittal view

Unhappy triad. T2 fat-suppressed magnetic resonance imaging through the intercondylar notch shows anterior cruciate ligament tear (arrow).

Anterior view

F

P

T

Fibular head

Opening for anterior tibial vessels

Interosseous membrane

Opening for perforating branch of fibular artery

Medial malleolus

Lateral malleolus

Figure 6.38
Tibiofibular joint. F = femur, P = patella, T = tibia.

C. Tibiofibular joint

As shown in Figure 6.38, the **tibiofibular joint** is a syndesmosis fibrous joint held together by an interosseous membrane that spans between the tibial and fibular shafts as well as distal tibiofibular ligaments (anterior, interosseous, and posterior). The collection of distal tibiofibular ligaments provides additional support to maintain the integrity of the ankle joint. Trace movement occurs at the distal end of this joint during ankle dorsiflexion. Branches from the fibular artery and anterior and posterior tibial arteries supply this joint, while innervation is mediated by branches of the tibial, deep fibular, and saphenous nerves.

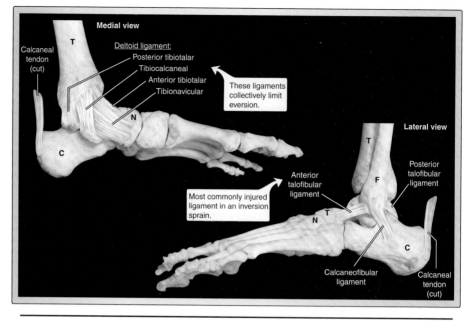

Figure 6.39
Ankle joint. C = calcaneus, F = fibula, N = navicular, T = tibia.

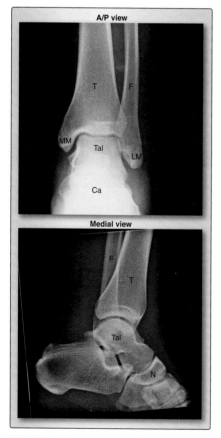

Figure 6.40
Plain film radiographs of normal ankle. A/P = anterior/posterior, Ca = calcaneus, F = fibula, LM = lateral malleolus, MM = medial malleolus, N = navicula, T = tibia, Tal = talus.

Movements of the foot are complex and described as *triplanar*. In the foot, *supination* refers to the combination of ankle plantarflexion and subtalar inversion and internal rotation. Foot *pronation* refers to the combination of ankle dorsiflexion and subtalar eversion and external rotation. These terms are often used when describing gait and running foot mechanics.

D. Ankle joint

As shown in Figures 6.39 and 6.40, the **ankle joint** is composed of the distal tibia and fibula articulating with the superior articular surface of the talus.

1. **Movement:** This joint allows only flexion and extension movement in the sagittal plane. All other foot movements (eversion, inversion, rotation) occur in the subtalar regions.

2. **Ligaments:** The ankle joint is supported medially by the strong fan-shaped **deltoid ligament**, which consists of the **tibionavicular part**, **tibiocalcaneal part**, and the **anterior** and **posterior tibiotalar parts**. This collection of ligaments resists eversion of the ankle joint. Laterally, the ankle is supported by the **anterior** and **posterior talofibular ligaments** and the **calcaneofibular ligament**. Collectively, these ligaments resist inversion, but they are weaker than their medial counterparts.

3. **Vasculature: Malleolar branches** from the posterior and anterior tibial and fibular arteries supply the ankle joint.

4. **Articular innervation:** Ankle joint innervation is mediated by branches of the deep fibular and tibial nerves.

E. Foot joints

Joints of the foot are numerous and include the **subtalar, talocalcaneonavicular, calcaneocuboid, cuneonavicular, tarsometatarsal, intermetatarsal, metatarsophalangeal,** and **interphalangeal joints** (Fig. 6.41). Figure 6.42 shows plain film of the foot and bones.

1. **Movement:** Owing to the multiplane nature of the foot, interarticular movements include inversion, eversion, gliding, rotation, sliding, circumduction, flexion, extension, abduction, and adduction. These articulations allow the foot to adjust to changes in the ground and transmit forces superiorly through the kinetic chain during the gait cycle. The **subtalar joint** is a plane synovial articulation between the talus and calcaneus where most of the eversion and inversion occurs. The **calcaneocuboid joint** also contributes to eversion and inversion. Flexion, extension, abduction, and adduction occur at the **metatarsophalangeal joints,** whereas **interphalangeal joints** allow for flexion and extension only.

2. **Ligaments:** Major supporting ligaments of the foot include the **plantar calcaneonavicular ligament** (spring ligament), **long plantar ligament,** and the **short plantar ligament** (plantar calcaneocuboid ligament). These ligaments passively support the longitudinal and transverse arches of the foot.

3. **Vasculature:** Branches from **dorsalis pedis** and **MP** and **LP arteries** give rise to **tarsal** and **digital arteries** to supply the foot and toes.

4. **Articular innervation:** Collectively, joints of the foot receive innervation from articular branches of the MP and LP nerves and the deep fibular nerves. Digital branches serve the toes.

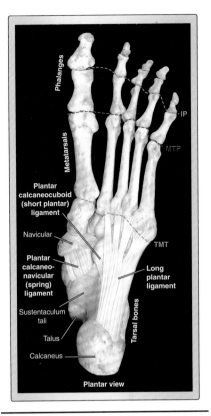

Figure 6.41
Foot joints. Supporting ligamentous structures. IP = interphalangeal joints, MTP = metatarsophalangeal joints, TMT = tarsometatarsal joint.

Clinical Application 6.14: Pes Planus

The medial longitudinal arch of the foot is supported dynamically by the tibialis posterior and passively by bony arrangement and ligamentous support. When any of these factors change, the arch can drop, leading to pes planus (flat foot). Orthotic shoe inserts may improve arch support.

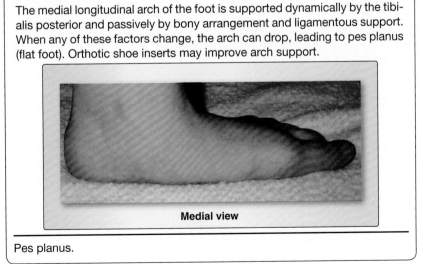

Medial view

Pes planus.

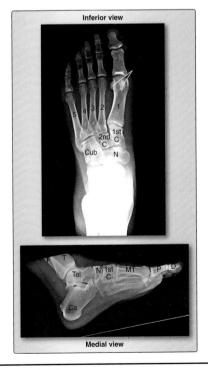

Figure 6.42
Plain film radiographs of normal foot.
C = cuneiform, Ca = calcaneus,
Cub = cuboid, D = distal phalange, F = fibula,
MT = metatarsals (1–5), N = navicula,
P = proximal phalange, T = tibia, Tal = talus.

Chapter Summary

- The lower limb is divided regionally into hip, thigh, leg, ankle, and foot.
- The upper limb develops in advance of the lower limb. The lower limb undergoes a 90° medial rotation.
- Lateral plate mesoderm forms the skeletal component of the lower limb. Somitomeric mesoderm forms the muscular component of the lower limb.
- The zone of polarizing activity (ZPA) is a zone of mesoderm. The apical ectodermal ridge (AER) is a thickened ridge of ectoderm.
- The lower limb is covered in a deep fascial layering (fascia lata and crural fascia) that assists in venous return proximally and compartmentalizes the thigh and leg.
- Superficial and deep veins are connected via perforating veins. When the valves of these venous structures fail, varicosities may occur. Lymphatic vessels follow both superficial and deep veins and drain into either popliteal or inguinal lymph nodes.
- The femoral artery is the main arterial supply to the lower limb. It is found in the femoral triangle, travels through the adductor canal, and exits the adductor hiatus posteriorly, where it is renamed popliteal artery.
- The femoral triangle is organized lateral to medial with the nerve, artery, vein, and lymphatics. Clinically, this area is important for venipuncture, arterial pulse detection, lymph drainage, and as a potential herniation site.
- The lumbosacral plexus innervates lower limb structures and is made up of a collection of anterior primary rami from L_2–L_5 and S_1–S_3.
- The thigh is divided into anterior (extensors), posterior (flexors), and medial (adductors) compartments. The leg is divided into anterior (dorsiflexors), posterior (plantarflexors), and lateral (evertors) compartments. The foot is divided into (extensors) and plantar (flexors) surfaces. The posterior hip includes the gluteal muscles (extensors and abductors) and lateral rotators, whereas the anterior hip is primarily made up of flexors.
- A lesion of the femoral nerve will cause loss of leg extension. A lesion of the common fibular will lead to foot drop. Superior gluteal nerve lesion will result in a Trendelenburg gait, whereas inferior gluteal nerve lesion will limit hip extension.
- The plantar foot is organized into four layers. Most of the intrinsic foot muscles are innervated by the lateral plantar nerve (branch of tibial nerve). The arches of the foot are dynamically and passively supported by tendons and ligaments/bony structure, respectively.
- Dorsalis pedis artery is used to measure heart rate in a supine (recumbent) patient. It is the continuation of the anterior tibial artery.
- Hip dislocations typically occur posteriorly. The unhappy triad in the knee involves damage to the anterior cruciate ligament (ACL), medial collateral ligament (MCL), and medial meniscus. Inversion ankle sprains are the most common type and may involve fracture of the distal fibula and tibia if the force is great.

Study Questions:

Choose the ONE correct answer.

6.1 Which of the following arteries gives rise to the axis artery of the lower limb?

    A. External iliac artery.

    B. Femoral artery.

    C. Profunda femoris artery.

    D. Umbilical artery.

    E. Inferior gluteal artery.

> Correct answer = D. Early in development, the umbilical artery gives rise to the axis artery.

6.2 During a routine ultrasound of an 18-week female fetus, it is discovered that she is missing her right fibula—a condition known as fibular hemimelia. A moderate leg length discrepancy was noted, along with underdeveloped and malformed right femur and tibia. Based on your understanding of lower limb development, all three of these bones develop from which of the following embryologic germ layers?

A. Somite mesoderm.
B. Lateral plate mesoderm.
C. Intermediate mesoderm.
D. Extraembryonic mesoderm.
E. Sclerotome mesoderm.

Correct answer = B. All bones of the lower limb form from lateral plate mesoderm that condenses along the central axis of the lower limb bud.

6.3 A 21-year old male was admitted to the Emergency Department after a motorcycle accident. Once stable, it was discovered that he suffered a crush injury to the right fibular head and a right tibial plateau fracture. Motor and sensory tests revealed loss of function at the ankle and altered sensation between his right first and second toes. The mechanism of injury and subsequent impairments suggest a nerve lesion that affected which of the following muscles and actions?

A. Tibialis posterior / ankle plantarflexion
B. Extensor digitorum longus / dorsiflexion.
C. Flexor hallicus longus / first toe flexion.
D. Popliteus / unlocking knee.
A. Tibialis anterior / plantarflexion.

Correct answer = B. Crush injury at the level of the fibular head would most likely affect the common fibular nerve. Lesion of the common fibular nerve would denervate anterior and lateral leg muscles, as well as dorsal foot muscles. Therefore, extensor digitorum longus, which assists in dorsiflexion, would be affected.

6.4 A 56-year old female presents with pain and paresthesia in her lower limb and significant weakness in hip extension, knee flexion and ankle and foot movements, indicative of sciatic nerve compression. Sciatic nerve compression most often occurs:

A. When it splits in the popliteal fossa.
B. As it enters the femoral triangle.
C. As it exits the pelvis inferior to the piriformis muscle.
D. As it courses through the adductor canal.
A. Within the tarsal tunnel.

Correct answer = C. The sciatic nerve can be compressed by the piriformis muscles in the gluteal region. Divisions of the sciatic nerve may even pierce the piriformis muscle as they exit the pelvis. This is often referred to as "Piriformis Syndrome." Symptoms would include impairment of hip extension, knee flexion, dorsiflexion, plantar flexion, eversion, inversion, and toe movements, as well as sensory changes, mainly in the leg and foot.

6.5 A 32-year old male, semi-professional downhill skier is seen in the outpatient clinic with complaints of pain in the posterior knee. Upon physical examination, pain is reproduced in with palpation in the popliteal fossa, with resisted knee flexion and at end range of full passive range of motion into knee extension. The patient describes pain with walking and ascending stairs, and has been unable to ski for 2 weeks. You suspect popliteus tendonitis, and ask the patient to walk up and down the clinic hall so that you can assess his gait. Which of the following actions would be most difficult for this patient during ambulation?

A. Moving from an extended to flexed thigh.
B. Dorsiflexing the ankle to make initial contact with the ground when stepping.
C. Moving from an extended to flexed leg.
D. Keeping the pelvis level.
A. Plantarflexing the ankle during push off.

Correct answer = C. The popliteal muscle unlocks the knee during ambulation, allowing for the fully extended leg to transition into a flexed leg from mid- to terminal-stance. A painful popliteus tendonitis would make this transition difficult.

6.6   A 75-year old male is being seen for left pes planus. The patient is morbidly obese, reports a sedentary lifestyle, and has a past medical history of diabetes, peripheral arterial disease, and hypertension (high blood pressure). He has a healing ulcer on the plantar surface of his left foot, and decreased sensation to light touch and pinprick in his left posterior leg and plantar foot. Upon inspection, atrophy of his left leg muscles is noted posteriorly. Nerve conduction studies indicate decreased left tibial nerve function at the level of the popliteal fossa. Based on these findings, which of the following muscles is most likely affected and contributing to this patient's pes planus?

A. Tibialis anterior.
B. Extensor digitorum brevis.
C. Gastrocnemius.
D. Tibialis posterior.
E. Soleus.

Correct answer = D. Tibilalis posterior, along with fibularis longus, provides dynamic support to the medial longitudinal arch of the foot. It is innervated by the tibial nerve. Denervation of the tibialis posterior as a result of proximal tibial nerve lesion would contribute to the changes in the medial arch of the foot, causing varying degrees of pes planus (flat foot).

6.7   A 24-year old female professional basketball player was carried off of the court after suffering what appeared to be an inversion ankle sprain. In addition to ligamentous damage, imaging revealed an avulsion fracture of the lateral malleolus. Based on the mechanism of injury and clinical findings, which of the following ligaments is most likely still intact?

A. Anterior talofibular.
B. Tibiocalcaneal.
C. Posterior talofibular.
D. Calcaneofibular.

Correct answer = B. An inversion sprain affects the ligaments on the lateral side of the ankle. Tibiocalcaneal ligament is located on the medial side of the ankle and would be most likely injured in an eversion sprain.

Upper Limb

7

I. OVERVIEW

The upper limbs are designed for mobility and manipulation (completion of a task). The upper limb is divided into shoulder, arm, forearm, and hand regions. The arrangement of joints and increased range of motion of the upper limb allow for bilateral coordination of crude and fine motor skills. Fine motor skills are achieved directly through the hand and fingers, but range of motion and strength at the more proximal joints are necessary for proper positioning of the hand.

Proximally, the shoulder (pectoral) girdle—comprising the manubrium of the sternum, the clavicles, and the scapulae—forms an incomplete bony ring that connects the upper limb to the axial skeleton. Posteriorly, the bony ring is supported by muscular attachments between the scapula and vertebral column.

II. OSTEOLOGY

Bones of the upper limb (proximal to distal) include the **clavicle**, **scapula**, **humerus**, **radius**, **ulna**, **carpal bones**, **metacarpals**, and **phalanges**.

A. Clavicle

The clavicle is an S-shaped bone that acts as a strut to connect the upper limb to the axial skeleton (Fig. 7.1). Medially, the clavicle is convex anteriorly and articulates with the manubrium (**sternal end**). Laterally, the clavicle is concave anteriorly and flattens to articulate with the acromion process (**acromial end**). The rough inferior surface of the clavicle has raised areas for ligament and muscle attachment, including the impression for the costoclavicular ligament, groove for the subclavius muscle, and **trapezoid line** and **conoid tubercle** for the two parts of the **coracoclavicular ligament**.

B. Scapula

The scapula is a triangular bone characterized by **medial**, **lateral**, and **superior borders** and **superior** and **inferior angles** (Fig. 7.2). Scapular structures are often best appreciated from lateral, posterior, and anterior views.

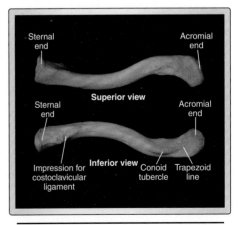

Figure 7.1
Clavicular osteology.

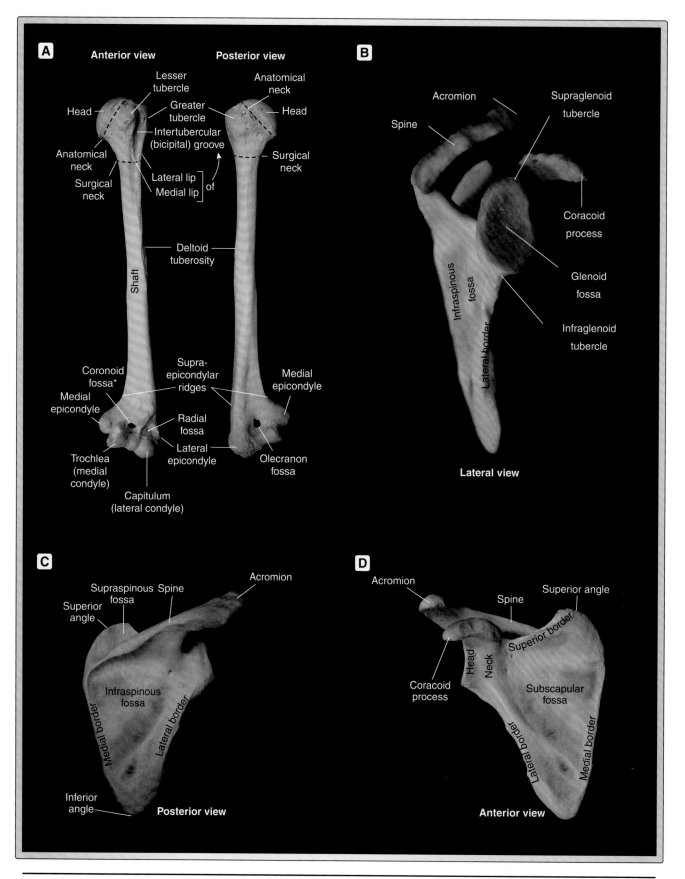

Figure 7.2
Humeral and scapular osteology. A. Humerus. B-D. Scapula. Hole is an artifact in the bone (*).

Clinical Application 7.1: Clavicle Fracture

The clavicle is the most commonly fractured bone in the body. Fractures typically occur between the middle and lateral thirds from direct trauma to the shoulder or indirect force from falling on an out-stretched upper limb. The proximal clavicle (PC) is pulled superiorly by the sternocleidomastoid (yellow arrow), while the distal clavicle (DC) is depressed inferiorly because of the weight of the upper limb. Brachial plexus divisions and axillary vasculature are at risk of secondary injury.

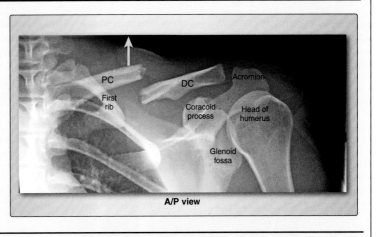

A/P view

Plain film radiograph of left clavicular fracture.

1. **Lateral:** The **glenoid fossa** serves as the shallow socket portion of the **glenohumeral** (shoulder) **joint**, which articulates with the head of the humerus laterally. **Supraglenoid** and **infraglenoid tubercles** are located superior and inferior to the fossa, respectively.

2. **Posterior:** The scapula is unevenly divided posteriorly into **supra-spinous** and **infraspinous fossae** by a ridge of bone called the **spine** of the scapula. The spine extends laterally and ends at the **acromion process** (point of the shoulder).

3. **Anterior:** The scapula has a concave anterior surface called the **subscapular fossa**. Arising from the **neck** of the scapula of the anterior superior surface is the beak-like **coracoid process**. The **suprascapular notch** lies medial to the root of the coracoid process.

C. Humerus

The **humerus** (arm; brachium) is the largest bone of the upper limb (see Fig. 7.2). Humeral structures can be described from proximal to distal.

1. **Proximal:** The proximal humerus is characterized by a round **head** (ball portion of the shoulder joint) that is covered with articular cartilage. The **anatomical neck** lies between the head and **greater** and **lesser tubercles**—two bony prominences that serve as muscle attachment sites (Fig. 7.3). The greater tubercle is positioned more superolaterally, whereas the lesser is more inferomedially. The intertubercular groove (sulcus; bicipital groove) lies between the tubercles. Extending inferiorly from the greater and lesser tubercle are the **lateral** and **medial lips of the intertubercular groove**, respectively. The **surgical neck** is found just distal to the tubercles.

2. **Shaft:** The humeral shaft is primarily smooth, except for a small mid-shaft **deltoid tubercle** laterally and a **spiral (radial) line** posteriorly.

3. **Distal**: The distal humerus has a spool-shaped **medial condyle (trochlea)** and a rounded **lateral condyle (capitulum)** that articulate with the **ulna** and **radius**, respectively. Superior to the condyles are the **medial** and **lateral epicondyles**. The **coronoid** and **radial fossae** are located between the epicondyles anteriorly and the **olecranon fossa** posteriorly.

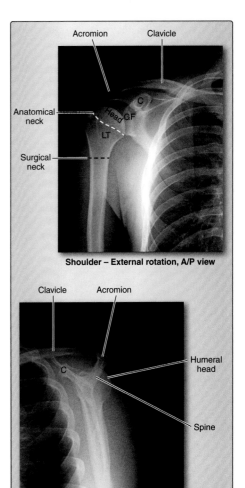

Shoulder – External rotation, A/P view

Shoulder – Scapular y-view

Figure 7.3

Plain film radiographs of shoulder complex. C = coracoid process, GF = glenoid fossa, GT = greater tubercle, LT = lesser tubercle.

Clinical Application 7.2: Humeral Fractures

Several nerve/artery pairs travel in close proximity to the humerus and are, therefore, at risk of secondary injury when humeral fractures occur. Common sites of fracture include the anatomical neck, surgical neck, midshaft, supraepicondylar ridge, medial epicondyle, and greater tubercle. Fracture of the surgical neck is common in geriatric population with osteoporosis and may injure the axillary nerve and circumflex humeral vessels. Midshaft or spiral groove fractures may injure the radial nerve and profunda brachii vessels. Supraepicondylar ridge fractures may injure the median nerve and brachial vessels. Medial epicondyle fractures may injure the ulnar nerve and superior ulnar collateral vessels.

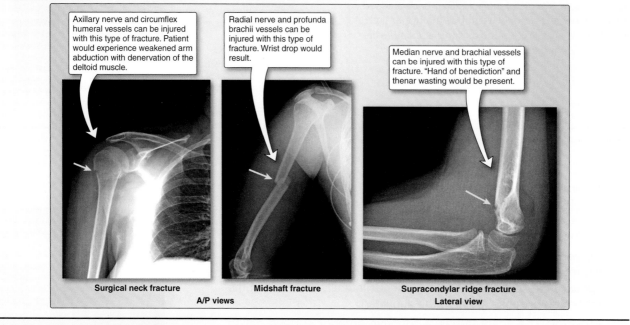

Axillary nerve and circumflex humeral vessels can be injured with this type of fracture. Patient would experience weakened arm abduction with denervation of the deltoid muscle.

Radial nerve and profunda brachii vessels can be injured with this type of fracture. Wrist drop would result.

Median nerve and brachial vessels can be injured with this type of fracture. "Hand of benediction" and thenar wasting would be present.

Surgical neck fracture   **Midshaft fracture**   **Supracondylar ridge fracture**
A/P views   **Lateral view**

Plain film radiographs of common humeral fractures. Yellow arrows indicate site(s) of fracture.

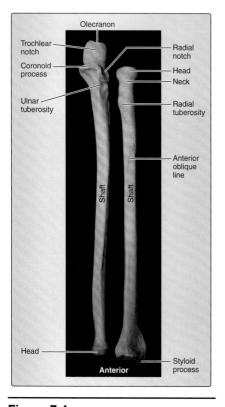

Figure 7.4
Forearm osteology (ulna and radius).

D. Ulna and radius

The bones of the forearm (antebrachium) include the **ulna** medially and the **radius** laterally (Figs. 7.4 and 7.5). These bones articulate proximally at the elbow with the humerus and distally at the wrist with the carpal bones. They are connected along their length by an interosseous membrane.

1. **Ulnar features:** The ulna is characterized proximally by a large **trochlear notch** framed anteriorly by the **coronoid process** and posteriorly by the **olecranon process**, a shallow **radial notch**, and a raised **ulnar tuberosity**. The trochlear notch articulates with the trochlea of the humerus, while the radial notch articulates with the head of the radius. Distally, the ulna tapers into a **head** and **styloid process**.

2. **Radial features:** The radius is characterized proximally by a **head**, **neck**, and raised **radial tuberosity**. The head articulates with the capitulum of the humerus. Distally, the radius expands and possesses a **styloid process**.

Clinical Application 7.3: Colles Fracture

Colles fracture ("dinner fork" deformity) is a fracture through the distal radius, resulting in the proximal segment moving anteriorly and the distal segment moving posteriorly, giving the distal forearm the appearance of a dinner fork.

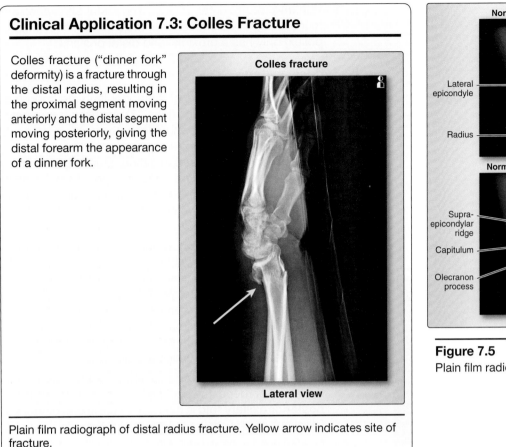

Colles fracture

Lateral view

Plain film radiograph of distal radius fracture. Yellow arrow indicates site of fracture.

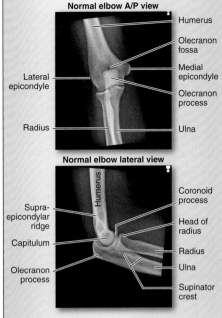

Normal elbow A/P view

Humerus
Olecranon fossa
Lateral epicondyle
Medial epicondyle
Olecranon process
Radius
Ulna

Normal elbow lateral view

Humerus
Supra-epicondylar ridge
Coronoid process
Head of radius
Capitulum
Radius
Olecranon process
Ulna
Supinator crest

Figure 7.5
Plain film radiographs of the elbow.

E. Carpal and metacarpal bones and phalanges

The carpal and metacarpal bones make up the bony structure of the hand (palm and dorsum), while the phalanges form digits one through five (Fig. 7.6). Carpal bones are arranged into proximal and distal rows, with bones of the proximal row contributing to the wrist (radiocarpal) joint.

1. **Carpal bones:** The carpal bones are arranged in a proximal and a distal row.

    a. **Proximal row:** From lateral to medial (radial to ulnar), the proximal row consists of the **scaphoid**, **lunate**, **triquetrum**, and **pisiform**. The scaphoid, lunate, and triquetrum articulate with the distal radius to form the wrist joint.

    b. **Distal row:** The distal row consists of the **trapezium**, **trapezoid**, **capitate**, and **hamate**. The distal row articulates with the bases of the five **metacarpal** bones.

2. **Metacarpals:** Metacarpals have a proximal base, middle shaft, and distal head. Metacarpal heads articulate with the base of the proximal **phalanges**.

3. **Phalanges:** Proximal, middle, and distal phalanges are found in digits two through five, while the first digit (thumb; pollex) only has a proximal and distal phalanx.

F. Surface anatomy

Several surface landmarks of the upper limb are important during physical examination (Fig. 7.7). Assessing symmetry of the upper limb, from the shoulder to the hand, is essential when formulating a diagnosis. Symmetry and level of these landmarks can be assessed in sitting, standing, or supine positions to determine where along the upper limb deviation may be occurring. Palpating soft-tissue structures, such as tendons, is made easier when patient is asked to actively engage the targeted muscle.

1. **Scapula**: Posteriorly, the **medial** and **inferior borders** of the scapula can be palpated as well as the **spine** (T_3 level), superior angle (T_2 level), and inferior angle (T_7 level). Follow the spine out laterally to the point of the shoulder where it becomes the **acromion**. The articulation between the distal clavicle and acromion (**acromioclavicular joint**) can be palpated anteriorly and the **coracoid process** just inferomedial to the acromioclavicular joint.

2. **Axillary folds:** The **anterior axillary fold** is made up of the lateral border of the pectoralis major muscle, while the **posterior axillary fold** is made up of the lateral borders of latissimus dorsi and teres major muscles. These folds provide anterior and posterior boundaries for the axilla, respectively.

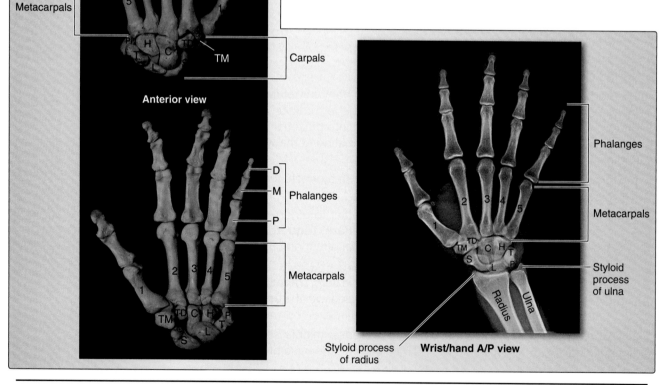

Figure 7.6

Osteology of the hand with plain film radiograph. C = capitate, H = hamate, L = lunate, Pi = pisiform, S = scaphoid, T = triquetrum, TD = trapezoid, TM = trapezium.

Clinical Application 7.4: Hand Fractures

Scaphoid fracture: The scaphoid is the most frequently fractured carpal bone. Fracture typically occurs through the narrowest part of the scaphoid following a fall on an extended, radially deviated palm. Pain with palpation of the anatomical snuff box as well as delayed radiographic imaging after swelling has subsided will confirm scaphoid fracture. Complications include avascular necrosis of the proximal fragment of the scaphoid due to poor blood supply and healing.

Boxer fracture: Fracture of the fifth metacarpal (or fourth) at the junction of the distal shaft and head (neck) is caused by striking a stationary object with a closed fist.

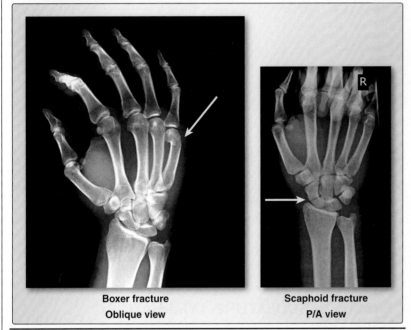

Boxer fracture	Scaphoid fracture
Oblique view	P/A view

Plain film radiographs of hand fracture. Yellow arrows indicate site(s) of fracture.

3. **Proximal and distal bony landmarks:** Proximal humeral bony landmarks include the **greater tubercle** found just inferolateral to the acromion. Moving medially, the **intertubercular groove** can be palpated and the **lesser tubercle** most medially. The long head of the biceps brachii tendon lies in the intertubercular groove. Distally, the **medial** and **lateral epicondyles** are easily palpated and serve as common tendon attachment sites for the forearm flexors and extensors, respectively. At the elbow, the **olecranon process** is easily palpated posteriorly, but the other proximal ulnar structures may be difficult to identify. With passive or active pronation/supination, the **radial head** can be located just distal to the lateral epicondyle.

4. **Cubital fossa (anterior elbow):** The **biceps brachii tendon** can be palpated easily with active elbow flexion. The **brachial artery** pulse can be found just medial to the biceps tendon. Superficially, the **median cubital vein** may be visible through the skin (site for venous puncture).

5. **Wrist**: Both **ulnar** and **radial styloid processes** can be palpated with abduction and adduction of the hand, respectively. The **radial**

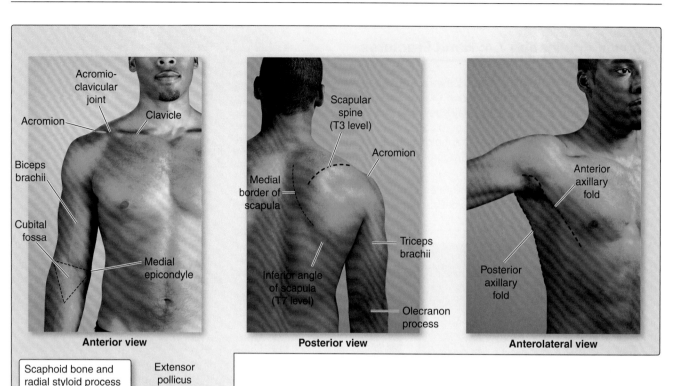

Figure 7.7
Surface landmarks of the upper limb.

artery pulse is found just lateral to the flexor carpi radialis tendon and the wrist. On the dorsum of the hand, the **anatomical snuff box** boundaries can be easily visualized with active thumb abduction and extension. The **scaphoid bone** and **radial styloid process** can be palpated within this space. In the hand, the thenar and hypothenar eminences represent the underlying intrinsic thumb and fifth digit ("pinky") muscles, respectively.

III. FASCIA, VASCULATURE, LYMPHATICS, INNERVATION

Many structures in the upper limb can be described as either superficial or deep, including fascial layers, venous vessels, and lymphatic vessels and nodes. The following section describes the organization of these structures in addition to the arterial and nervous supply of the upper limb.

A. Superficial fascia

Deep to the skin of the upper limb lies a **superficial fascia** that contains varying amounts of loose connective and adipose tissues. Superficial veins, lymphatic vessels, and cutaneous nerves travel in this fascia, which is continuous with the superficial fascia of the neck and trunk.

B. Deep fascia

Deep to the superficial fascia is a **deep fascia** that is divided into several regions, including **deltoid**, **pectoral**, **axillary**, **clavipectoral**, **brachial**, **antebrachial**, and **palmar** (Fig. 7.8). These **deep fasciae** are continuous with each other at different locations and collectively invest the upper limb muscle compartments. Medial and lateral intermuscular septa project internally to attach to bone and create the rigid compartments of the arm (anterior and posterior) and forearm (anterior and posterior).

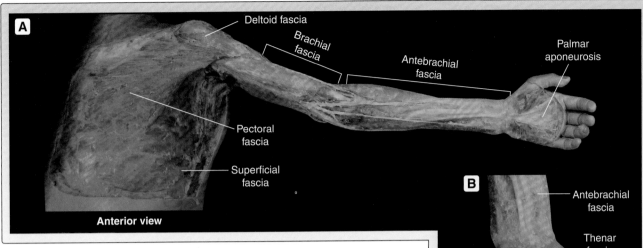

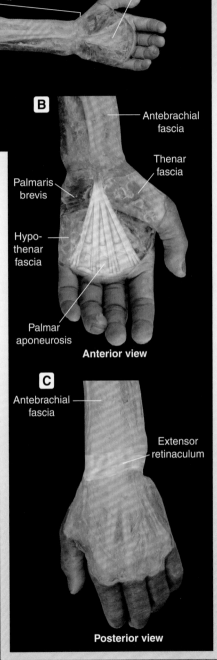

1. **Shoulder and arm fascia:** The pectoral fascia covers the pectoralis major muscle and is continuous with the axillary fascia (Fig. 7.9). The clavipectoral fascia lies deep to the pectoralis major muscle, encapsulates the pectoralis minor and subclavius muscles, and is continuous superiorly with the deep cervical fascia. Continuous with the deltoid, pectoral, and axillary fascia is the brachial fascia, which contains the muscles of the arm in anterior and posterior compartments.

2. **Forearm and hand fascia:** Distally, the brachial fascia continues into the forearm as the antebrachial fascia, also arranged in anterior and posterior compartments. At the wrist, the antebrachial fascia thickens into an anterior **flexor retinaculum** and posterior **extensor retinaculum**, which function to maintain tendon position at the wrist. The fascia of the palm thickens into the **palmar aponeurosis**, which further compartmentalizes the hand.

C. Venous drainage

Venous drainage of the upper limb occurs through a superficial and deep venous network (Fig. 7.10).

1. **Superficial network:** Superficially, the **cephalic vein** and **basilic vein** travel superiorly from the dorsum of the hand to drain into the axillary vein. The cephalic vein travels laterally and the basilic medially. Multiple, small tributary veins drain into these two main superficial veins, and they are connected at the cubital fossa by the **median cubital vein**.

   a. **Cephalic vein:** The cephalic vein travels along the lateral forearm and arm and within the **deltopectoral groove** before piercing the **costocoracoid membrane** and clavipectoral fascia to drain into the proximal portion of the axillary vein.

   b. **Basilic vein:** The basilic vein travels along the medial forearm and pierces the brachial fascia midway along the arm to join the brachial vein. The merging of the basilic and brachial veins forms the axillary vein.

   c. **Perforating veins:** Multiple **perforating veins** pierce the deep fascia of the upper limb along the course of the superficial veins to connect superficial to deep veins. Both superficial and perforating veins have valves to ensure—under normal conditions—unidirectional blood return toward the heart.

Figure 7.8
Fascia of the upper limb. A, Abducted upper limb showing continuity of fascia. B, Palmar aponeurosis. C, Dorsum of hand with extensor retinaculum.

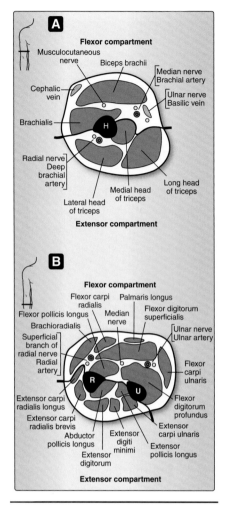

Figure 7.9
Cross-sectional anatomy of the upper limb. A, Arm. B, Forearm. H = humerus, R = radius, U = ulna.

2. **Deep network:** Deep veins of the upper limb travel with all major upper limb arteries and branches and typically carry the same name (see III. E).

D. Lymphatics

Lymphatics of the upper limb are closely associated with the venous system (Fig. 7.11).

1. **Superficial lymphatic vessels:** These travel with the cephalic and basilic veins and drain into associated lymph nodes. Lymphatics that travel with the cephalic vein primarily drain into **apical axillary lymph nodes** first before being drained by the **subclavian lymphatic trunk**. Those that travel with the basilic vein partially drain into the **cubital nodes** located just superior to the medial epicondyle. From the cubital nodes, efferent lymph vessels travel to the **humeral axillary nodes** along deep veins.

2. **Deep lymphatic vessels:** These travel with deep veins in the upper limb, which first drain into **humeral axillary nodes**, then **central axillary nodes**, and finally **apical axillary nodes**, before being drained by the subclavian lymphatic trunk. **Pectoral** and **subscapular axillary lymph nodes** drain those respective regions of the upper limb.

E. Arterial supply

Upper limb structures receive arterial blood supply from branches of the **subclavian, axillary, brachial, ulnar,** and **radial arteries** (Fig. 7.12).

1. **Subclavian artery:** This artery sends branches to posterior axioappendicular muscles, which also contribute to collateral flow around the scapula. Branches include **transverse cervical** (to trapezius), **dorsal scapular** (to rhomboid major/minor and levator scapulae), and **suprascapular** (to supraspinatus and infraspinatus) **arteries**.

2. **Axillary artery:** After passing the lateral border of the first rib, the subclavian artery continues as the **axillary artery**. It is divided into three parts that correspond to the position of the pectoralis minor muscle.

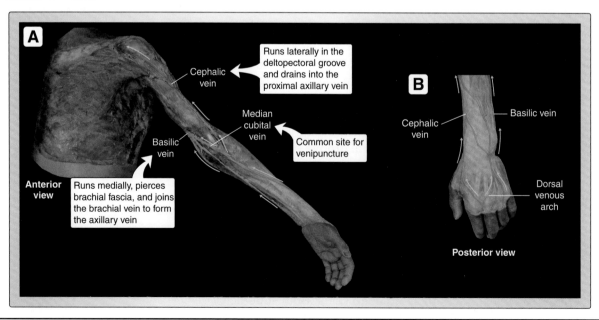

Figure 7.10
Superficial veins. A, Upper limb superficial vein network. B, Dorsum of hand venous network. Green arrows indicate direction of blood flow.

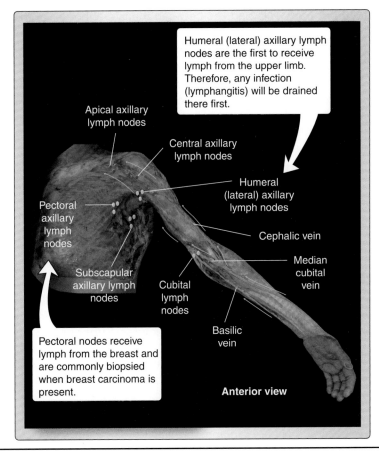

Apical axillary lymph nodes

Central axillary lymph nodes

Humeral (lateral) axillary lymph nodes are the first to receive lymph from the upper limb. Therefore, any infection (lymphangitis) will be drained there first.

Humeral (lateral) axillary lymph nodes

Pectoral axillary lymph nodes

Cephalic vein

Median cubital vein

Subscapular axillary lymph nodes

Cubital lymph nodes

Basilic vein

Pectoral nodes receive lymph from the breast and are commonly biopsied when breast carcinoma is present.

Anterior view

Clinical Application 7.5: Venipuncture

Superficial veins are generally easily used for blood draws or placement of intravenous (IV) lines (see Fig. 7.12). The median cubital vein is easily accessible for blood sampling, while the superficial dorsal venous network and distal basilic or cephalic veins are common sites for IV placement. Special attention needs to be taken when performing venipuncture because of variations in venous organization and the presence of valves because these structures will interrupt blood flow.

Figure 7.11
Lymphatics of the upper limb. Green arrows indicate direction of lymph flow.

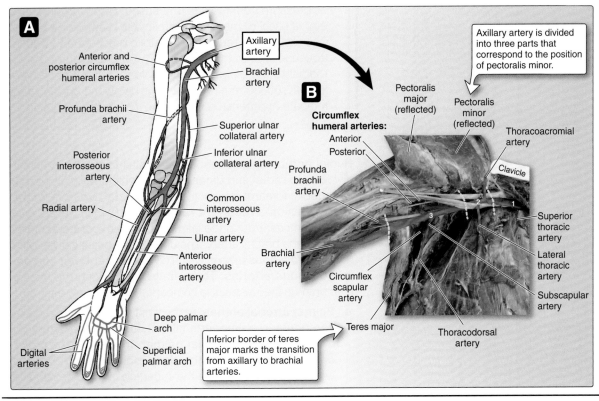

Anterior and posterior circumflex humeral arteries

Profunda brachii artery

Posterior interosseous artery

Radial artery

Deep palmar arch

Digital arteries

Superficial palmar arch

Axillary artery

Brachial artery

Superior ulnar collateral artery

Inferior ulnar collateral artery

Common interosseous artery

Ulnar artery

Anterior interosseous artery

Brachial artery

Inferior border of teres major marks the transition from axillary to brachial arteries.

Axillary artery is divided into three parts that correspond to the position of pectoralis minor.

Pectoralis major (reflected)

Pectoralis minor (reflected)

Thoracoacromial artery

Clavicle

Circumflex humeral arteries:
Anterior
Posterior

Profunda brachii artery

Circumflex scapular artery

Teres major

Thoracodorsal artery

Superior thoracic artery

Lateral thoracic artery

Subscapular artery

Figure 7.12
Arterial supply. A, Axillary artery through palmar arches. B, Dissection of axillary artery and branches (brachial plexus terminal nerves reflected). Numbers correspond to the three different parts of the axillary artery.

a. **First part:** This part lies between the lateral border of the first rib and the medial border of pectoralis minor and gives off one branch—**superior thoracic artery**—to the second intercostal space.

b. **Second part:** This part lies deep to the pectoralis minor and gives off two branches—**thoracoacromial** and **lateral thoracic arteries**. The thoracoacromial artery gives off clavicular, pectoral, deltoid, and acromial branches that serve those respective structures. The lateral thoracic supplies the lateral pectoral region and serratus anterior muscle.

c. **Third part:** This part lies between the lateral border of pectoralis minor and the inferior border of teres major and gives off three branches—**anterior** and **posterior circumflex humeral** and **subscapular arteries**. The circumflex humeral arteries anastomose around the surgical neck of the humerus. The subscapular artery further divides into **circumflex scapular** and **thoracodorsal arteries**.

3. **Brachial artery:** After crossing the inferior border of the teres major, the axillary artery continues as the **brachial artery**. It supplies structures in the anterior arm and gives off a **profunda brachii artery** to serve the posterior arm structures. **Superior** and **inferior ulnar collateral arteries** arise from the brachial artery medially and travel posterior and anterior to the medial epicondyle, respectively, to contribute to the collateral blood flow of the elbow.

> Blood pressure is commonly assessed at the brachial artery. The artery is occluded against the humeral shaft by a blood pressure cuff, and arterial sounds are observed with a stethoscope over the brachial artery in the cubital fossa as pressure from the cuff is released. A sphygmomanometer is used to measure systolic and diastolic pressures. The first sound represents systolic pressure and the first absence of sound, diastolic. Brachial pulse can be felt medial to the bicipital tendon. Normal blood pressure is 90–120/60–80 mm Hg. Readings below the normal range indicate hypotension and above indicate hypertension.

4. **Radial and ulnar arteries:** In the cubital fossa, the brachial artery divides into **radial** and **ulnar arteries**, which travel along the lateral and medial forearm, respectively. Just distal to its origin, the radial artery gives off a **recurrent radial artery**, which travels proximally to anastomose around the lateral elbow with collateral branches of the profunda brachii artery. The ulnar artery quickly gives off a **common interosseous artery**, which divides into **anterior** and **posterior interosseous arteries**. These travel deep along the interosseous membrane in their respective compartments to supply deep structures.

a. **Palmar arterial arches:** At the wrist, the ulnar and radial arteries contribute to palmar arterial arches. The ulnar artery primarily makes up the **superficial palmar arch**, while the radial artery contributes mainly to the **deep palmar arch**. Both arteries anastomose to complete the superficial and deep palmar arches.

Clinical Application 7.7: Raynaud Disease

Raynaud disease is vasoconstriction of the digital arteries of idiopathic origin. Overactive postganglionic sympathetic fibers are believed to cause the vasoconstriction. Cold temperatures and emotional stimuli may trigger the ischemic event, which is characterized by numbness, pain, and skin color changes due to ischemia and reperfusion. Surgical correction in the upper limb may include presynaptic sympathectomy. This can also occur in the lower limb.

b. **Digital supply:** The radial artery also gives off the **princeps pollicis** and **radialis indicis arteries** to the first and second digits, respectively. **Common palmar digital arteries** arise from the superficial palmar arch and give rise to **proper palmar digital arteries** in the digits. **Dorsal digital arteries arise** from the dorsal carpal arch.

F. Innervation

Upper limb structures are innervated by branches of the **brachial plexus**, a collection of anterior primary rami from C_5–C_8 and T_1 (Fig. 7.13).

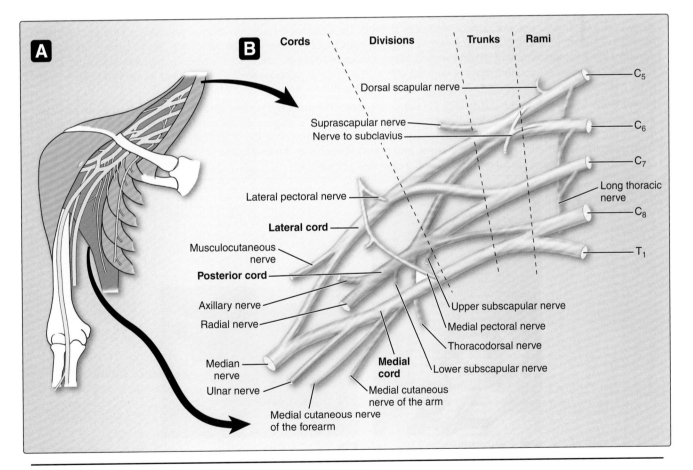

Figure 7.13
Brachial plexus organization. A, In situ. Note rami and trunks in posterior triangle of neck, divisions running deep to clavicle, and chords and terminal branches in axilla. B, Schematic representation of right brachial plexus from rami to terminal nerves.

1. **Brachial plexus:** The brachial plexus is divided into five parts from proximal to distal—**rami**, **trunks** (upper, middle, and lower), **divisions** (anterior and posterior), **cords** (lateral, medial, and posterior), and **terminal branches**. Small branches arise from rami, trunks, and cords. Cords and branches are contained within the axilla.

   a. **Rami (C_5–C_8, T_1):** Anterior rami branch from spinal nerves exiting the vertebral column in the neck and emerge between the anterior and middle scalene muscles. The **dorsal scapular** (C_5) **nerve** arises from C_5 anterior rambus.

   b. **Trunks:** In the posterior triangle of the neck, anterior rami from C_5–C_6 merge to form the upper trunk, C_7 continues as the middle trunk, and C_8 and T_1 merge to form the lower trunk. The **nerve to subclavius** (C_5–C_6) and the **suprascapular** (C_5–C_6) **nerve** arise from the upper trunk.

   c. **Divisions:** Trunks divide into anterior and posterior divisions that serve pre- and postaxial structures, respectively. Divisions are found deep to the clavicle and have no branches.

Clinical Application 7.8: Brachial Plexus Injuries

Upper trunk injury (Erb-Duchenne palsy): Excessive separation or stretch between the shoulder and neck can cause injury to the C_5 and C_6 anterior rami or the upper trunk of the brachial plexus, resulting in paralysis of shoulder and arm muscles. Muscles innervated by suprascapular, axillary, subscapular, musculocutaneous, and lateral pectoral nerves are more notably affected. A patient will present with his or her upper limb in a "waiter's tip" position, where the arm is adducted, extended and internally rotated, elbow extended, and forearm pronated because of the number of muscles paralyzed. Loss of sensation on the lateral arm/forearm is also typically present.

Lower trunk injury (Klumpke paralysis): Excessive separation or stretch between the arm and trunk can injure the lower trunk of the brachial plexus or C_8 and T_1 anterior rami directly, resulting in paralysis of muscles innervated by the ulnar and medial pectoral nerves. A patient will present with "claw hand" mainly because of the paralysis of the medial lumbricals. Over time, the fourth and fifth digits will move into hyperextension at the metacarpophalangeal joints and flexion at the proximal interphalangeal joints, giving the hand a claw-like appearance.

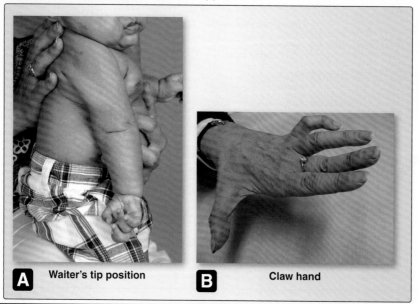

A Waiter's tip position   **B** Claw hand

Brachial plexus injuries. A, Upper trunk injury showing "waiter's tip" position in an infant. B, Lower trunk injury showing "claw hand" presentation.

d. **Cords:** Anterior divisions from the upper and middle trunks join to form the lateral cord. Posterior divisions from all trunks join to form the posterior cord. The anterior division from the lower trunk continues as the medial cord. Cords are named by their relationship with the axillary artery.

   [1] **Lateral cord:** This gives off the **lateral pectoral nerve** (C_5–C_7).

   [2] **Medial cord:** This gives off the **medial pectoral** (C_8–T_1), **medial brachial cutaneous** (C_8–T_1), and **medial antebrachial cutaneous** (C_8–T_1) nerves.

   [3] **Posterior cord:** This gives off **upper subscapular** (C_5–C_6), **thoracodorsal** (middle subscapular, C_6–C_8), and **lower subscapular** (C_5–C_6) nerves.

e. **Terminal branches:** Each cord terminates in two terminal branches. The **median nerve** (C_5–C_8, T_1) is made up of the lateral and medial roots (Fig. 7.14).

   [1] **Lateral cord:** This divides into the lateral root of the median nerve and **musculocutaneous nerve** (C_5–C_7).

   [2] **Medial cord:** This divides into the medial root of the median nerve and **ulnar nerve** (C_8–T_1).

   [3] **Posterior cord:** This divides into **axillary** (C_5–C_6) and **radial** (C_5–C_8, T_1) **nerves**.

> Brachial plexus nerve block is anesthesia given at different regions of the brachial plexus to allow for surgical intervention without general anesthesia. Common sites include supraclavicular, axillary sheath, and interscalene.

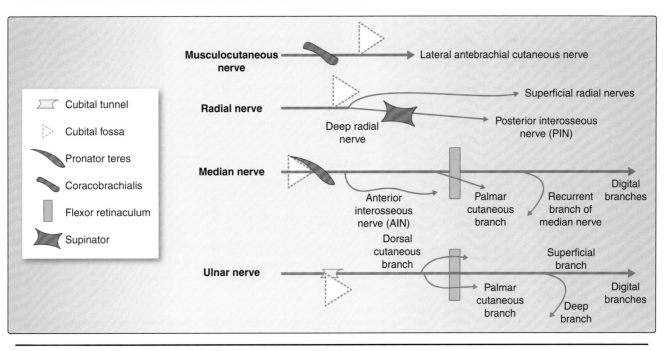

Figure 7.14
Terminal nerve distribution. Schematic drawings of terminal nerve pathway and branches (blue lines) and relationship between adjacent osseous, fascial, and muscular structures.

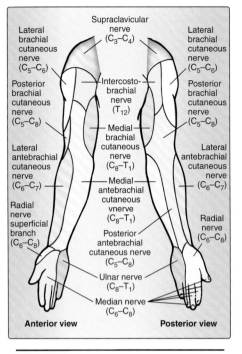

Figure 7.15
Cutaneous distribution in the upper limb.

2. **Cutaneous innervation:** Cutaneous innervation of the upper limb is relayed primarily through branches of the brachial plexus terminal nerves as well as **supraclavicular** (C_3–C_4) and **intercostobrachial** (T_2) nerves (Fig. 7.15). Postganglionic sympathetic fibers travel with branches to provide general visceral afferent and general visceral efferent innervation to upper limb structures. Parasympathetic fibers do not travel in the upper limb. See also Figure 6.19 for a dermatome map.

IV. EMBRYOLOGY

At the end of week 4, the upper limb buds form pronounced protrusions from the lateral body wall at the C5–T2 level (Fig. 7.16). In general, the upper limb bud consists of a core of mesoderm that is covered by ectoderm. Mesoderm from the lateral plate (**lateral plate mesoderm**) migrates into the upper limb bud and condenses in the center of the limb bud to eventually form the **skeletal component** (i.e., bone, ligaments, tendons, and dermis) of the upper limb. Mesoderm from the somites (**somitomeric mesoderm**) migrates into the upper limb bud and condenses into a posterior extensor condensation and an anterior flexor condensation to eventually form the **muscular component** of the upper limb.

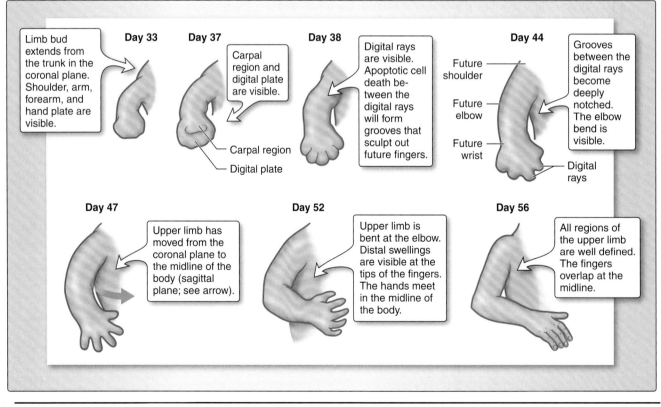

Figure 7.16
Embryologic development of the upper limb.

> Limb development occurs over a 5-week period extending from week 4 to week 8. The upper limbs develop in advance of the lowers limbs. The upper limb bud appears first at day 24, whereas the lower limb bud appears second at day 28.

A. Special development zones

The upper limb bud displays two specialized areas called the **zone of polarizing activity** (**ZPA**) and the **apical ectodermal ridge** (**AER**) that play an important role in the development of the upper limb. The ZPA consists of mesodermal cells located just beneath the AER along the caudal margin of the upper limb bud. The AER is a thickened ridge of ectoderm at the tip of the upper limb bud.

B. Development axes

The upper limb bud develops with respect to three axes. The **proximal-distal axis** runs from the shoulder to the fingers. The **cranial–caudal axis** runs from the thumb to the little finger. The **posterior–anterior axis** runs from the back of the hand to the palm of the hand.

> Numerous genes are involved in limb development: *WNT3, WNT7a, SHH, LMBR1, GLI3, TBX3, TBX4, TBX5, PITX1, TP73L (P63), DLX5, HOXD13, HOXA13, HOXD11, NIPBL, GDF5, ROR2, IHH, FGFR2,* and *EN1.* Mutations in any one of these genes will result in a congenital limb anomaly.

C. Bone formation

The lateral plate mesoderm migrates into the upper limb bud and condenses in the center of the upper limb bud to eventually form the **skeletal component** of the upper limb. The lateral plate mesoderm forms the **scapula, clavicle, humerus, radius, ulna, carpals, metacarpals,** and **phalanges**. All the bones of the upper limb undergo endochondral ossification. However, the clavicle undergoes both membranous and endochondral ossification.

D. Muscle formation

The upper limb bud site lies opposite somites C4–C8, T1, and T2. During week 5, mesoderm from these somites (myotomes) migrates into the limb bud and forms a **posterior extensor condensation** of mesoderm and an **anterior flexor condensation** of mesoderm. The mesoderm of these condensations differentiates into myoblasts. Then, the condensations split into anatomically recognizable muscles of the upper limb, although little is known about this process.

1. **Posterior extensor condensation of mesoderm:** In general, this gives rise to the **extensor and supinator musculature** (Table 7.1).

2. **Anterior flexor condensation of mesoderm:** In general, this gives rise to the flexor and pronator musculature (see Table 7.1).

Table 7.1: Posterior and Anterior Mesoderm Condensations Into Muscle

Posterior Extensor Condensation	Anterior Flexor Condensation
Deltoid	Biceps brachii
Supraspinatus	Brachialis
Infraspinatus	Coracobrachialis
Teres minor	Pronator teres
Teres major	Flexor carpi radialis
Subscapularis	Palmaris longus
Triceps brachii	Flexor carpi ulnaris
Anconeus	Flexor digitorum superficialis
Brachioradialis	Flexor digitorum profundus
Extensor carpi radialis longus	Flexor pollicis brevis
Extensor carpi radialis brevis	Flexor pollicis longus
Extensor digitorum	Pronator quadratus
Extensor digiti minimi	Abductor pollicis brevis
Extensor carpi ulnaris	Opponens pollicis
Supinator	Adductor pollicis
Abductor pollicis longus	Abductor digiti minimi
Extensor pollicis brevis	Flexor digiti minimi brevis
Extensor pollicis longus	Opponens digiti minimi
Extensor indicis	Lumbricals
	Palmar interossei
	Dorsal interossei

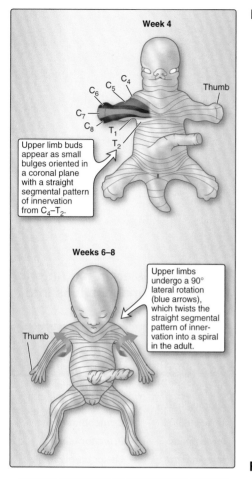

Figure 7.17
Rotation of the upper limb.

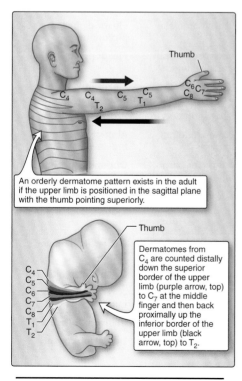

Figure 7.18
Dermatome pattern of the upper limb.

E. Brachial plexus formation

The axons within **anterior primary rami from C_5–C_8** and **T_1** arrive at the base of the upper limb bud and mix in a specific pattern to form the **upper trunk**, **middle trunk**, and **lower trunk** of the brachial plexus.

1. **Axon migration and directionality:** At this point, axon migration pauses at the base of the upper limb bud and then subsequently resumes so that axons are directed to either the posterior extensor condensation or the anterior flexor condensation. The direction that the axons take is controlled by the ***homeobox gene Lim1*** and its downstream target ***ephrin type A receptor 4*** (***EPHA4***), allowing axons to enter the posterior extensor condensation but avoiding the anterior flexor condensation.

2. **Cord formation:** The posterior divisions of the trunks grow into the posterior extensor condensation of mesoderm and join to form the **posterior cord**. The anterior divisions of the trunks grow into the anterior flexor condensation of mesoderm and join to form the **medial cord** and **lateral cord**.

3. **Terminal branch formation:** With further development of the limb musculature, the posterior cord branches into the **axillary nerve (C_5, C_6)** and **radial nerve (C_5–C_8, T_1)**, thereby innervating all the muscles that form from the posterior extensor condensation of mesoderm. With further development of the limb musculature, the medial cord and lateral cord branch into terminal nerves including the **musculocutaneous nerve (C_5–C_7)**, **ulnar nerve (C_8, T_1)**, and **median nerve (C_5–C_8, T_1)**, thereby innervating all the muscles that form from the anterior flexor condensation of mesoderm.

F. Upper limb vasculature formation

The upper limb vasculature formation involves the fates of the subclavian artery and the axis artery.

1. **Fate of the subclavian artery:** The **subclavian artery** enters the upper limb bud as the **axis artery**, which ends in a **terminal plexus** near the tip of the upper limb bud. The **terminal plexus** participates in the formation of the **deep palmar arch** and the **superficial palmar arch**.

2. **Fate of the axis artery:** The **axis artery** initially sprouts the **posterior interosseous artery** and the **median artery**. The median artery is typically regresses in the adult. The axis artery later sprouts the **radial artery** and **ulnar artery**. The axis artery persists in the adult as the **axillary artery**, **brachial artery**, **anterior interosseous artery**, and **deep palmar arch**.

G. Rotation and dermatome pattern

At week 4, the upper limb buds appear as small bulges oriented in the **coronal plane** (Fig. 7.17). In week 6, the upper limb buds undergo a horizontal movement, so that they are now oriented in the **sagittal plane**. During weeks 6–8, the upper limbs undergo a **90° lateral rotation**, such that the elbow points posteriorly, the extensor compartment lies posterior, and the flexor compartment lies anterior. The 90° lateral rotation of the upper limb bud alters the originally straight segmental pattern of innervation in the embryo; that is, the pattern of innervation becomes "twisted in a spiral" in the adult (Fig. 7.18).

Clinical Application 7.9: Congenital Limb Anomalies

Congenital anomalies of the limbs fall into four general categories:
1. In reduction defects, a part of the limb is missing (meromelia), or the entire limb is missing (amelia).
2. In duplication defects, extra digits are present (polydactyly).
3. In dysplasia defects, fusion of digits occurs (syndactyly), or a disproportionate growth of the limb occurs.
4. In deformation defects, physical forces damage the developing limb (e.g., amniotic band syndrome).

Numerous drugs (teratogens) cause limb anomalies: 5′-fluoro-2-deoxyuridine, acetazolamide, valproic acid, phenytoin, warfarin, thalidomide, alcohol, and cocaine.

V. MUSCULATURE

The muscles of the upper limb are organized into specific compartments or regions: shoulder, arm, forearm, and hand. The muscles in these compartments commonly share similar neurovascular supply and overall function(s), with a few exceptions. The following section details the contents of each compartment.

A. Shoulder

The shoulder region is the most proximal portion of the upper extremity, serving as the connection between the upper limb and the trunk. It comprises a collection of joints organized in the shoulder girdle and is characterized by its ability to move through an extensive range of motion. The health and functionality of the shoulder complex often suffer as a result of the region's freedom of movement. Muscles of the shoulder complex include **anterior** and **posterior axioappendicular muscles** and **intrinsic scapular muscles**. The pectoral region makes up the anterior axioappendicular muscles, while superficial back muscles (previously described in Chapter 2) make up the posterior axioappendicular muscles. These two groups connect the upper limb (scapula, clavicle, and humerus) to the axial skeleton (vertebral column, sternum, and ribs). The **axilla** (armpit) is a pyramid-shaped space that is bound by the musculature and bones of this region. It contains important neurovascular structures that serve the upper limb. Movements at the shoulder complex include elevation, depression, rotation, protraction and retraction of the scapula and flexion, extension, abduction, adduction, medial (internal) rotation, lateral (external) rotation, and circumduction of the humerus (arm), as shown in Figure 7.19.

1. **Anterior axioappendicular muscles:** This group of muscles originates from the ribs, sternum, and clavicle to insert onto the humerus, scapula, and clavicle (Fig. 7.20).

    a. **Pectoralis major:** This muscle has clavicular and sternocostal heads (origins) that collectively insert onto the lateral lip of intertubercular groove and adduct and medially rotate the arm.

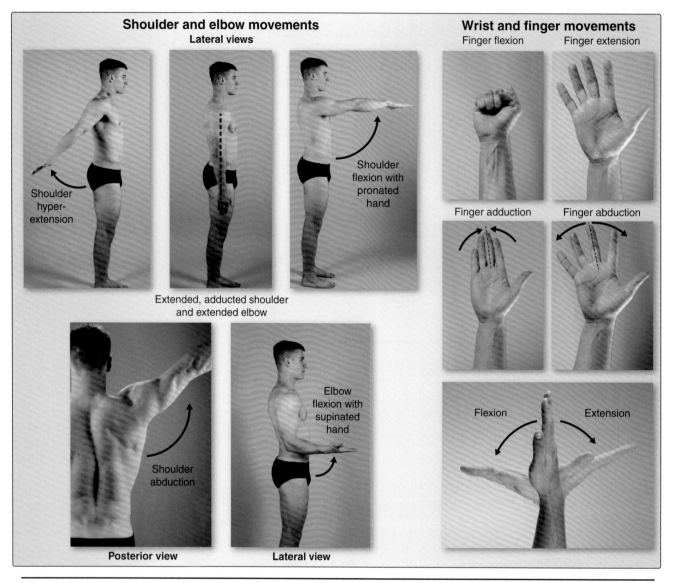

Figure 7.19
Movements of the upper limb joints.

    [1] Clavicular head: This also flexes the arm and is innervated by the lateral pectoral nerve.

    [2] Sternocostal head: This also extends arm from a flexed position and is innervated by the medial pectoral nerve.

  b. Pectoralis minor: This muscle originates from ribs 3 to 5 to insert onto the coracoid process. It stabilizes the scapula by depressing and pulling anteriorly and is innervated by the medial pectoral nerve.

  c. Serratus anterior: This muscle originates from ribs 1 to 8 and inserts onto the anterior medial border of the scapula. It protracts and rotates the scapula and stabilizes the scapula against the thoracic cage. It is innervated by the long thoracic nerve.

  d. Subclavius: This muscle originates from the first rib and inserts onto the inferior clavicle. It anchors the clavicle and is innervated by the nerve to the subclavius.

2. **Posterior axioappendicular muscles:** This group of muscles originates from the axial skeleton (pelvis, spine, and occiput) and inserts onto the scapula, clavicle, and humerus (Fig. 7.21; see also Figs. 2.28 and 2.29).

a. **Trapezius:** This muscle originates from the external occipital protuberance, nuchal ligament, and thoracic spinous processes and inserts along the superior border of the scapular spine, acromion, and lateral third of the clavicle. It is innervated by the accessory nerve (cranial nerve XI) and has proprioceptive fibers from anterior rami C_3–C_4. This muscle has an upper, middle, and lower portion.

[1] **Upper:** This portion elevates and rotates the scapula upward.

[2] **Middle:** This portion retracts the scapula.

[3] **Lower:** This portion depresses and rotates the scapula upward.

b. **Latissimus dorsi:** This muscle originates from the iliac crest and thoracolumbar fascia and inserts into the floor of the intertubercular groove. It extends, adducts, and medially rotates the arm and is innervated by the thoracodorsal nerve.

c. **Rhomboid major and minor:** This pair of muscles originates from the inferior portions of the nuchal ligament (minor) and upper thoracic spinous processes (major) and inserts along the medial border of the scapula at the level of the spine (minor) and inferior (major). They retract and downwardly rotate the scapula and are innervated by the dorsal scapular nerve.

d. **Levator scapulae:** This muscle originates from cervical transverse processes and inserts along the superior medial border of the scapula. It elevates and downwardly rotates the scapula. Its upper slips are innervated by anterior rami C_3–C_4 and lower slips by the dorsal scapular nerve.

Scapular rotation occurs at the scapulothoracic interface in the frontal plane around a sagittal (anterior/posterior) axis. Upward rotation of the scapula is necessary after 30° of humeral abduction to reach full range of motion. After 30°, the scapula rotates 1° for every 2° of humeral abduction. This is referred to as *scapulohumeral rhythm*. Therefore, any limitation of scapular rotation will also limit humeral abduction.

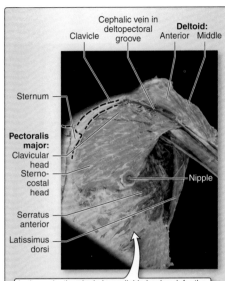

In the male, the nipple is a reliable landmark for the fourth intercostal space. Owing to variable amounts of adipose in the female breast, this relationship does not always exist.

Anterior view, superficial

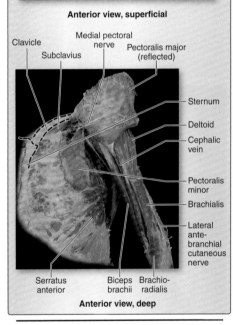

Anterior view, deep

Figure 7.20
Anterior axioappendicular muscles.

Clinical Application 7.10: Winged Scapula

Lesion of the long thoracic nerve will paralyze the serratus anterior muscle, resulting in a "winged" scapula. The medial border and inferior angle of the affected scapula will protrude posteriorly away from the thoracic cage, especially when the patient pushes against resistance. Full abduction of the affected limb is impossible because the serratus anterior is unable to assist with upward scapular rotation.

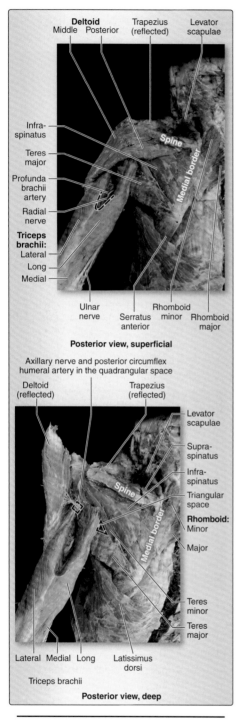

Posterior view, superficial

Axillary nerve and posterior circumflex
humeral artery in the quadrangular space

Posterior view, deep

Figure 7.21
Posterior axioappendicular muscles.

3. **Intrinsic scapular muscles:** Intrinsic scapular muscles arise directly from the scapula to insert onto the humerus (Fig. 7.22). This group includes the deltoid, teres major, supraspinatus, infraspinatus, teres minor, and subscapularis. The latter four comprise the **rotator cuff muscles**, which collectively work to stabilize the humeral head in the glenoid fossa and support the glenohumeral joint.

   a. **Deltoid:** This muscle originates along the inferior border of the scapular spine, acromion, and lateral third of the clavicle and inserts onto the deltoid tubercle. It is innervated by the axillary nerve. It is divided into anterior, middle, and posterior parts.

   [1] **Anterior:** This part flexes and medially rotates the arm.

   [2] **Middle:** This part is the main abductor of the arm.

   [3] **Posterior:** This part extends and laterally rotates the arm.

   b. **Teres major:** This muscle originates from the lateral border of the scapula and inserts onto the medial lip of the intertubercular

---

Clinical Application 7.11: Rotator Cuff Pathology

The supraspinatus tendon is more commonly implicated in rotator cuff injuries, primarily because of the small osseoligamentous path by which it travels to insert onto the greater tubercle. Repetitive overhead activities, paired with poor mechanics and unbalanced muscles, drive the humeral head superiorly into the underside of the acromion and cause microtrauma to the supraspinatus tendon. Chronic inflammation can lead to calcification within the tendon and partial or complete tear. Owing to the proximity of the subacromial bursa, bursitis may also accompany rotator cuff pathology. Pain associated with rotator cuff injury and bursitis is often exacerbated when patient is asked to abduct his or her arm above 50° ("painful arc syndrome").

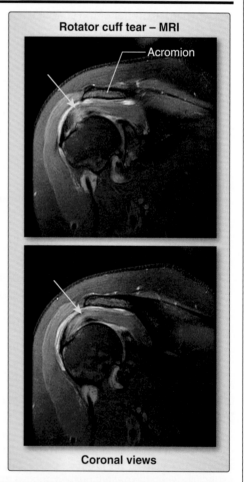

Coronal views

Rotator cuff pathology. MRI showing supraspinatus tendon tear (yellow arrows).

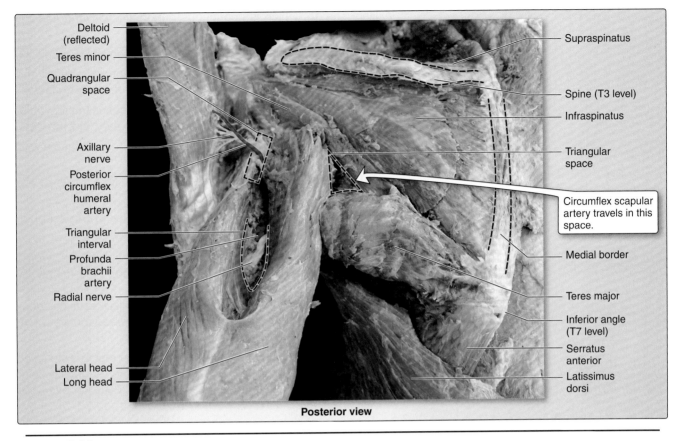

Deltoid (reflected)
Teres minor
Quadrangular space
Axillary nerve
Posterior circumflex humeral artery
Triangular interval
Profunda brachii artery
Radial nerve
Lateral head
Long head

Supraspinatus
Spine (T3 level)
Infraspinatus
Triangular space
Circumflex scapular artery travels in this space.
Medial border
Teres major
Inferior angle (T7 level)
Serratus anterior
Latissimus dorsi

Posterior view

Figure 7.22
Intrinsic scapular muscles.

groove. It adducts and medially rotates the arm and assists in arm extension. It is innervated by the lower subscapular nerve.

c. **Supraspinatus:** This muscle originates from the supraspinous fossa and inserts onto the (superior) greater tubercle. It initiates and assists in arm abduction and is innervated by the suprascapular nerve.

d. **Infraspinatus:** This muscle originates from the infraspinous fossa and inserts onto the (middle) greater tubercle. It laterally rotates the arm and is innervated by the suprascapular nerve.

e. **Teres minor:** This muscle originates from the lateral border of the scapula and inserts onto the (inferior) greater tubercle. It laterally rotates the arm and is innervated by the axillary nerve.

f. **Subscapularis:** This muscle originates from the subscapular fossa and inserts onto the lesser tubercle. It adducts and medially rotates the arm and is innervated by the upper and lower subscapular nerves.

4. **Axilla:** The axilla is a pyramid-shaped space that spans between the root of the neck and arm (Fig. 7.23). It contains the infraclavicular portions of the brachial plexus (chords and terminal branches), axillary vessels and branches, lymph vessels and nodes, and fat. Axillary vessels and nervous structures are contained within a fascial

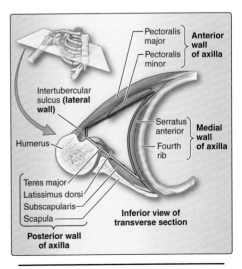

Pectoralis major
Pectoralis minor
Anterior wall of axilla
Intertubercular sulcus **(lateral wall)**
Serratus anterior
Fourth rib
Medial wall of axilla
Humerus
Teres major
Latissimus dorsi
Subscapularis
Scapula
Inferior view of transverse section
Posterior wall of axilla

Figure 7.23
Axilla.

axillary sheath, which is continuous proximally with the cervical prevertebral fascia (Fig. 7.24).

a. **Boundaries:** The boundaries of the axilla are shown in Figure 7.23.

[1] **Anterior:** This includes subclavius, pectoralis major and minor (anterior axillary fold) muscles, and overlying fascia.

[2] **Posterior:** This includes the scapula and subscapularis, latissimus dorsi, and teres major (posterior axillary fold) muscles.

[3] **Medial:** This includes the serratus anterior muscle and underlying ribs.

[4] **Lateral:** This includes the intertubercular groove of the humerus.

[5] **Apex:** This includes the superior border of the scapula, clavicle, and first rib (cervicoaxillary canal).

[6] **Base:** This includes skin and axillary fascia.

b. **Blood supply:** The shoulder complex is supplied mainly by branches from the axillary artery (see III. E). Posterior axioappendicular and intrinsic scapular muscles also receive vasculature from subclavian artery branches (suprascapular, dorsal scapular, and transverse cervical).

5. **Innervation:** Cutaneous innervation of the shoulder region is mediated by superior lateral brachial cutaneous (from axillary) supraclavicular and intercostobrachial nerves (see Fig. 7.15). The skin overlying

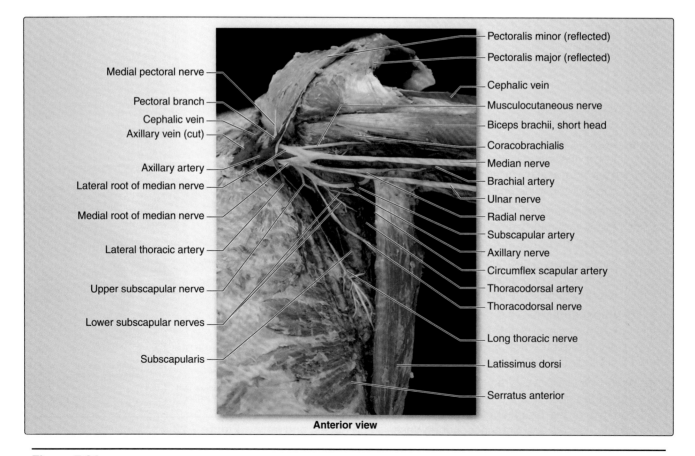

Medial pectoral nerve
Pectoral branch
Cephalic vein
Axillary vein (cut)
Axillary artery
Lateral root of median nerve
Medial root of median nerve
Lateral thoracic artery
Upper subscapular nerve
Lower subscapular nerves
Subscapularis

Pectoralis minor (reflected)
Pectoralis major (reflected)
Cephalic vein
Musculocutaneous nerve
Biceps brachii, short head
Coracobrachialis
Median nerve
Brachial artery
Ulnar nerve
Radial nerve
Subscapular artery
Axillary nerve
Circumflex scapular artery
Thoracodorsal artery
Thoracodorsal nerve
Long thoracic nerve
Latissimus dorsi
Serratus anterior

Anterior view

Figure 7.24
Boundaries of axilla.

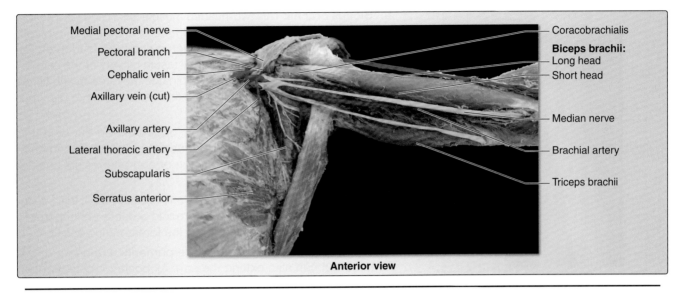

Figure 7.25
Superficial arm structures.

the superficial back muscles (posterior axioappendicular group) is segmentally innervated by posterior primary rami. The main dermatomes in the shoulder region are C_4–C_6 and T_2–T_4 (see Fig. 6.19).

B. Arm

The humerus is the main bone of the arm, which spans between the shoulder (glenohumeral) and elbow (humeroradial, humeroulnar, and proximal radioulnar) joints. Brachial fascia divides the arm into anterior and posterior compartments. Muscles of the arm cross both the shoulder and elbow joints; thus, some act at both joints. Muscles of the arm flex and extend the arm and flex, extend, and supinate the forearm.

1. **Anterior arm:** These muscles are primarily flexors of the forearm, but can also flex the arm. All anterior compartment muscles are innervated by the musculocutaneous nerve (C_5–C_7). Branches from the brachial artery serve this compartment. Anterior arm muscles are shown in Figures 7.25 and 7.26.

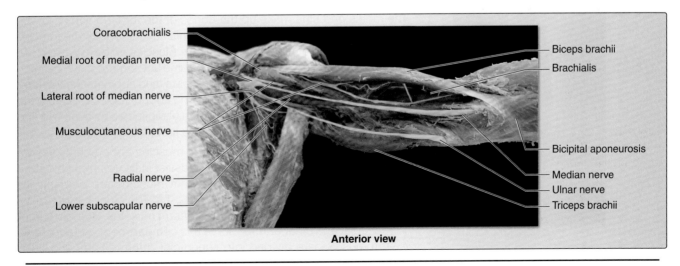

Figure 7.26
Deep anterior arm structures.

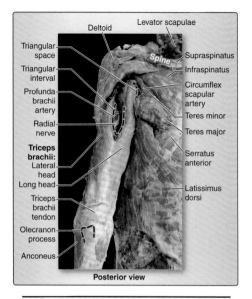

Figure 7.27
Posterior arm structures.

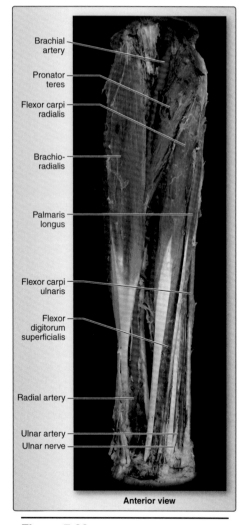

Figure 7.28
Flexor forearm structures. Superficial
and intermediate layers.

a. **Biceps brachii:** This two-headed muscle (short and long heads) originates from the supraglenoid tubercle (long) and coracoid process (short) and inserts through a common tendon on the radial tuberosity and antebrachial fascia by way of the bicipital aponeurosis. It flexes the arm, supinates the forearm and flexes the forearm when it is supinated, and resists anterior glenohumeral dislocation.

b. **Coracobrachialis:** This muscle originates on the coracoid process and inserts along the medial midshaft of humerus. It assists in flexion and adduction of arm and resists anterior glenohumeral dislocation.

c. **Brachialis:** This muscle originates on the distal half of the anterior humerus and inserts onto the coronoid process and tuberosity of ulna. It is the primary flexor of the forearm (any position).

2. **Posterior arm:** These muscles are primarily extensors of the forearm, but can also extend the arm. All posterior compartment muscles are innervated by the radial nerve (C_5–C_8, T_1). Branches from the profunda brachii artery serve this compartment. Posterior arm muscles are shown in Figure 7.27.

a. **Triceps brachii:** This three-headed muscle (long, lateral, and medial heads) originates from the infraglenoid tubercle (long), lateral to the radial groove (lateral), and medial to the radial groove (medial) and inserts through a common tendon on the olecranon process and antebrachial fascia. It extends the arm (long head) and the forearm.

b. **Anconeus:** This muscle originates from the lateral epicondyle of the humerus and inserts onto the olecranon and posterior proximal ulna. It assists in terminal extension of the arm and stabilizes the elbow.

3. **Innervation:** Cutaneous innervation of the arm is mediated primarily by **inferior lateral brachial cutaneous** (from radial), **medial brachial cutaneous**, and **posterior brachial cutaneous** (from radial) **nerves** (see Fig. 7.15). The main dermatomes in the arm are C_5–C_6 and T_1–T_2 (see Fig. 6.19).

C. Forearm

The radius and ulna make up the bones of the forearm, which spans between the elbow and wrist. Antebrachial fascia divides the forearm into anterior and posterior compartments. Muscles of the forearm cross the elbow, wrist, and hand joints; thus, some act at more than one joint. Muscles of the forearm flex, extend, pronate, and supinate the forearm; flex, extend, abduct (radial deviation), and adduct (ulnar deviation) the hand; and assist in flexion and extension of digits two through five and flexion, extension, and abduction of the first digit (thumb).

1. **Anterior forearm:** Anterior forearm muscles are primarily flexors of the hand and digits, but can also assist in flexion and pronation of the forearm. Anterior compartment muscles are primarily innervated by the median nerve (C_5–C_8, T_1). The ulnar nerve (C_8–T_1) innervates one and a half anterior forearm muscles. Branches from the radial and ulnar arteries serve this compartment. Anterior forearm muscles are divided into superficial, intermediate, and deep groups (Fig. 7.28).

a. **Superficial:** The common flexor tendon serves as the collective origin for most muscles in this group.

   [1] **Pronator teres:** This muscle originates from the medial epicondyle of the humerus and the coronoid process of the ulna and inserts onto the midshaft lateral radius. It pronates and flexes the forearm and is innervated by the median nerve.

   [2] **Flexor carpi radialis:** This muscle originates from the medial epicondyle of the humerus and inserts onto the second metacarpal base. It flexes and abducts the hand and is innervated by the median nerve.

   [3] **Palmaris longus:** This muscle, when present, originates from the medial epicondyle of the humerus and inserts into the palmar aponeurosis. It flexes the hand and puts tension on the palmar aponeurosis. It is innervated by the median nerve.

   [4] **Flexor carpi ulnaris:** This muscle originates from the olecranon and inserts onto the carpal (pisiform and hamate) and fifth metacarpal bones. It flexes and adducts the hand and is innervated by the ulnar nerve.

b. **Intermediate:** The **flexor digitorum superficialis** is the muscle that originates from the medial epicondyle of the humerus, coronoid process of the ulna, and the proximal radius and inserts onto the shafts of the middle phalanges of digits two through five (see Fig. 7.28). It assists in hand flexion and flexes the second through fifth proximal interphalangeal (PIP) and metacarpophalangeal (MCP) joints. It is innervated by the median nerve.

c. **Deep:** Figure 7.29 shows muscles in this group.

   [1] **Flexor digitorum profundus:** This muscle originates from the proximal ulna and interosseous membrane and inserts onto the base of distal phalanges of digits two through five. It assists in hand flexion and flexes the second through fifth distal interphalangeal (DIP) joints. Its lateral half is innervated by the anterior interosseous nerve (deep branch of median nerve). Its medial half is innervated by the ulnar nerve.

   [2] **Flexor pollicis longus:** This muscle originates from the middle radius and interosseous membrane and inserts onto the base of the distal phalanx of the thumb. It flexes the interphalangeal (IP) joint of the thumb and is innervated by the anterior interosseous nerve.

Anterior view

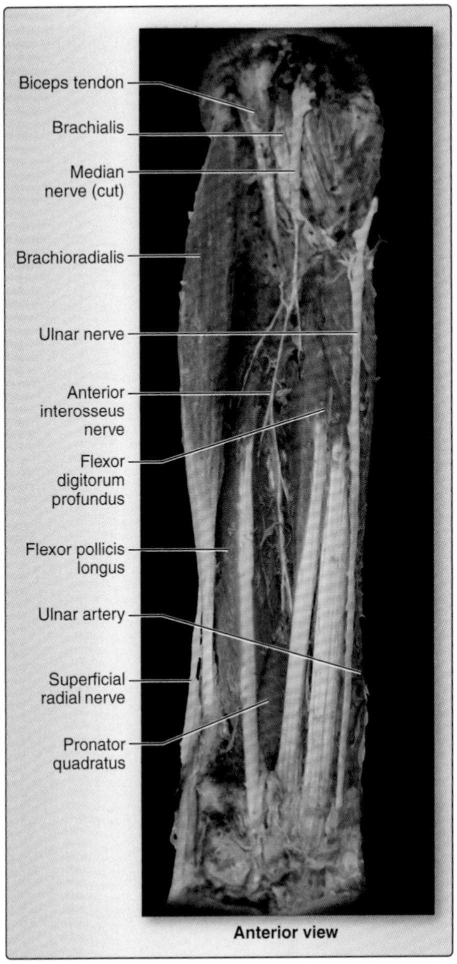

Figure 7.29
Flexor forearm structures. Deep layer.

Clinical Application 7.12: Tendonitis and Tenosynovitis

The upper limb is vulnerable to tendonitis (inflammation of the tendon) and tenosynovitis (inflammation of tendon and synovial sheath) at different locations. Common sites for inflammation include supraspinatus (rotator cuff tendonitis), biceps brachii, common flexor and extensor tendons (golf and tennis elbow, respectively), and outcropping muscles (De Quervain tenosynovitis). Inflammation can be acute or chronic and typically occurs as a result of overuse paired with poor mechanics.

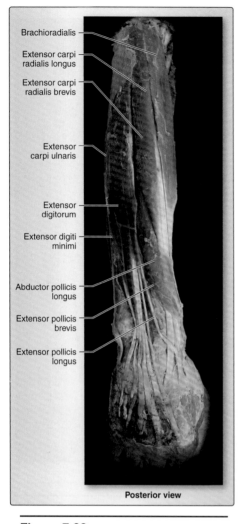

Brachioradialis

Extensor carpi
radialis longus

Extensor carpi
radialis brevis

Extensor
carpi ulnaris

Extensor
digitorum

Extensor digiti
minimi

Abductor pollicis
longus

Extensor pollicis
brevis

Extensor pollicis
longus

Posterior view

Figure 7.30
Extensor forearm structures.
Superficial layer.

[3] Pronator quadratus: This muscle originates on the distal ulna and inserts onto the distal radius. It pronates the forearm and supports the distal radioulnar joint. It is innervated by the anterior interosseous nerve.

2. **Posterior forearm:** Posterior forearm muscles are primarily extensors of the hand and digits, but can also assist in flexion and supination of the forearm (Fig. 7.30). Posterior compartment muscles are innervated by the radial nerve (C_5–C_8, T_1) and its branches (Figs. 7.31 and 7.32). Branches from the radial and ulnar arteries serve this compartment. Posterior forearm muscles are divided into superficial and deep groups.

a. **Superficial:** The common extensor tendon serves as the collective origin for a portion of this group.

   [1] Brachioradialis: This muscle originates from the supraepicondylar ridge of the humerus and inserts onto the distal lateral radius. It assists in flexion of the forearm (when in the midpronated position) and is innervated by the radial nerve.

   [2] Extensor carpi radialis longus: This muscle originates from the lateral supraepicondylar ridge of the humerus and inserts onto the second metacarpal base. It extends and abducts the hand and is innervated by the radial nerve.

   [3] Extensor carpi radialis brevis: This muscle originates from the lateral epicondyle of the humerus and inserts onto the third metacarpal base. It extends and abducts the hand and is innervated by the deep radial nerve.

   [4] Extensor digitorum: This muscle originates from the lateral epicondyle of the humerus and inserts onto the extensor expansions of digits two through five. It extends digits two through five at MCP joints and assists in IP extension. It is innervated by the posterior interosseous nerve.

   [5] Extensor digiti minimi: This muscle originates from the lateral epicondyle of the humerus and inserts onto the extensor expansion of the fifth digit. It extends the fifth digit at MCP joints and assists in IP extension. It is innervated by the posterior interosseous nerve.

   [6] Extensor carpi ulnaris: This muscle originates from the lateral epicondyle of the humerus and posterior ulna and inserts onto the dorsal base of the fifth metacarpal. It extends and adducts the hand and is innervated by the posterior interosseous nerve.

b. **Deep:** Figure 7.33 shows muscles in this group.

   [1] Supinator: This muscle originates from the lateral epicondyle of the humerus, radial ligaments, ulnar crest, and supinator fossa. It supinates the forearm and is innervated by the deep radial nerve.

   [2] Outcropping muscles: All **outcropping muscles** in the deep compartment are innervated by the posterior interosseous nerve.

   a. **Abductor pollicis longus:** This muscle originates from the proximal ulna, radius, and interosseous membrane and inserts onto the base of the first metacarpal bone.

It abducts the thumb and aids in extension at the carpometacarpal (CMC) joint.

b. **Extensor pollicis longus:** This muscle originates from the midshaft of the ulna and interosseous membrane and inserts onto the base of the distal phalanx of the thumb. It extends all thumb joints.

c. **Extensor pollicis brevis:** This muscle originates from the distal radius and interosseous membrane and inserts onto the base of the proximal phalanx of the thumb. It extends the MCP and CMC joints.

d. **Extensor indicis:** This muscle originates from the distal ulna and interosseous membrane and inserts onto the extensor expansion of the second digit. It extends the second digit (allows for extension independent of other digits) and assists in wrist extension.

3. **Cubital fossa:** The **cubital fossa** is a triangular-shaped region on the anterior elbow surface (Fig. 7.34). It is bound medially by the pronator teres, laterally by the brachioradialis, and superiorly by an imaginary line through the medial and lateral epicondyles of the humerus. The floor of the fossa is made up of the supinator and brachialis muscles, and the roof is the overlying fascia, adipose, and skin. Important neurovascular structures course within and superficial to the fossa, and their anatomical relationships are important to understand because the cubital fossa is a common area for drawing blood samples.

a. **Contents:** From lateral to medial, the contents are radial nerve and divisions (deep and superficial radial nerves), biceps brachii tendon, terminal portion of the brachial artery as it branches into radial and ulnar arteries (with accompanying deep veins), and the median nerve.

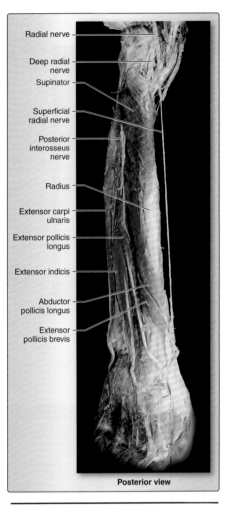

Posterior view

Figure 7.31
Extensor forearm structures. Deep layer.

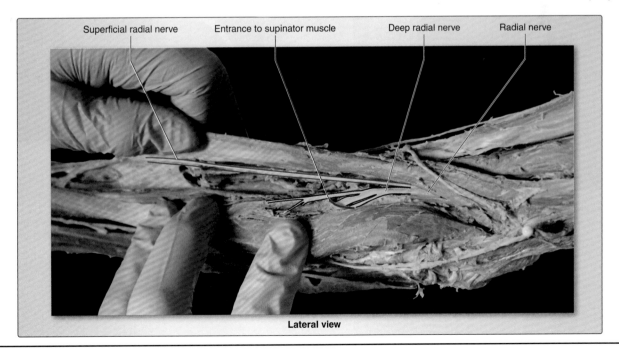

Lateral view

Figure 7.32
Branching of radial nerve at elbow.

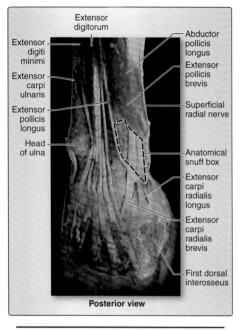

Figure 7.33
Anatomical snuffbox and dorsum
of hand.

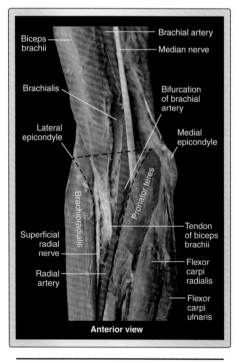

Figure 7.34
Cubital fossa. Black dotted line marks
cubital fossa boundaries.

Clinical Application 7.13: Radial Nerve Injury

Depending on the level of lesion, radial nerve injury can result in full loss of
elbow extension because of paralysis of the triceps brachii (proximal injury) and
wrist drop or just wrist drop (at or distal to spiral groove) with elbow
extension spared. Muscular branches to the triceps brachii long and lateral
heads are typically given off proximally. Wrist drop occurs because of paralysis
of wrist and finger extensors. The deep branch of the radial nerve can also
become impinged as it travels deep to the supinator muscle. Muscles of the
deep posterior forearm compartment would be affected.

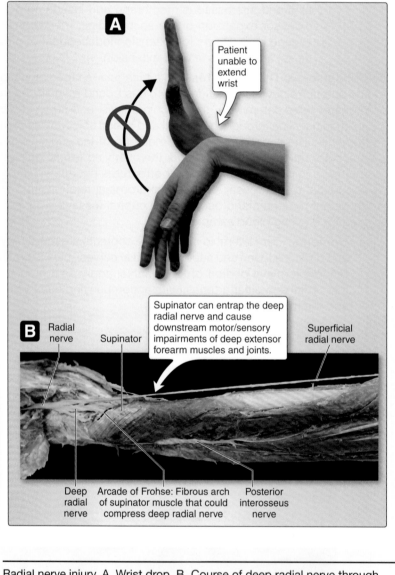

Radial nerve injury. A, Wrist drop. B, Course of deep radial nerve through
supinator muscle.

b. **Innervation:** Superficially, the median cubital vein courses across the cubital fossa, connecting cephalic and basilic veins. Medial and lateral antebrachial cutaneous nerves travel superficially alongside the basilic and cephalic veins, respectively.

4. **Innervation:** Cutaneous innervation of the forearm is mediated primarily by lateral antebrachial cutaneous (from musculocutaneous), medial antebrachial cutaneous, and posterior antebrachial cutaneous (from radial) nerves (see Fig. 7.15). The main dermatomes in the arm are C_5–C_8 and T_1 (see Fig. 6.19).

D. Hand

The hand is the distalmost portion of the upper limb and is connected to the forearm at the wrist. The hand is made up of 2 rows of **carpal** bones, 5 **metacarpals**, and a total of 14 **phalangeal** bones. The hand can be separated into three compartments, the **thenar eminence** (first digit muscular mass), **hypothenar eminence** (fifth digit muscular mass), and a **central compartment**. The deep fascia of the hand—**palmar aponeurosis**—covers the central compartment and further separates it from the thenar and hypothenar eminences. Terminal branches of the radial and ulnar arteries anastomose in a series of arterial arches to supply the hand. Hand movements include flexion, extension, abduction, and adduction of the digits as well as opposition of the first and fifth digits (Fig. 7.35; also see Fig. 7.19). The third digit represents the midline of the hand.

1. **Thenar compartment:** The thenar eminence is the muscular mass associated with the first digit—the thumb. Muscles in this compartment are innervated by the recurrent branch of the median nerve and include the **abductor pollicis brevis**, **flexor pollicis brevis**, and **opponens pollicis** (Fig. 7.36). Although not directly in the thenar eminence, the **adductor pollicis** does contribute to thumb movement. It is innervated by the deep branch of the ulnar nerve. Movement of the thumb is complex and imparts precision with fine motor tasks. At the CMC joint, abduction and adduction occur out of the palm in the sagittal plane, while flexion and extension occur in the frontal plane. Opposition is a complex motion that combines CMC extension, abduction, and medial rotation with MCP flexion. Flexor pollicis longus, abductor pollicis longus, extensor pollicis longus, and extensor pollicis brevis assist the intrinsic thumb muscles in achieving these movements.

2. **Hypothenar compartment:** The hypothenar eminence is the muscular mass associated with the fifth digit—the little finger. Muscles in this compartment are innervated by the deep branch of the ulnar nerve and include the **abductor digiti minimi**, **flexor digiti minimi brevis**, and **opponens digiti minimi** (Fig. 7.37). **Palmaris brevis** overlies the hypothenar group and shares a common innervation. It is located superficially to the hypothenar eminence and aids in increasing grip by wrinkling the skin on the medial palm.

3. **Central compartment:** The central compartment of the hand contains tendons of the long flexors and short intrinsic hand muscles—four **lumbricals** and seven **interossei** (three palmar and four dorsal). The lateral two lumbricals are innervated by the median nerve, while the

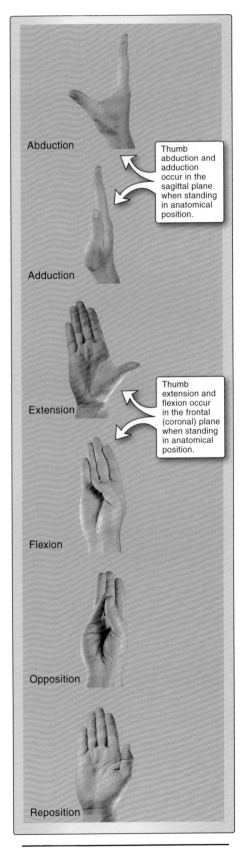

Abduction

Adduction

Thumb abduction and adduction occur in the sagittal plane when standing in anatomical position.

Extension

Flexion

Thumb extension and flexion occur in the frontal (coronal) plane when standing in anatomical position.

Opposition

Reposition

Figure 7.35
Movements of the thumb (first digit).

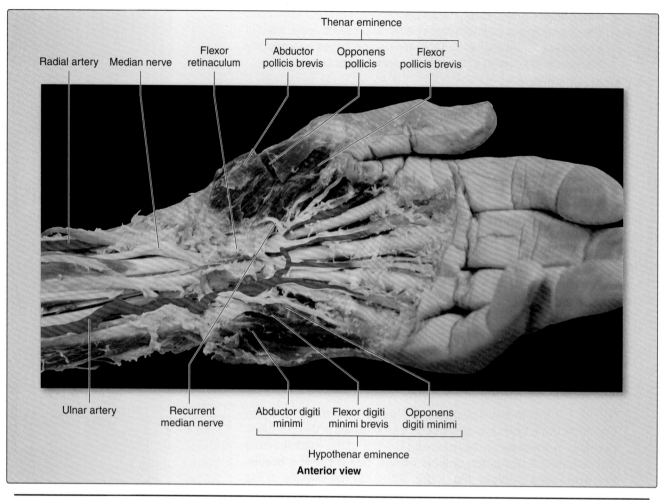

Thenar eminence

Radial artery   Median nerve   Flexor
retinaculum   Abductor
pollicis brevis   Opponens
pollicis   Flexor
pollicis brevis

Ulnar artery   Recurrent
median nerve   Abductor digiti
minimi   Flexor digiti
minimi brevis   Opponens
digiti minimi

Hypothenar eminence

Anterior view

Figure 7.36
Superficial palmar hand.

remaining central compartment muscles are innervated by the deep branch of the ulnar nerve (see Figs. 7.36 and 7.37A). Lumbricals arise from the tendons of the flexor digitorum profundus and insert into the lateral extensor expansions of digits two through five (see Fig. 7.37B). They flex the MCP joints and extend the IP joints of these digits. Dorsal interossei are bipennate muscles found between the metacarpals. Dorsal interossei abduct digits two through four. Palmar interossei are also found between metacarpals and adduct digits two, four, and five.

4. **Carpal tunnel:** The **carpal tunnel** is an osseofascial space that is bound posterolaterally by carpal bones and anteriorly by the thickened flexor retinaculum. The space is occupied by the median nerve and long tendons of flexor digitorum superficialis (4), flexor digitorum profundus (4), and flexor pollicis longus (1). Prior to entering the carpal tunnel, the median nerve gives off a cutaneous branch to the skin of the lateral palm—**palmar cutaneous**

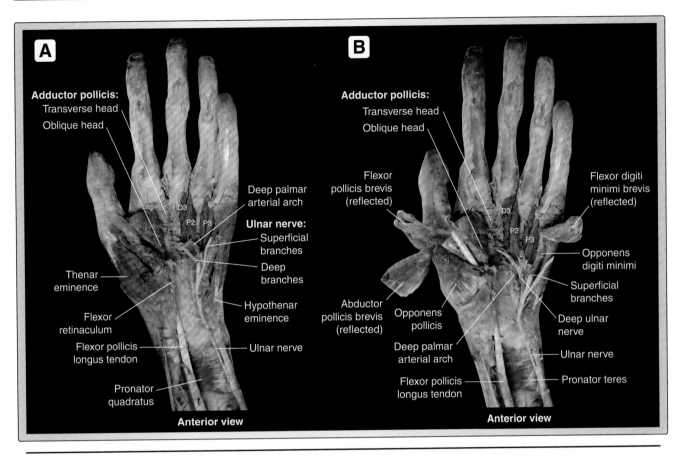

Figure 7.37
Deep palmar hand. A, Thenar and hypothenar eminences intact. B, Thenar and hypothenar eminences reflected to show deeper structures. D – dorsal, P – palmar

Clinical Application 7.14: Dupuytren Contracture

Dupuytren contracture is contracture of the medial half of the palmar deep fascia of genetic origin. Bands of the palmar aponeurosis associated with the fourth and fifth digits begin to shorten and fibrose, causing these digits to move into a flexed position. This disease is more common in males and is often bilateral. Surgical intervention to excise the fibrotic tissue is a common treatment option. Less common is collagenase injections to break down contracted tissue.

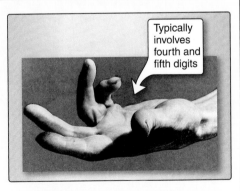

Dupuytren contracture.

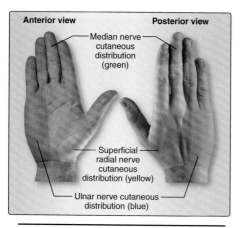

Figure 7.38
Cutaneous and dermatome map of the hand. Cutaneous map of palm and dorsum of hand. Green region is supplied by the median nerve, yellow region is supplied by the radial nerve (superficial branch), and blue region is supplied by the ulnar nerve.

branch of the median nerve. After passing through the carpal tunnel, the median nerve divides into three to four palmar digital nerves and the recurrent branch of the median nerve to serve the thenar muscles; lumbricals (1 and 2); and the skin overlying digits one, two, three, and half of four. Compromise of the median nerve within the carpal tunnel may cause downstream motor and sensory impairments.

5. **Innervation:** Cutaneous innervation of the hand is mediated through branches of the ulnar, median, and radial nerves (Fig. 7.38). The median nerve innervates the skin over the lateral palm; thumb; and digits two, three, and half of four (extending to dorsum of the fingers to the DIP joint). The ulnar nerve innervates the skin over the medial palm and dorsum of the hand and digits five and half of four. The superficial radial nerve serves the lateral dorsum of the hand up to the PIP joints of digits two, three, and half of four. Dermatomes of the hand include C_6 (thumb), C_7 (digits two and three), and C_8 (digits four and five; see also Fig. 6.19).

Clinical Application 7.15: Carpal Tunnel Syndrome

Carpal tunnel syndrome involves compression of the median nerve in the carpal tunnel due to any space-occupying lesion (inflammation, swelling, synovial cysts, etc.). Symptoms include numbness and tingling in the lateral three and a half digits, pain, thenar eminence atrophy, and decreased thumb strength. Surgical release of the flexor retinaculum may relieve pressure on the median nerve.

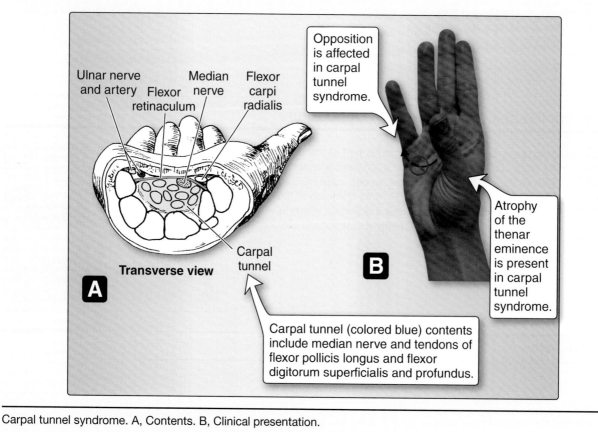

Carpal tunnel syndrome. A, Contents. B, Clinical presentation.

Clinical Application 7.16: Median Nerve Lesion

A lesion of the median nerve at the elbow results in denervation of most flexor forearm muscles as well as the thenar eminence muscles and lumbricals 1 and 2. This type of lesion may occur because of a distal humeral fracture or as an entrapment syndrome as the median nerve travels between the two heads of the pronator teres muscle ("pronator syndrome"). Clinically, a patient with a median nerve lesion at the elbow presents with the inability to flex digits one through three completely ("hand of benediction"). Thenar wasting and loss of thumb opposition would also be present over time ("simian" or "ape hand"). Cutaneous sensory deficits in the median nerve hand distribution are also present (green region in figure 7.38). In

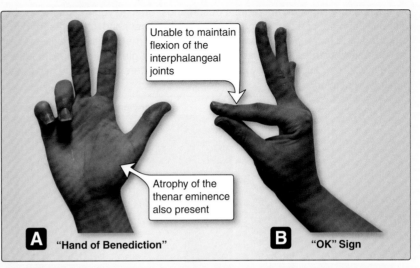

Unable to maintain flexion of the interphalangeal joints

Atrophy of the thenar eminence also present

A "Hand of Benediction" **B** "OK" Sign

some cases, a lesion of the anterior interosseous branch of the median nerve may occur. This nerve serves the muscles in the deep flexor forearm, including flexor pollicis longus (FPL), pronator quadratus, and the lateral half of flexor digitorum profundus (FDP). With this type of lesion, the patient is unable to make an "OK" sign with digits one and two because of the loss of FPL and FDP to the second digit. The other long flexors of the forearm are spared, as are the thenar muscles and median nerve cutaneous sensory distribution.

Clinical presentation of median nerve lesion. A, At elbow. B, Anterior interosseous nerve lesion in deep forearm flexor compartment.

VI. JOINTS AND LIGAMENTS

Joints of the upper limb include all joints of the shoulder complex, elbow (**humeroradial** and **humeroulnar**), forearm (**proximal** and **distal radio-ulnar**), and hand (**wrist**, **intercarpal**, **CMC**, **MCP**, and **IP**). A series of ligaments and capsular structures support these upper limb joints and permit a wide range of movement.

A. Shoulder complex

Shoulder complex joints include the **glenohumeral**, **acromioclavicular**, and **sternoclavicular** joints (Figs. 7.39 and 7.40).

1. **Glenohumeral:** This is a synovial ball-and-socket joint between the head of the humerus and shallow glenoid fossa. It is supported by a joint capsule, **glenohumeral** and **coracohumeral** ligaments, and rotator cuff muscles. The joint is deepened by fibrocartilaginous **glenoid labrum**.

   a. **Movement:** This joint permits flexion, extension, abduction, adduction, medial rotation, lateral rotation, and circumduction. Its wide range of motion makes it vulnerable to injury.

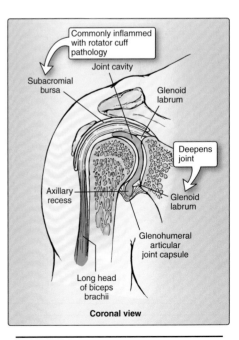

Commonly inflamed with rotator cuff pathology

Joint cavity

Subacromial bursa

Glenoid labrum

Deepens joint

Axillary recess

Glenoid labrum

Glenohumeral articular joint capsule

Long head of biceps brachii

Coronal view

Figure 7.39
Glenohumeral joint.

Clinical Application 7.17: Glenohumeral Joint (Shoulder) Dislocation

Dislocation of the glenohumeral joint occurs most often in young athletes and in the anteroinferior direction. Overuse, as in baseball pitchers, or direct injury can drive the humeral head in an anterior direction, especially if the shoulder is extended, abducted, and externally rotated. Depending on the mechanism of injury and amount of force, dislocation in this direction can be paired with a glenoid labrum tear. Posterior glenohumeral dislocations are less common because the posterior capsule is further supported by rotator cuff musculature. The axillary nerve and circumflex humeral vessels are vulnerable in this type of injury.

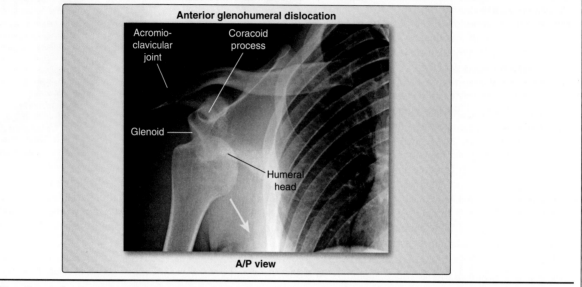

Anterior glenohumeral dislocation

Acromio-clavicular joint

Coracoid process

Glenoid

Humeral head

A/P view

Plain film A/P radiograph of anterior glenohumeral dislocation. Yellow arrow indicates direction of dislocation of humeral head from the glenoid fossa. Note that the acromioclavicular joint is unaffected in a glenohumeral dislocation.

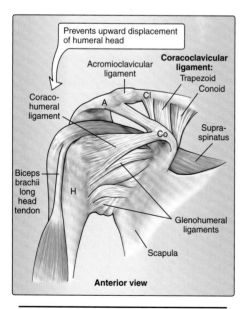

Prevents upward displacement of humeral head

Acromioclavicular ligament

Coracoclavicular ligament:
Trapezoid
Conoid

Coraco-humeral ligament

Supra-spinatus

Biceps brachii long head tendon

Glenohumeral ligaments

Scapula

Anterior view

Figure 7.40
Capsular and ligamentous support of shoulder complex.

b. **Blood supply:** This joint is supplied by anterior and posterior circumflex humeral arteries and suprascapular, axillary, and lateral pectoral nerves.

c. **Associated bursae:** These include the subacromial/subdeltoid and subscapular bursae.

2. **Acromioclavicular:** This is a synovial plane joint between the acromion and the acromial end of the clavicle. It is supported by a joint capsule, directly by the **acromioclavicular ligament** and indirectly by the **coracoclavicular ligament** (**conoid** and **trapezoid** portions).

a. **Movement:** This joint permits rotation of the acromion on the clavicle during scapular movement.

b. **Blood supply:** This joint is supplied by branches of the suprascapular and thoracoacromial arteries and supraclavicular, lateral pectoral, and axillary nerves.

3. **Sternoclavicular:** This is a synovial saddle joint (functionally ball and socket) between the manubrium and the sternal end of the clavicle. It is supported by a joint capsule and anterior and posterior **sternoclavicular**, **interclavicular**, and **costoclavicular ligaments**. It has an articular disc.

Clinical Application 7.18: Shoulder Separation

Injury to the acromioclavicular ligament can result from a direct blow or fall on the shoulder and is common in contact sports, such as football and hockey. Rupture of the coracoclavicular ligaments can also occur, which increases the severity of the shoulder separation. In this case, the weight of the upper limb pulls it inferiorly, accentuating the point of the acromion through the lateral shoulder skin and giving the shoulder a less rounded, squarer appearance.

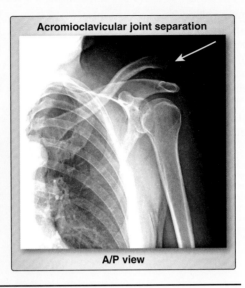

Acromioclavicular joint separation

A/P view

Shoulder separation. Plain film radiograph of acromioclavicular joint dislocation. Note distal clavicle overriding acromion.

    a. **Movement:** This joint permits clavicular elevation, depression, and anterior/posterior movement during humeral movement.

    b. **Blood supply:** This joint is supplied by branches of the internal thoracic and suprascapular arteries and medial supraclavicular and subclavius nerves.

B. Elbow

The elbow is a synovial hinge-shaped joint, supported by a fibrous capsule. It allows for flexion and extension movements and is supplied by anastomoses around joint (from brachial, profunda brachii, radial, and ulnar arteries) and median, radial, and ulnar nerves (see Fig. 7.5).

    1. **Humeroradial:** This joint articulates between the capitulum and radial head and is supported by **radial collateral** and **anular ligaments** (also supports proximal radioulnar joint by maintaining position of radial head in radial notch of ulna).

    2. **Humeroulnar:** This joint articulates between the trochlea and trochlear notch and is supported by the **ulnar collateral ligament** (anterior, posterior, and oblique bands).

C. Forearm

Synovial pivot-type joints allow for pronation and supination of the forearm. They are supported by a fibrous capsule and ligaments.

Clinical Application 7.19: Nursemaid's Elbow

Dislocation of the humeroradial joint ("nursemaid's elbow") can occur when the anular ligament is partially or completely torn. This often happens in young children as a result of a forceful pull on the upper limb. The radial head becomes dislocated and appears as a palpable mass in the cubital fossa. The biceps brachii pulls the radial head anteriorly and superiorly once dislocated. Children will commonly splint their injured arm against their bodies and complain of pain. The source of pain is believed to be the torn anular ligament being pinched in the joint. The joint may be reduced by "screwing" the head back in place—supinating the forearm while the elbow is flexed.

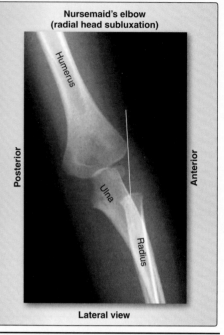

Nursemaid's elbow (radial head subluxation). Lateral plain film radiograph indicating anterior displacement of radial heads in reference to humerus (yellow line).

Clinical Application 7.20: Ulnar Collateral Ligament Reconstruction

When the ulnar collateral ligament is torn—common in baseball pitchers—surgical repair involves harvesting a tendon (often the palmaris longus) and passing it through drilled holes around the humeroulnar joint in a figure eight pattern to stabilize the joint. This repair is often referred to as "Tommy John surgery" (after a famous major league pitcher). Extensive rehabilitation is necessary before returning to play.

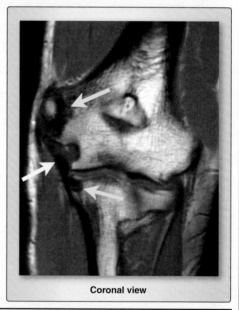

Ulnar ligament damage. Intact Tommy John graft. Postoperative changes can be seen in the epicondyle and the sublime tubercle after Tommy John surgery on the T1-weighted images (yellow arrows). The intact graft is a continuous low-signal linear structure (white arrows).

1. **Proximal radioulnar:** This joint articulates between the radial head and radial notch of the ulna and allows for rotation of the head in the notch. It is supported by the anular ligament and supplied by elbow anastomoses and musculocutaneous, median, and radial nerves.

2. **Distal radioulnar:** This joint articulates between the ulnar head and ulnar notch of the radius with an articular disc. The ulna is relatively fixed, allowing the radius to move during pronation/supination. It is supported by weak anterior and posterior ligaments and the interosseous membrane and supplied by anterior and posterior interosseous arteries and nerves.

> **Pronation** and **supination** occur at the proximal and distal radioulnar joints. At the proximal radioulnar joint, the radial head rotates in the radial notch. This connection is supported by the anular ligament. At the distal radioulnar joint, the distal radius is parallel to the ulna in the supinated position and crosses anterior and medial to the ulna in the pronated position. The palm of the hand faces anteriorly when the forearm is supinated and posteriorly when the forearm is pronated. An easy way to remember this is to pair *supin*ation with the *supine* position (face up) and *pron*ation with the *prone* position (face down).

D. Wrist and hand

The wrist and hand are made up a collection of small synovial joints that permit fine movement at the wrist and fingers, including flexion, extension, abduction, adduction, and opposition (first and fifth digits only). Collectively, these joints are supplied by the carpal arterial arches and associated digital branches and radial, median, and ulnar nerves.

1. **Wrist:** The **radiocarpal joint** articulates between the radius and proximal row of carpal bones (minus pisiform). The ulna does not contribute to this joint, which is supported by radial and ulnar collateral ligaments of the wrist and radiocarpal ligaments (palmar and dorsal).

2. **Hand:** The hand is a collection of intercarpal, CMC, MCP, and IP joints that are supported by fibrous capsules and ligaments (named for joint). The **Pisohamate ligament** creates an osseofibrous tunnel **(Guyon's canal)** through which the deep branch of the ulnar nerve travels, a potential site for nerve compression.

> The CMC joint of the thumb is between the trapezium and the base of the first metacarpal. It is unique in that it is a saddle joint, whereas the other CMC joints are plane. It has its own articular capsule and allows for movement in all planes, which is essential for opposition (see Fig. 7.35).

Chapter Summary

- The upper limb develops in advance of the lower limb and undergoes a 90° lateral rotation.
- Lateral plate mesoderm forms the skeletal component of the upper limb. Somitomeric mesoderm forms the muscular component of the upper limb.
- The zone of polarizing activity (ZPA) is a zone of mesoderm. The apical ectodermal ridge (AER) is a thickened ridge of ectoderm.
- The upper limb is divided regionally into shoulder, arm, forearm, and wrist and hand.
- The upper limb is covered in a deep fascial layering (brachial, antebrachial, palmar, and dorsal fascia) that compartmentalizes the arm, forearm, and hand.
- Superficial and deep veins are connected via perforating veins. The cephalic vein runs superficially on the lateral surface of the upper limb, and the basilic runs medially. The basilic vein joins the brachial to form the axillary vein, into which the cephalic vein drains. Lymphatic vessels follow both superficial and deep veins and drain into either cubital or axillary lymph nodes.
- The axillary is the main arterial supply to the shoulder/axilla region. Distal to the teres major muscle, it continues as the brachial artery, which supplies the arm. At the cubital fossa, the brachial artery divides into radial and ulnar arteries, which supply the forearm and form arterial arches in the hand.
- The axilla is a pyramid-shaped space that contains important neurovascular structures (axillary artery and vein, brachial plexus cords, and terminal nerves) of the upper limb.
- The brachial plexus innervates upper limb structures and is made up of a collection of anterior primary rami from C_5–C_8 and T_1.
- Muscles that attach from the axial skeleton to the shoulder complex are called axioappendicular muscles, while intrinsic scapular muscles connect the scapula/clavicle to the humerus. The arm and forearm are divided into anterior (flexors) and posterior (extensors) compartments.
- Rotator cuff muscles include the supraspinatus, infraspinatus, teres minor, and subscapularis. They function as a collective unit to maintain the humeral head in the glenoid fossa, thus supporting the glenohumeral joint. The most frequently injured rotator cuff muscle is supraspinatus.
- Lesions of the radial, ulnar, and median nerves are associated with clinical presentations of wrist drop, claw hand, and hand of benediction/ape hand, respectively.
- The palm is organized into thenar, hypothenar, and central compartments. Most of the intrinsic hand muscles are innervated by the deep ulnar nerve.
- Shoulder dislocations typically occur anteriorly and inferiorly. Shoulder separation involves injury to the acromioclavicular and, potentially, the coracoclavicular ligaments.

Study Questions:

Choose the ONE correct answer.

7.1 A 45-year old female patient is seen for symptoms of carpal tunnel syndrome. An ultrasound of the carpal tunnel reveals an arterial structure that is not typically seen in this space. Thinking back to upper limb embryology, you recall that this artery is one of the first branches to form from the upper limb axis artery. The artery is the:

A. Radial artery
B. Ulnar artery
C. Axillary artery
D. Median artery
E. Brachial artery

> Correct answer = D. The median artery is one of the first branches to form from the axis artery. In the adult, the median artery does not persist and is probably reduced to a small, unnamed vessel. This is why the median nerve does not have an accompanying artery in the adult like the ulnar nerve (ulnar artery) and radial nerve (radial artery).

> Correct answer = B. All bones of the upper limb form from lateral plate mesoderm that condenses alone the central axis of the upper limb bud.

7.2 The humerus develops from which of the following germ layers?

A. Somite mesoderm
B. Lateral plate mesoderm
C. Intermediate mesoderm
D. Extraembryonic mesoderm
E. Sclerotome mesoderm

7.3   A professional javelin thrower is being seen for a torn triceps brachii (long head) muscle, an injury she suffered during the last Summer Olympic games. During treatment, you begin to discuss development of upper limb structures. When you begin to explain the development of the triceps brachii, you tell her it develops from:

A. Doral extensor condensation
B. Ventral flexor condensation
C. Lateral plate mesoderm
D. Extraembryonic mesoderm
E. Sclerotome mesoderm

> Correct answer = A. Somite mesoderm migrates into the limb bud and forms two condensations. The dorsal extensor condensation of the upper limb gives rise to the extensors of the upper limb, which attain a posterior location in the adult because of the lateral rotation of 90°

7.4   A 89-year old female patient with a history of falls and osteoporosis is admitted to the Emergency Department after falling in the bathroom earlier that evening. Plain-film images reveal a mid-shaft humeral fracture and multiple rib fractures on the right. Which of the following nerve/artery pairs would most likely be damaged with this type of humeral fracture?

A. Median/brachial.
B. Ulnar/superior ulnar collateral.
C. Axillary/posterior circumflex humeral.
D. Radial/profunda brachii.
E. Musculocutaneous/brachial.

> Correct answer = D. The radial nerve and profunda brachii artery travel directly on the surface of the humerus in the radial groove. Therefore, a mid-shaft fracture would most likely damage this pair for structures.

7.5   A 19-year old male patient is admitted to the Emergency Department following a shoulder injury suffered during an intramural rugby tournament. Upon physical examination, you notice loss of shoulder roundness on the left and increased pain with horizontal adduction (shoulder flexed to 90 degrees and moved medially in transverse plane). You suspect shoulder separation and order imaging. Which of the following structures is most likely involved in this patient?

A. Glenohumeral ligaments.
B. Glenoid laburm.
C. Acromioclavicular ligament.
D. Coracohumeral ligament.
E. Supraspinatus tendon.

> Correct answer = C. Shoulder separation involves damage to the acromioclavicular ligament and potentially the coracoclavicular ligament parts. Shoulder separation is not the same as shoulder (glenohumeral) dislocation, which involves glenohumeral ligaments and can involve the glenoid labrum.

7.6   During a difficult vaginal delivery of a 42-week newborn, the newborn's right shoulder became blocked in the vaginal canal at the pubic symphysis, requiring additional physical manipulation to complete delivery. The manipulation caused excess separation between the newborn's right shoulder and neck, resulting in an upper brachial plexus injury. This injury would eliminate which of the following actions in the right upper limb of this newborn?

A. Metacarophalangeal flexion and interphalangeal extension at digits 4 and 5.
B. Opposition of the thumb.
C. Abduction of the arm.
D. Extension of the forearm.
E. Pronation of the forearm.

> Correct answer = C. Upper brachial plexus injury causes damage to C_5–C_6 rami or the upper trunk. Therefore, axillary and suprascapular nerves are damaged, which denervates the deltoid and supraspinatus muscles—the two abductors of the arm.

The following clinical scenario should be used to answer questions 7 and 8:

A 43-year old male patient is seen in your outpatient office with complaints of weakness and pain in his left shoulder. He states that he felt like he slept on his arm "weird" 2-weeks ago, and has been experiencing symptoms ever since. He denies any falls or traumatic injury leading up to this visit. Upon visual inspection of his left shoulder, you do not notice any obvious atrophy, bruising, or swelling. He has tenderness to palpation over the left posterior deltoid and proximal triceps, and decreased sensation over the middle head of the deltoid near the insertion. Muscle testing at the shoulder reveals marked weakness in full range of motion in abduction as well as weakness in shoulder flexion, extension, medial and lateral rotation on the left side, when compared to the right. You suspect a nerve entrapment and write an order for physical therapy evaluation and treatment.

Based on these findings and your current knowledge of shoulder anatomy, answer the following questions:

7.7   Which of the following nerves is entrapped in the above scenario?

   A. Radial.
   B. Axillary.
   C. Median.
   D. Ulnar.
   E. Musculocutaneous.

Correct answer = B. The axillary nerve innervates deltoid and teres minor muscles and mediates sensation from the superolateral humerus. Motor and sensory changes indicate axillary nerve involvement, specifically loss of full shoulder abduction and decreased sensation over medial head of deltoid.

7.8   Through which of the following spaces does the entrapped nerve travel?

   A. Triangular interval.
   B. Cubital fossa.
   C. Triangular space.
   D. Quadrangular space.
   E. Guyon's canal.

Correct answer = D. The axillary nerve and posterior circumflex humeral vessels travel around the surgical neck of the humerus and through the quadrangular space to supply the deltoid and teres minor muscles. Axillary nerve entrapment can occur as the nerve travels through the quadrangular space.

The following clinical scenario should be used to answer questions 9 and 10:

A 35-year old right-hand-dominant patient comes to you complaining of numbness, tingling and pain in several fingers on her right hand. She also reports weakness in her thumb. These symptoms worsens at night and when she is working. She works as a court reporter, and often is seated and typing for several hours continuously. She reports that her symptoms began approximately five months ago and have progressively gotten worse. Upon visual inspection, you notice that her thenar eminence appears smaller on the right when compared to the left. Flexion of interphalangeal joints on digits 2-5 is normal. Based on your findings, you suspect a nerve entrapment.

7.9   Which of the following nerves is most likely entrapped?

   A. Deep ulnar.
   B. Recurrent median.
   C. Median.
   D. Deep radial.
   E. Superficial radial.

Correct answer = C. The median nerve is most likely entrapped in the carpal tunnel in this clinical scenario. Numbness and tingling in her digits with thenar wasting and decreased thumb function suggests median nerve entrapment proximal to where the recurrent median nerve branches to innervate thenar muscles.

7.10 Which of the following muscles would still be functional in the above clinical scenario?

   A. Flexor pollicis brevis.
   B. Opponens pollicis.
   C. Abductor pollicis brevis.
   D. Lumbricals 1 and 2.
   E. Adductor pollicis.

Correct answer = E. The adductor pollicis is innervated by the deep ulnar nerve, and would not be affected in this scenario. All other muscles listed are innervated by the median nerve, distal to the site of entrapment.

Head and Cranial Nerves

8

I. OVERVIEW

The head is the rostral most structure of the human body, connected to the trunk by the cervical spine. It is characterized by a bony cranium (skull), which houses the brain and serves as a scaffold for facial structures, including those associated with the orbits, nasal cavities, and oral cavity. To aid understanding of the arrangement and neuromuscular supply of these head structures, embryologic development is discussed first in most sections in this chapter. Twelve cranial nerves (CNs) arise from the brain and brainstem, and a brief description of their courses and structures innervated is also included in this chapter to provide a complete, yet concise, overview.

II. CRANIUM

The cranium, or skull, comprises a collection of singular and paired bones that articulate and fuse over the course of development. Covering the top part of the skull is the multilayered scalp.

A. Osteology

The skull comprises two parts: the **neurocranium** and the **viscerocranium**. Bones that contribute to the complete formation of the skull include (Fig. 8.1) paired (parietal, temporal, maxilla, inferior turbinate [nasal concha], zygomatic, palatine, nasal, and lacrimal) and singular (frontal, ethmoid, sphenoid, occipital, mandible, and vomer) bones.

1. **Embryology:** The neurocranium consists of the flat bones of the calvaria (membranous neurocranium) and the cranial base (cartilaginous neurocranium). The neurocranium develops from **cranial neural crest cells**, except for the basilar part of the occipital bone, which forms from **mesoderm of the occipital sclerotomes** (Fig. 8.2). The viscerocranium consists of the bones of the face involving the pharyngeal arches. The viscerocranium develops from **cranial neural crest cells**, except for the laryngeal cartilages, which form from **mesoderm within pharyngeal arches 4 and 6.**

   a. **Sutures:** During fetal life and infancy, the flat bones of the skull are separated by dense connective tissue (fibrous joints) called **sutures**. There are five sutures: **frontal, sagittal, lambdoid, coronal,** and **squamous sutures**. Sutures allow the flat bones of the skull to deform during childbirth (called **molding**) and

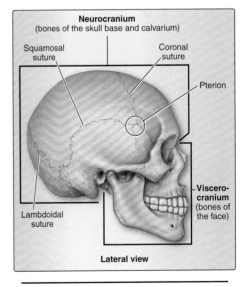

Figure 8.1
Adult cranium showing neurocranium and viscerocranium and associated sutures.

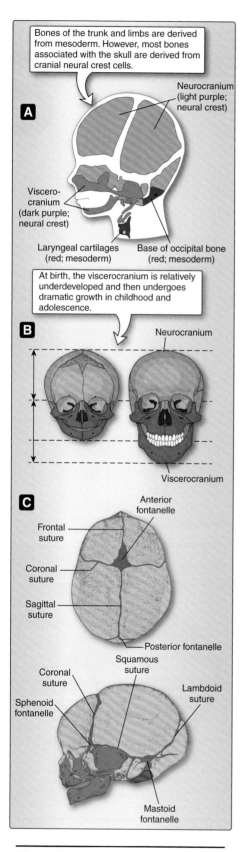

Figure 8.2
A, Newborn skull. B, Postnatal growth of skull. C, Sutures and fontanelles.

Clinical Application 8.1: Craniosynostosis

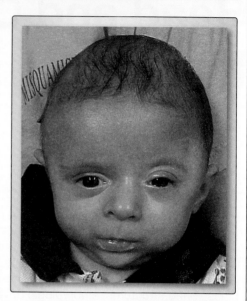

Craniosynostosis involves premature closure of sutures, resulting in distinct malformation of the skull. **Oxycephaly** (**turricephaly** or **acrocephaly**) is a **tower-like skull** caused by premature closure of the lambdoid and coronal sutures. **Plagiocephaly** is an asymmetrical skull caused by premature closure of the lambdoid and coronal sutures on one side of the skull. **Brachycephaly** is a short, square-shaped skull caused by premature closure of the coronal sutures. **Scaphocephaly** is a long skull (in the anterior/posterior plane) caused by premature closure of the sagittal suture. **Kleeblattschädel** is a cloverleaf skull caused by premature closure of all sutures, forcing the brain growth through the anterior and sphenoid fontanelles.

to expand during childhood as the brain grows. Typically, the frontal suture closes by the eighth year of life, while the others slowly close into adulthood.

b. **Fontanelles:** Fontanelles are large, fibrous areas where several sutures meet. There are six fontanelles: **anterior, posterior, two sphenoid,** and **two mastoid fontanelles.** The anterior fontanelle is the largest fontanel and is readily palpable in the infant. The anterior fontanel pulsates because of the underlying cerebral arteries and can be used to obtain a blood sample from the underlying **superior sagittal sinus.** The anterior fontanelle and the mastoid fontanelles close at about age 2 years when the main growth of the brain ceases. The posterior fontanelle and the sphenoid fontanelles close at about age 6 months.

2. **Adult skull:** The adult bony skull can be divided into two parts: the **neurocranium** and the **viscerocranium.** Figures 8.3 through 8.5 provide various views of the skull.

a. **Neurocranium:** Collectively, the neurocranium is made up of **frontal,** paired **parietal,** paired **temporal, ethmoid, sphenoid,** and **occipital** bones. The superior portions of the frontal, parietal, and occipital bones contribute to the formation of the **calvaria** (skull cap).

[1] **Calvaria:** Distinguishing features of the calvaria include the sagittal, coronal, and lambdoid sutures, previously described. The junctions of the sagittal suture with the coronal and lambdoidal sutures are termed **bregma** and **lambda,** respectively. These junctions represent the closure sites of the anterior and posterior fontanelles, respectively.

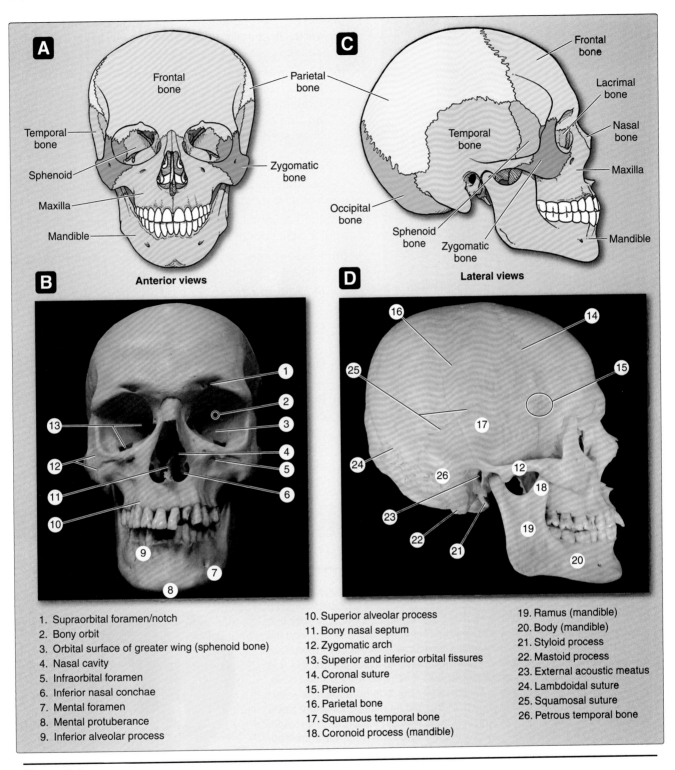

1. Supraorbital foramen/notch
2. Bony orbit
3. Orbital surface of greater wing (sphenoid bone)
4. Nasal cavity
5. Infraorbital foramen
6. Inferior nasal conchae
7. Mental foramen
8. Mental protuberance
9. Inferior alveolar process
10. Superior alveolar process
11. Bony nasal septum
12. Zygomatic arch
13. Superior and inferior orbital fissures
14. Coronal suture
15. Pterion
16. Parietal bone
17. Squamous temporal bone
18. Coronoid process (mandible)
19. Ramus (mandible)
20. Body (mandible)
21. Styloid process
22. Mastoid process
23. External acoustic meatus
24. Lambdoidal suture
25. Squamosal suture
26. Petrous temporal bone

Figure 8.3
Adult cranium. A and C, Color-coded bones. B and D, Skeletal specimens.

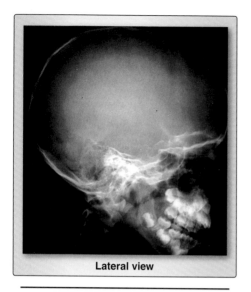

Lateral view

Figure 8.4
Plain film radiograph (child skull, face and upper cervical spine).

(a) **Vertex:** The superiormost point of the calvaria is the **vertex**, located approximately midway along the sagittal suture.

(b) **Temporal fossa:** Laterally, the **pterion** represents the junction of the frontal, parietal, sphenoid, and temporal (squamosal) bones and is situated in a region called the temporal fossa. Superior and inferior temporal lines serve as superior and posterior boundaries of this region, which is comprised of mainly by the parietal and temporal (squamous) bones, with anterior contributions from the sphenoid (greater wing) and frontal bones.

[2] **Base:** The frontal, ethmoid, sphenoid, petrous temporal, and occipital bones form the cranial base.

(a) **Fossae:** Internally, the cranial base is further divided into anterior, middle, and posterior fossae (Fig. 8.5E):

(i) **Anterior fossa:** Frontal, ethmoid, and sphenoid bones contribute to the anterior fossa.

(ii) **Middle fossa:** Sphenoid and temporal bones contribute to the middle fossa.

(iii) **Posterior fossa:** Sphenoid and occipital bones contribute to the posterior fossa.

(b) **Foramina and fissures:** Bilateral foramina and fissures are present in each fossa, allowing for the passage of important neurovascular structures (Table 8.1; also see Fig. 8.5). Additional foramina occur throughout the base of the skull to transmit emissary veins, including the foramen cecum (frontal) and condylar and mastoid foramina (occipital).

Clinical Application 8.2: Skull Fractures

Trauma to the skull can result in various types of fractures, including linear—most common, occurring at impact site; depressed—bone depressed inwardly; comminuted—multiple fractured pieces; and contrecoup—fracture opposite of impact site. Basilar fractures involve bones that make up with the cranial base and may cause damage to vasculature and CNs associated with the ventral surface of the brain. Basilar fractures may result in otorrhea and rhinorrhea and leakage of cerebrospinal fluid (CSF) into the ears and nose, respectively. Fracture at the pterion should be considered a medical emergency because the anterior branches of the middle meningeal artery travel adjacent to the site in the potential epidural space. Rupture of the middle meningeal artery will lead to an epidural hematoma and, if left untreated, can lead to acute death.

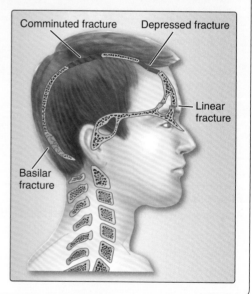

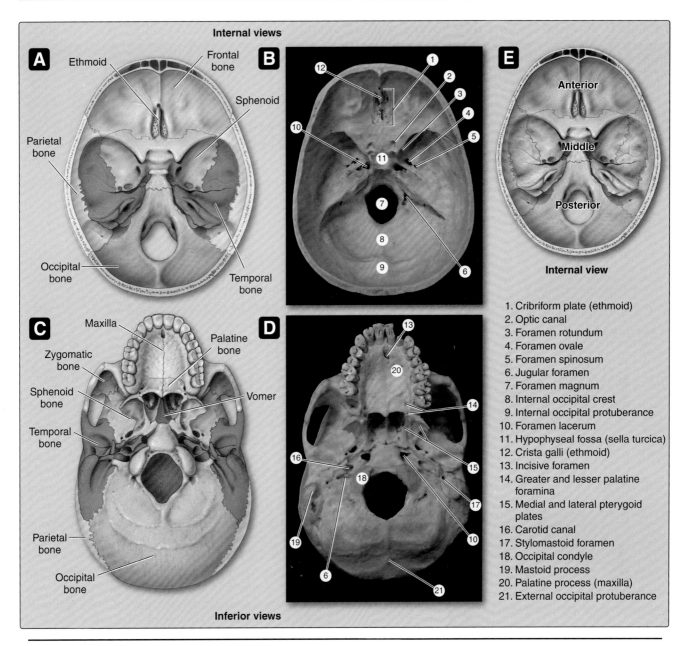

Figure 8.5
Adult cranium. A and C, Color-coded bones. B and D, Skeletal specimens. E, Cranial fossae.

(c) **External surface features:** Inferiorly, the external cranial base has several surface features that serve as attachment sites for muscles and fascia as well as regions of bony articulations. Of particular importance are the paired **occipital condyles**, superior sites for articulation with C1 (atlas) to form the **atlanto-occipital joint**. The **mastoid** and **styloid processes** (petrous temporal) are located laterally to the occipital condyles. Many of the

Table 8.1:   Internal Neurocranial Foramina and Contents

Foramen	Structures Transmitted

Anterior fossa
    Cribriform plate
    Ethmoidal foramina
	
	Olfactory nerve (CN I)
	Anterior and posterior ethmoidal nerves and arteries

Middle fossa
    Optic canal
    Superior orbital fissure
	
	Optic nerve (CN II), ophthalmic artery, retinal artery and vein
	Oculomotor nerve (CN III), trochlear nerve (CN IV), trigeminal nerve (ophthalmic division, CN V$_1$), ophthalmic vein

Foramen rotundum **Foramen ovale**	Trigeminal nerve (maxillary division, CN V$_2$) Trigeminal nerve (mandibular division, CN V$_3$), lesser petrosal nerve (glossopharyngeal nerve branch, CN IX), accessory meningeal artery
Foramen spinosum **Foramen lacerum** **Carotid canal** **Facial hiatus**	Middle meningeal artery Empty (covered with cartilage in living person) Internal carotid artery, postganglionic sympathetic plexus Greater petrosal nerve (branch of facial nerve, CN VII)
Posterior fossa **Internal acoustic meatus**	 Facial nerve (CN VII), vestibulocochlear nerve (CN VIII), labyrinthine artery
Jugular foramen **Hypoglossal canal** **Foramen magnum**	Glossopharyngeal nerve (CN IX), vagus nerve (CN X), spinal accessory nerve (CN XI), sigmoid sinus Hypoglossal nerve (CN XII) Medulla, CN XI (cervical component), vertebral arteries

Table 8.2:   Inferior Neurocranial Foramina and Contents

Foramen	Structure Transmitted
Incisive canal	Nasopalatine nerve (branch of maxillary division of trigeminal nerve, CN V$_2$), greater palatine artery
Greater palatine foramen	Greater palatine verve (branch of maxillary division of trigeminal nerve, CN V$_2$), greater palatine artery
Lesser palatine foramen	Lesser palatine verve (branch of maxillary division of trigeminal nerve, CN V$_2$), lesser palatine artery
Stylomastoid foramen	Facial nerve (CN VII)

previously mentioned foramina are visible inferiorly, and additional foramina include the opening of the **incisive canal** (maxilla), **greater** and **lesser palatine foramina** (palatine), **stylomastoid foramen** (petrous temporal), and the entry site for the **carotid canal** (petrous temporal) (see Table 8.2; also see Fig. 8.5).

(d) **Occipital bone:** Externally, the occipital bone represents the majority of the posterior portion of the skull, with additional contribution from the parietal bones superiorly and the mastoid processes (petrous temporal) inferiolaterally. Posteriorly, the occipital bone is characterized by a midline palpable elevation of bone called the **external occipital protuberance**. The **superior nuchal line** extends laterally from the protuberance, serving as the superiormost attachment site for neck structures. The less prominent inferior nuchal line lies inferior to the protuberance.

b. **Viscerocranium:** Located anteriorly, the **viscerocranium** represents the bony scaffold of the face and is made up of bones that surround and form three main facial regions—orbit, nose, and mouth. Bones that contribute to the formation of the viscerocranium include parasagittal paired **maxillae**, **zygomatic**, **nasal**, **lacrimal**, and **inferior turbinate** (nasal concha) bones and midline singular **mandible**, **ethmoid**, and **vomer** bones (see Figs. 8.3 and 8.5).

[1] Frontal bone: This bone forms the majority of the forehead of the face and contributes to the superior rim (supraorbital margin) of the orbit. Bilateral supraorbital notches are found medially along the supraorbital margins. A smooth, midline depression, the **glabella**, sits between the paired supraciliary arches and is easily palpated between the eyebrows, superior to the nasal bridge—formed by paired nasal bones.

[2] Zygomatic and maxillary bones: These bones complete the orbital margin inferiolaterally and inferomedially, respectively. Each zygomatic bone has a zygomaticotemporal foramen anterior to the temporal process of the zygomatic bone. This process articulates with the zygomatic process of the temporal bone to form the **zygomatic arch**. The **external acoustic meatus** (petrous temporal) lies just posterior to the zygomatic arch. Bilateral **infraorbital foramina** are located just inferior to the infraorbital margin on the superior aspect of the maxilla. The intermaxillary suture represents the fusion site for the paired maxillae, forming the upper jaw and characterized by alveolar processes that support the upper (maxillary) teeth.

[3] Mandible: The jaw is completed inferiorly by the U-shaped **mandible**, also characterized by **alveolar processes** that support the lower (mandibular) teeth. A midline **mental protuberance** is found inferiorly and is framed by bilateral **mental foramina**. Laterally, the mandible is characterized by a body, angle, and ramus. Superior to the ramus, the **coronoid process** and **head of the mandible** are situated anteriorly and posteriorly, respectively. The head of the mandible articulates with the **mandibular fossa** (petrous temporal) to form the **temporomandibular joint**.

[4] Foramina: Refer to Table 8.3 for additional details about viscerocranial foramina.

Table 8.3: Viscerocranial Foramina and Contents

Foramen	Structure Transmitted
Supraorbital notch	Supraorbital nerve (branch of ophthalmic division of trigeminal nerve, CN V_1), supraorbital artery
Infraorbital foramen	Infraorbital nerve (branch of maxillary division of trigeminal nerve, CN V_2), infraorbital artery
Zygomaticofacial foramen	Zygomatic nerve (branch of maxillary division of trigeminal nerve, CN V_2)
Mental foramen	Mental nerve (branch of mandibular division of trigeminal nerve, CN V_3), mental artery

B. Scalp

The **scalp** is a multilayer structure that covers the neurocranium, spanning between the supraorbital margins anteriorly to the superior nuchal lines posteriorly and extending laterally to the zygomatic arches.

From superficial to deep, the layers of the **SCALP** are: **S**kin, **C**onnective tissue, **A**poneurosis, **L**oose connective tissue, and **P**ericranium.

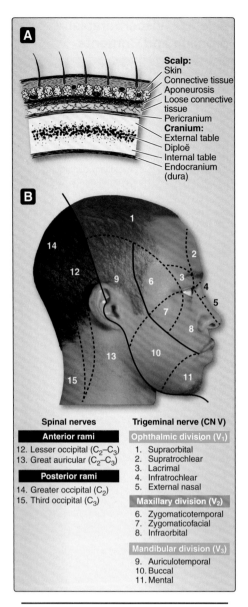

Figure 8.6
Scalp. A, Layers. B, Innervation of the scalp and face.

1. **Scalp proper:** The first three layers of the scalp are called the scalp proper and comprise skin, connective tissue, and aponeurosis. The skin of the scalp has a rich blood supply and contains multiple sweat and sebaceous glands and hair follicles. The thick subcutaneous connective tissue layer also has a substantial neuromuscular supply. The aponeurosis layer provides a tendon-like bridge between the anterior and posterior bellies of the **occipitofrontalis** muscle and also serves as an attachment site for the superior auricular muscle (Fig. 8.6A).

2. **Loose connective tissue layer:** Deep to the aponeurosis, the loose connective tissue layer allows for movement of the scalp proper on the skull and contains emissary veins.

3. **Pericranium:** Finally, the innermost layer, the pericranium, is a dense connective tissue layer that is firmly attached to the calvaria, forming the periosteum.

4. **Innervation:** The skin of the scalp is innervated by branches of the trigeminal nerve and cervical anterior and posterior rami (see Fig. 8.6B).

   a. **Anterior and superior scalp:** This area is innervated by the supratrochlear and infratrochlear nerves (CN V_1, ophthalmic).

   b. **Anterolateral scalp:** This area is innervated by the zygomaticotemporal (CN V_2, maxillary) and auriculotemporal (CN V_3, mandibular) nerves.

   c. **Posterolateral scalp:** This area is innervated by the lesser occipital nerve (anterior rami C_2, C_3).

   d. **Posterior and superior scalp:** This area is innervated by the greater occipital nerve (posterior rami C_2).

5. **Vasculature:** The scalp receives blood supply primarily from branches of the **external carotid artery**, including **posterior auricular**, **occipital**, and **superficial temporal arteries**. The anterior scalp is supplied by vessels that indirectly arise from the **internal carotid artery**, including the **supratrochlear** and **supraorbital arteries**. Typically, veins of the same name drain the superficial scalp. There are no lymph nodes in the superficial scalp, so all lymph is drained into the superficial ring of lymph nodes located at the intersection of the head and neck.

III. BRAIN AND MENINGES

The brain is made up of a **cerebrum** (telencephalon and diencephalon), a **cerebellum** (metencephalon), and a **brainstem** (mesencephalon = midbrain; mesencephalon = pons; myelencephalon = medulla). Protective and physiologic membranous coverings, called **meninges**, surround structures of the brain.

A. Embryology

The central nervous system (CNS), that is, the brain and spinal cord, begins to form in **week 3** of development, during which time the process of **neurulation** occurs (Fig. 8.7). **Neurulation** refers to the formation and closure of the neural tube in which **BMP-4** (bone morphogenetic protein), **noggin** (an inductor protein), **chordin** (an inductor protein), **FGF-8** (fibroblast growth factor), and **N-CAM** (neural cell adhesion molecule) play a role.

1. **Brain development:** Neurulation begins when the **primitive node/ notochord** induces the overlying ectoderm to form the **neural plate**, which is a thick plate of pseudostratified, columnar neuroepithelial cells called **neuroectoderm**. The neural plate is shaped with a broad cranial portion that gives rise to the brain and a narrow caudal portion that gives rise to the spinal cord.

    Even before neurulation begins, the primordia of the three **primary brain vesicles** (i.e., **prosencephalon**, **mesencephalon**, and **rhombencephalon**) are apparent as broadenings of the neural plate. The three primary brain vesicles further develop into five **secondary brain vesicles** (i.e., **telencephalon, diencephalon, mesencephalon, metencephalon**, and **myelencephalon**). During week 5, the prosencephalon subdivides into the telencephalon and the diencephalon, and the rhombencephalon subdivides into the metencephalon and the myelencephalon. The mesencephalon does not subdivide. From these five secondary brain vesicles, the adult derivatives of the brain form.

    a. **Ventricles:** Within each of the brain vesicles, the neural canal develops into the definitive ventricular system of the brain. The neural canal of the telencephalon becomes the paired **lateral ventricles**. The neural canal of the diencephalon becomes the **third ventricle**. The neural canal of the mesencephalon becomes the **cerebral aqueduct**. The neural canal of the metencephalon and myelencephalon (or the rhombencephalon) becomes the **fourth ventricle**.

    b. **Neural tube folding:** During weeks 4–8, the neural tube folds sharply at three locations. The first fold that develops is a ventral folding called the **cephalic flexure** located at the mesencephalon. The second fold that develops is a ventral folding called the **cervical flexure** located at the junction of the myelencephalon and the spinal cord. The third fold that develops is a dorsal folding called the **pontine flexure** located at the pons. Refer to Table 8.4 for additional details.

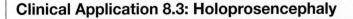

Clinical Application 8.3: Holoprosencephaly

Holoprosencephaly occurs when the prosencephalon fails to cleave down the midline such that the telencephalon contains a single ventricle. It is characterized by the absence of olfactory bulbs and tracts (arhinencephaly) and is commonly seen in trisomy 13 (Patau syndrome), trisomy 18 (Edward syndrome), short arm deletion of chromosome 18, and Meckel syndrome. Because the fetal face develops at the same time as the brain, facial anomalies (e.g., cyclopia, cleft lip, cleft palate) are commonly seen with holoprosencephaly. Holoprosencephaly is the most severe manifestation of **fetal alcohol syndrome** resulting from alcohol abuse during pregnancy (especially in the first 4 weeks of pregnancy). A sonogram will show a single, horseshoe-shaped ventricle and fused thalami.

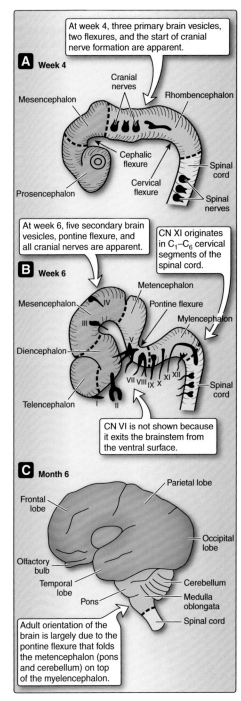

Figure 8.7
Embryology of the brain (A–C).

Table 8.4: Primary and Secondary Brain Vesicles

Primary Vesicles	Secondary Vesicles	Adult Derivatives	Cranial Nerve	Ventricle
Prosencephalon	Telencephalon	Cerebral hemispheres, caudate, putamen, amygdaloid, claustrum, lamina terminalis, olfactory bulbs, hippocampus	CN I	Lateral ventricles
	Diencephalon	Epithalamus, subthalamus, thalamus, hypothalamus, mammillary bodies, neurohypophysis, pineal gland, globus pallidus, retina, epithelium of iris and ciliary body, optic nerve (CN II), optic chiasm, optic tract	CN II	Third ventricle
Mesencephalon	Mesencephalon	Midbrain	CNs III, IV	Cerebral aqueduct
Rhombencephalon	Metencephalon	Pons, cerebellum	CNs V–VIII CNs IX, X, XII	Fourth ventricle
	Myelencephalon	Medulla		

2. **Neural tube histogenesis:** The cells of the neural tube are derived from neuroectoderm that form **neuroblasts** and **glioblasts**. The neuroblasts form all the neurons in the CNS. The glioblasts form the supporting cells (or **neuroglial cells**) of the CNS. The two main types of supporting cells are the **astrocytes** and the **oligodendrocytes**. The other important neuroglial cells in the CNS are the **microglia**. The microglia are actually macrophages within the CNS that arise from monocytes (i.e., mesoderm) that invade the developing nervous system in week 3 along with the developing blood vessels (Fig. 8.8).

   a. **Astrocyte:** Astrocytes project foot processes to capillaries that contribute to the blood–brain barrier and play a role in the metabolism of neurotransmitters (e.g., glutamate, γ-aminobutyric acid, serotonin). Astrocytes buffer the [K$^+$] of the CNS extracellular space and form the external and internal glial-limiting membrane in the CNS. In reaction to CNS injury, astrocytes undergo hypertrophy and hyperplasia and form glial scars in a damaged area of the CNS (i.e., astrogliosis). The astrocyte contains **glial fibrillary acidic protein** (**GFAP**) and **glutamine synthetase**, which are good markers for astrocytes. The two types of astrocytes are fibrous and protoplasmic.

   [1] **Fibrous astrocyte: Fibrous astrocytes** are found predominately in the white matter, and about 80% of adult primary tumors arise from fibrous astrocytes.

   [2] **Protoplasmic astrocyte: Protoplasmic astrocytes** are found predominately in the gray matter.

   b. **Oligodendrocyte:** The oligodendrocyte may project up to 40 cell processes, each of which is involved in myelination. Each oligodendrocyte cell process produces a myelin sheath that surrounds and insulates a portion of only one axon. Because one oligodendrocyte may project up to 40 cells processes, it may myelinate a portion of up to 40 different axons. Because the junction between adjacent oligodendrocyte cell processes lacks myelin, this segment of the axon is exposed to the extracellular milieu due to gaps in the myelin sheath. This segment of the axon is called the **node of Ranvier**.

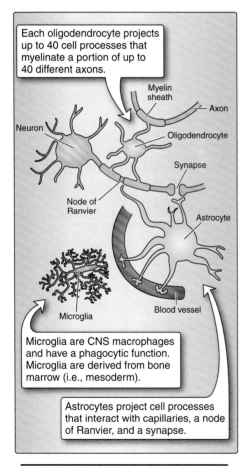

Each oligodendrocyte projects up to 40 cell processes that myelinate a portion of up to 40 different axons.

Myelin sheath
Axon
Neuron
Oligodendrocyte
Synapse
Node of Ranvier
Astrocyte
Microglia
Blood vessel

Microglia are CNS macrophages and have a phagocytic function. Microglia are derived from bone marrow (i.e., mesoderm).

Astrocytes project cell processes that interact with capillaries, a node of Ranvier, and a synapse.

Figure 8.8
Histogenesis during brain development. CNS, central nervous system.

c. **Microglia:** Microglia are the smallest neuroglia and have a phagocytic function. They are derived from **colony-forming unit-granulocyte monocyte cells** found in the bone marrow (i.e., mesoderm). Microglia normally comprise 1% of all the neuroglia in the CNS but proliferate in regions of injury or disease. These are then called **reactive microglia.**

3. **Hypophysis development and histology:** The hypophysis (or pituitary gland) forms from two distinct embryologic sources (Fig. 8.9). The first source is from **ectoderm** that lines the **stomodeum** (or the primitive mouth). The second source is from **neuroectoderm** associated with the **diencephalon.** The hypophysis comprises two embryologically distinct components, the **adenohypophysis** and the **neurohypophysis** (Fig. 8.10).

a. **Adenohypophysis:** At week 3, an upward evagination of ectoderm that lines the stomodeum called **Rathke's pouch** appears. Rathke's pouch grows dorsally toward the diencephalon and, by week 8, loses its connection with the stomodeum and comes into close contact with the infundibulum of the diencephalon. Rathke's pouch eventually forms the **adenohypophysis,** which includes three subdivisions: **pars distalis, pars tuberalis,** and **pars intermedia.**

[1] **Pars distalis:** The pars distalis contains the majority of endocrine cells, including **somatotropes, mammotropes, corticotropes, gonadotropes,** and **thyrotropes.** Table 8.5 provides a summary of hormones produced by these cells.

[2] **Pars tuberalis:** The pars tuberalis surrounds the median eminence and infundibular stem of the neurohypophysis. The par tuberalis contains some corticotropes and gonadotropes. In addition, the pars tuberalis contains the portal venules of the hypothalamo-hypophyseal portal system.

[3]. **Pars intermedia:** The pars intermedia (rudimentary in humans) contains numerous colloid-filled cysts called **Rathke's cysts.**

b. **Neurohypophysis:** At week 3, a downward evagination of neuroectoderm associated with the diencephalon called the **infundibulum** appears. The infundibulum grows ventrally toward Rathke's pouch and, by week 8, maintains its connection to the diencephalon (specifically the hypothalamus) and comes into close contact with Rathke's pouch. The infundibulum eventually forms the **neurohypophysis.** The neurohypophysis consists of two subdivisions, the **pars nervosa** and the **infundibulum.**

A remnant of Rathke's pouch may persist and give rise to a **craniopharyngioma.** A craniopharyngioma is the most common supratentorial tumor occurring in childhood and is the most common cause of hypopituitarism in children. A craniopharyngioma may form within the roof of the pharynx or within the sella turcica of the sphenoid bone but is most commonly found above the sella turcica where it can compress the optic chiasm and hypothalamus.

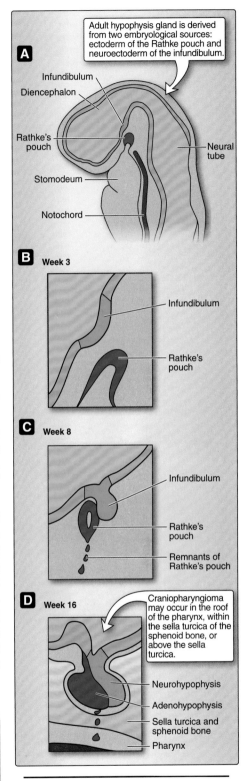

Figure 8.9
Hypophysis embryology (A–D).

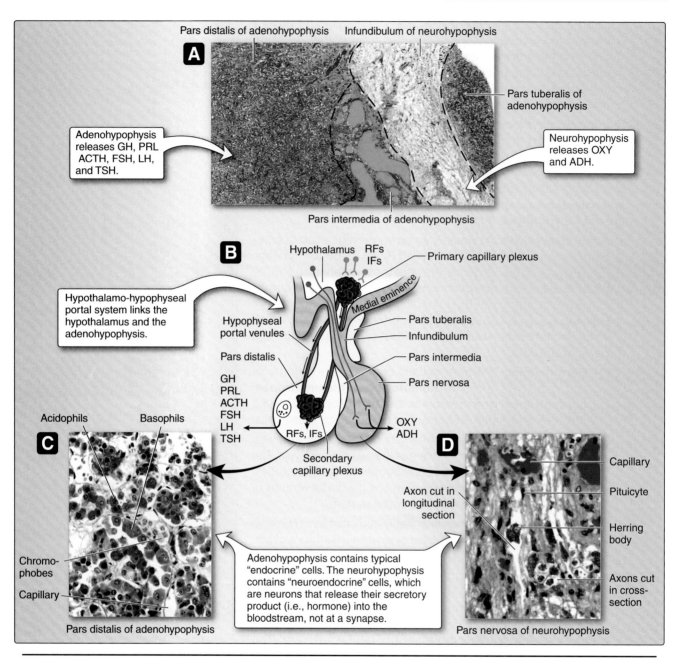

Figure 8.10

Hypophysis histology. A, Gross histology. B, Hypothalamo-hypophyseal portal system. C and D, Cell types.
ACTH = adrenocorticotropic hormone, ADH = antidiuretic hormone, FSH = follicle-stimulating hormone, GH = growth
hormone, IFs = inhibiting factors, LH = luteinizing hormone, OXY = oxytocin, PRL = prolactin, RFs = releasing factors,
TSH = thyroid-stimulating hormone.

[1] **Pars nervosa:** The pars nervosa contains the unmyelinated
axons and axon terminals that belong to neuroendocrine cells
whose cell bodies are located in the **supraoptic nucleus**
and the **paraventricular nucleus** of the hypothalamus. The
pars nervosa also contains glial-like cells called **pituicytes**.

(a) **Hormones:** The cell bodies of the neuroendocrine cells
located in the hypothalamic supraoptic and paraventricular nuclei synthesize **oxytocin** and **antidiuretic**

Table 8.5: Hormones of the Adenohypophysis and Neurohypophysis

Endocrine Cell	Hormone Secretion	Receptor	Hypothalamic Factors	Function
Somatotrope (50%) Acidophil	GH	GH receptor Receptor tyrosine kinase	GHRF Somatostatin	In muscle, decreases glucose uptake and increases protein synthesis In adipose tissue, decreases glucose uptake and increases lipolysis In hepatocytes, increases gluconeogenesis, increases glycogen degradation, and stimulates release of IGF-1 (somatomedin C), which increases protein synthesis in chondrocytes at the epiphyseal growth plate and, therefore, causes linear bone growth (pubertal growth spurt)
Mammotrope (15%–20%) Acidophil	PRL	PRL receptor Receptor tyrosine kinase	TRF Dopamine	Promotes milk production (lactogenesis) in lactating women Promotes growth of mammary gland during pregnancy Inhibits release of GNRF and thereby prevents ovulation (in women) or spermatogenesis (in men)
Corticotrope (15%–20%) Basophil	ACTH	ACTH receptor G-protein–linked receptor	CRF	Stimulates the enzyme desmolase that converts cholesterol → pregnenolone, a key step in the synthesis of all steroids Stimulates zona fasciculata and zona reticularis to secrete cortisol, androstenedione, and DHEA
Gonadotrope (10%) Basophil	FSH	FSH receptor	GNRF	In women, promotes growth of secondary follicles → Graafian follicles In men, maintains spermatogenesis and stimulates synthesis of ABP in Sertoli cells
	LH	LH receptor G-protein–linked receptors		In women, promotes ovulation (i.e., the LH surge), formation of corpus luteum (leutinization), and progesterone secretion In men, stimulates testosterone secretion from Leydig cells
Thyrotrope (5%) Basophil	TSH	TSH receptor G-protein–linked receptor	TRF	Stimulates T_3 and T_4 secretion from thyroid follicular cells
Neuroendocrine cell (SO, PV)	Oxytocin	OXTR receptor G-protein–linked receptor		Causes milk ejection and uterine contractions
	ADH	V_1, V_2, V_3 receptor G-protein–linked receptor		Increases water reabsorption by medullary collecting ducts in the kidney

Abbreviations: ACTH = adrenocorticotropic hormone, CRF = corticotropin-releasing factor, FSH = follicle-stimulating hormone, GH = growth hormone, GHRF = growth hormone–releasing factor, GNRF = gonadotropin-releasing factor, IGF-1 = insulin-like growth factor 1, LH = luteinizing hormone, OXTR= oxytocin receptor, PRL= prolactin, PV = paraventricular nucleus, SO = supraoptic nucleus, T_3 = triiodothyronine, T_4 = thyronine, TRF = thyrotropin-releasing factor, TSH = thyroid-stimulating hormone, V_1 = vasopressin.

hormone (**ADH**; see Table 8.5). Their unmyelinated axons project to the pars nervosa and carry large aggregations of neurosecretory vesicles called **Herring bodies**. The Herring bodies contain oxytocin or ADH along with the carrier protein **neurophysin**. The axon terminals of the neuroendocrine cells secrete oxytocin and ADH into a capillary plexus formed by the inferior hypophyseal artery.

(b) **Pituicyte:** Pituicytes are glial-like cells that resemble astrocytes. The pituicyte contains intermediate filaments assembled from **GFAP**. It has cell processes that project to fenestrated capillaries and the perivascular space.

[2] **Infundibulum:** The infundibulum is a stalk that connects the pars nervosa to the hypothalamus.

B. Adult brain

The brain is made up of a **cerebrum** (telencephalon and diencephalon), **brainstem** (mesencephalon = midbrain; mesencephalon = pons; myelencephalon = medulla), and a **cerebellum** (metencephalon), as shown in Figure 8.11.

1. **Cerebrum:** The cerebrum is divided into right and left cerebral hemispheres, which are separated in the midline along a longitudinal fissure. The cerebral surface (cortex) is characterized by multiple gyri (folds) and sulci (grooves). This gyri/sulci arrangement allows for greater cortical surface area. A general organization of sulci and gyri is maintained within each hemisphere, although no two brains are identical.

   a. **Lobes:** Each cerebral hemisphere is further divided into four lobes. Both right and left cerebral hemispheres have a **frontal**,

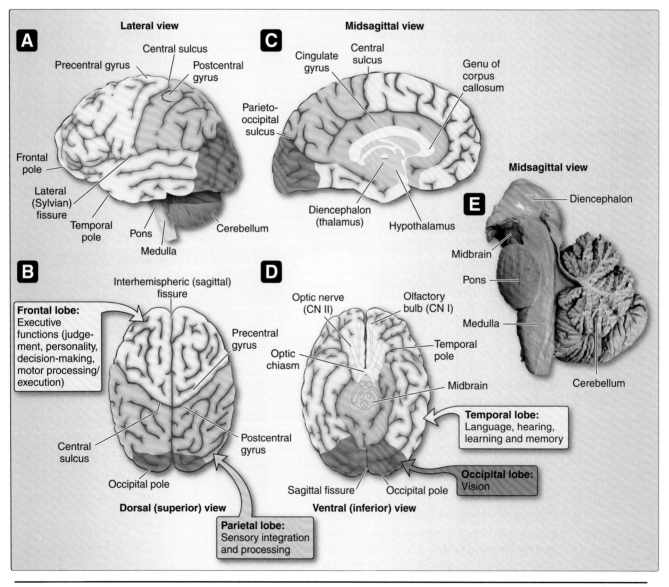

Figure 8.11

Organization of the brain. A–D, Frontal lobe, parietal lobe, occipital lobe, temporal lobe, limbic lobe/system. E, Brainstem and cerebellum.

parietal, temporal, and occipital lobe. Laterally, the temporal lobe is separated from the frontal and parietal lobes by the **lateral fissure**. The ventral surface of the cerebrum sits within the cranial base, so that the frontal lobes are located in the anterior cranial fossa and the temporal lobes in the middle cranial fossa.

b. **Diencephalic structures:** A midsagittal view of a cerebral hemisphere reveals diencephalic structures, including the **thalamus**, **hypothalamus**, **pineal gland**, and **epithalamus**.

2. **Brainstem:** The brainstem begins at the junction of the middle and posterior cranial fossae and extends to the **foramen magnum** where it continues inferiorly as the spinal cord. The **midbrain** is the most rostral portion of the brainstem, followed by the **pons** and **medulla** caudally. Multiple **CNs** arise from regions of the brainstem and is discussed in detail later in this chapter.

3. **Cerebellum:** The cerebellum occupies the remaining space in the posterior cranial fossa. Latin for "little brain," the cerebellum also possesses right and left hemispheres, which are united in the midline by the **vermis**.

B. Ventricular system

The ventricular system of the brain is made up of **CSF**-filled paired **lateral ventricles** and singular midline **third** and **fourth ventricles** (Fig. 8.12). The tuft-like **choroid plexus** found throughout the ventricular

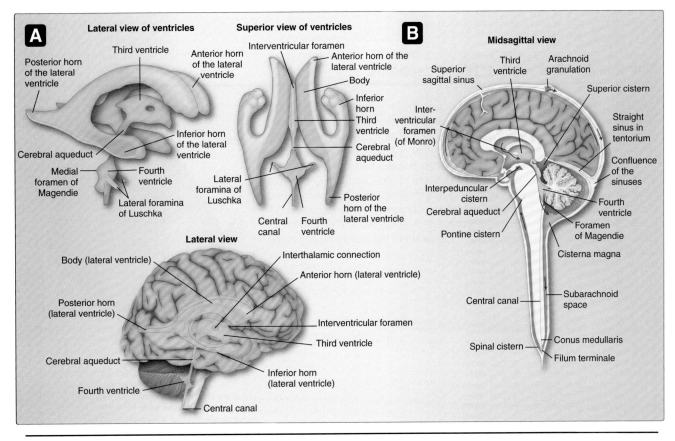

Figure 8.12
Ventricular system. A, Schematic views of ventricles (blue). B, Brain with ventricles in situ and cisterns. Note direction of cerebrospinal fluid (CSF) flow (red arrows) and relationship between arachnoid granulations and superior sagittal sinus.

system is responsible for CSF production. Each ventricle is associated with a specific region of the brain: right and left lateral ventricles, **telencephalon**; third ventricle, **diencephalon**; and fourth ventricle, **mesencephalon** (pons/cerebellum) and **myelencephalon** (medulla).

> The choroid plexuses produce approximately 600–700 ml of CSF per day. Constant reabsorption of CSF into the dural venous sinuses ensures that an average of only 100–160 ml is present at any given time.

1. **Cerebrospinal fluid flow:** Flow through the ventricular system occurs normally as long at the ventricles can communicate freely. Flow occurs from the lateral ventricles, through the **interventricular foramen** (of Monro) into the third ventricle. A narrow conduit through the midbrain, called the **cerebral aqueduct**, connects the third and fourth ventricles. From the fourth ventricle, CSF either continues inferiorly into the **central canal** of the spinal cord or can flow out into the subarachnoid space through a median aperture (of Magendie) or through paired lateral apertures (of Lusaka).

2. **Subarachnoid cisterns:** From the ventral surface of the brain, CSF may pool in a series of enlarged subarachnoid spaces called **cisterns**, primarily localized adjacent to the cerebellum, brainstem,

Clinical Application 8.4: Hydrocephalus

Hydrocephalus is characterized by an excess of CSF in the brain. This condition may be caused by CSF flow blockage or excess production. Increased CSF in the brain causes expansion of associated ventricles and potentially harmful pressure on adjacent structures. Hydrocephalus may be temporarily tolerated in an infant or toddler, due to open sutures that can partially accommodate for the increase in fluid. The skulls of older children and adults cannot expand. Symptoms may include altered motor function, urinary and fecal incontinence, and impaired cognition. Diagnostic tools include computed tomography (CT), magnetic resonance imaging (MRI), CSF sampling, and intracranial pressure monitoring. Surgical shunt placement is performed to alleviate the pressure.

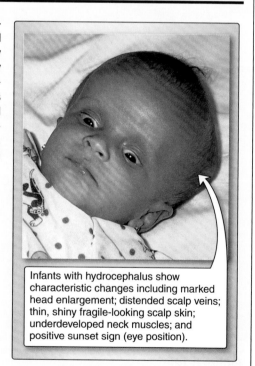

Infants with hydrocephalus show characteristic changes including marked head enlargement; distended scalp veins; thin, shiny fragile-looking scalp skin; underdeveloped neck muscles; and positive sunset sign (eye position).

and ventral structures. CSF flows superiorly within the subarachnoid space, bathing the sulci and gyri and functioning to nourish and cushion the brain within the cranial vault. Circulating CSF within the cranium is absorbed into the dural venous sinus system by way of **arachnoid granulations**.

C. Cranial meninges

Like spinal meninges, **cranial meninges** collectively surround, support, and protect the brain within the cranium (Fig. 8.13). Dural layers serve both to protect the brain in the cranium and to form partitions and venous sinuses (Fig. 8.14). From superficial to deep, these layers are described below.

1. **Dura mater: Dura mater** (L. *tough mother*) is the outermost, thick connective tissue layer. In the skull, the dura has two layers, a periosteal layer that is attached directly to the calvaria and cranial base and a meningeal layer that forms dural inholdings and is continuous with the dura surrounding the spinal cord. These layers are fused together, except for where they separate to form dural venous sinuses. A potential **epidural (extradural) space** exists between the periosteal dura and skull. Dura is pain sensitive, receiving innervation from branches of the trigeminal nerve (CN V) and vagus nerve (CN X). Meningeal arteries provide vascular supply to the dura and travel in the epidural space.

2. **Arachnoid mater: Arachnoid mater** is the delicate, weblike intermediate layer. It creates a true **subarachnoid space**, which contains CSF and cerebral vasculature. Collagenous **arachnoid trabeculae** connect the arachnoid to the underlying pia mater. Under normal conditions, the arachnoid and dura are tightly associated, obliterating the potential **subdural space** between these two layers. Specializations, called **arachnoid granulations**, arise from this layer and project into dural venous sinuses, functioning to transfer CSF into the venous system.

3. **Pia mater: Pia mater** is the innermost meningeal layer and is closely adhered to the surface of the brain. Pia extends into sulci and fissures, separating the brain substance from CSF in the subarachnoid space. Cerebral vessels pierce the pia through the perivascular space to reach the brain parenchyma.

> Collectively, arachnoid and pia mater are known as "leptomeninges" (*lepto* = delicate, slender). Embryologically, these two layers are derived from neural crest cells.

4. **Reflections:** Reflections of meningeal dura serve as dividing structures throughout different regions of the cranium.
   a. **Falx cerebri:** The cerebral hemispheres are partially separated by a sickle-shaped reflection called the **falx cerebri**, which sits in the longitudinal fissure and attaches anteriorly to the crista gali (ethmoid).
   b. **Tentorium cerebelli and tentorial notch:** Posteriorly, the occipital lobes and cerebellum are separated by the **tentorium cerebelli** (tent of the cerebellum). The tentorium attaches anteriorly to the

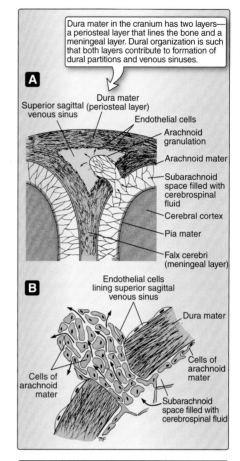

Figure 8.13
Meninges and arachnoid granulations. A, Relationship with superior sagittal sinus. B, Cellular organization.

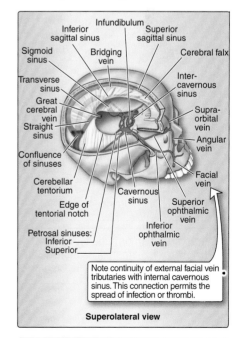

Figure 8.14
Dural reflections/sinuses: right calvarium and brain removed to view dural partitions (white) and venous sinuses (blue).

posterior crinoid processes (sphenoid) and along the petrous ridges of the temporal bones and is interrupted in the midline by the **tentorial notch**, which allows for the brainstem to enter the posterior cranial fossa and exit the skull. Posteriorly, the tentorium attaches to the parietal and occipital bones.

Clinical Application 8.5: Intracranial Hemorrhage

Intracranial hemorrhages may occur in cases of head trauma. The three main types—epidural, subdural, and subarachnoid hemorrhages—lead to the collection of blood, hematoma, in these spaces.

- Epidural hematoma typically involves damage to the middle meningeal artery as a result of a skull fracture, likely at the site of the pterion. Arterial blood extrudes into the potential epidural space, between the periosteal dura and bone, forming an epidural hematoma. Patients may present with loss of consciousness, followed by lucidity, and, if not treated, coma and death may occur, because of continuous pressure. Epidural blood is seen on CT scan as a lens-shaped pattern. Blood evacuation and vascular occlusion is indicated as treatment.
- Subdural hematoma (SDH) typically involves damage to the bridging veins that connect the superior cerebral veins to the superior sagittal sinus. This commonly occurs with shearing forces sustained during head injury. Venous blood pools between the meningeal dura and arachnoid, thus forming a subdural space and presenting in a crescent-shaped pattern on CT scan. However, magnetic resonance imaging (MRI) may be more sensitive for diagnosing SDH. Patients commonly present with coma and require surgical intervention. Blood evacuation and vascular occlusion is indicated as treatment. Patients with cerebral atrophy have a higher risk of developing an SDH.
- Subarachnoid hematoma (SAH), associated with hemorrhagic strokes, typically involves rupture of saccular aneurysms and escape of arterial blood into the subarachnoid space. Patients' primary complaint is a sudden, severe headache, which may cause nausea or vomiting and, in some cases, a brief loss of consciousness. Noncontrast CT scan and lumbar puncture are key diagnostic tools when SAH is suspected. Hyperdense clotted blood in the subarachnoid space, as well as blood following sulci and fissures, can often be identified on CT. If not managed quickly, aneurysmal SAH can be fatal. Common surgical treatment includes clipping and endovascular coiling.

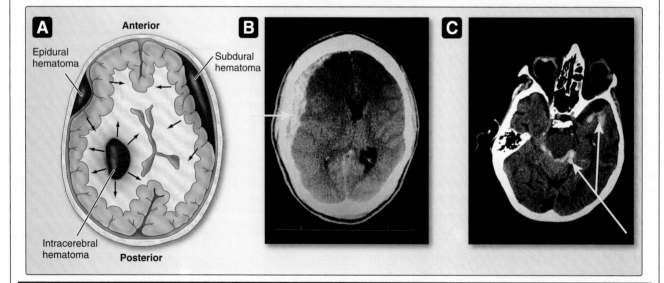

A, Intracranial hemorrhage types. B, CT subdural hematoma. Note collection of blood along right border of calvarium (arrow) with ~1.2-cm midline shift to left, compressing ventricular system on right. C, CT subarachnoid hematoma. Note blood around brainstem and left temporal lobe (arrows).

c. **Falx cerebelli:** A small **falx cerebelli** partially separates the cerebellar hemispheres in the posterior cranial fossa.

d. **Diaphragma sellae:** The **diaphragma sellae** is the smallest dural reflection, spanning the sellae turcica to cover the pituitary gland.

5. **Dural venous sinuses:** These primarily occur where there is a separation of periosteal and meningeal dura layers. Select sinuses occur between duplications of meningeal dura. These endothelial-lined sinuses drain venous blood and reabsorbed CSF directly or indirectly into the internal jugular veins. The primary sinuses are detailed below and shown in Figure 8.15. Smaller sinuses include the superior and inferior petrosal sinuses, occipital sinus, sphenoparietal sinus, and cavernous sinus.

a. **Superior sagittal sinus:** Located in the superior border of the falx cerebri, running from the crista gali to the **confluence of sinuses**, the **superior sagittal sinus** is the main site for CSF reabsorption via arachnoid granulations. It receives venous blood from superior cerebral veins and CSF from arachnoid granulations that project directly into the sinus or from small adjacent collections of granulations in **lateral venous lacunae**.

b. **Inferior sagittal sinus:** Located in the free border of the falx cerebri, the **inferior sagittal sinus** terminates in the straight sinus.

c. **Straight sinus:** Located at the junction of the falx cerebri and tentorium, the **straight sinus** is formed by the union of the inferior sagittal sinus and the great cerebral vein (of Galen) and terminates at the confluence.

d. **Transverse sinus:** The bilateral **transverse sinus** projects laterally from the confluence between a groove in the occipital and parietal bones and the tentorium. It terminates in the sigmoid sinus.

e. **Sigmoid sinus:** The bilateral S-shaped **sigmoid sinus** in the posterior cranial fossa exits the skull through the jugular foramen, terminating in the internal jugular vein. It receives venous blood from the superior and inferior petrosal sinuses at its origin and termination, respectively.

f. **Confluence of sinuses:** The **confluence of sinuses** is located at the site of the internal occipital protuberance. In general, flow travels from anterior to posterior, where the superior sagittal and straight sinuses drain into the confluence. The confluence also receives the occipital sinus. Venous blood travels laterally from the confluence through the transverse and sigmoid sinuses, before draining into jugular system.

Clinical Application 8.6: Ischemic and Hemorrhagic Stroke

Stroke can be classified as either ischemic (lack of blood supply, 80%) or hemorrhagic (ruptured blood vessel, 20%). A transient ischemic accident ("mini-stroke") is characterized by temporary periods of neurologic dysfunction, whereas acute ischemic stroke (cerebrovascular accident) typically causes permanent dysfunction. Ischemia is further divided by cause into thrombosis, embolism, and systemic hypoperfusion categories. Antithrombotic therapy is indicated within 48 hours of a thrombotic stroke. Hemorrhagic stroke commonly involves the rupture of a saccular aneurysm, most typically a berry aneurysm, in vessels of the circle of Willis.

Stroke warning signs include sudden typically unilateral numbness and weakness in extremities, slurred speech, altered mental state, loss of balance and difficulty walking, severe headache, and visual impairment. Even transient symptoms should be considered a medical emergency and addressed immediately.

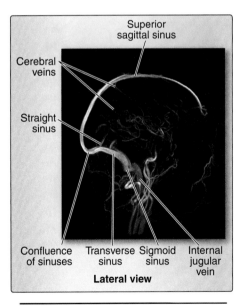

Figure 8.15
Venography of dural venous sinus system.

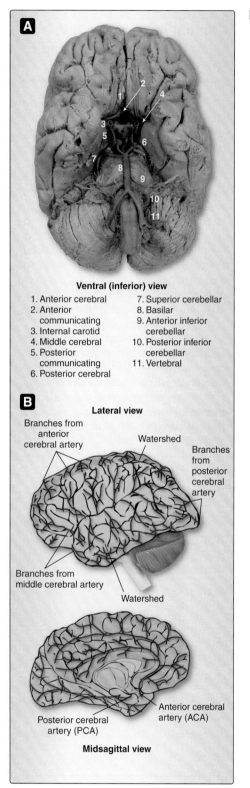

Ventral (inferior) view

1. Anterior cerebral
2. Anterior communicating
3. Internal carotid
4. Middle cerebral
5. Posterior communicating
6. Posterior cerebral
7. Superior cerebellar
8. Basilar
9. Anterior inferior cerebellar
10. Posterior inferior cerebellar
11. Vertebral

Lateral view

Branches from anterior cerebral artery

Watershed

Branches from posterior cerebral artery

Branches from middle cerebral artery

Watershed

Anterior cerebral artery (ACA)

Posterior cerebral artery (PCA)

Midsagittal view

Figure 8.16
Arterial blood supply to the brain. A, Gross specimen with cerebral arterial circle. B, Arterial distribution to cerebrum.

D. Vasculature

Arterial blood supply to the brain arises from multiple sources to allow for adequate flow in the event of peripheral blockage. Specialized dural venous sinuses work not only to drain deoxygenated blood from the brain substance but also to recycle CSF back into the venous system.

1. **Arterial supply:** Cerebral arterial blood supply arises from branches of the vertebral/basilar arterial and the internal carotid systems (Figs. 8.16 and 8.17). Collectively, these two sets of arteries form an arterial circle (circle of Willis), located on the ventral surface of the brain.

   a. **Vertebral/basilar system:** Arising from the subclavian artery, the vertebral artery ascends the cervical region through transverse foramina in cervical vertebra and enters the posterior cranial fossa through the foramen magnum. The pair of vertebral arteries unites near the pontomedullary junction to form the basilar artery. The following branches arise directly from the vertebral and basilar system.

      [1] **Vertebral arteries:** Singular anterior and paired posterior spinal arteries serve the spinal cord, and paired **posterior inferior cerebellar arteries** serve the cerebellum.

      [2] **Basilar arteries:** Paired **anterior inferior cerebellar arteries** and paired superior cerebellar arteries serve the cerebellum, multiple pontine arteries serve the pons, and **posterior cerebral arteries** (PCAs; terminal branches of the basilar artery) serve the occipital lobe.

   b. **Internal carotid system:** Coursing up through the carotid canal, the internal carotid arteries travel through the cavernous sinus and pierce the dura to enter the middle cranial fossa. The following paired branches arise directly from the internal carotid system:

      [1] **Ophthalmic artery:** This artery supplies the eye.

      [2] **Posterior communicating artery:** This artery anastomoses with PCA, thus connecting the internal carotid system to the vertebral/basilar system.

      [3] **Anterior choroidal artery:** This artery supplies portions of the choroid plexus.

      [4] **Anterior cerebral artery (ACA):** The ACA enters the longitudinal fissure, is connected by a short anterior communicating artery, and serves the midline frontal and parietal lobes.

      [5] **Middle cerebral artery (MCA):** The MCA is not considered part of the circle of Willis. It travels laterally between the frontal and temporal lobes and serves lateral temporal, parietal, and frontal lobes and deep nuclei.

2. **Venous supply:** Venous blood in the brain is drained by thin, valveless **cerebral veins** (see Fig. 8.15). These veins travel with the arteries in the subarachnoid space and must pierce the arachnoid and meningeal dura to drain into the dural venous sinus system. This primarily occurs at the superior sagittal sinus, although a collection of cerebral veins drain deeper structures into the straight sinus by way of the **great cerebral vein** (of Galen). Transverse and petrosal sinuses also receive cerebral veins.

Clinical Application 8.7: Cavernous Sinus Thrombosis

Communication occurs between internal dural sinuses and valveless external structures like emissary and facial veins, thus setting up an environment for the spread of infection. Of special consideration is the cavernous sinus, which sits on either side of the sella turcica and communicates externally via emissary veins. Infection or thrombosis within the cavernous sinus can lead to downstream CN deficits. The oculomotor (CN III), trochlear (CN IV), and trigeminal (CN V_1 and V_2) nerves travel in the lateral wall of the sinus, while the internal carotid artery and abducens nerve (CN VI) travel within the trabeculated center—making CN VI more susceptible to inflammatory damage than those in the lateral wall of the sinus. The spread of infection may occur through connection with facial veins, adjacent internal sinuses, or the pterygoid venous plexus, found in the infratemporal fossa. Patients may present with headache, extraocular muscle paralysis (lateral gaze palsy, CN VI), diplopia (double vision), ptosis (eyelid drooping), and mydriasis (dilated pupil). Internal carotid artery damage in the cavernous sinus may also cause pressure on the surrounding CNs. Antibiotic therapy remains the mainstay treatment for the infective component of this condition.

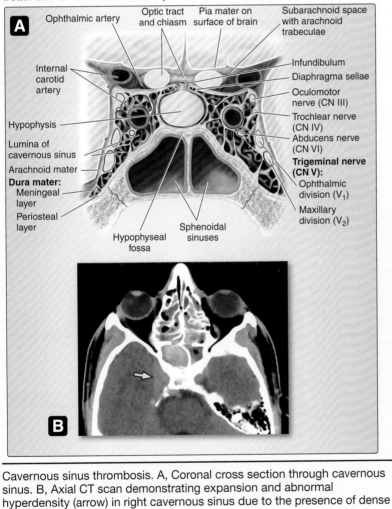

Cavernous sinus thrombosis. A, Coronal cross section through cavernous sinus. B, Axial CT scan demonstrating expansion and abnormal hyperdensity (arrow) in right cavernous sinus due to the presence of dense thrombosis.

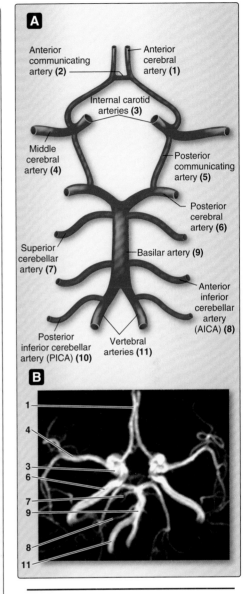

Figure 8.17
Arterial circle (of Willis). A, Schematic. B, Angiogram.

IV. FACE

The face, which spans between the ears and extends superior to inferior from the forehead to the chin, represents the anterior portion of the head. The general shape of the face is determined by the underlying bony scaffold of the viscerocranium and the overlying muscles, fascia, subcutaneous adipose, and skin. Cartilaginous extensions of the nose, eyelids, and external ears also provide unique features to each person's face.

A. Embryology

The pharyngeal apparatus gives rise to adult head and neck structures. For completeness, all head and neck adult derivatives are mentioned in this chapter with details on structures of the head. A detailed description of adult neck structures can be found in Chapter 9.

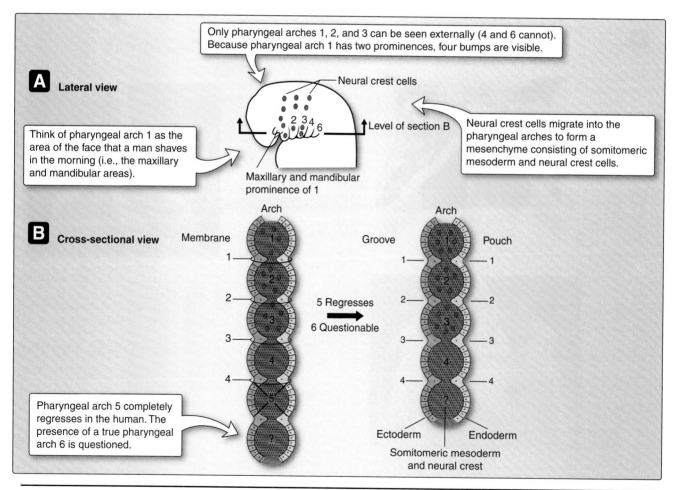

A Lateral view

Only pharyngeal arches 1, 2, and 3 can be seen externally (4 and 6 cannot). Because pharyngeal arch 1 has two prominences, four bumps are visible.

Neural crest cells

↑ Level of section B

Neural crest cells migrate into the pharyngeal arches to form a mesenchyme consisting of somitomeric mesoderm and neural crest cells.

Think of pharyngeal arch 1 as the area of the face that a man shaves in the morning (i.e., the maxillary and mandibular areas).

Maxillary and mandibular prominence of 1

B Cross-sectional view

Membrane   Groove   Pouch

5 Regresses
6 Questionable

Pharyngeal arch 5 completely regresses in the human. The presence of a true pharyngeal arch 6 is questioned.

Ectoderm   Endoderm

Somitomeric mesoderm and neural crest

Figure 8.18
Pharyngeal apparatus.

1. **Pharyngeal apparatus development:** The pharyngeal apparatus contributes greatly to the formation of the head and neck region of the body (Figs. 8.18 and 8.19). The pharyngeal apparatus consists of the **pharyngeal arches** (five), **pouches** (four), **grooves** (four), and **membranes** (four). At week 4, the pharyngeal apparatus is first observed and gives the embryo its distinctive appearance. The particular fates of the elements of the pharyngeal apparatus are described below and shown in Table 8.6.

Table 8.6: Fate of Pharyngeal Apparatus

Arch	Cranial Nerve	Adult Derivative
1	CN V	**Mesoderm:** Muscles of mastication, mylohyoid, anterior belly of digastric, tensor veli palatini, tensor tympani **Neural crest:** Maxilla, mandible, malleus, incus, zygomatic bone, squamous temporal bone, palatine bone, vomer, spheno-mandibular ligament, and Meckel's cartilage
2	CN VII	**Mesoderm:** Muscles of facial expression, posterior belly of digastric, stylohyoid, stapedius **Neural crest:** Stapes, styloid process, stylohyoid ligament, lesser horn and upper body of hyoid bone, and Reichert's cartilage
3	CN IX	**Mesoderm:** Stylopharyngeus, common carotid arteries, internal carotid arteries **Neural crest:** Greater horn and lower body of hyoid bone
4	CN X (superior laryngeal nerve)	**Mesoderm:** Muscles of soft palate (except tensor veli palatini), muscles of the pharynx (except stylopharyngeus), cricothyroid, cricopharyngeus, laryngeal cartilages, right subclavian artery, arch of aorta **Neural crest:** None
6	CN X (recurrent laryngeal nerve)	**Mesoderm:** Intrinsic muscles of larynx (except cricothyroid), upper muscles of the esophagus, laryngeal cartilages, pulmonary arteries, ductus arteriosus **Neural crest:** None
Pouch		
1		Epithelial lining of auditory tube and middle ear cavity
2		Epithelial lining of palatine tonsil crypts
3		Chief and oxyphil cells of the inferior parathyroid gland Thymic epitheliocytes of the thymus
4		Chief and oxyphil cells of the superior parathyroid gland Parafollicular cells (C cells) of the ultimopharyngeal body*
Groove		
1		Epithelial lining of the external auditory meatus
2, 3, 4		Obliterated
Membrane		
1		Tympanic membrane
2, 3, 4		Obliterated

*Neural crest cells migrate into the ultimobranchial body to form parafollicular cells (C cells) of the thyroid, which secrete calcitonin.

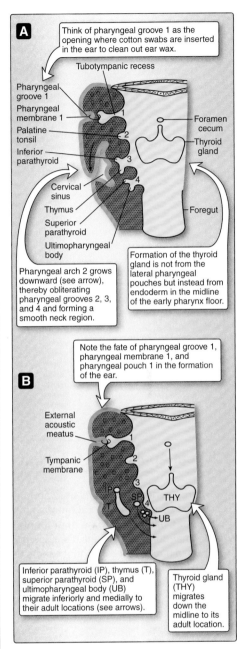

Figure 8.19

Pharyngeal pouch, groove, and membrane fate. A, 5 weeks. B, 7 weeks.

> ‖ Pharyngeal arch 1 has two identifiable prominences called the **maxillary prominence** and the **mandibular prominence**.

a. **Pharyngeal arches:** The pharyngeal arches (1, 2, 3, 4, and 6) contain **somitomeric mesoderm** and **neural crest cells**. The somitomeric mesoderm differentiates into various adult **muscles** and **arteries** (i.e., aortic arches 1–6) in the head and neck region. The neural crest cells differentiate into various adult **bones** and **connective tissue** in the head and neck region. In addition, each pharyngeal arch has a **cranial nerve** associated with it.

b. **Pharyngeal pouches:** The pharyngeal pouches (1, 2, 3, 4) are evaginations of the endoderm that lines the foregut.

[1] **Pharyngeal pouch 1:** This pouch elongates toward the surface and forms the **tubotympanic recess**. The endoderm lining the tubotympanic recess eventually forms the epithelial lining of the auditory tube and the middle ear cavity.

[2] **Pharyngeal pouch 2:** This pouch grows into the underlying mesenchyme and forms pitlike depressions that are lined by endoderm. This endoderm eventually forms the epithelial lining of the palatine tonsil crypts. The mesenchyme surrounding

Clinical Application 8.8: First Arch Syndrome

First arch syndrome results from abnormal development of **pharyngeal arch 1** and produces various facial anomalies. It is caused by a lack of migration of neural crest cells into pharyngeal arch 1. Two well-described first arch syndromes are **Treacher Collins syndrome (mandibulofacial dysostosis)** and **Pierre Robin syndrome**. Treacher Collins syndrome is an autosomal-dominant genetic disorder caused by a mutation in the *TCOF1* **gene** on **chromosome 5q32-q33.1** for the **treacle protein**, a nucleolar protein that seems to be involved in microtubule dynamics. Clinical features include hypoplasia of the zygomatic bones and mandible, resulting in midface hypoplasia, micrognathia, and retrognathia; external ear abnormalities, including small, absent, malformed, or rotated ears; and lower eyelid abnormalities, including coloboma.

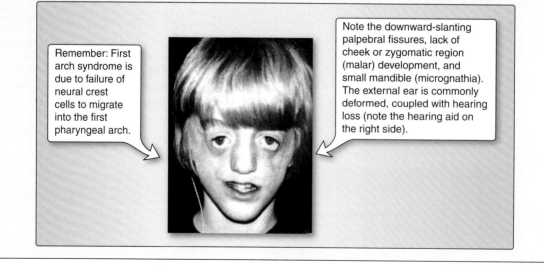

Remember: First arch syndrome is due to failure of neural crest cells to migrate into the first pharyngeal arch.

Note the downward-slanting palpebral fissures, lack of cheek or zygomatic region (malar) development, and small mandible (micrognathia). The external ear is commonly deformed, coupled with hearing loss (note the hearing aid on the right side).

the crypts later becomes populated by lymphoid tissue forming the palatine tonsil.

[3] Pharyngeal pouch 3: This pouch expands and forms a solid dorsal portion related to the **inferior parathyroid gland** and a hollow ventral portion related to the **thymus gland**.

(a) Dorsal portion: The endoderm lining the solid dorsal portion progressively differentiates and eventually forms the **chief cells** and **oxyphil cells** of the inferior parathyroid gland. The bilateral primordia of the inferior parathyroid glands migrate inferiorly and medially where they come to lie on the dorsal surface of the lower part of the thyroid gland.

(b) Ventral portion: The endoderm lining the hollow ventral portion proliferates and forms solid cords of cells that grow into the underlying mesenchyme. The endoderm progressively differentiates and eventually forms the **thymic epitheliocytes** of the thymus gland. The mesenchyme surrounding the solid cords of cells later becomes populated by lymphoid tissue. The bilateral primordia of the thymus migrate inferiorly and medially where they fuse to form the bilobed thymus gland, which then descends into the superior mediastinum.

[4] Pharyngeal pouch 4: This pouch expands and forms a solid dorsal portion related to the **superior parathyroid gland** and an elongated ventral portion related to the **ultimopharyngeal body**.

(a) Dorsal portion: The endoderm lining the solid dorsal portion progressively differentiates and eventually forms the **chief cells** and **oxyphil cells** of the superior parathyroid gland. The bilateral primordia of the superior parathyroid glands migrate inferiorly and medially where they come to lie on the dorsal surface of the upper part of the thyroid gland.

(b) Ventral portion: Very soon after the elongated ventral portion forms, it becomes populated by **neural crest cells** that form the ultimopharyngeal body. The bilateral ultimopharyngeal bodies detach from the pharyngeal wall and fuse with the dorsal surface of the thyroid gland. The neural crest cells within the ultimopharyngeal bodies disperse throughout the thyroid gland and differentiate into the **parafollicular cells** (or **C cells**).

c. Pharyngeal grooves: The pharyngeal grooves (1, 2, 3, 4) are invaginations of the **ectoderm** that covers the surface of the embryo. They are located between each pharyngeal arch (see Fig. 8.19).

[1] Pharyngeal groove 1: This groove elongates toward the pharynx, and the ectoderm forms the epithelial lining of the external auditory meatus.

[2] Pharyngeal grooves 2, 3, and 4: These grooves are obliterated as pharyngeal arch 2 grows downward and fuses with the lower portion of the neck, thereby forming the smooth, contoured surface seen in the adult.

Clinical Application 8.9: DiGeorge Syndrome

DiGeorge syndrome (DS; "catch 22"; 22q11 syndrome) is caused by a microdeletion of a region in chromosome 22q11.2 that is also called the "DiGeorge chromosomal region." This results in the failure of **pharyngeal pouches 3 and 4** to differentiate into the thymus and parathyroid glands. DS is usually accompanied by facial anomalies resembling first arch syndrome (micrognathia, low-set ears) due to abnormal neural crest cell migration, cardiovascular anomalies due to abnormal neural crest cell migration during formation of the aorticopulmonary septum, immunodeficiency due to the absence of the thymus gland, and hypocalcemia due to the absence of parathyroid glands.

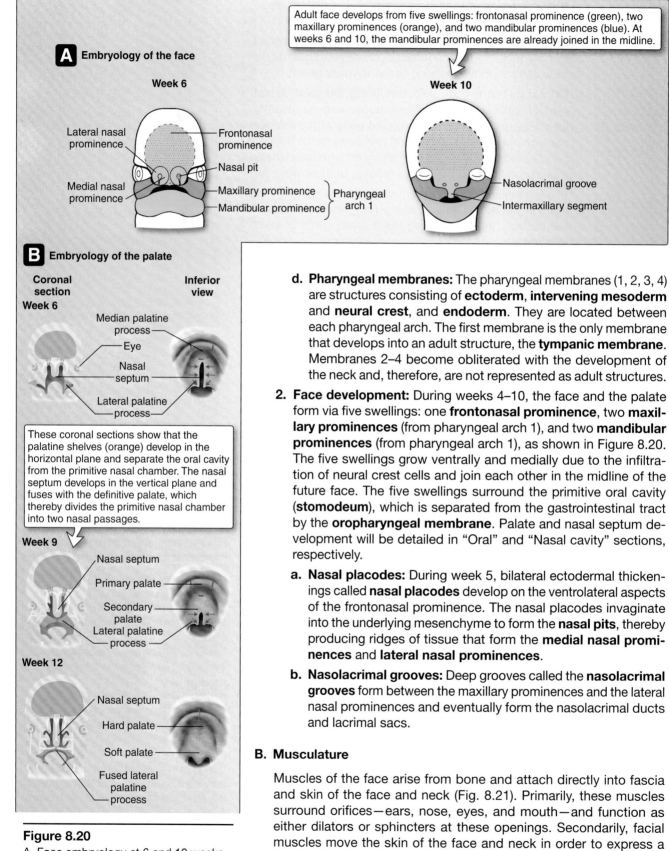

A Embryology of the face

Week 6

Lateral nasal prominence
Frontonasal prominence
Nasal pit
Medial nasal prominence
Maxillary prominence
Mandibular prominence
} Pharyngeal arch 1

Adult face develops from five swellings: frontonasal prominence (green), two maxillary prominences (orange), and two mandibular prominences (blue). At weeks 6 and 10, the mandibular prominences are already joined in the midline.

Week 10

Nasolacrimal groove
Intermaxillary segment

B Embryology of the palate

Coronal section
Week 6

Inferior view

Median palatine process
Eye
Nasal septum
Lateral palatine process

These coronal sections show that the palatine shelves (orange) develop in the horizontal plane and separate the oral cavity from the primitive nasal chamber. The nasal septum develops in the vertical plane and fuses with the definitive palate, which thereby divides the primitive nasal chamber into two nasal passages.

Week 9

Nasal septum
Primary palate
Secondary palate
Lateral palatine process

Week 12

Nasal septum
Hard palate
Soft palate
Fused lateral palatine process

Figure 8.20
A, Face embryology at 6 and 10 weeks.
B, Embryology of the palate at 6, 9, and 12 weeks.

d. **Pharyngeal membranes:** The pharyngeal membranes (1, 2, 3, 4) are structures consisting of **ectoderm**, **intervening mesoderm** and **neural crest**, and **endoderm**. They are located between each pharyngeal arch. The first membrane is the only membrane that develops into an adult structure, the **tympanic membrane**. Membranes 2–4 become obliterated with the development of the neck and, therefore, are not represented as adult structures.

2. **Face development:** During weeks 4–10, the face and the palate form via five swellings: one **frontonasal prominence**, two **maxillary prominences** (from pharyngeal arch 1), and two **mandibular prominences** (from pharyngeal arch 1), as shown in Figure 8.20. The five swellings grow ventrally and medially due to the infiltration of neural crest cells and join each other in the midline of the future face. The five swellings surround the primitive oral cavity (**stomodeum**), which is separated from the gastrointestinal tract by the **oropharyngeal membrane**. Palate and nasal septum development will be detailed in "Oral" and "Nasal cavity" sections, respectively.

a. **Nasal placodes:** During week 5, bilateral ectodermal thickenings called **nasal placodes** develop on the ventrolateral aspects of the frontonasal prominence. The nasal placodes invaginate into the underlying mesenchyme to form the **nasal pits**, thereby producing ridges of tissue that form the **medial nasal prominences** and **lateral nasal prominences**.

b. **Nasolacrimal grooves:** Deep grooves called the **nasolacrimal grooves** form between the maxillary prominences and the lateral nasal prominences and eventually form the nasolacrimal ducts and lacrimal sacs.

B. **Musculature**

Muscles of the face arise from bone and attach directly into fascia and skin of the face and neck (Fig. 8.21). Primarily, these muscles surround orifices—ears, nose, eyes, and mouth—and function as either dilators or sphincters at these openings. Secondarily, facial muscles move the skin of the face and neck in order to express a myriad of emotions. The main muscles of the face and their actions are described below.

1. **Orbicularis oculi:** This muscle is the sphincter of the eye. Its palpebral portion closes the eyelid gently, and its orbital portion closes the eyelid tightly.

2. **Orbicularis oris:** This muscle is the sphincter of the mouth. It closes and protrudes the lips.

3. **Buccinator:** The cheek muscle keeps the bolus of food between the teeth during mastication.

4. **Zygomaticus major:** The "smile muscle" pulls the angle of the mouth superiorly and laterally.

5. **Other muscles:** A number of smaller muscles around the eye, nose, ear, and mouth are devoted to actions, including lip elevation and depression, nostril dilation, and skin wrinkling on the bridge of the nose and chin. Although these muscles are not detailed here, their anatomical arrangement is partially shown in Figure 8.21.

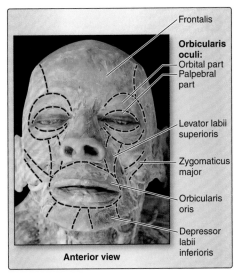

Anterior view

Figure 8.21
Face muscles.

> ‖ Observing patterns of asymmetry in facial expression is a powerful diagnostic tool, aiding in the differentiation of upper verses lower motor neuron lesions.

C. Innervation

Muscles of facial expression are derived from the second pharyngeal arch, so it makes sense that they receive motor innervation from the CN also associated with the second arch—**facial nerve** (CN VII), as shown in Figures 8.22. The face receives sensory innervation from the **trigeminal nerve** (CN V) (Fig. 8.23).

1. **Facial nerve branches:** The facial nerve provides branchiomotor (special visceral efferent [SVE]) innervation to all muscles of facial expression through regional terminal branches that reach the face after passing through the substance of the parotid gland. The five branches are temporal, zygomatic, buccal, marginal mandibular, and cervical.

> ‖ A helpful mnemonic for facial nerve branches is:
>
> To (temporal) Zanzibar (zygomatic) by (buccal) motor (mandibular) car (cervical).

2. **Trigeminal nerve branches:** Sensory (general somatic afferent [GSA]) innervation of the face is supplied by branches of the **trigeminal nerve** (CN V).

   a. **CN V₁:** Supratrochlear, supraorbital, infratrochlear, and external nasal nerves supply the skin over the upper eyelids, bridge of the nose, and forehead.

   b. **CN V₂:** Infraorbital, zygomaticofacial, and zygomaticotemporal nerves supply the skin over the lateral nose, superior lip, inferior eyelids, cheekbone, and anterior temporal fossa.

   c. **CN V₃:** Mental, buccal, and auriculotemporal nerves supply the skin over the inferior lip, chin, flesh of the cheek, and temporal fossa and parotid regions.

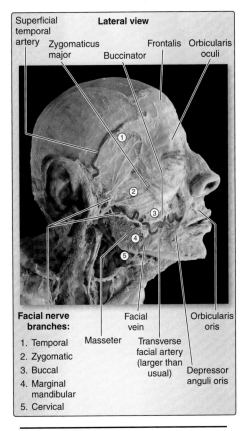

Facial nerve branches:
1. Temporal
2. Zygomatic
3. Buccal
4. Marginal mandibular
5. Cervical

Figure 8.22
Face motor innervation. Facial nerve brances (CN VII).

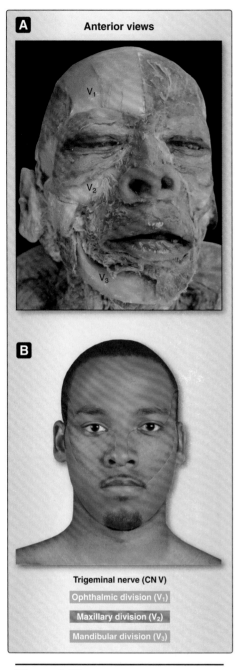

A Anterior views

V₁

V₂

V₃

B

Trigeminal nerve (CN V)
Ophthalmic division (V₁)
Maxillary division (V₂)
Mandibular division (V₃)

Figure 8.23
Face sensory innervation. Terminal branches of trigeminal nerve (CN V) divisions. A, Cadaveric specimen showing distal fibers. B, Trigeminal division distribution.

Clinical Application 8.10: Trigeminal Neuralgia

Trigeminal neuralgia (TN) is a common cause of unilateral facial pain within the distribution of one of more divisions of the trigeminal nerve. The condition is characterized by recurrent episodes of pain, commonly described as electric shock-like or stabbing, and more predominant in women. Classically, vascular compression of the trigeminal nerve root at the mid-pons level accounts for most cases of TN. Secondarily, TN can be caused by herpes zoster viral infection, post-traumatic neuropathy, or a nonvascular space–occupying lesion. Initial treatment commonly includes carbamazepine therapy. Patients who cannot tolerate pharmacologic therapies may be candidates for surgery to alleviate the pain.

D. Vasculature

The face is primarily supplied by direct or indirect branches of the external carotid artery. Venous tributaries of the face typically drain into the jugular venous system.

1. **Arterial supply:** Superficial structures of the face are primarily supplied by the **facial artery**, a direct branch of the external carotid artery (Fig. 8.24). From its origin in the carotid triangle of the neck, the facial artery follows a tortuous path, deep to the superficial part of the submandibular gland and crosses the inferior border of the mandible, anterior to the masseter muscle. At the angle of the mouth, it gives off **inferior** and **superior labial arteries**, to supply the structures of the lower and upper lips, respectively. The facial artery continues toward the nose, where it is renamed the **angular artery**. Additional arteries that supply the face include branches of the superficial temporal artery.

2. **Venous supply:** Tributaries of the **facial vein** drain the majority of the face, including the angular, superior and inferior labial, and deep facial veins (see Fig. 8.24). The facial vein unites with the anterior branch of the **retromandibular vein** to form the **common facial vein**, which drains directly into the **internal jugular vein**. The posterior branch of the retromandibular vein joins the posterior auricular vein to form the external jugular vein.

> The "danger triangle" of the face refers to the region of skin around the nose and upper lip. Infection in this area may spread through valveless connections between the facial vein tributaries and the cavernous sinus.

3. **Lymphatic supply:** Lymph nodes of the face are only found in the parotid and buccal regions (Fig. 8.25). The majority of lymph is drained, along with lymph from the scalp, through the superficial ring of lymph nodes at the intersection of the head and neck (including parotid, occipital, mastoid, submental, and submandibular nodes). Once drained through the superficial ring, lymph travels through the deep cervical nodes adjacent to the internal jugular vein to the jugular lymphatic duct. Lymph eventually drains into the thoracic duct on the left of the subclavian/internal jugular vein junction on the right.

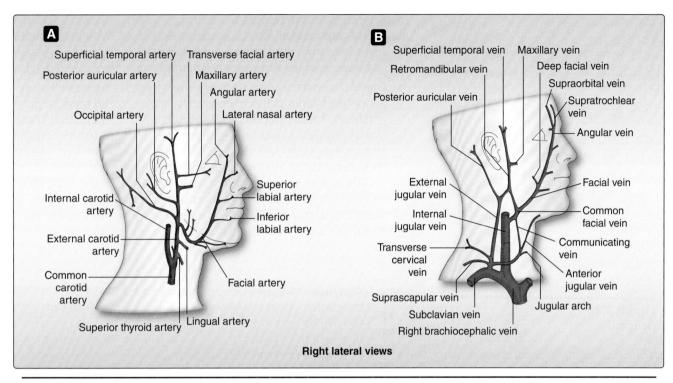

Right lateral views

Figure 8.24
Blood supply to face A, Arterial supply. B, Venous supply.

V. ORBIT

The **orbits** are paired pyramid-shaped cavities that house the eyeballs and associated muscular, neuromuscular, glandular, and connective tissue structures (Fig. 8.26). Each orbit is angled such that the apex faces posteromedially and the base anterolaterally. The apex is located at the optic canal and the base at the orbital rim.

A. Osteology

A number of neurocranial and viscerocranial bones contribute to the formation of the bony orbit. A periosteal layer called the **periorbita** lines the bones that form the orbit and is continuous posteriorly with periosteal dura, anteriorly with the pericranium, and internally with the extraocular muscle and orbital fasciae. For descriptive purposes, the orbit is divided into superior (roof), inferior (floor), medial, and lateral walls.

1. **Superior wall:** The frontal bone (orbital portion) and sphenoid (lesser wing) contribute superiorly.

2. **Inferior wall:** The maxilla and zygomatic bones contribute inferiorly, with the palatine bone also making a small contribution.

3. **Medial wall:** Frontal, ethmoid, lacrimal, and sphenoid bones contribute medially.

4. **Lateral wall:** Zygomatic (frontal process) and sphenoid (greater wing) bones contribute laterally.

B. Eyelids and lacrimal apparatus

Collectively, upper and lower **eyelids** function to protect the anterior surface of the eyeball and aid in corneal lubrication (Fig. 8.27). Eyelids

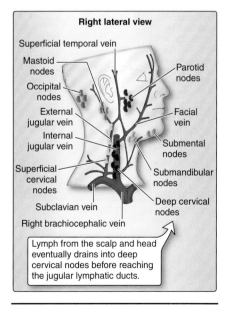

Right lateral view

Lymph from the scalp and head eventually drains into deep cervical nodes before reaching the jugular lymphatic ducts.

Figure 8.25
Head lymphatics. Figure showing primary lymph nodes of head.

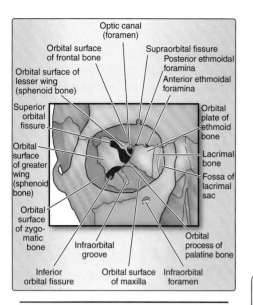

Figure 8.26
Bony orbit.

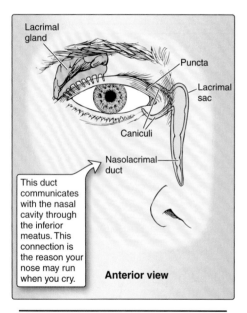

Figure 8.27
Lacrimal apparatus.

possess an outer thin layer of skin and an inner mucous membrane, the **palpebral conjunctiva**. The substance between these two layers includes muscle fibers from **orbicularis oculi** (palpebral portion) superficially and extensions of **levator palpebrae superioris** (upper eyelid only).

1. **Eyelid:** Deep to the muscle fibers, each eyelid is supported by superior and inferior plates of connective tissue, called **tarsi** (singular = tarsus). **Tarsal glands** are dispersed within each tarsus. These glands produce a lipid-rich secretion that functions to lubricate the eyelid's free edge and form a boundary for lacrimal fluid. Medial and lateral tarsal ligaments extend from the tarsi to support the eyelids and connect them to the medial and lateral orbital walls, respectively. A broad **orbital septum** completes the connection to the orbital margin. Eyelashes extend from the free edge of each eyelid and are associated with sebaceous ciliary glands.

> A sty results from obstruction of a ciliary gland duct in the eyelid. The red swelling may produce pus and is often painful until it has resolved. A chalazion results from obstruction or cysts of the tarsal glands. If uninfected, both types of obstructions typically resolve on their own.

2. **Conjunctival sac:** The space between the palpebral conjunctiva surface of the eyelids and the bulbar conjunctiva of the eyeball is called the **conjunctival sac**. Superior and inferior conjunctival fornices serve as superior and inferior limits of this specialized bursa-like space, thus allowing for free movement of the eyelids on the eyeball.

3. **Lacrimal apparatus:** The **lacrimal apparatus** is structurally and functionally related to the eyelid and eyeball.

    a. **Lacrimal gland:** The small lacrimal gland sits in the superolateral wall of the orbit, in a depression called the **lacrimal fossa**. It produces lacrimal fluid, which is secreted to the surface of the eyeball through a series of 8–12 ducts. Stimulation of fluid production is under autonomic control through parasympathetic fibers from the facial nerve (CN VII).

    b. **Lacrimal sac:** Aided by gravity and the blinking motion of the eyelids, fluid spreads across the cornea in a lateral-to-medial direction toward the lacrimal lake at the medial angle of the eyelids. Fluid is taken up through lacrimal caruncles and deposited into the lacrimal sac. The **lacrimal sac** is a thin-walled structure that sits in a depression in the lacrimal bone along the medial wall of the orbit. Inferiorly, the sac communicates with the **nasolacrimal duct**, which serves as a conduit to transport lacrimal fluid from the sac to the nasal cavity and, eventually, the nasopharynx.

C. **Eye**

Understanding how the eye develops is critical to understanding its anatomy. In the developing eye, an optic cup of neuroectoderm is surrounded by an embryonic connective tissue called **mesenchyme**. The question is, What does this mesenchyme become? The answer is that the mesenchyme directly around the optic cup forms a vascular tunic called the **choroid**, and the outermost

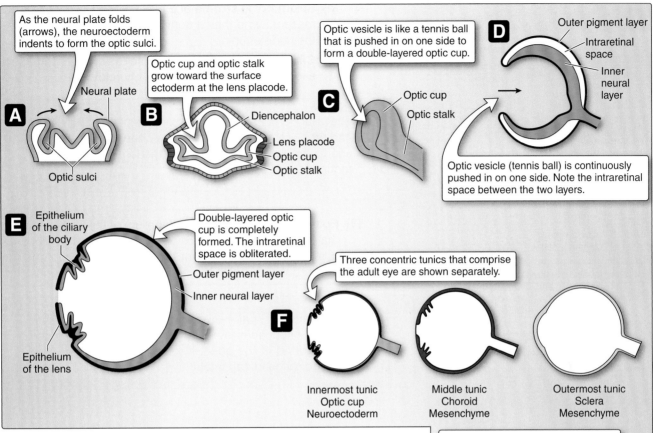

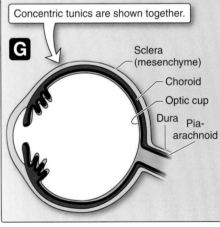

Figure 8.28
Optic vesicle development (A–G).

mesenchyme forms a fibrous tunic called the **sclera**. Consequently, the general feature of the adult eye is that it consists of three concentric tunics: the innermost tunic (optic cup; neuroectoderm), middle tunic (choroid; mesenchyme), and the outermost tunic (sclera; mesenchyme).

1. **Embryology:** At day 22, the eye begins to develop when the neural plate in the forebrain region (i.e., the future diencephalon) begins to fold to form a closed neural tube.

   a. **Optic vesicle development:** The neural plate (neuroectoderm) on each side indents to form the **optic sulci** (Fig. 8.28). Each optic sulcus expands from the forebrain to form the **optic vesicle**. The optic vesicle grows toward the surface ectoderm and induces the formation of the **lens placode**.

   b. **Optic cup development:** At day 28, the optic vesicle invaginates to form a double-layered **optic cup** of neuroectoderm. The optic cup remains attached to the forebrain by the **optic stalk**. The double-layered optic cup consists of an **outer pigment layer** and an **inner neural layer**. The optic cup gives rise to the **retina**, the **epithelium of the ciliary body**, and the **epithelium of the iris**.

   [1] **Retina:** The outer pigment layer of the optic cup gives rise to the **outer pigment layer of the retina**. The inner neural layer of the optic cup gives rise to the **inner neural layer of the retina**.

   [2] **Epithelium of the ciliary body:** The epithelium of the ciliary body is unique in that it consists of two opposing layers of epithelium continuous with the outer pigment layer of the optic cup and the other continuous with the inner neural layer of the optic cup (Fig. 8.29).

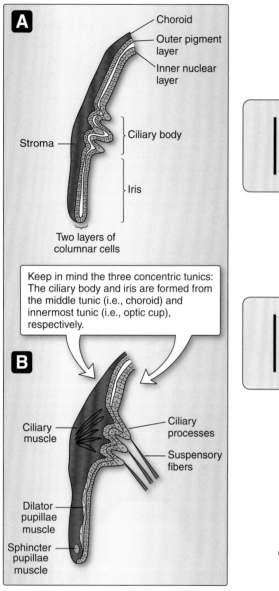

Figure 8.29
Ciliary body and iris development
(A and B).

(a) **Stroma:** The **stroma** of the ciliary body is derived from mesenchyme that is continuous with the choroid (i.e., the middle tunic).

(b) **Ciliary muscle:** The ciliary muscle is derived from mesenchyme continuous with the choroid.

> The ciliary processes are components of the ciliary body and produce aqueous humor. The ciliary processes give rise to the suspensory fibers of the lens, which are attached to and suspend the lens.

[3] **Epithelium of the iris:** The epithelium of the iris is unique in that it consists of two opposing layers of epithelium continuous with the outer pigment layer of the optic cup and the other continuous with the inner neural layer of the optic cup.

> The intraretinal space separates the outer pigment layer from the inner neural layer. Although the intraretinal space is obliterated in the adult, it remains a weakened area prone to retinal detachment.

(a) **Stroma:** The **stroma** of the iris is derived from mesenchyme that is continuous with the choroid (i.e., the middle tunic).

(b) **Muscles:** The **dilator pupillae muscle** and **sphincter pupillae muscle** are formed from the epithelium of the outer pigment layer by a transformation of these epithelial cells into contractile cells.

c. **Optic stalk development:** At day 28, the ventral portion of the optic stalk invaginates to form the **optic fissure** (Fig. 8.30). The optic fissure contains the **hyaloid artery and vein.** The hyaloid artery supplies the developing retina and the developing lens vesicle. The fully mature lens ceases to need a blood supply, so the portion of the hyaloid artery that crosses the vitreous body degenerates and leaves a remnant called the **hyaloid canal.** At week 7, the optic fissure seals and entraps the hyaloid artery and vein, which later become the **central artery and vein of the retina.** As the inner neural layer continues to proliferate, the increasing number of axons from the ganglion cell layer of the retina obliterate the intraretinal space. The optic stalk forms the **optic nerve (CN II)**, **optic chiasm**, and **optic tract** in the adult.

> The adult retina is vascularized by two sources. The first source is from the highly vascularized choroid (middle tunic). The second source is the central artery of the retina. When a physician examines the eye with an ophthalmoscope, the blood vessels that are seen are small branches of the central artery of the retina.

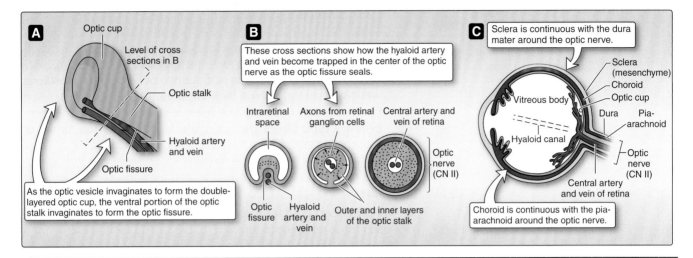

Figure 8.30
Optic stalk development (A–C).

The optic nerve (CN II) is really a tract of the diencephalon and has the following characteristics:
- It is not completely myelinated by oligodendrocytes until 3 months after birth.
- It is not capable of regeneration after transection.
- It is invested by the meninges and, therefore, is surrounded by a subarachnoid space, which plays a role in papilledema.

d. **Cornea development:** The cornea develops from both surface ectoderm and mesenchyme that lies anterior to the anterior chamber and that is continuous with the sclera (i.e., the outermost tunic), as shown in Figure 8.31. The surface ectoderm forms upper and lower infoldings that eventually develop into the upper and lower eyelids (Recall that the space between the two layers of ectoderm is the conjunctival sac.). A portion of the surface ectoderm reflects over the mesenchyme that is continuous with the sclera. The surface ectoderm forms the **anterior epithelium of the cornea**, which has a high regenerative capacity. The mesenchyme forms the **substantia propria of the cornea** (i.e., **Bowman layer**, **stroma**, and **Descemet membrane**) and the **corneal endothelium**.

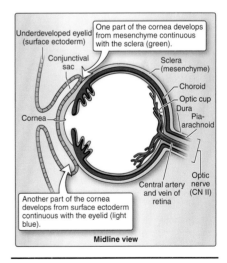

Figure 8.31
Cornea development.

The corneoscleral junction contains a trabecular network and the canal of Schlemm, which are involved in the flow of aqueous humor. The flow of aqueous humor follows this route: posterior chamber to anterior chamber → trabecular network → canal of Schlemm → aqueous veins → episcleral veins. The drainage rate of aqueous humor is balanced by the secretion rate of aqueous humor from the ciliary epithelium, thus maintaining a constant intraocular pressure of 23 mm Hg. An obstruction of aqueous humor flow will increase intraocular pressure, causing a condition called glaucoma.

e. **Lens development:** When the optic vesicle gets close to the surface ectoderm, the surface ectoderm in that vicinity thickens to form the **lens placode** (Fig. 8.32). The lens placode invaginates shortly thereafter to form the **lens pit** and then completely separates from the surface ectoderm to become the hollow **lens vesicle** surrounded by a **lens capsule**. At day 33, the cells on the posterior surface of the lens vesicle differentiate to form **primary lens fibers** that elongate to obliterate the lumen of the lens vesicle to form the **lens body**. The cells on the anterior surface of the lens vesicle remain mitotically active throughout life, migrate to the **lens equator**, and form the **secondary lens fibers**.

2. **General histologic features of the eye:** Recall that the eye comprises three concentric tunics (Fig. 8.33). The **lens** is suspended by **zonular fibers** (forming the suspensory ligament) that originate from the ciliary body. The **posterior** and **anterior chambers** of the eye are filled with aqueous humor, which is a clear, plasma-like fluid secreted by the epithelium of the ciliary body. The **vitreous cavity** is filled with the **vitreous body**, which is a transparent gelatinous substance that consists of water, some collagen fibers, and hyaluronan.

   a. **Tunics:** The adult eye wall contains the corneoscleral, uveal, and retinal tunics.

      [1] **Corneoscleral tunic:** The outermost fibrous tunic consists of the white, opaque sclera and transparent cornea. Covering the posterior five-sixths of the eyeball, the sclera is a thick, opaque layer of collagen and elastic fibers produced by fibroblasts. The tendons of the extraocular muscles attach to the sclera. The **corneoscleral junction** (or **limbus**) is the junction of the transparent cornea and the opaque sclera.

      [2] **Uveal tunic:** The middle vascular tunic consists of the **choroid**, the **stroma of the ciliary body**, and the **stroma of the iris**. The choroid is a connective tissue layer, between the sclera and retina, that contains fibroblasts, collagen fibers, elastic fibers, macrophages, lymphocytes, mast cells, plasma cells, and numerous melanocytes that give this layer its characteristic brown/black appearance. The inner portion of the choroid is highly vascularized and is called the **choriocapillary layer**.

      [3] **Retinal tunic:** The innermost tunic consists of the pigment epithelium, the neural retina, the epithelium of the ciliary body, and the epithelium of the iris.

   b. **Cornea:** Covering the anterior sixth of the eyeball, the cornea is an avascular, transparent structure composed of five layers: **corneal** and **Bowman layers**, **stroma**, **Descemet membrane**, and **corneal endothelium**.

      [1] **Corneal layer:** The **corneal epithelium** is a nonkeratinized stratified squamous epithelium that covers the anterior surface of the cornea (i.e., the surface exposed to air). The cornea, more so than the lens, is responsible for retracing light, thus allowing for the focusing of an inverted image on the retinal fundus.

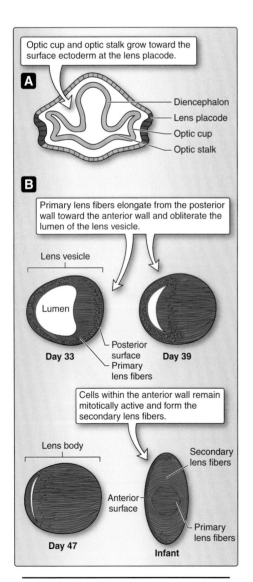

Figure 8.32
Lens development (A and B).

The corneal epithelium is innervated by free nerve endings from CN V_1 (i.e., the ophthalmic division of the trigeminal nerve), has a high capacity for regeneration, and is continuous with the bulbar conjunctiva at the limbus. The cornea surface is very sensitive to touch. Integrity of CN V_1 can be tested by touching the cornea with a wisp of cotton, thus stimulating the corneal blink reflex. If the patient does not blink (blink action is mediated by the facial nerve, CN VII), a CN V_1 lesion may be suspected.

[2] **Bowman layer:** This layer is not considered a true basal lamina but is a distinctive portion of the corneal stroma that contains randomly arranged type I collagen fibers.

[3] **Stroma:** The **stroma** is the thickest layer of the cornea and consists of connective tissue composed of fibroblasts, ground substance, and types I and V collagen fibers. The stroma is orderly arranged in about 60 layers. The collagen fibrils in each layer are oriented perpendicular to the collagen fibrils in the adjacent layer.

[4] **Descemet membrane:** The **Descemet membrane** is the thick basal lamina that lies beneath the corneal endothelium.

[5] **Corneal endothelium:** This simple squamous epithelium covers the posterior surface of the cornea (i.e., the surface exposed to aqueous humor).

c. **Ciliary body:** Posterior to the corneoscleral junction sits the thickened, ringlike ciliary body, which serves as an attachment site for the lens. Folds of tissue, called the ciliary process, extend internally from the ciliary body. The ciliary body and ciliary processes consist of an **epithelium** and a **stroma**.

[1] **Ciliary epithelium:** This consists of two layers of simple columnar epithelium, only one of which is heavily pigmented by melanin. The two layers of simple columnar epithelium are continuous with the outer pigmented layer of the retina and the inner nonpigmented neural layer of the retina. The inner, nonpigmented layer of the ciliary epithelium associated with the ciliary processes, secretes **aqueous humor** into the posterior chamber and produces the **zonular fibers** that attach to the lens capsule.

[2] **Stroma:** The highly vascularized stroma consists of fibroblasts, melanocytes, collagen fibers, and the **ciliary muscle**. The ciliary muscle functions in the process of accommodation, whereby the lens becomes flatter to focus on distant objects or rounder to focus on nearby objects.

d. **Iris:** The iris is located on the anterior surface of the lens. It consists of an **epithelium** and a **stroma**.

[1] **Epithelium:** The iris epithelium consists of two layers of simple columnar epithelium both of which are heavily pigmented by melanin. The two layers of simple columnar epithelium are continuous with the outer pigmented layer of the retina and the inner nonpigmented neural layer of the retina.

[2] **Stroma:** The stroma of the iris forms an irregular surface with numerous grooves and ridges. The highly vascularized stroma

Clinical Application 8.11: Altered Pupillary Function

Pathology that compromises this sympathetic pathway will result in Horner syndrome, which causes miosis (constriction of the pupil due to paralysis of the dilator pupillae muscle), ptosis (drooping of the eyelid due to paralysis of the superior tarsal muscle), and hemianhydrosis (loss of sweating on one side). Lesions involving CN III (oculomotor nerve) will result in a fixed and dilated pupil.

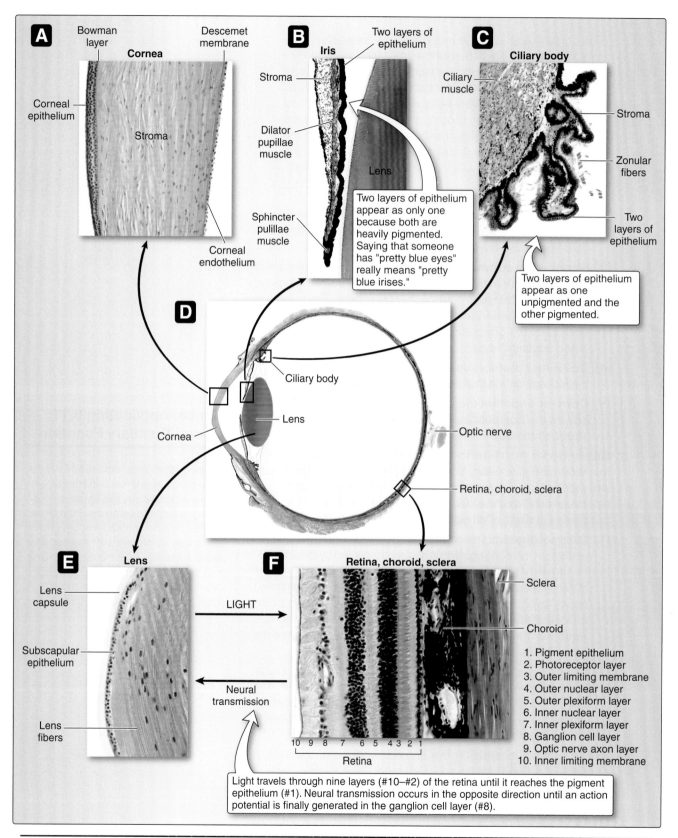

A Cornea — Bowman layer, Corneal epithelium, Stroma, Descemet membrane, Corneal endothelium

B Iris — Two layers of epithelium, Stroma, Dilator pupillae muscle, Lens, Sphincter pulillae muscle

Two layers of epithelium appear as only one because both are heavily pigmented. Saying that someone has "pretty blue eyes" really means "pretty blue irises."

C Ciliary body — Ciliary muscle, Stroma, Zonular fibers, Two layers of epithelium

Two layers of epithelium appear as one unpigmented and the other pigmented.

D — Ciliary body, Lens, Cornea, Optic nerve, Retina, choroid, sclera

E Lens — Lens capsule, Subscapular epithelium, Lens fibers

LIGHT

Neural transmission

F Retina, choroid, sclera — Sclera, Choroid

1. Pigment epithelium
2. Photoreceptor layer
3. Outer limiting membrane
4. Outer nuclear layer
5. Outer plexiform layer
6. Inner nuclear layer
7. Inner plexiform layer
8. Ganglion cell layer
9. Optic nerve axon layer
10. Inner limiting membrane

10 9 8 7 6 5 4 3 2 1
Retina

Light travels through nine layers (#10–#2) of the retina until it reaches the pigment epithelium (#1). Neural transmission occurs in the opposite direction until an action potential is finally generated in the ganglion cell layer (#8).

Figure 8.33
Eye histology (A–F).

consists of fibroblasts, melanocytes, collagen fibers, the **dilator pupillae muscle**, and the **sphincter pupillae muscle**. The dilator pupillae muscle is radially arranged around the entire circumference of the iris and is innervated by the sympathetic nervous system. The sphincter pupillae muscle is circularly arranged around the entire circumference of the iris and is innervated by the parasympathetic nervous system. Coordination of these muscles changes the diameter of the iris's aperture, the pupil, in response to light and other stimulation.

e. **Lens:** The lens is a biconvex, transparent, avascular structure located posterior to the iris. It consists of a **lens capsule**, a **subcapsular epithelium**, and **lens fibers**. The lens is attached to the ciliary processes by zonular fibers that constitute the suspensory ligament of the lens. For distance vision, ciliary muscles are relaxed, and the lens assumes a stretched, thin shape. For near vision, ciliary muscles contract, and the lens assumes a thicker, more spherical shape.

   [1] **Lens capsule:** The lens capsule is a thick basal lamina containing type IV collagen that completely surrounds the lens.

   [2] **Subcapsular epithelium:** This simple cuboidal epithelium is located beneath the lens capsule only on the anterior surface and at the equatorial region (i.e., no epithelium is found on the posterior surface). The subcapsular epithelium is mitotically active and migrates to the equatorial region of the lens where the cells elongate and rotate so that they are parallel to the lens surface.

   [3] **Lens fibers:** The lens fibers are prismatic remnants of the subcapsular epithelium that have lost their nuclei and organelles. The lens fibers are filled with the cytoskeletal protein α, β, γ-crystallin, which maintains the conformation and transparency of the lens. The newer lens fibers are located at the periphery of the lens, whereas the older lens fibers are displaced toward the center of the lens.

f. **Retina:** The innermost eye layer, the retina, is divided into two areas. The posterior two-thirds of the retina is a light-sensitive area called the **pars optica**. The anterior third is a light-insensitive area called the **pars ciliaris** and **pars iridis**. These two areas are separated by the **ora serrata**. The light-sensitive pars optica consists of the following 10 layers.

   [1] **Pigment epithelium:** The pigment epithelium synthesizes and contains melanin, transports nutrients, phagocytizes shed tips of rod outer segments, converts 11-trans retinal to 11-cis retinal, and forms the blood–retinal barrier through zonula occludens (tight junctions).

   [2] **Photoreceptor layer:** The photoreceptor layer consists of the outer segments, connecting cilium, and inner segments of rods and cones.

   [3] **Outer limiting membrane:** The outer limiting membrane consists of zonula adherens between rods/cones and Müller cells.

   [4] **Outer nuclear layer:** The outer nuclear layer consists of nuclei of rods and cones.

   [5] **Outer plexiform layer:** The outer plexiform layer consists of synapses between bipolar cells and horizontal cells with rods and cones.

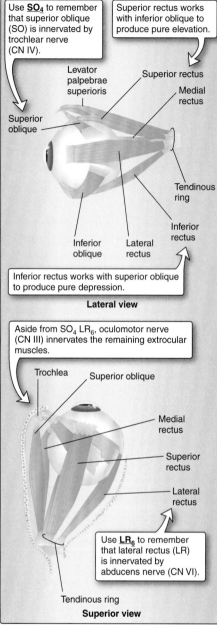

Superior rectus works with inferior oblique to produce pure elevation.

Levator palpebrae superioris

Superior rectus

Medial rectus

Superior oblique

Tendinous ring

Inferior rectus

Inferior oblique

Lateral rectus

Inferior rectus works with superior oblique to produce pure depression.

Lateral view

Aside from SO₄ LR₆, oculomotor nerve (CN III) innervates the remaining extrocular muscles.

Trochlea   Superior oblique

Medial rectus

Superior rectus

Lateral rectus

Use **LR₆** to remember that lateral rectus (LR) is innervated by abducens nerve (CN VI).

Tendinous ring

Superior view

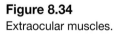

Figure 8.34
Extraocular muscles.

[6] **Inner nuclear layer:** The inner nuclear layer consists of nuclei of horizontal cells, bipolar cells, amacrine cells, and Müller cells.

[7] **Inner plexiform layer:** The inner plexiform layer consists of synapses between bipolar cells and amacrine cells with ganglion cells.

[8] **Ganglion cell layer:** The ganglion cell layer consists of nuclei of ganglion cells.

[9] **Optic nerve axon layer:** The optic nerve axon layer consists of unmyelinated axons of ganglion cells.

[10] **Inner limiting membrane:** The inner limiting membrane consists of the termination of Müller cells and their basal lamina.

> Upon examination of the retina, clinicians look at structures on the internal surface of the posterior portion of the eye, known as the fundus. Health of structures such as the optic disc (papilla), macula, and associated retinal vasculature is assessed using an ophthalmoscope. A detached retina will appear as wrinkled, typically due to the presence of fluid between the neural and pigmented retinal layers.

3. **Musculature:** The eye has both intrinsic and extrinsic muscles (Fig. 8.34). Intrinsic muscles include the pupillary sphincter and dilator as well as the ciliary muscle, which have been described previously. This section focuses on the attachments, functions, and innervations of the six extraocular muscles: **medial rectus**, **lateral rectus**, **superior rectus**, **inferior rectus**, **superior oblique**, and **inferior oblique**.

   a. **Movement:** Unlike most of the pharyngeal-derived musculature of the head and neck, the six **extraocular muscles** arise embryologically from myotomes. They function, often in pairs, to allow for specific movements of the eye in various directions and planes. To understand their synchronous actions, it is important to understand that the eye moves around three axes (Fig. 8.35).

      [1] **Anterior/posterior:** Movement around this axis results in medial (intorsion) and lateral (extorsion) rotation.

      [2] **Horizontal:** Movement around this axis results in elevation and depression.

      [3] **Vertical:** Movement around this axis results in abduction and adduction.

   b. **Function:** Due to the position of the eye in the orbit, only the medial and lateral rectus act to move the eye around one axis—the vertical—producing pure adduction and abduction, respectively. The other four muscles do not run in parallel with the eye and, therefore, produce movements around all three axes. These four muscles function in pairs to produce pure elevation and depression of the eye, where secondary and tertiary movements are cancelled out. The superior rectus and inferior oblique function together to produce pure elevation, while the inferior rectus and superior oblique function together to produce pure depression.

      [1] **Superior rectus:** This muscle elevates, abducts, and medially rotates the eye.

[2] Inferior rectus: This muscle depresses, adducts, and laterally rotates the eye.

[3] Superior oblique: This muscle depresses, abducts, and medially rotates the eye.

[4] Inferior oblique: This muscle elevates, adducts, and laterally rotates the eye.

> Testing ocular muscle function is an important component of any neurologic examination. Asking a patient to visually track the shape of an "H" allows clinicians to place these muscles in their optimal fictional position. Alterations in eye movement, unilaterally and bilaterally, could indicate a possible lesion of CNs III, IV, and VI.

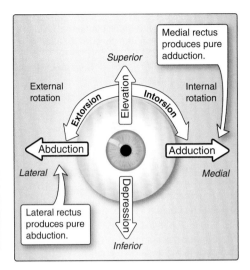

Figure 8.35
Eye movements.

4. **Innervation:** Five CNs (CNs II, III, IV, V$_1$, VI) enter the orbit to innervate structures associated with the eye (Fig. 8.36).

 a. **Special senses (vision):** The largest of these is the **optic nerve** (CN II), which traverses the optic canals as anterior extensions of the forebrain to mediate vision. The **optic sheath**, a covering made up of cranial dura and arachnoid mater layers, surrounds the nerve and is continuous with the fascia of the sclera.

 b. **Somatic motor and sensory:** As shown in Figure 8.34, the medial rectus, superior rectus, inferior rectus, and inferior oblique muscles are innervated by the **oculomotor nerve** (CN III). The superior oblique and the lateral rectus are innervated by the **trochlear nerve** (CN IV) and **abducens nerve** (CN VI), respectively. The **nasociliary nerve** of V$_1$ mediates somatic sensory to the eyeball.

 c. **Autonomic motor:** Postganglionic sympathetic fibers arise from the superior cervical ganglion and travel with the long ciliary nerve to provide autonomic motor innervation to the **dilator pupillae** and autonomic sensory to the iris and cornea. Postganglionic sympathetic fibers also travel with the lacrimal nerve to reach the lacrimal gland. Preganglionic parasympathetic fibers travel in CN III to the ciliary ganglion where they synapse on postganglionic parasympathetic neurons. Postganglionic parasympathetic fibers distribute to the ciliary muscles and sphincter pupillae muscles. Postganglionic parasympathetic fibers also arise from the **pterygopalatine ganglion** and travel from the zygomatic branch of V$_2$ to the lacrimal nerve of V$_1$ to reach the lacrimal gland. Innervation details are listed in Table 8.7.

> Reflexes of the eye include the pupillary light reflex and the corneal reflex. Both reflexes can be assessed to determine potential CN deficits or lesions. The pupillary light reflex involves the optic nerve (CN II) as the afferent limb (light shining into pupil) and the oculomotor nerve (CN III) as the efferent limb (pupillary constriction). The corneal reflex involves the ophthalmic division of the trigeminal nerve (CN V$_1$) as the afferent limb (touch cornea with tip of cotton swab) and the facial nerve (CN VII) as the efferent limb (blink response is through activation of orbicularis oculi).

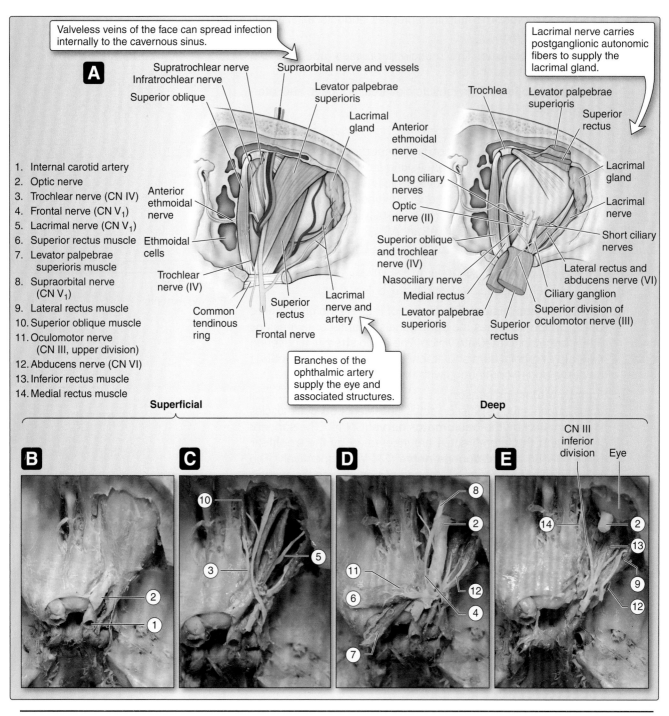

Figure 8.36
Superior view of orbit, superficial to deep. A, Schematics. B–E, Gross specimens.

Table 8.7: Nerves of the Eye

Nerve	Branch	Somatic Motor	Autonomic Motor	Sensory
Oculomotor	Superior division	Levator palpebral superioris, superior rectus		
	Inferior division	Medial rectus, inferior rectus, inferior oblique	Pupillary sphincter, ciliary muscles	
Trigeminal: ophthalmic division	Nasociliary, infratrochlear			Skin of conjunctiva (medial eye); lacrimal sac
	Nasociliary, long ciliary			Eyeball
	Nasociliary, long root of ciliary ganglion			Eyeball
	Lacrimal		Carries postganglionic autonomic fibers to lacrimal gland	Lacrimal gland, lateral lid, conjunctiva
Trochlear		Superior oblique		
Abducens		Lateral rectus		

5. **Arterial supply:** Blood supply to the eye and structures housed in the orbit occurs primarily by way of the **ophthalmic artery**, a branch of the internal carotid artery. The ophthalmic artery travels with the optic nerve (CN II) through the optic canal to enter the orbit posteriorly. In the orbit, it gives off a series of branches including ethmoid air cell branches, **supratrochlear**, **supraorbital**, and **retinal** arteries.

6. **Venous supply:** Venous drainage occurs by way of the valveless **superior** and **inferior ophthalmic veins**, which communicate externally with the facial vein network and internally with the cavernous sinus and pterygoid venous plexus. Typically, the central retinal vein drains directly into the cavernous sinus.

VI. EAR

The ear is the organ of balance and hearing. What we commonly call the "ear" actually consists of the three components: an **internal ear**, a **middle ear**, and an **external ear**.

A. Internal ear

The internal ear is found in the petrous temporal bone and houses the specialized organs of balance (vestibular system) and hearing (auditory system).

Clinical Application 8.12: Ocular Stroke

Compromise of the arterial and venous supply of the retina can lead to various degrees of loss of vision. Blockage of the retinal artery typically occurs by way of an embolism. Patients commonly experience immediate loss of vision without pain. This condition should be treated as an emergency to avoid permanent damage. Blockage of the central retinal vein typically occurs by way of a thrombus from the cavernous sinus. In contrast to a retinal artery occlusion, patients with retinal vein blockage experience a slow loss of vision also without pain. Both types typically occur unilaterally.

1. **Embryology:** At week 4, the internal ear develops from a thickening of the surface **ectoderm** called the **otic placode** (Fig. 8.37). The otic placode invaginates into the underlying mesenchyme adjacent to the rhombencephalon and becomes the **otic vesicle**. The otic vesicle divides into an upper **utricular portion** and a lower **saccular portion**.

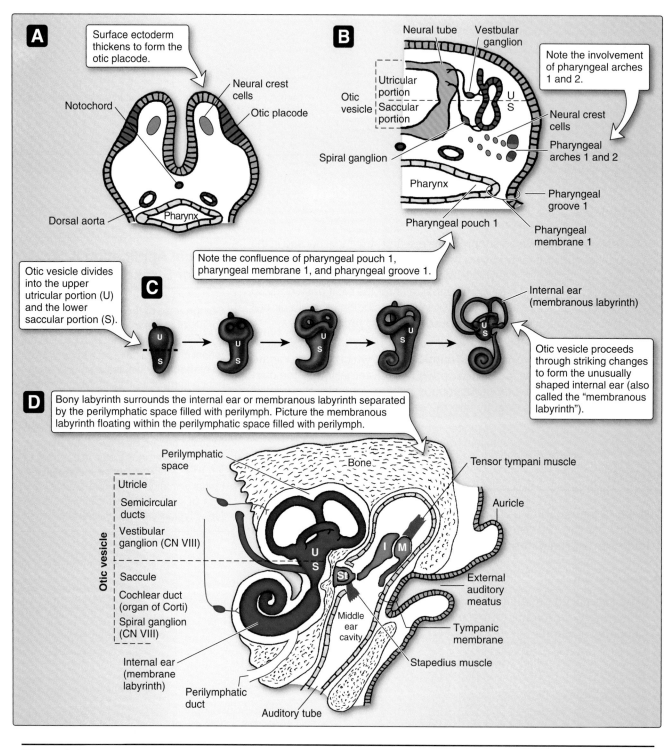

Figure 8.37

Internal, middle, and external ear development (A–D). I = incus, M = malleus, ST = stapes.

a. Utricular portion: The upper portion of the otic vesicle gives rise to the following.

    [1] Utricle: This structure contains the sensory hair cells and otoliths located in a specific region called the **macula of the utricle**. The utricle responds to **linear acceleration** and the **force of gravity**.

    [2] Semicircular ducts: These contain the sensory hair cells of the cristae ampullares. The semicircular ducts respond to **angular acceleration**.

    [3] Vestibular ganglion of CN VIII: This lies at the base of the internal auditory meatus.

    [4] Endolymphatic duct and sac: This membranous duct connects the saccule to the utricle and terminates in a blind sac beneath the dura. The endolymphatic sac is involved in fluid exchange.

b. Saccular portion: The lower portion of the otic vesicle gives rise to the following.

    [1] Saccule: This structure contains the sensory hair cells and otoliths located in a specific region called the **macula of the saccule**. The saccule responds to **linear acceleration** and the **force of gravity**.

    [2] Cochlear duct (organ of Corti): Involved in hearing, this duct has pitch (tonopic) localization whereby high-frequency sound waves (20,000 Hz) are detected at the base, and low-frequency sound waves (20 Hz) are detected at the apex.

    [3] Spiral ganglion of CN VIII: This lies in the modiolus of the bony labyrinth.

c. Membranous labyrinth: At week 8, the utricular and saccular portions of the otic vesicle have formed the abovementioned structures, sometimes collectively referred to as the **membranous labyrinth**. The terms "membranous labyrinth" and "bony labyrinth" cause much confusion, but an understanding of them is crucial in order to appreciate the anatomical and physiologic functions of the internal ear.

    [1] Endolymph: The soft, cellular membranous labyrinth is filled with **endolymph** and consists of all the ectodermal structures derived from the utricular portion and the saccular portion of the otic vesicle. The endolymph is similar to intracellular fluid and is exchanged using the endolymphatic duct and sac. The membranous labyrinth is completely surrounded by neural crest cells that form a connective tissue covering. This connective tissue becomes cartilaginous and then ossifies to become the bony labyrinth of the temporal bone.

    [2] Perilymph: However, the connective tissue directly opposed to the membranous labyrinth degenerates, thus forming the perilymphatic space filled with perilymph that lies between the membranous labyrinth and the bony labyrinth. This establishes an interesting anatomical relationship in which the membranous labyrinth filled with endolymph floats within the bony labyrinth filled with **perilymph**. The perilymph is similar to CSF and communicates with the subarachnoid space via the perilymphatic duct.

2. **Histology:** The internal ear (or the membranous labyrinth) is composed of two divisions: **vestibular** and **cochlear labyrinths**. The vestibular labyrinth consists of the **semicircular ducts**, the **utricle**, and the **saccule**. The cochlear labyrinth consists of the **cochlear duct**.

a. **Vestibular labyrinth:** The three semicircular ducts (i.e., anterior, posterior, and horizontal) each have a swelling at one end where it joins the utricle called the ampulla (Fig. 8.38). On the floor of each ampulla rests an ampullary crest.

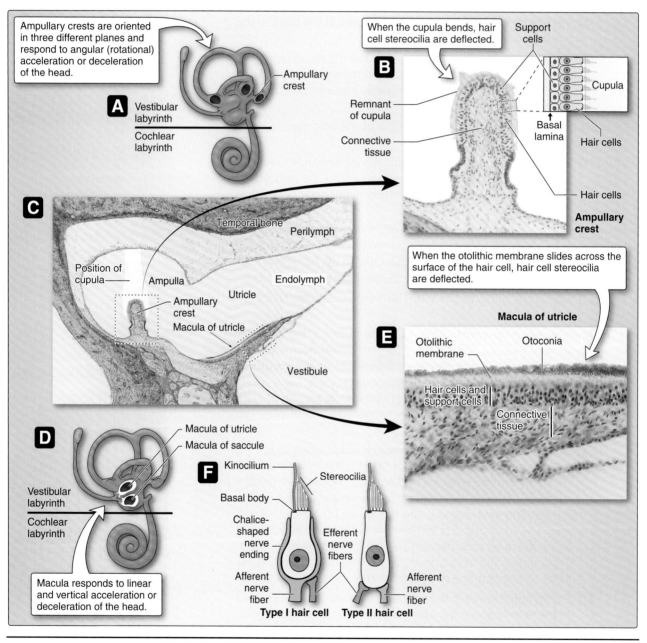

Figure 8.38

Vestibular labyrinth histology. A, Location of ampullary crests (red) within the ampulla (blue) at the base of each semicircular duct. B, Light micrograph of the left boxed area in C (arrow). C, Light micrograph showing the ampullary crest on the floor of the ampulla (filled with endolymph) and its relationship to the cupula as well as the macula of the utricle on the floor of the utricle (filled with endolymph). D, Location of the macula of the utricle (red) and macula of the saccule (red) within two swellings called the utricle (blue) and saccule (blue). E, Light micrograph of the right boxed area in C (arrow). The macula of the utricle consists of a connective tissue base covered by hair cells and support cells. F, Morphology of types I and II hair cells and their relationship to afferent and efferent nerve fibers.

[1] Ampullary crest: The ampullary crest is an elevated ridge of connective tissue covered by an **epithelium** and the **cupula**. The epithelium consists of **type I hair cells**, **type II hair cells**, and **support cells**. The cupula is a gelatinous mass that covers the epithelium and extends to the roof of the ampulla.

(a) Type I hair cell: Pear shaped with a basally located nucleus, the type I hair cell forms a single, **chalice-like synapse** with bipolar afferent neurons from the vestibular ganglion of CN VIII. Efferent neurons are also present that set the sensitivity of the type I hair cell. The type I hair cell has a single **kinocilium** and 40–100 **stereocilia** of varying lengths embedded in the cupula.

(b) Type II hair cell: Cylinder shaped with a centrally located nucleus, the type II hair cells form multiple, small, **bouton-like synapses** with bipolar afferent neurons from the vestibular ganglion of CN VIII. Efferent neurons are also present that set the sensitivity of the type II hair cell. The type II hair cell has a single **kinocilium** and 40–100 **stereocilia** of varying lengths embedded in the cupula.

(c) Support cells: These rest on the basal lamina and provide support by cradling the hair cells.

The semicircular ducts respond to **rotational (angular) acceleration** or **deceleration of the head**. Head rotation drags the cupula through the endolymph, causing the cupula to bend, thereby deflecting hair cell stereocilia. When stereocilia are deflected toward the kinocilium, action potential discharge increases (depolarization). When stereocilia are deflected away from the kinocilium, action potential discharge decreases (repolarization).

[2] Macula: On the floor of both the utricle and saccule rests a region of specialized epithelium called the macula (i.e., macula of the utricle and macule of the saccule), as shown in Figure 8.38. The histology of the macula of the utricle and that of the macula of the saccule is the same. The macula is a region of connective tissue covered by an **epithelium**, the **otolithic membrane**, and **otoconia**. The epithelium consists of the same **types I and II hair cells** and **support cells** as those of the ampullary crest (see above). The otolithic membrane is a gelatinous mass that covers the epithelium. The otoconia are tiny calcium carbonate ($CaCO_3$) crystals that are attached to the surface of the otolithic membrane.

b. Cochlear labyrinth: The cochlear duct is a triangle-shaped duct that is coiled ~2.75 times, much like the tail of a snail (Fig. 8.39). The cochlear duct is suspended across the bony labyrinth, so that the space above the cochlear duct is the **scala vestibuli** and filled with perilymph, and the space below the cochlear duct is the **scala tympani** and also filled with perilymph. The lumen of the cochlear duct is called the **scala media**, which contains endolymph.

[1] Boundaries: The boundaries of the cochlear duct are the **vestibular membrane** that forms the roof, the **basilar membrane** that forms the floor, the **stria vascularis** that

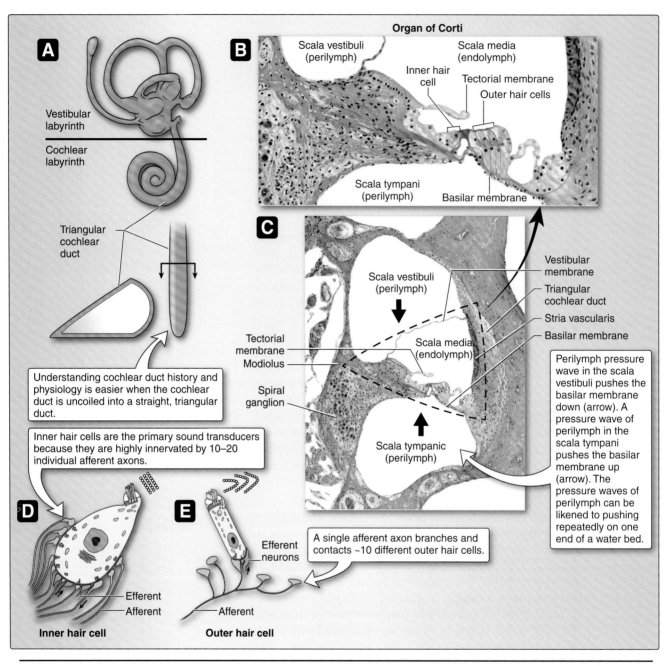

A

Vestibular labyrinth

Cochlear labyrinth

Triangular cochlear duct

Understanding cochlear duct history and physiology is easier when the cochlear duct is uncoiled into a straight, triangular duct.

Inner hair cells are the primary sound transducers because they are highly innervated by 10–20 individual afferent axons.

D

Efferent
Afferent

Inner hair cell

E

Efferent neurons

Afferent

Outer hair cell

A single afferent axon branches and contacts ~10 different outer hair cells.

B

Organ of Corti

Scala vestibuli (perilymph)

Scala media (endolymph)

Inner hair cell

Tectorial membrane

Outer hair cells

Scala tympani (perilymph)

Basilar membrane

C

Scala vestibuli (perilymph)

Tectorial membrane
Modiolus

Spiral ganglion

Scala media (endolymph)

Scala tympanic (perilymph)

Vestibular membrane

Triangular cochlear duct

Stria vascularis

Basilar membrane

Perilymph pressure wave in the scala vestibuli pushes the basilar membrane down (arrow). A pressure wave of perilymph in the scala tympani pushes the basilar membrane up (arrow). The pressure waves of perilymph can be likened to pushing repeatedly on one end of a water bed.

Figure 8.39
Cochlear labyrinth histology (A–E).

forms the lateral wall, and the bony **modiolus** that forms the medial wall.

[2] **Stria vascularis:** The stria vascularis is a highly vascularized stratified epithelium that produces the endolymph and maintains the high K⁺ concentration in the endolymph.

[3] **Organ of Corti:** The **organ of Corti** rests on the basilar membrane and is a band of connective tissue covered by an **epithelium** and the **tectorial membrane**, a gelatinous mass that covers the epithelium and extends to the spiral

limbus. The epithelium consists of a single row of 3,500 **inner hair cells**, three rows of 20,000 **outer hair cells**, and a number of different types of **supporting cells** (i.e., border cells, phalangeal cells, pillar cells, cells of Boettcher, and cells of Claudius).

(a) **Inner hair cell:** Pear shaped with a basally located nucleus that is completely surrounded by inner phalangeal cells, the inner hair cell forms multiple synapses with bipolar afferent neurons from the spiral ganglion of CN VIII. Efferent neurons are also present that set its sensitivity. The inner hair cell lacks a kinocilium but has 40–100 **stereocilia** of varying lengths arranged in a **straight line** and embedded in the tectorial membrane.

(b) **Outer hair cell:** Cylinder shaped with a centrally located nucleus that is only partially surrounded by outer phalangeal cells, the outer hair cell forms multiple synapses with bipolar afferent neurons from the spiral ganglion of CN VIII. Efferent neurons are also present that set its sensitivity. The outer hair cell lacks a kinocilium but has 40–100 **stereocilia** of varying lengths arranged in a **V-shaped pattern** and embedded in the tectorial membrane.

[4] **Function:** The cochlear duct responds to **sound**. The motion of the stapes at the oval window sets up a pressure wave in the perilymph within the scala vestibuli. This pressure wave travels down the scala vestibuli, through the helicotrema at the apex, and then back up the scala tympani to the round window. The pressure wave in the scala vestibuli pushes the basilar membrane of the organ of Corti down, thereby deflecting hair cell stereocilia away from the tallest length. When the stereocilia are deflected away from the tallest length, action potential discharge decreases. The pressure wave in the scala tympani pushes the basilar membrane of the organ of Corti up, thereby deflecting stereocilia toward the tallest length. When stereocilia are deflected toward the tallest length, action potential discharge increases.

> The inner hair cells are the primary sound transducers. About 95% of the afferent (sensory) axons in the auditory nerve synapse on the inner hair cells. A single afferent axon typically contacts only one inner hair cell. Each inner hair cell makes synaptic contact with 10–20 afferent axons.

3. **Anatomy:** The internal ear cavity lies deep within the otic capsule of the petrous temporal bone and houses the **vestibulocochlear organ complex** (Fig. 8.40). The bony and membranous labyrinths are contained within the otic capsule. The components of the vestibular complex include the semicircular canals, semicircular ducts, vestibule, utricle, and saccule. The vestibular complex is located posterosuperior to the cochlear complex. The cochlear complex consists of the **cochlea**, **cochlear duct**, **scala tympani**, and **scala vestibuli**, as previously described.

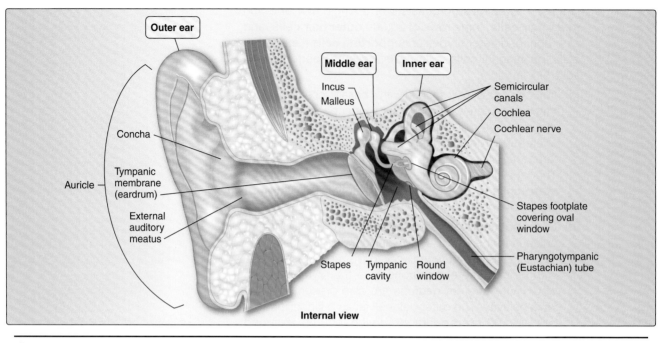

Figure 8.40
Ear anatomy.

The **vestibulocochlear nerve** (CN VIII) passes from the pons through the internal acoustic meatus to provide special sensory (SS) innervation to these structures (outlined above).

B. **Middle ear**

The middle ear houses the ear ossicles that function to transfer sound waves into mechanical energy for interpretation of sounds.

1. **Embryology:** At week 4, the middle ear begins to develop from a number of different sources: pharyngeal arch 1, pharyngeal arch 2, pharyngeal pouch 1, and pharyngeal membrane 1 (see Fig. 8.37).

   a. **Ossicles:** The ossicles of the middle ear include the malleus, incus, and stapes.

      [1] **Malleus:** The **malleus** develops from Meckel's cartilage derived from **neural crest cells** within **pharyngeal arch 1**. It is attached to the tympanic membrane and is moved by the **tensor tympani muscle** derived from **mesoderm** within **pharyngeal arch 1**. The tensor tympani muscle is innervated by CN V_3 and functions to dampen loud sounds.

      [2] **Incus:** The **incus** develops from Meckel's cartilage derived from **neural crest cells** within **pharyngeal arch 1**. The incus articulates with the malleus and stapes.

      [3] **Stapes:** The **stapes** develops from Reichert's cartilage derived from **neural crest cells** within **pharyngeal arch 2**. The stapes is attached to the oval window of the vestibule and is moved by the **stapedius muscle** derived from **mesoderm** within **pharyngeal arch 2**. The stapedius muscle is innervated by CN VII and functions to dampen loud sounds.

b. **Epithelial linings:** The epithelial lining of the auditory tube and epithelial lining of the middle ear cavity develop from endoderm of pharyngeal pouch 1.

c. **Tympanic membrane:** The **tympanic membrane** develops from **ectoderm, intervening mesoderm and neural crest cells,** and **endoderm** of **pharyngeal membrane 1.** The tympanic membrane separates the middle ear from the external auditory meatus of the external ear. The tympanic membrane receives general visceral afferent (GVA) innervation internally by the tympanic plexus of the glossopharyngeal (CN IX) nerve.

2. **Anatomy:** The air-filled middle ear cavity is housed within the petrous temporal bone, deep to the tegmen tympani (Fig. 8.41).

a. **Walls:** The lateral (membranous) wall of this cavity is associated with the tympanic membrane, the medial (labyrinthine) wall with the promontory and oval window with the stapes base, the roof (tegmental wall) with the tegmen tympani of the temporal bone, the floor (jugular wall) with the temporal bone adjacent to the jugular foramen, the posterior (mastoid) wall with the aditus (opening to mastoid air cells), and the anterior (carotid) wall with the auditory (pharyngotympanic) tube.

b. **Contents:** Auditory ossicles are housed within the middle ear, forming a kinetic chain that propagates vibrations from the external environment to the internal ear for processing. Both the **stapedius** and **tensor tympani** muscles function to dampen loud sounds by limiting the oscillation of the **stapes** and **malleus.** Both muscles extend into the middle ear cavity to insert onto their respective bones. The middle ear cavity also houses portions of two CNs—**chorda tympani nerve** (branch from the

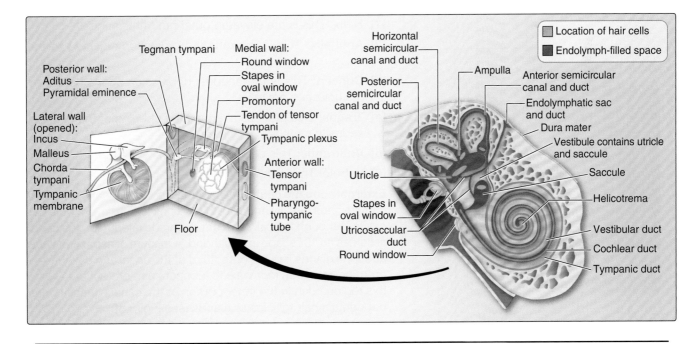

Figure 8.41
Middle and inner ear anatomy. Note boundaries and associated structures in middle ear (black arrow).

facial nerve) and the **tympanic plexus** (from the glossopharyngeal nerve). The chorda tympani nerve passes through the middle ear cavity en route to the **infratemporal fossa**. The tympanic plexus provides GVA innervation to the middle ear cavity before exiting as the **lesser petrosal nerve**.

C. External ear

The external ear is represented externally as a semirigid structure that is designed to funnel sounds wave toward the middle ear.

1. **Embryology:** At week 4, the external ear begins to develop from a number of different sources: pharyngeal groove 1, pharyngeal arch 1, and pharyngeal arch 2 (see Fig. 8.37).

   a. **Auditory meatus:** The **epithelial lining of the external auditory meatus** develops from **ectoderm** of **pharyngeal groove 1**. The external auditory meatus becomes filled with ectodermal cells that form a temporary **meatal plug** that disappears before birth. The external auditory meatus is innervated by CNs V_3 and IX.

   b. **Auricle:** The **auricle** develops from six **auricular hillocks** that form as six mesenchymal proliferations associated with pharyngeal arches 1 and 2. The six auricular hillocks surround pharyngeal groove 1. The auricle is innervated by CNs V_3, VII, IX, and X and cervical nerves C_2 and C_3.

2. **Anatomy:** The external ear is characterized externally by the **auricle** (pinna), which contains an elastic cartilage core and overlying skin (Fig. 8.42).

   a. **Auricle:** The auricular cartilage imparts the shape of the external ear. It functions to funnel sounds in to the external acoustic canal toward the middle ear cavity. Features of the auricle are described below.

      [1] **Helix:** This is the elevated outer rim of the auricle.

      [2] **Antihelix:** This is the rounded projection adjacent to the helix.

      [3] **Concha:** This is the deepest depression and is bound by the helix and antihelix.

      [4] **Tragus:** This process overlaps the opening of the external acoustic meatus.

      [5] **Antitragus:** This process lies opposite the tragus.

      [6] **Lobule:** This is the ear lobe absent cartilage.

   b. **External acoustic canal:** The external acoustic canal is one-third cartilaginous distally and two-thirds bony toward the middle ear cavity. Although typically straight during development, the canal assumes an "S" shape in adulthood. A mixture of sebaceous and apocrine glands line the outer third of the canal and collectively produce **cerumen** (ear wax) to lubricate and protect the skin in this region. Skin in the inner portion of the canal typically does not contain hair follicles or glands (see Fig. 8.40).

      [1] **Innervation:** The canal receives sensory (GSA) innervation from the **auriculotemporal branch** (CN IX) and **auricular branches** (CN X). These branches also supply sensory innervation to the outer surface of the **tympanic membrane**,

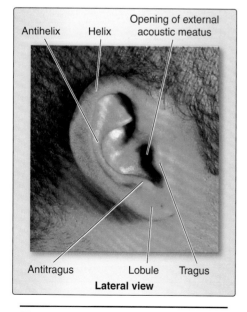

Figure 8.42
External ear anatomy.

(Labels in figure: Antihelix, Helix, Opening of external acoustic meatus, Antitragus, Lobule, Tragus, **Lateral view**)

in addition to the **posterior auricular branch** of the facial nerve (CN VII).

[2] **Lymphatics:** Lymphatic drainage from the external ear occurs either through parotid (anterior superior), mastoid (posterior superior), or superficial cervical (inferior) nodes associated with the external jugular vein.

> The outer surface of the tympanic membrane is visible with the use of an **otoscope**. The examiner should be able to identify the handle of the malleus near the middle of the membrane. A cone of light should be visible inferior to the handle, as a reflection of the otoscope's light. Under healthy conditions, the membrane should appear translucent, in a neutral position and pinkish gray in color. Deviation from this normal appearance may indicate middle ear pathology. One of the most common pathologies is **otitis media** (middle ear infection). In the case of otitis media, the tympanic membrane may appear red, cloudy, and bulging.

VII. TEMPORAL REGION

The **temporal region** is located laterally on the skull and includes both the temporal and infratemporal fossae (Fig. 8.43). This region contains muscles of mastication, branches of the mandibular division of the trigeminal nerve (CN V$_3$), and terminal branches of the external carotid artery.

A. Temporal fossa

The **temporal fossa** is bound by the superior and inferior temporal lines posteriorly and superiorly, frontal and zygomatic bones anteriorly, infratemporal crest inferiorly, and the zygomatic arch laterally. The **temporalis muscle** fills the majority of this bound space, projecting inferiorly into the infratemporal fossa. The bony intersection known as the **pterion** is contained within the temporal fossa.

B. Infratemporal fossa

The **infratemporal fossa** lies inferior to the zygomatic arch and is bound anteriorly by the posterior maxilla, posteriorly by the condylar process of the mandible, medially by the lateral pterygoid plate, laterally by the ramus of the mandible, and superiorly by the infratemporal crest (Figs. 8.44 and 8.45). Inferiorly, the space is closed by the **medial pterygoid muscle**. The contents of the infratemporal fossa include the maxillary artery and branches, the mandibular division of the trigeminal nerve (CN V$_3$) and branches, the pterygoid venous plexus, medial and lateral pterygoid muscles and the inferior portion of the temporalis muscle, the otic ganglion, and the chorda tympani nerve (branch of CN VII).

1. **Maxillary artery:** The **maxillary artery**, a terminal branch of the external carotid artery, travels deep to the neck of the mandible to enter the infratemporal fossa. Within the fossa, it gives off a number of branches that serve structures of the temporomandibular joint

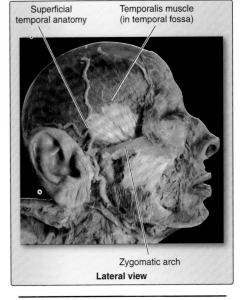

Superficial temporal anatomy

Temporalis muscle (in temporal fossa)

Zygomatic arch

Lateral view

Figure 8.43
Temporal region.

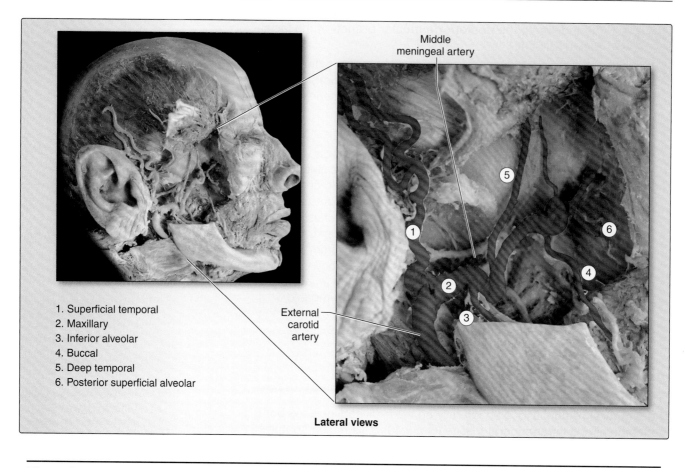

Middle meningeal artery

1. Superficial temporal
2. Maxillary
3. Inferior alveolar
4. Buccal
5. Deep temporal
6. Posterior superficial alveolar

External carotid artery

Lateral views

Figure 8.44
Infratemporal fossa: maxillary artery and branches (lateral pterygoid and masseter muscles, mandibular condyle, coronoid process, and ramus removed; temporalis reflected superiorly).

(TMJ), external ear, meninges, lower jaw and teeth, and muscles of mastication. The terminal part of the maxillary artery travels into the pterygopalatine fossa to serves structures of the palate, nasal cavity, and upper jaw and teeth. Of clinical significance is the **middle meningeal artery** branch that travels into the middle cranial fossa through the **foramen spinosum**. This vessel travels deep to the pterion and is a great risk for damage and subsequent **epidural hematoma** (see Clinical Application 8.5).

2. **Mandibular division of the trigeminal nerve:** CN V₃ enters the infratemporal fossa through the **foramen ovale**, where it divides into anterior (mainly motor) and posterior (mainly sensory) divisions. Prior to dividing, CN V₃ gives off a small sensory branch (spinous nerve) to the dura and lining of the mastoid cells and a small branchiomotor branch to the medial pterygoid muscle. The motor branches of CN V₃ provide branchiomotor innervation to the muscles of mastication, mylohyoid, and anterior belly of the digastric muscle. The main sensory nerves of CN V₃ include:

   a. **Lingual nerve:** The **lingual nerve** continues into the oral cavity, where it is anatomically associated with the **submandibular ganglion**. This relationship is further discussed in the "Oral cavity" section.

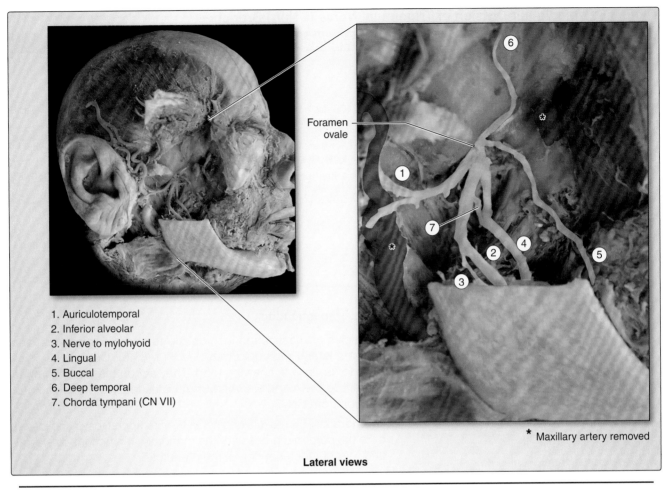

Foramen ovale

1. Auriculotemporal
2. Inferior alveolar
3. Nerve to mylohyoid
4. Lingual
5. Buccal
6. Deep temporal
7. Chorda tympani (CN VII)

* Maxillary artery removed

Lateral views

Figure 8.45
Infratemporal fossa: maxillary division of trigeminal nerve (V_3). (Lateral pterygoid and masseter muscles, mandibular condyle, coronoid process, and ramus removed; temporalis reflected superiorly.)

b. **Inferior alveolar nerve:** After giving off the **nerve to mylohyoid**, the **inferior alveolar nerve** enters the mandibular foramen to travel through the lower jaw. It exits through the mental foramen to the face and is renamed the **mental nerve**.

c. **Buccal nerve**: The buccal nerve travels anteriorly in the infratemporal fossa to enter the oral cavity and provide sensory innervation to the mucosa of the cheek. Do not confuse this nerve with the buccal branch of the facial nerve.

3. **Otic ganglion:** The **otic ganglion** lies high in the fossa, medially to and anatomically associated with CN V_3. Details are listed in Table 8.8.

> The pterygoid venous plexus directly communicates with the veins of the face and the cavernous sinus. A deep face infection or thrombosis can potentially spread through the pterygoid plexus into the cavernous sinus and cause serious impairments with CNs associated with the space. See Clinical Application 8.7 for more details.

Table 8.8: Mandibular Division of Trigeminal Nerve (CN V₃) Branches

Divisions	Branch	Branchiomotor	Autonomic Motor	Sensory
Anterior	Muscular branches	Masseter, temporalis, lateral pterygoid		
	Buccal			Cheek mucosa and gingiva
Posterior	Auriculotemporal		Carries postganglionic parasympathetic fibers from otic ganglion to parotid gland; sympathetic fibers arise from the superior cervical ganglion	Parotid gland, temporomandibular joint, external acoustic meatus, external surface of tympanic membrane, superficial temporal region
	Lingual		Carries preganglionic parasympathetic fibers from chorda tympani to submandibular gland	Anterior two-thirds of the tongue (chorda tympani rides along to provide taste to anterior two-thirds of the tongue)
	Inferior alveolar	Gives off nerve to mylohyoid to innervate the mylohyoid and anterior belly of digastric		Mandibular teeth and gums; skin of chin, lower lip, and adjacent mucosa (mental branch)

C. Muscles of mastication

The muscles of mastication include the temporalis, masseter, and medial and lateral pterygoid muscles (Fig. 8.46). Collectively, they function to assist with chewing food. They act on the TMJ, to impart movement to the mandible. All four muscles receive branchiomotor innervation from CN V₃.

1. **Temporalis:** This muscle originates from temporal fossa and inserts onto the coronoid process of the mandible. It functions to elevate and retract (posterior fibers) the mandible.

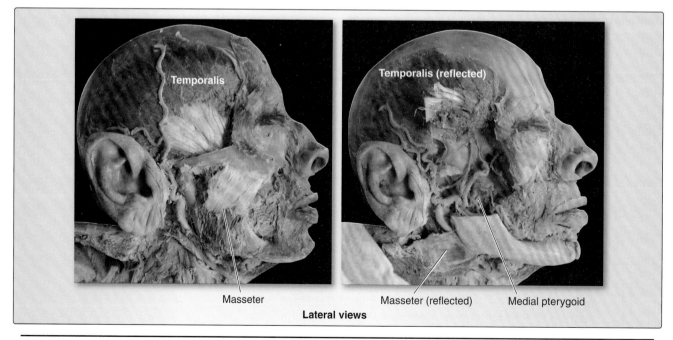

Lateral views

Figure 8.46

Muscles of mastication. (Zygomatic arch, mandibular condyle, coronoid process, ramus, and lateral pterygoid muscle removed in right image.)

2. **Masseter:** This muscle originates from the zygomatic arch and inserts onto the lateral surface of the mandibular ramus. It functions to elevate, protrude, and retract (deep fibers) the mandible.

3. **Medial pterygoid:** This muscle originates from the medial surface of the lateral pterygoid plate, posterolateral palatine bone, and maxillary tubercle and inserts onto the medial surface of the mandibular ramus. It functions bilaterally to elevate and protrude the mandible and unilaterally and alternating to produce a side-to-side grinding motion.

4. **Lateral pterygoid:** This muscle originates from the infratemporal crest and lateral surface of the lateral pterygoid plate and inserts onto the mandibular neck and TMJ capsule. Like the medial pterygoid, it functions bilaterally to protrude the mandible and unilaterally and alternating to produce a side-to-side grinding motion.

5. **Temporomandibular joint:** The TMJ occurs between the head of the mandible and the mandibular fossa and articular tubercle of the temporal bone (Fig. 8.47). This synovial joint is enclosed in a loose joint capsule, which contains an articular disc and supporting internal ligaments. The TMJ is a triplanar joint that allows for elevation, depression, protrusion, retraction, and side-to-side movements of the mandible.

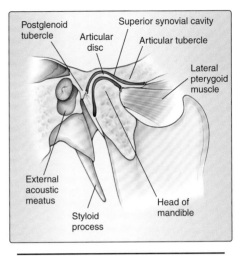

Figure 8.47
Temporomandibular joint (TMJ).

VIII. ORAL REGION

Structures of the oral region include those found in the oral cavity and the transitional region between the **oral cavity** and the **oropharynx**, including the teeth, tongue, gums, soft and hard palates, and palatine tonsils.

A. Oral cavity

The oral cavity (mouth) represents the beginning of the gastrointestinal tract (Fig. 8.48). Food is ingested into the oral cavity and prepared for digestion. The roof of the oral cavity is formed by the **hard** and **soft palates**, whereas the floor is formed by the **tongue** and associated mucous membrane. The **mylohyoid** and **geniohyoid** muscles lie superficial to the mucosa and further support the floor of the mouth. Sensory innervation to the roof and floor of the oral cavity is mediated through branches of the maxillary and mandibular divisions of the trigeminal nerve (V_2 and V_3), respectively. The oral cavity receives blood supply from branches of the maxillary, facial, and lingual arteries. The oral cavity can be divided into the following two regions.

1. **Oral vestibule:** This is a U-shaped interval between the lips/cheeks and teeth/gums. The parotid duct opens into this space opposite the upper second molar.

2. **Oral cavity proper:** This is the area between the arches of the teeth, containing the tongue, sublingual mucosa, frenulum, and submandibular gland ducts.

B. Palate

The formation of the adult palate occurs as a result of the embryologic development and fusion of the **primary** and **secondary palates**.

1. **Embryology:** During week 7, the intermaxillary segment forms when the two medial nasal prominences fuse together at the midline due

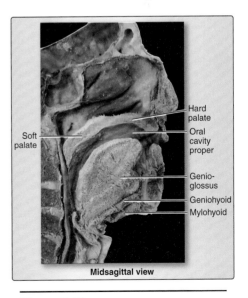

Figure 8.48
Oral cavity.

to the growth of the maxillary prominences of pharyngeal arch 1 toward the midline (see Fig. 8.20B).

   a. Primary palate: The intermaxillary segment forms the philtrum of the lip, four incisor teeth, and the primary palate.

   b. Secondary palate: The secondary palate forms from horizontal outgrowths of the maxillary prominences of pharyngeal arch 1 called the **palatine shelves**. Initially, the palatine shelves project downward on either side of the tongue but later attain a horizontal position and fuse along the **palatine raphe** to form the **secondary palate**.

   c. Definitive palate: The primary and secondary palates fuse at the **incisive foramen** to form the **definitive palate**. Bone develops in both the primary palate and anterior part of the secondary palate. Bone does not develop in the posterior part of the secondary palate, which eventually forms the **soft palate** and **uvula**.

   d. Nasal septum: The **nasal septum** develops from the frontonasal prominence and medial nasal prominences and grows down vertically from the roof of the primitive **nasal chamber**. The nasal septum eventually fuses with the definitive palate and divides the primitive nasal chamber into two **nasal passages**.

2. Anatomy: The **hard** and **soft palates** collectively form the roof of the oral cavity and the floor of the nasal cavity (Fig. 8.49).

   a. Hard palate: Anteriorly, the hard palate represents two-thirds of the palate and is made up of the maxillae (palatine processes) and palatine (horizontal plate) bones, covered in a thick mucosa that contains **palatine glands**.

   b. Soft palate: The soft palate makes up the posterior third of the palate and marks the transitional area between the oral cavity and the oropharynx superiorly. This mobile soft tissue partition arches posteroinferiorly in the midline as the **uvula** and receives support from a strong **palatine aponeurosis**.

   c. Musculature: Muscles of the palate include the tensor veli palatini, levator veli palatini, musculus uvulae, palatoglossus, and palatopharyngeus. The palatoglossus and palatopharyngeus muscles form the palatine arches that contain palatine tonsils and mark the transition from the oral cavity to the oropharynx inferiorly.

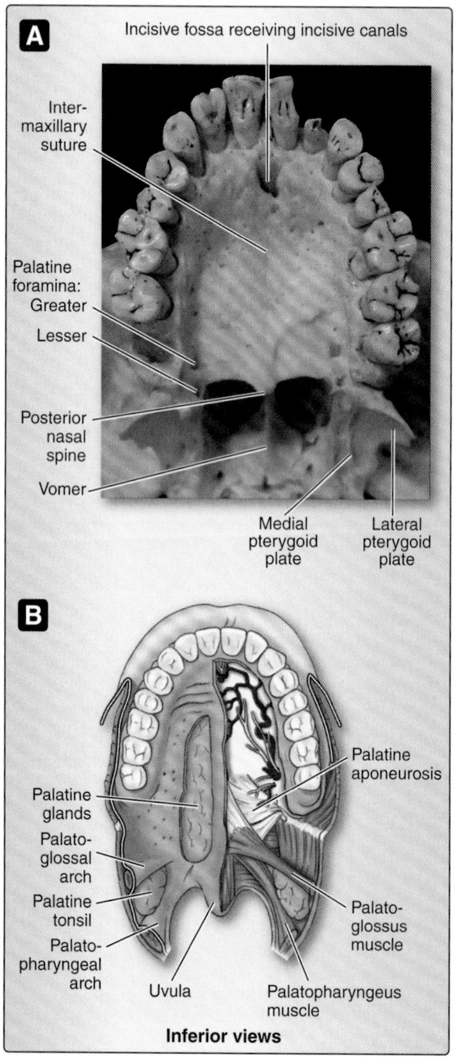

Figure 8.49
Palate. A, Hard palate. B, Soft palate.

Clinical Application 8.13: Cleft Palate and Lip

Cleft palate is classified as **anterior cleft palate** or **posterior cleft palate**. An anterior cleft palate occurs when the palatine shelves fail to fuse with the primary palate. A posterior cleft palate occurs when the palatine shelves fail to fuse with each other and with the nasal septum.

Cleft palate and **cleft lip** are distinct embryologic malformations even though they often occur together. A **unilateral cleft lip** is the most common embryologic malformation of the head and neck region. A unilateral cleft lip occurs when the maxillary prominence fails to fuse with the medial nasal prominence.

[1] Tensor veli palatini: This muscle is innervated by CN V_3 and functions to tense the soft palate and open the auditory tube during swallowing and yawning (think popping ears with changes in altitude).

[2] Levator veli palatini: This muscle is innervated by the vagus nerve (CN X) and functions to elevate the soft palate.

[3] Musculus uvulae: This muscle is innervated by CN X and functions to pull the uvula superiorly.

[4] Palatoglossus: This muscle is innervated by CN X and functions to depress the soft palate and elevate the tongue.

[5] Palatopharyngeus: This muscle is innervated by CN X and functions to tense the soft palate and move the pharyngeal walls during swallowing.

d. Innervation: Terminal branches of V_2 and the maxillary artery reach the palate by way of one of three bony foramina—incisive canal/fossa, greater palatine foramen, and lesser palatine foramen. Nerves of the palate include the **nasopalatine** and **greater** and **lesser palatine** branches of V_2. These nerves provide general sensation to the palate and also carry postganglionic autonomic fibers to the palatine glands. The mucosa overlying the region of the palatal arches and tonsils is primarily served by the glossopharyngeal nerve (CN IX). Stroking of this mucosa typically elicits the gag reflex and tests the integrity of CN IX. The greater and lesser palatine arteries supply the hard and soft palates, respectively.

C. Tongue and salivary glands

The **body** (oral part; anterior two-thirds) of the **tongue** fills the floor of the oral cavity, and the **root** (pharyngeal part; posterior third) of the tongue occupies the anterior portion of the oropharynx. The tongue is a strong, moveable organ composed of intrinsic musculature covered in a thick mucous membrane. The tongue functions in mastication, speech, taste, expression, and swallowing.

1. Embryology: Late in week 4, a number of swellings appear in the floor of the pharynx, which consist of mounds of mesoderm covered by endoderm (Fig. 8.50). These swellings are responsible for forming the oral part of the tongue (i.e., the anterior two-thirds of the tongue), the pharyngeal part of the tongue (i.e., the posterior third of the tongue), and the tongue musculature.

a. Oral part: The **oral part** of the tongue forms from the **median tongue bud** and two **distal tongue buds** consisting of mounds of mesoderm covered by endoderm. The median tongue bud and two distal tongue buds develop in the floor of the pharynx due to a proliferation of mesoderm associated with pharyngeal arch 1. The distal tongue buds overgrow the median tongue bud and fuse in the midline, forming the median sulcus.

[1] Taste buds: The oral part of the tongue is characterized by **filiform papillae** (no taste buds), **fungiform papillae** (taste buds present), **foliate papillae** (taste buds present), and **circumvallate papillae** (taste buds present).

[2] General sensation: General sensation from the mucosa (derived from endoderm) of the oral part of the tongue is carried by the **lingual branch** of the trigeminal nerve (CN V).

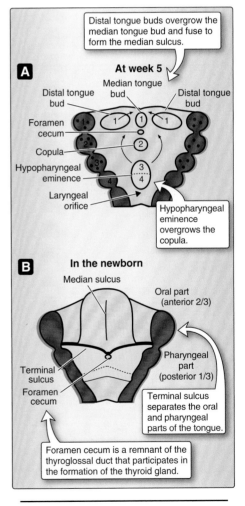

Distal tongue buds overgrow the median tongue bud and fuse to form the median sulcus.

A   **At week 5**

Median tongue bud

Distal tongue bud   Distal tongue bud

Foramen cecum

Copula

Hypopharyngeal eminence

Laryngeal orifice

Hypopharyngeal eminence overgrows the copula.

B   **In the newborn**

Median sulcus

Oral part (anterior 2/3)

Pharyngeal part (posterior 1/3)

Terminal sulcus

Foramen cecum

Terminal sulcus separates the oral and pharyngeal parts of the tongue.

Foramen cecum is a remnant of the thyroglossal duct that participates in the formation of the thyroid gland.

Figure 8.50
Development of the tongue (A and B).

[3] Taste sensation: Taste sensation from the mucosa (derived from endoderm) of the oral part of the tongue is carried by the **chorda tympani** branch of the facial nerve (CN VII). Special visceral afferent neurons convey taste sensation from the oral part of the tongue to the CNS. The cell bodies for these neurons lie in the **geniculate ganglion**. The peripheral processes run with the lingual nerve and chorda tympani nerve. The central processes enter the brainstem via the intermediate nerve and terminate in the rostral portion of the solitary nucleus.

b. Pharyngeal part: The pharyngeal part of the tongue forms from the **copula** and the **hypopharyngeal eminence**, which consist of mounds of mesoderm covered by endoderm. The copula develops in the floor of the pharynx due to a proliferation of mesoderm associated with pharyngeal arch 2. The hypopharyngeal eminence develops in the floor of the pharynx due to a proliferation of mesoderm associated with pharyngeal arches 3 and 4. The hypopharyngeal eminence (pharyngeal arches 3 and 4) overgrows the copula (pharyngeal arch 2), thereby eliminating any contribution of the copula (pharyngeal arch 2) in the formation of the definitive adult tongue.

[1] Tonsils: The line of fusion between the oral and pharyngeal parts of the tongue is indicated by the **terminal sulcus**. The **pharyngeal part** is characterized by the **lingual tonsil**, which forms along with the palatine tonsil and **pharyngeal tonsil** (adenoids) Waldeyer's ring.

[2] General and taste sensations: General and taste sensations from the mucosa (derived from endoderm) of the pharyngeal part of the tongue are carried primarily by the glossopharyngeal nerve (CN IX).

c. Musculature: The intrinsic muscles and most of the extrinsic muscles of the tongue are derived from myoblasts that migrate into the tongue region from occipital myotomes. The motor innervation to these muscles is supplied by the hypoglossal nerve (CN XII).

[1] Extrinsic muscle: The extrinsic muscle of the tongue that is the exception is the **palatoglossus muscle**, which is derived from mesoderm probably associated with pharyngeal arch 4 and is innervated by the **pharyngeal plexus** of nerves derived from the vagus nerve (CN X).

> The swellings that participate in the formation of the tongue are initially attached to the floor of the pharynx. This attachment eventually regresses in the anterior portion of the tongue but persists in the posterior portion as the frenulum. Ankyloglossia (tongue-tie) is a condition that occurs if regression in the anterior portion of the tongue fails to happen.

2. Histology: The tongue consists of a **mucosa** (stratified squamous epithelium and connective tissue), **skeletal muscle**, and **seromucous glands** (Fig. 8.51). The intrinsic skeletal muscle bundles are arranged in three separate planes (longitudinal, transverse, and vertical) at right angles to one another. The seromucous glands and their ducts are found interspersed between the skeletal muscle bundles.

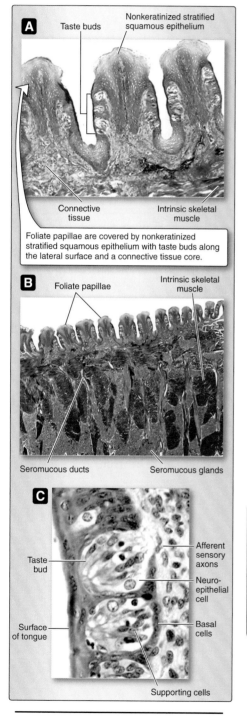

A Taste buds — Nonkeratinized stratified squamous epithelium

Connective tissue — Intrinsic skeletal muscle

Foliate papillae are covered by nonkeratinized stratified squamous epithelium with taste buds along the lateral surface and a connective tissue core.

B Foliate papillae — Intrinsic skeletal muscle

Seromucous ducts — Seromucous glands

C Taste bud — Afferent sensory axons

Neuro-epithelial cell

Surface of tongue — Basal cells

Supporting cells

Figure 8.51
Tongue histology (A–C).

a. **Mucosa:** The ventral mucosa consists of nonkeratinized stratified squamous epithelium and connective tissue similar to the lining of the oral cavity. The dorsal mucosa is highly specialized, consisting of four types of **papillae** that consist of a keratinized stratified squamous epithelium and connective tissue.

[1] **Filiform papillae:** These are the most numerous and smallest of the four types of papillae. The filiform papillae cover the entire anterior two-thirds of the tongue. They contain no taste buds but instead help in chewing and mixing food.

[2] **Fungiform papillae:** These are less numerous and taller than filiform papillae. The fungiform papillae are found near the tip and sides of the tongue. They contain taste buds along their apical surface.

[3] **Foliate papillae:** These are found along the posterior lateral edge of the tongue as a series of parallel ridges. The foliate papillae are not well developed in humans: in young individuals, foliate papillae can be observed, but, in older individuals, they may not be. The foliate papillae contain taste buds along their lateral surface.

[4] **Circumvallate papillae:** These are the largest of the four types of papillae. The circumvallate papillae (10–14 in number) are found in a single row just anterior to the sulcus terminalis of the tongue. They are surrounded by a deep groove into which serous glands (glands of von Ebner) open. The circumvallate papillae contain taste buds along their lateral surface.

b. **Taste buds:** The **taste buds** are oval, light-staining structures found within the nonkeratinized stratified squamous epithelium that sense the contents of the oral cavity through the taste pore. They consist of the following cells.

[1] **Neuroepithelial cells:** The neurosensory cells have a large, round, light-staining nucleus and apical microvilli that extend into the taste pore. The neurosecretory cells synapse with afferent sensory nerve axons at their basal surface.

[2] **Supporting cells:** The supporting cells have a narrow, flat, dark-staining nucleus and apical microvilli that extend into the taste pore.

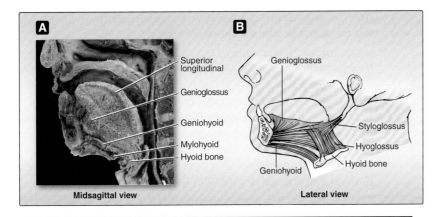

Figure 8.52
Intrinsic and extrinsic tongue muscles. A, Cadaveric specimen. B, Primary extrinsic tongue muscles (palatoglossus not shown).

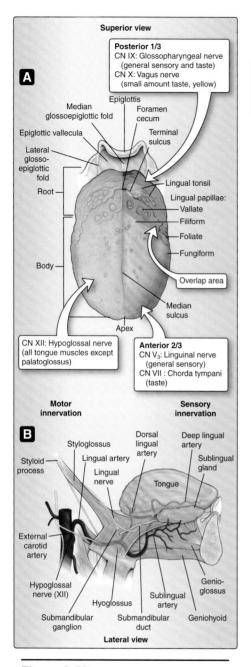

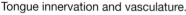

Figure 8.53
Tongue innervation and vasculature.

[3] Basal cells: The basal cells are small cells located at the base of the taste bud and serve as stem cells.

> The neuroepithelial cells react to five basic stimuli or tastants: sweet, salty, bitter, sour, and umami.

3. **Anatomy:** The tongue can move and change shape through coordinated movements of intrinsic and extrinsic muscles.

   a. **Intrinsic muscles:** These are contained within the tongue and have no bony attachments. Intrinsic muscles are arranged in longitudinal, transverse, and vertical bands. These muscles primarily act to alter the shape of the tongue. All intrinsic muscles are innervated by the **hypoglossal nerve** (CN XII).

   b. **Extrinsic muscles:** Extrinsic tongue muscles arise from bone and insert into various parts of the tongue (Fig. 8.52). These muscles primarily act to alter the position of the tongue. All extrinsic tongue muscles, with the exception of the palatoglossus, are innervated by the hypoglossal nerve (CN XII). The palatoglossus is innervated by the vagus nerve (CN X). Extrinsic tongue muscles include the following.

      [1] Genioglossus: Originating from the mental spine of the mandible, this muscle's functions include tongue depression, protrusion, and lateral movements.

      [2] Hyoglossus: Originating from the hyoid bone, this muscle functions primarily to depress the tongue.

      [3] Styloglossus: Originating from the styloid process, this muscle functions primarily to retract the tongue.

      [4] Palatoglossus: Originating from the palatine aponeurosis, this muscle functions to elevate the posterior tongue toward the soft palate.

   c. **General sensation:** General sensation to the anterior two thirds and posterior third is mediated by the lingual nerve (CN V_3) and the glossopharyngeal nerve (CN IX), respectively (Fig. 8.53).

   d. **Taste sensation:** Taste to the anterior two thirds and posterior third is mediated by the chorda tympani nerve (CN VII) and glossopharyngeal nerve, respectively (see Fig. 8.53). The vagus nerve (CN X) also mediates a small area of taste on the root of the tongue adjacent to the epiglottis.

   e. **Vasculature:** Vasculature of the tongue includes branches of the **lingual artery**, which arises from the external carotid artery (see Fig. 8.53). Passing deep to the hyoglossus muscle to reach the tongue, the lingual artery gives off dorsal, deep, and sublingual branches. Dorsal and deep **lingual veins** drain the tongue. Lymphatic drainage occurs by way of the superior and inferior deep cervical lymph nodes for the posterior third and anterior two thirds, respectively. The lateral surfaces of the tongue are drained into the submandibular lymph nodes.

   f. **Organization:** The arrangement of structures associated with the tongue is such that the lingual nerve with the submandibular ganglion and the hypoglossal nerve passes lateral to the hyoglossus muscle to reach the tongue mucosa and musculature, respectively. The lingual artery passes medial to the hyoglossus muscle to reach the tongue.

4. **Salivary glands:** Salivary glands produce and secrete saliva into the oral vestibule and cavity (Fig. 8.54). These include the parotid, submandibular, and sublingual glands, in addition to the smaller mucous glands of the palate.

   a. **Parotid gland:** The **parotid gland** sits in the parotid bed situated between the mandibular ramus and mastoid process, anterior to the external ear and inferior to the zygomatic arch. The largest of the salivary glands in the head, it is encased in a thick connective tissue sheath—the **parotid sheath**—and is traversed by several important structures of the head and face. In particular, the facial nerve divides the gland into superficial and deep lobes. The retromandibular vein and external carotid artery pass through the deep lobe.

      [1] Parotid duct: The **parotid duct** (Stensen's duct) extends anteriorly across the masseter, often running with the buccal branch of the facial nerve (CN VII), and pierces the **buccinator muscle** to enter the oral cavity at the level of the second maxillary molar tooth.

      [2] Innervation: Sensory innervation to the parotid sheath and overly skin is mediated by the great auricular nerve (C2–C3) of the cervical plexus. Parasympathetic autonomic innervation (general visceral efferent [GVE]) is provided by a branch of the glossopharyngeal nerve (CN IX)—lesser petrosal nerve—which synapses in the otic ganglion in the infratemporal fossa, and postganglionic fibers ride on the auriculotemporal nerve (CN V₃) to reach the parotid gland. Postganglionic sympathetic fibers from the superior cervical ganglion reach the parotid gland through the external carotid plexus.

   b. **Submandibular gland:** The **submandibular gland** is the next largest gland. It can be divided into superficial and deep portions, with the superficial portion occupying part of the submandibular triangle in the neck and the deep portion lying medial to the body of the mandible. The submandibular duct arises from the deep portion and travels anteriorly before opening into the floor of the mouth on either side of the **frenulum** of the tongue at the sublingual papillae.

   c. **Sublingual glands:** The **sublingual glands** are the smallest and deepest of the salivary glands. They lie deep to the mucosa of the oral cavity floor and join bilaterally to form a U-shaped elevation beneath the mucosal lining. A series of small ducts extend superiorly from the glands to empty into the floor of the mouth.

   d. **Innervation:** The submandibular and sublingual glands receive parasympathetic autonomic (GVE) innervation from postganglionic fibers that arise from the submandibular ganglion that is suspended from the lingual nerve (CN V₃). Preganglionic fibers from the chorda tympani nerve (CN VII) synapse in the submandibular ganglion to complete this autonomic chain.

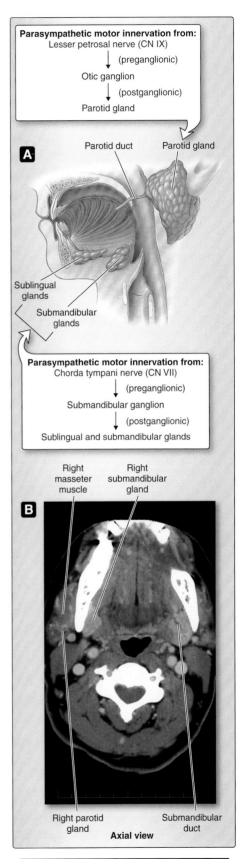

Figure 8.54
Salivary glands. A, Glands and associated structures. B, CT scan showing parotid and submandibular glands. C, Axial CT image. CT = computed tomography.

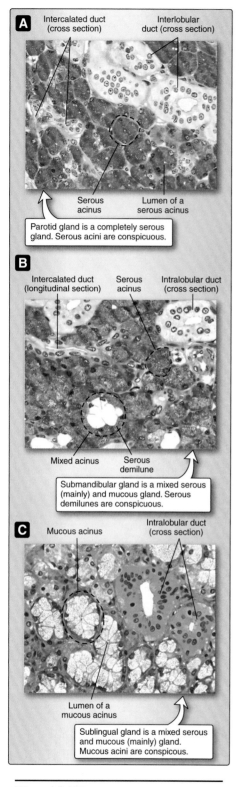

A
Intercalated duct (cross section)
Interlobular duct (cross section)
Serous acinus
Lumen of a serous acinus

Parotid gland is a completely serous gland. Serous acini are conspicuous.

B
Intercalated duct (longitudinal section)
Serous acinus
Intralobular duct (cross section)
Mixed acinus
Serous demilune

Submandibular gland is a mixed serous (mainly) and mucous gland. Serous demilunes are conspicuous.

C
Mucous acinus
Intralobular duct (cross section)
Lumen of a mucous acinus

Sublingual gland is a mixed serous and mucous (mainly) gland. Mucous acini are conspicous.

Figure 8.55
Salivary glands histology. A, Parotid gland. B, Submandibular gland. C, Sublingual gland.

Although the largest of the three paired salivary glands in the head and neck, the parotid gland only produces up to 50% of the total volume of saliva. Collectively, the parotid, submandibular, and sublingual glands produce 0.5–2.0 liters of saliva per day. Saliva aids in maintaining moisture of the oral mucosa and contains digestive enzymes.

5. **Histology:** Figure 8.55 shows the histology of the salivary glands.

   a. **Parotid gland:** The parotid gland is a **serous gland** arranged as a **compound tubuloacinar gland**. The parotid gland is surrounded by a connective tissue capsule that divides the gland into lobes and lobules.

   [1] **Serous cells:** These are pyramidal-shaped cells with a broad basal surface abutting the connective tissue and a narrow apical surface abutting the lumen of the acinus. Serous cells have a round, basally located nucleus. They are protein-secreting cells (they also secrete H_2O and ions) with basophilia located at the basal cytoplasm representing the rough endoplasmic reticulum.

   [2] **Duct system:** The duct system of the parotid gland consists of **intercalated**, **intralobular (striated)**, and **interlobular ducts** and the **main excretory duct**. The intercalated duct is lined by a simple low cuboidal epithelium and receives secretions from the serous acinus directly. The intralobular (striated) duct is lined by a simple columnar epithelium characterized by basal infoldings that modify the initial secretion from the acini by altering the concentration of various electrolytes. The interlobular duct and excretory ducts are lined by a pseudostratified, stratified cuboidal, or stratified columnar epithelium and are located within connective tissue septae from the capsule.

   b. **Submandibular gland:** The submandibular gland is a **mixed serous (mainly) gland** and **mucous gland** arranged as a **compound tubuloacinar gland**. It is surrounded by a connective tissue capsule that divides the gland into lobes and lobules. Secretory acini that contain both serous and mucous cells are called "mixed acini."

   [1] **Serous cells:** These are the same as those of the parotid gland as described above. They are located at the periphery of mixed acini and are called **serous demilunes** because they appear as a half-moon shape.

   [2] **Mucous cells:** These are pyramidal-shaped cells with fairly distinct basal, lateral, and apical margins. Mucous cells have a flat, oval-shaped nucleus. They are glycoprotein-secreting cells with basophilia located at the basal cytoplasm representing the rough endoplasmic reticulum and apical mucous droplets that appear as clear vacuoles because mucus is extracted during histologic processing.

   [3] **Duct system:** The duct system of the submandibular gland is the same as that of the parotid gland as described above.

c. **Sublingual gland:** The sublingual gland is a **mixed serous gland** and **mucous** (mainly) **gland** arranged as a **compound tubuloacinar gland**. It is surrounded by a connective tissue capsule that divides the gland into lobes and lobules.

[1] **Serous and mucous cells:** These are the same as those described above; however, serous demilunes are not prominent in the sublingual gland.

[2] **Duct system:** The duct system of the sublingual gland consists of intercalated ducts, intralobular ducts, interlobular ducts, and the main excretory duct. The intercalated duct is lined by a simple low cuboidal epithelium and receives secretions from the acinus directly. The intercalated ducts in the sublingual gland are short and, therefore, difficult to observe. The intralobular duct is lined by a simple columnar epithelium and is not characterized by basal infoldings. The interlobular duct and excretory ducts are lined by a pseudostratified, stratified cuboidal, or stratified columnar epithelium and are located within connective tissue septae from the capsule.

6. **Teeth and gums:** In the adult, 32 **teeth** are typically housed in the upper and lower jaws (Fig. 8.56). These permanent teeth include four incisors, two canines, four premolars, and six molars in each jaw.

a. **Anatomy:** Teeth have three main parts—**crown**, **neck**, and **root**. The root is anchored tightly into dental alveoli by a **periodontal membrane**. The neck represents the transition zone between the root and the crown. The crown extends into the oral cavity from the gingiva (gums). Enamel covers the surface of the crown, whereas dentine forms the majority of the core of each tooth.

b. **Innervation:** The teeth and gums associated with the maxilla receive sensory innervation from the posterior, middle, and anterior superior alveolar branches from the **maxillary division** of the trigeminal nerve (CN V$_2$). The teeth associated with the mandible receive sensory innervation from dental branches of the inferior alveolar nerve, a branch of the **mandibular division** of the trigeminal nerve (CN V$_3$). The buccal and lingual gums of the mandible receive sensory innervation from the buccal and lingual nerves (CN V$_3$), whereas the palatal gingiva receives sensory innervation from the nasopalatine, greater palatine, and lesser palatine nerves (CN V$_2$).

c. **Arterial supply:** Blood supply to the upper and lower jaw structures includes branches of the **maxillary artery**, including the posterior superior alveolar, inferior alveolar, buccal, greater and lesser palatine, and sphenopalatine arteries.

IX. PTERYGOPALATINE FOSSA

The **pterygopalatine fossa** is a small, inverted pyramid-shaped space nestled medial to the infratemporal fossa, lateral to the nasal cavity, and superior to the palate (Fig. 8.57). This space is associated with terminal branches of the **maxillary artery** and **maxillary division** (V$_2$) of the trigeminal nerve.

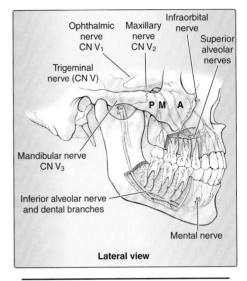

Figure 8.56
Teeth and gum innervations: trigeminal nerve, mandibular (V$_2$) and maxillary (V$_3$) divisions. A = anterior, M = middle, P = Posterior.

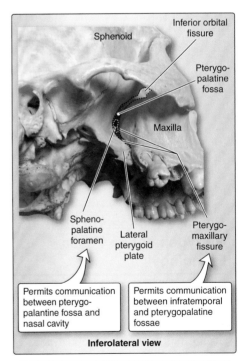

Figure 8.57
Pterygopalatine fossa. White circle is located within the pterygopalatine fossa. Yellow dotted line outlines sphenopalatine foramen.

A. Anatomy

The space is bound by the maxilla and palatine bones anteriorly, maxilla and sphenoid bones laterally, the sphenoid posteriorly, and the sphenoid and palatine bones medially.

1. **Foramina and fissures:** Nerves and vessels enter and exit the pterygopalatine fossa by way of several foramina and fissures.

   a. **Laterally:** The pterygomaxillary fissure connects to the infratemporal fossa.

   b. **Medially:** The sphenopalatine foramen connects to the nasal cavity.

   c. **Inferiorly:** The palatine canal and greater and lesser palatine foramina connect to the oral cavity.

   d. **Anteriorly:** The infraorbital fissure connects to the face and forms the roof of the maxillary sinus.

   e. **Posteriorly:** The foramen rotundum and pterygoid canal connect to middle cranial fossa, and the pharyngeal canal connects to the pharynx.

B. Vasculature

The maxillary artery terminates in the pterygopalatine fossa and sends arterial branches to associated structures, including the nasal cavity, palate, pharynx, oral cavity, and face.

1. **Arterial supply:** Vessels of the pterygopalatine fossa include terminal branches of the maxillary artery, which enters the space through the **pterygomaxillary fissure**. These branches include the **sphenopalatine, descending palatine** (divides into greater and lesser palatine), **pharyngeal, pterygoid canal, posterior superior alveolar,** and **infraorbital** (gives off middle and anterior superior alveolar branches) arteries.

2. **Venous drainage:** Structures associated with the pterygopalatine fossa, including the palate and nasal cavity, are drained by tributaries of the pterygoid plexus and submucosal venous plexus, respectively.

C. Innervation

The main nerve of the pterygopalatine fossa is the maxillary division (V$_2$) of the trigeminal nerve, which enters the space posteriorly through the foramen rotundum (Fig. 8.58).

   a. **Maxillary division of the trigeminal nerve:** Once in the fossa, V$_2$ gives off the following sensory (GSA) branches.

   [1] **Pharyngeal:** This nerve exits posteriorly through the pharyngeal canal to innervate the pharyngeal mucosa.

   [2] **Greater and lesser palatine:** These nerves exit inferiorly through the palatine canal to innervate the hard and soft palates, respectively. Posterior superior and inferior lateral nerves are branches of the palatine nerves.

   [3] **Nasopalatine:** This nerve exits medially through the sphenopalatine foramen to innervate the nasal and palatal mucosa.

   [4] **Infraorbital nerve:** This nerve represents the continuation of V$_2$ anteriorly through the inferior orbital fissure. The infraorbital nerve travels in the floor of the orbit and roof of the maxillary sinus. Terminal branches travel through the infraorbital

---

Clinical Application 8.14: Pterygopalatine Fossa Pathology

Pathology within the pterygopalatine fossa most often involves invasion from adjacent tumor growth as with nasopharyngeal carcinomas or juvenile nasopharyngeal angiofibromas. Radiographic diagnosis involves detecting changes in the fat content of the fossa as well as observing enlargement of associated foramina and fissures.

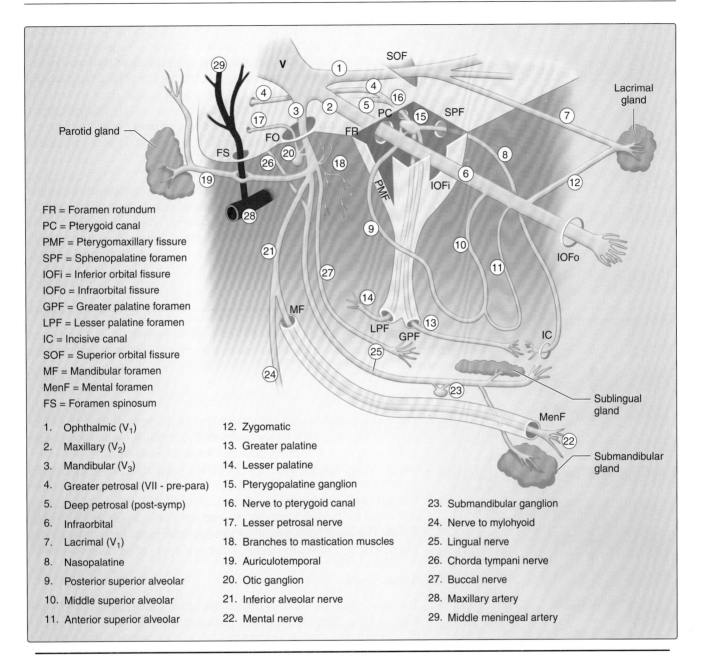

FR = Foramen rotundum
PC = Pterygoid canal
PMF = Pterygomaxillary fissure
SPF = Sphenopalatine foramen
IOFi = Inferior orbital fissure
IOFo = Infraorbital fissure
GPF = Greater palatine foramen
LPF = Lesser palatine foramen
IC = Incisive canal
SOF = Superior orbital fissure
MF = Mandibular foramen
MenF = Mental foramen
FS = Foramen spinosum

1. Ophthalmic (V₁)
2. Maxillary (V₂)
3. Mandibular (V₃)
4. Greater petrosal (VII - pre-para)
5. Deep petrosal (post-symp)
6. Infraorbital
7. Lacrimal (V₁)
8. Nasopalatine
9. Posterior superior alveolar
10. Middle superior alveolar
11. Anterior superior alveolar

12. Zygomatic
13. Greater palatine
14. Lesser palatine
15. Pterygopalatine ganglion
16. Nerve to pterygoid canal
17. Lesser petrosal nerve
18. Branches to mastication muscles
19. Auriculotemporal
20. Otic ganglion
21. Inferior alveolar nerve
22. Mental nerve

23. Submandibular ganglion
24. Nerve to mylohyoid
25. Lingual nerve
26. Chorda tympani nerve
27. Buccal nerve
28. Maxillary artery
29. Middle meningeal artery

Figure 8.58
Pterygopalatine fossa with associated structures, maxillary division of trigeminal nerve (CN V₂) and adjacent divisions associated with the orbit (V₁) and infratemporal fossa (V₃).

foramen to innervate skin of the face. Its branches include the following [5]–[7].

[5] Posterior superior alveolar: These nerves exit laterally through the pterygomaxillary fissure to innervate the upper posterior teeth and gums.

[6] Zygomatic: This nerve travels laterally in the floor of the orbit to innervate skin over the zygomaticotemporal region.

[7] Middle and anterior superior alveolar: These nerves travel within the maxilla to contribute to the superior dental plexus.

b. Preganglionic and postganglionic fibers: Although V₂ is a purely sensory (GSA) nerve, it does carry parasympathetic and sympathetic autonomic fibers (GVE) that distribute to the nasal, palatal, pharyngeal, and lacrimal glands. Preganglionic parasympathetic fibers travel by way of the **greater petrosal nerve** (branch of the facial nerve, CN VII), which enters the pterygopalatine fossa through the **pterygoid canal**. Prior to entering the canal, the greater petrosal nerve is met by postganglionic sympathetic fibers called the **deep petrosal nerve**, forming the **nerve to the pterygoid canal**. Preganglionic fibers synapse in the **pterygopalatine ganglion**, which is anatomically associated with V_2, whereas postganglionic fibers pass through the ganglion. Postganglionic fibers distribute along the nasopalatine, greater and lesser palatine, posterior lateral nasal, pharyngeal, and alveolar nerves. Additionally, autonomic fibers are carried on the zygomatic nerve to a communicating branch that connects to the lacrimal nerve (V_1), to bring innervation to the lacrimal gland.

X. NASAL REGION

The nasal region is composed of the external features of the nose and the internal nasal cavity. This region is involved in respiration and the special sense of smell.

A. Nose

The **nose** projects anteriorly from the face, representing the main external feature of the **nasal cavities** (Fig. 8.59). A cartilaginous core covered in skin, the nose, has two anterior openings into the nasal cavity, called **nares** (nostrils). Nares are separated in the midline by a cartilaginous septum, which attaches posteriorly to a bony septum that separates the nasal cavities. Superiorly, the bridge of the nose is formed by paired nasal bones and the nasal region of the frontal bones. The frontal process of the maxilla contributes to the lateral bony skeleton of the nose. (See IV.A.2. for details on nose development.)

B. Nasal cavity

The nasal cavity consists of paired triangular spaces, separated in the midline by a bony and cartilaginous **septum** (Fig. 8.60). The space spans from the nasal vestibule anteriorly to the **choana** posteriorly. The **vestibule** of the nasal cavity is lined with skin and hair and extends superiorly into the **atrium**, which is lined with nasal mucosa (respiratory mucosa). Posterior to the vestibule and atrium is the cranial portion of the nasal cavity, also lined with nasal mucosa and further divided

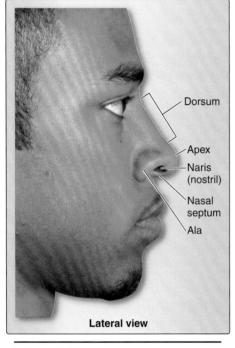

Lateral view

Figure 8.59
External nose.

Clinical Application 8.15: Spread of Nasal Infection

Due to the communication between the nasal cavity and the paranasal sinuses, spread of infection from the nasal cavity into the sinuses is common. Swelling and inflammation of the nasal and sinus mucosa can block drainage of mucus, causing pain and pressure in the sinus region. Infection from the nasal cavity can also spread into the middle ear cavity by way of the Eustachian (auditory) tube.

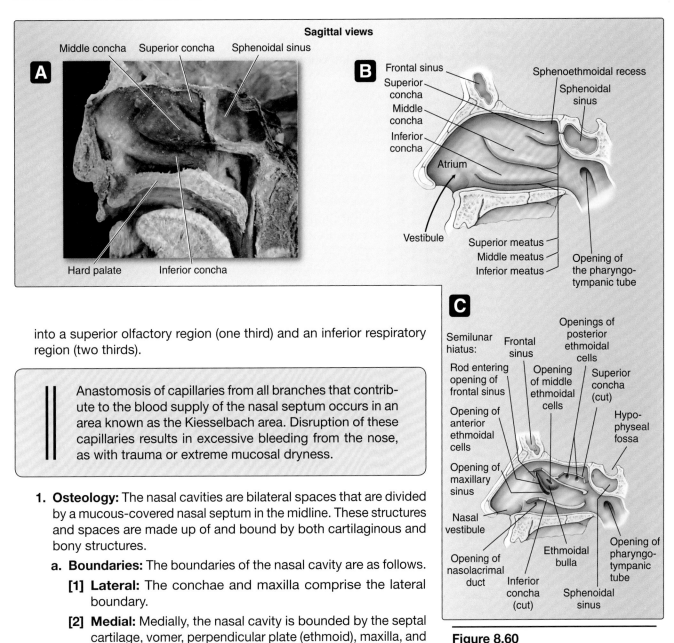

Sagittal views

A — Middle concha, Superior concha, Sphenoidal sinus, Hard palate, Inferior concha

B — Frontal sinus, Superior concha, Middle concha, Inferior concha, Atrium, Vestibule, Sphenoethmoidal recess, Sphenoidal sinus, Superior meatus, Middle meatus, Inferior meatus, Opening of the pharyngo-tympanic tube

C — Semilunar hiatus:, Rod entering opening of frontal sinus, Opening of anterior ethmoidal cells, Opening of maxillary sinus, Nasal vestibule, Opening of nasolacrimal duct, Frontal sinus, Openings of posterior ethmoidal cells, Opening of middle ethmoidal cells, Superior concha (cut), Hypophyseal fossa, Inferior concha (cut), Ethmoidal bulla, Sphenoidal sinus, Opening of pharyngo-tympanic tube

Figure 8.60
Nasal cavity lateral wall. A, Cadaveric specimen B, Conchae intact C, Conchae removed.

into a superior olfactory region (one third) and an inferior respiratory region (two thirds).

> Anastomosis of capillaries from all branches that contribute to the blood supply of the nasal septum occurs in an area known as the Kiesselbach area. Disruption of these capillaries results in excessive bleeding from the nose, as with trauma or extreme mucosal dryness.

1. **Osteology:** The nasal cavities are bilateral spaces that are divided by a mucous-covered nasal septum in the midline. These structures and spaces are made up of and bound by both cartilaginous and bony structures.

   a. **Boundaries:** The boundaries of the nasal cavity are as follows.

      [1] **Lateral:** The conchae and maxilla comprise the lateral boundary.

      [2] **Medial:** Medially, the nasal cavity is bounded by the septal cartilage, vomer, perpendicular plate (ethmoid), maxilla, and palatine bones.

      [3] **Floor:** The floor of the nasal cavity is made up of the palatine bones and palatine process of the maxilla.

   b. **Conchae:** Paired shelf-like projections, **conchae** (turbinates) extend from the lateral walls of the nasal cavity. **Superior** and **middle conchae** arise from the ethmoid bone, whereas the **inferior concha** is a separate bone. These bones are covered in mucosa and function to increase the surface area in the nasal cavity, thus assisting in warming and humidifying inspired air.

      [1] **Meatuses:** Deep to each concha is a space known as a **meatus**, making for a superior, middle, and inferior meatus bilaterally. Each meatus communicates with one or more paranasal sinus and/or the nasolacrimal duct. Connections among nasal cavity structures and sinuses aid in pressure

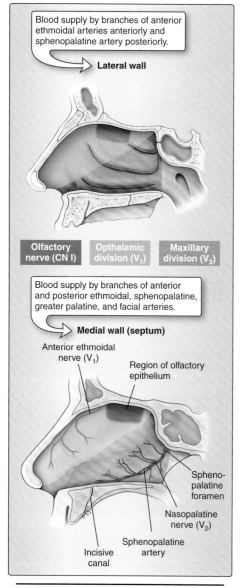

Figure 8.61
Nasal cavity. Innervation and blood supply to lateral and medial walls of nasal cavity.

equilibrium and mucous drainage from the paranasal sinuses and nasolacrimal duct.

     (a) Superior meatus: This communicates with the posterior ethmoid sinuses.

     (b) Middle meatus: This communicates with the frontal, anterior, and middle ethmoid and maxillary sinuses.

     (c) Inferior meatus: This communicates with the nasolacrimal duct.

   [2] Sphenoethmoidal recess: This lies posterosuperiorly to the superior concha and communicates with the sphenoid sinus.

2. **Arterial supply:** The nasal cavity is lined with a heavy vascularized mucosa. Blood supply to the lateral wall nasal mucosa occurs through branches of the anterior ethmoidal arteries anteriorly and the sphenopalatine artery posteriorly (Fig. 8.61). These arteries also contribute, along with branches of the posterior ethmoidal, greater palatine, and facial arteries, to the blood supply of the nasal septum.

3. **Innervation:** Innervation of the nasal cavity can be divided into the nerve(s) that serve the olfactory area versus the respiratory area (see Fig. 8.61). The mucosa of the olfactory area is supplied by the olfactory nerve (CN I), which mediates the special sense of olfaction (smell). Olfactory nerve branches extend superiorly through the cribriform plate of the ethmoid bone to converge into the olfactory bulb. The remaining respiratory area is supplied by branches of the ophthalmic and maxillary divisions of the trigeminal nerve (V_1 and V_2). Similar to the pattern of blood supply, anterior ethmoidal branches (V_1) supply a portion of the nasal septum and anterior lateral nasal wall. The nasopalatine nerve (V_2) is the main nerve of the nasal septum, traveling along with branches of the sphenopalatine artery. This nerve courses anteroinferiorly along the septum before traveling through the incisive foramen to supply the anterior hard palate. Posterior superior lateral nasal nerves (V_2) supply the posterior lateral nasal wall.

XI. CRANIAL NERVES

Twelve paired CNs extend from the ventral surface of the brain and brainstem (Fig. 8.62). These nerves primarily serve structures in the head in neck, with one exception—the vagus nerve (CN X).

A. Functional components

CNs contain at least one of the six functional nerve components previously described—GSA, general somatic efferent (GSE), GVA, GVE, branchiomotor or SVE, and SS. Parasympathetic autonomic fibers are contained within CNs III, VII, IX, and X. CNs do not contain sympathetic autonomic fibers. Postganglionic sympathetic fibers travel to structures of the head and neck by way of vascular plexuses, such as the internal carotid and maxillary plexuses.

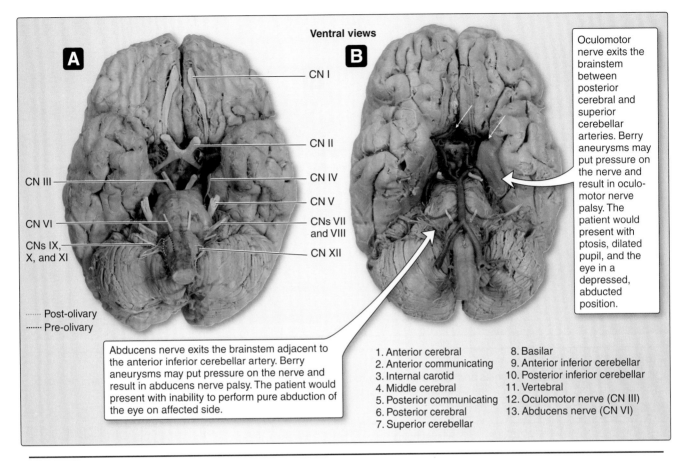

Ventral views

A

CN I

CN II

CN III

CN IV

CN V

CN VI

CNs VII and VIII

CNs IX, X, and XI

CN XII

...... Post-olivary
...... Pre-olivary

B

Oculomotor nerve exits the brainstem between posterior cerebral and superior cerebellar arteries. Berry aneurysms may put pressure on the nerve and result in oculomotor nerve palsy. The patient would present with ptosis, dilated pupil, and the eye in a depressed, abducted position.

Abducens nerve exits the brainstem adjacent to the anterior inferior cerebellar artery. Berry aneurysms may put pressure on the nerve and result in abducens nerve palsy. The patient would present with inability to perform pure abduction of the eye on affected side.

1. Anterior cerebral
2. Anterior communicating
3. Internal carotid
4. Middle cerebral
5. Posterior communicating
6. Posterior cerebral
7. Superior cerebellar
8. Basilar
9. Anterior inferior cerebellar
10. Posterior inferior cerebellar
11. Vertebral
12. Oculomotor nerve (CN III)
13. Abducens nerve (CN VI)

Figure 8.62
Cranial nerves. A, Nerves (yellow). B, Relationship between cranial nerves and cerebral arterial circle branches.

B. Courses and structures innervated

A brief description of each CN course and its structures innervated, supplemented by figures as well as tables, follows.

1. **Olfactory nerve (CN I):** CN I mediates smell (SS). Primary bipolar sensory neurons extend from the olfactory region of the nasal cavity superiorly through the cribriform plate to synapse on secondary (mitral and tufted cells) in the olfactory bulbs, which sit on either side of the crista galli (Fig. 8.63). Olfactory bulbs are continuous caudally with olfactory tracts, which divide into medial, intermediate, and lateral olfactory stria. These axons project to the medial, intermediate, and lateral olfactory areas in the brain, respectively.

2. **Optic nerve (CN II):** CN II mediates vision (SS). Light enters the pupil, passing to photoreceptors (rods and cones) in the deep retinal layers (Fig. 8.64; also see Fig. 8.31). Information is transmitted to bipolar cells (primary sensory neurons) and then to ganglion cells (secondary sensory neurons). These axons form the optic nerve, which extends posteromedially from the eyeball, exiting the orbit through the optic canal. At the optic chiasm, half of the optic nerve fibers cross, whereas the other half remain uncrossed. These fibers project to the lateral geniculate nucleus before projecting to the primary visual cortex (occipital lobe).

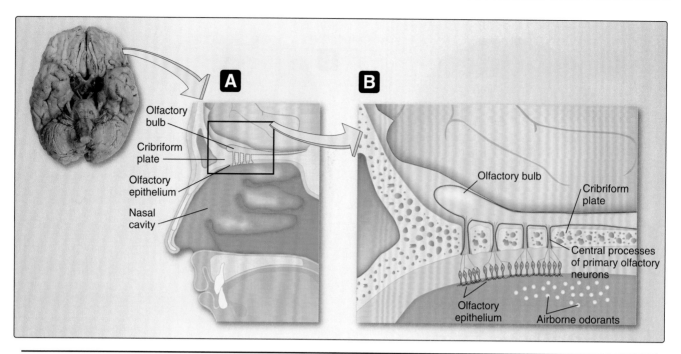

Figure 8.63
Olfactory nerve. A, Olfactory nerves and bulb relationship to nasal cavity. B, Magnified view of olfactory bulb and nerves.

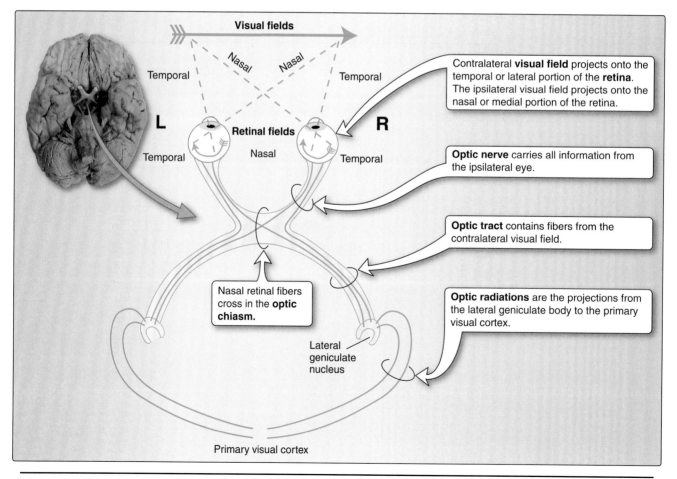

Figure 8.64
Optic nerve and visual pathway.

3. **Oculomotor nerve (CN III):** CN III provides motor innervation (GSE) to four extraocular muscles (superior rectus, medial rectus, inferior rectus, inferior oblique) and levator palpebral superioris as well as parasympathetic (GVE) innervation to constrictor pupillae and ciliary muscles by way of the ciliary ganglion (Fig. 8.65; also see Fig. 8.34). CN III exits the brain at the level of the caudal midbrain, emerging from the interpeduncular fossa between the superior cerebellar arteries and PCAs. It travels rostrally in the middle cranial fossa along the lateral wall of the cavernous sinus before entering the orbit through the superior orbital fissure. It divides into superior (GSE, superior rectus and levator palpebral superioris) and inferior divisions (GSE, inferior rectus and inferior oblique; GVE, ciliary and constrictor pupillae muscles). The ciliary ganglion is anatomically associated with the ophthalmic division of the trigeminal nerve (V_1) but functionally associated with the oculomotor nerve.

Clinical Application 8.16: Visual Field Deficits—Optic Pathway Lesions

Visual deficits are named by the visual field that is lost, rather than by the retinal field left dysfunctional. Visual fields are divided into quadrants—upper temporal, upper nasal, lower temporal, and lower nasal. The word *-anopia* or *-anopsia* is used to describe the amount of loss within one or more of these quadrants. Therefore, the term **hemianopsia** describes loss in two ipsilateral quadrants, or half of the visual field on one side. The terms **homonymous** and **heteronymous** describe visual loss in the same or opposite visual fields for both eyes, respectively.

Lesions along different parts of the visual pathway result in deficits in specific visual fields. The optic nerve, chiasm, and tract contain fibers from different visual fields. Therefore, a lesion at each location will present with a unique pattern of visual loss.
- The **optic nerve** carries all visual input from the ipsilateral eye (contralateral nasal visual field and ipsilateral temporal visual field). Therefore, lesion of the optic nerve will present as monocular blindness on the side of the lesion (as shown in A).
- The **optic chiasm** contains fibers from bilateral temporal visual fields. Therefore, lesion of the optic chiasm will present as bitemporal hemianopsia (as shown in B).
- The **optic tract** carries all visual input from the contralateral visual field. The left optic tract carries visual input from the right temporal and nasal visual fields, and the right optic nerve carries visual input from the left temporal and nasal visual fields. Therefore, lesion of the left optic tract would present as left homonymous hemianopsia (as shown in C).

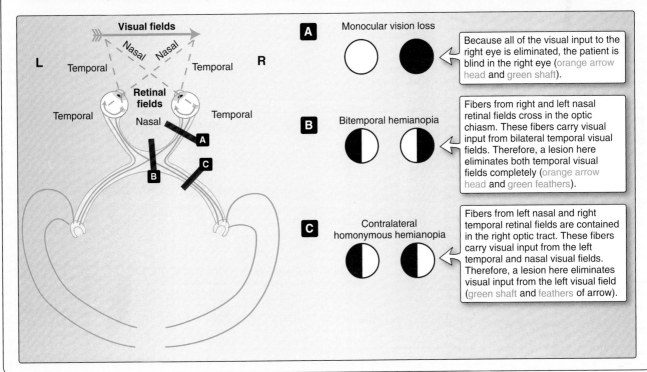

Visual fields

Nasal Nasal

L Temporal Temporal R

Retinal fields

Temporal Nasal Temporal

A | B | C

A Monocular vision loss

Because all of the visual input to the right eye is eliminated, the patient is blind in the right eye (orange arrow head and green shaft).

B Bitemporal hemianopia

Fibers from right and left nasal retinal fields cross in the optic chiasm. These fibers carry visual input from bilateral temporal visual fields. Therefore, a lesion here eliminates both temporal visual fields completely (orange arrow head and green feathers).

C Contralateral homonymous hemianopia

Fibers from left nasal and right temporal retinal fields are contained in the right optic tract. These fibers carry visual input from the left temporal and nasal visual fields. Therefore, a lesion here eliminates visual input from the left visual field (green shaft and feathers of arrow).

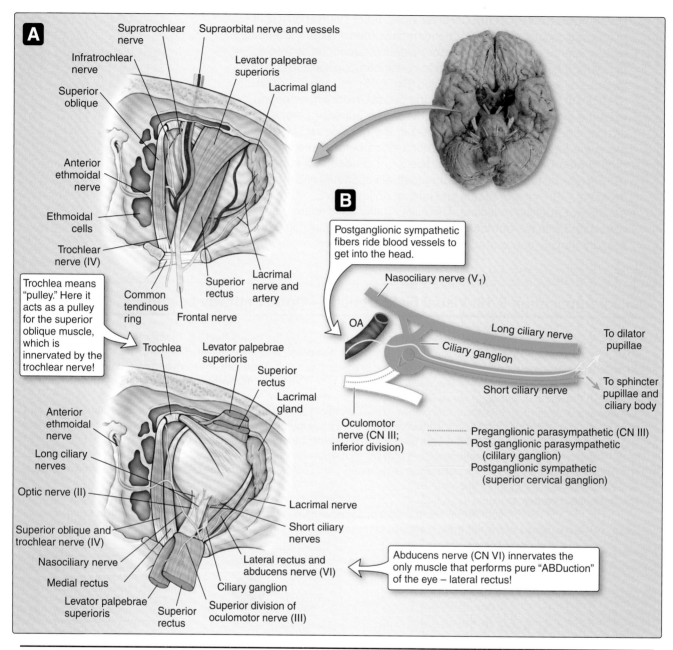

Figure 8.65
Motor and sensory nerves of the orbit. A, Ophthalmic. B, Functional and structural arrangement of autonomic structures in orbit (CN V₁; green; GSA), oculomotor (CN III; orange; GSE and GVE). OA = ophthalmic artery.

4. **Trochlear nerve:** CN IV provides motor innervation (GSE) to the superior oblique muscle (see Figs. 8.34 and 8.65). CN IV crosses in the midbrain tegmentum before exiting posteriorly at the level of the inferior colliculus. It courses anteriorly, along the free edge of the tentorium cerebelli, and through the cavernous sinus along the lateral wall before entering the orbit through the superior orbital fissure. It courses superomedially to enter the superior oblique muscle proximally.

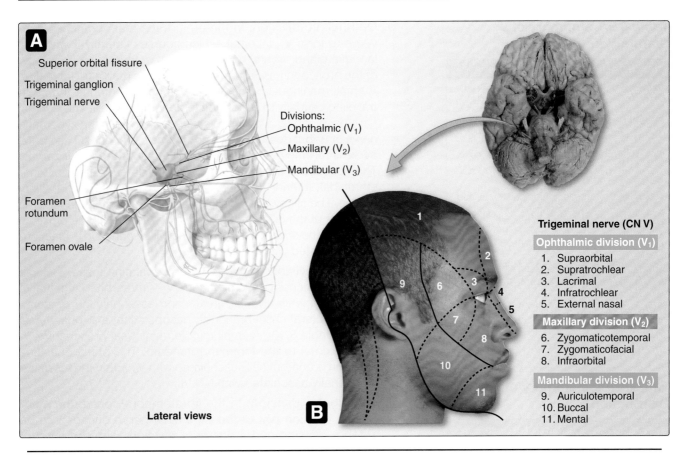

Figure 8.66
Trigeminal nerve. A, Distribution within head (skull ghosted to demonstrate nerve branching). B, Sensory distribution of trigeminal divisions on face.

5. **Trigeminal nerve (CN V):** CN V primarily mediates general sensation (GSA), with a small branchiomotor component (Fig. 8.66). CN V exits/enters the brainstem at the mid-pons level, with a large sensory root and a smaller motor root. Cell bodies for the sensory root are contained within the trigeminal ganglion, located within Meckel's cave in the middle cranial fossa. The trigeminal ganglion receives peripheral axons from each of the three trigeminal divisions—ophthalmic (V_1), maxillary (V_2), and mandibular (V_3)—by way of the superior orbital fissure, foramen rotundum, and foramen ovale, respectively. Each sensory division has a number of branches that mediate general sensation from structures associated with the face, orbit, sinuses, nasal cavity, oral cavity, meninges, and pharynx. The small motor root is only associated with the mandibular division of the trigeminal nerve, which also passes through the foramen ovale. Sympathetic and parasympathetic autonomic fibers do not originate in the trigeminal nerve but distribute to structures of the head by way of branches of each division. These relationships are detailed in "Orbit," "Pterygopalatine fossa," and "Infratemporal fossa" sections of this chapter (see Figs. 8.23, 8.34, 8.45, 8.56, 8.58, and 8.61).

Table 8.9: Summary of V₁ Distribution

Nerve	Structure
Lacrimal	Lacrimal: lateral upper eyelid, lacrimal gland, conjunctiva
Frontal	Supraorbital: anterior two-thirds of the forehead, scalp, upper eye lid Supratrochlear: bridge of nose, medial forehead, medial upper eyelid
Nasociliary	Anterior ethmoidal: frontal and ethmoid sinuses and nasal mucosa, dorsum of nose Posterior ethmoidal: sphenoid and posterior ethmoid sinus mucosa Inferior trochlear: side of nose, medial upper eyelid, lacrimal sac Long ciliary: sensory to the eyeball Short ciliary: sensory to the eyeball

Table 8.10: Summary of V₂ Distribution

Nerve	Structure
Infraorbital	Main: lateral nose, lower eyelid, and infra-orbital region Middle and inferior superior alveolar: upper teeth and gums
Zygomatic	Zygomatic and temporal areas
Posterior superior alveolar	Upper teeth and gums
Palatine	Greater: hard palate Lesser: soft palate
Posterior superior lateral nasal	Nasal cavity
Nasopalatine	Nasal cavity, nasopharynx, sphenoid and ethmoid sinuses
Pharyngeal	Nasopharynx

a. **Ophthalmic division:** In the orbit, three main branches converge to form V_1, lacrimal, which courses laterally toward the lacrimal gland; frontal, which courses anteriorly in the middle of the orbit; and nasociliary, which courses medially (Table 8.9). A small meningeal branch joins V_1 prior to entering the orbit, traveling caudally to supply the tentorium cerebelli. The lacrimal nerve is joined by a communicating branch from the zygomatic nerve of V_2 but does not have any intrinsic branches. The frontal nerve is formed by the supraorbital and supratrochlear nerves. The nasociliary nerve is formed by the anterior and posterior ethmoidal, inferior trochlear, and long ciliary and short ciliary nerves. The ciliary ganglion is anatomically associated with the long root of the ciliary ganglion, which represents the proximal portion of the short ciliary nerve. The ciliary ganglion is functionally associated with CN III.

b. **Maxillary division:** Within the pterygopalatine fossa, multiple sensory branches converge to form V_2—infraorbital, zygomatic, posterior superior alveolar, greater and lesser palatine, posterior superior lateral nasal branches, nasopalatine, and pharyngeal nerves (Table 8.10). A small middle meningeal branch joins V_2 just proximal to the foramen rotundum. The pterygopalatine ganglion is anatomically associated with V_2 within the fossa but functionally associated with CN VII.

c. **Mandibular division:** In the infratemporal fossa, the mandibular division (V_3) of the trigeminal nerve divides into an anterior division and a posterior division, with the anterior division primarily GSA and the posterior division primarily branchiomotor (Table 8.11). The GSA fibers associated with the posterior division travel with branchiomotor branches and carry proprioceptive information from respective muscles. V_3 enters the infratemporal fossa through the foramen ovale and divides, giving off buccal, lingual, inferior alveolar, auriculotemporal, and spinous nerves and motor branches to the muscles of mastication, tensor tympani, and tensor veli palatini. (The course of these nerves is described in VII.B.2.) The otic ganglion is anatomically associated with V_3, high in the infratemporal fossa, but functionally associated with the lesser petrosal nerve of the glossopharyngeal nerve (CN IX).

6. **Abducens nerve (CN VI):** CN VI provides motor innervation (GSE) to one extraocular muscle, the lateral rectus (see Fig. 8.34). CN V exits the ventral brainstem at the pontomedullary junction in close proximity to the bifurcation of the basilar artery and between the labyrinthine and anterior inferior cerebellar arteries. It travels rostrally from the posterior to middle cranial fossa, passes medially in the cavernous fossa, and then enters the orbit via the superior orbital fissure. The abducens nerve travels laterally to reach the medial

Table 8.11: Summary of V₃ Distribution

Nerve	Structure (Branchiomotor)	Structure (Sensory)
Muscular branches	Masseter, temporalis, lateral pterygoid, tensor tympani, tensor veli palatini	Proprioception from V₃ muscles
Buccal		Cheek mucosa and gingiva
Auriculotemporal		Parotid gland, temporomandibular joint, external acoustic meatus, external surface of tympanic membrane, superficial temporal region
Lingual		Anterior two-thirds of the tongue
Inferior alveolar	Gives off nerve to mylohyoid to innervate the mylohyoid and anterior belly of digastric	Mandibular teeth and gums; skin of chin, lower lip, and adjacent mucosa (mental branch)

surface of the lateral rectus muscle, which produces abduction of the eyeball.

7. **Facial nerve (CN VII):** CN VII mediates general somatic (GSA), visceral (GVA), and SS information and provides visceral (GVE) and branchiomotor innervation to glands and muscles in the head, respectively (Fig. 8.67). CN VII exits the brainstem at the pontocerebellar angle and enters the internal auditory meatus in the posterior cranial fossa, into the facial canal. The sensory cell bodies form the geniculate ganglion within the petrous temporal bone. Distal to the ganglion, the greater petrosal nerve branches and exits through the facial canal hiatus into the medial cranial fossa toward the pterygoid canal. The facial nerve continues through the facial canal, giving off a stapedial branch and the chorda tympani nerve in the middle ear cavity (Table 8.12). Branchiomotor and GSA fibers continue inferiorly and exit the skull through the stylomastoid foramen.

8. **Vestibulocochlear nerve (CN VIII):** CN VIII mediates the SSs of balance (vestibular division) and hearing (cochlear division). Sensory receptors for the vestibular and cochlear divisions are located in the inner ear and are associated with the semicircular canals/vestibule and cochlea, respectively (Fig. 8.68). Central processes of both sensory divisions travel through the petrous temporal bone, exit through the internal acoustic meatus, and enter the brainstem at the pontocerebellar angle to synapse on vestibular and cochlear nuclei, respectively.

9. **Glossopharyngeal nerve (CN IX):** CN IX mediates somatic (GSA), visceral (GVA), and SS information and provides branchiomotor and visceromotor innervation to structures in the head and neck (Fig. 8.69). CN IX emerges from the postolivary sulcus of the medulla and exits the skull through the jugular foramen. Superior and inferior glossopharyngeal ganglia are present at this junction. Prior to exiting the skull, the tympanic

Table 8.12: Summary of CN VII Distribution

Nerve	Structure
Greater petrosal	Preganglionic parasympathetic GVE to pterygopalatine ganglion (glands of palate, pharynx, nasal cavity, and lacrimal gland); small GVA and taste component to palate
Stapedial	Stapedius muscle
Chorda tympani	Taste to anterior two-thirds of the tongue; preganglionic parasympathetic fibers to submandibular ganglion (submandibular and sublingual glands)
Facial (main): temporal, zygomatic, buccal, mandibular, cervical, posterior auricular branches	Muscles of facial expression, posterior belly of digastric, stylohyoid (branchiomotor); GSA to posterior auricular muscle

Abbreviations: GSA = general sensory afferent, GVA = general visceral afferent, GVE = general visceral efferent.

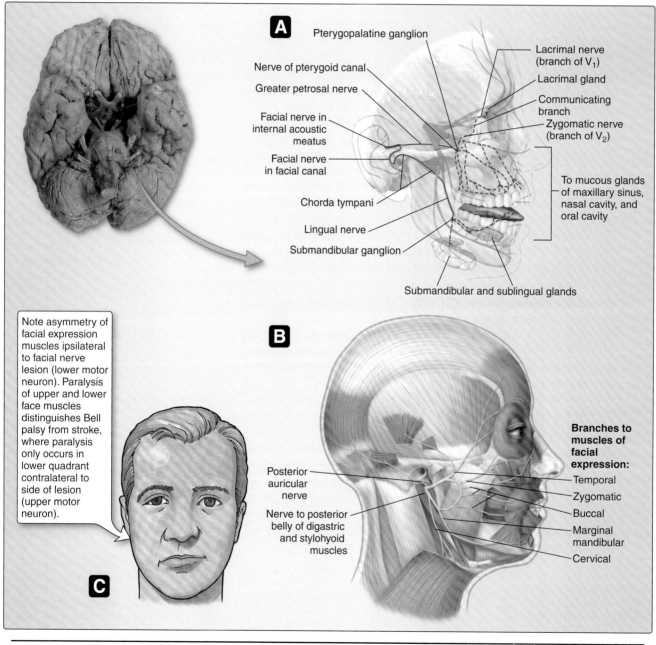

Figure 8.67

Facial nerve (CN VII). A, Pathway of branches with autonomic components (postganglionic = dotted line). B, Terminal branches to muscles of facial expression. C, Bell palsy presentation with ipsilateral paralysis of facial muscles.

nerve branches from the main nerve and travels through the middle ear, becoming plexiform as the tympanic plexus. The lesser petrosal nerve leaves the plexus and exits the middle ear through a small fissure into the middle cranial fossa before entering the infratemporal fossa via foramen ovale (Table 8.13). In the neck, CN IX passes laterally around the stylopharyngeus muscle and sends a motor branch to the muscle prior to passing between the superior and middle constrictor muscles to enter the pharynx. At this point, it joins the pharyngeal plexus with the vagus nerve and distributes throughout the pharynx, palatine tonsils, and posterior tongue region.

10. **Vagus nerve (CN X):** CN X mediates somatic (GSA), visceral (GVA), and SS information and provides branchiomotor and visceromotor to muscles (pharyngeal, laryngeal, palatal) and smooth muscle and glands in the thorax and abdomen, respectively (Fig. 8.70). CN X emerges from the postolivary sulcus of the medulla and exits the skull through the jugular foramen. The superior (jugular) ganglion is found at the foramen, and the inferior (nodose) ganglion is present inferiorly. These ganglia represent the sensory cell bodies for GSA (superior) and GVA and SS (inferior) components. While exiting the skull, the recurrent meningeal and auricular branches leave the main nerve to mediate sensation from the dura mater and auricle/external auditory meatus, respectively (Table 8.14). In the neck, the vagus nerve travels in the carotid triangle, posterior to the internal carotid artery and internal jugular vein within the carotid sheath. Branches of the vagus nerve in the neck include the carotid sinus nerve, pharyngeal branches, superior laryngeal nerve (internal and external laryngeal), and recurrent laryngeal nerve. The internal laryngeal nerve pierces the thyrohyoid membrane to enter the

Table 8.13: Summary of CN IX Distribution

Nerve	Structure
Tympanic	GVA from internal surface of tympanic membrane
Lesser petrosal	Preganglionic parasympathetic GVE to otic ganglion (parotid gland)
Auricular	GSA from auricle, external auditory meatus
Carotid branch	GVA from carotid sinus (pressoreceptors) and carotid body (chemoreceptors)
Stylopharyngeus branch	Branchiomotor to stylopharyngeus muscle
Pharyngeal plexus	GVA to pharyngeal mucosa, palatine tonsils, posterior third of the tongue; taste (SS) from posterior third of the tongue

Abbreviations: GSA = general sensory afferent, GVA = general visceral afferent, GVE = general visceral efferent, SS = special sensory.

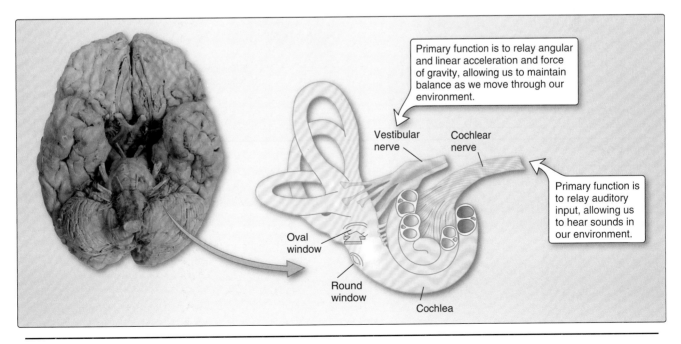

Figure 8.68
Vestibulocochlear nerve.

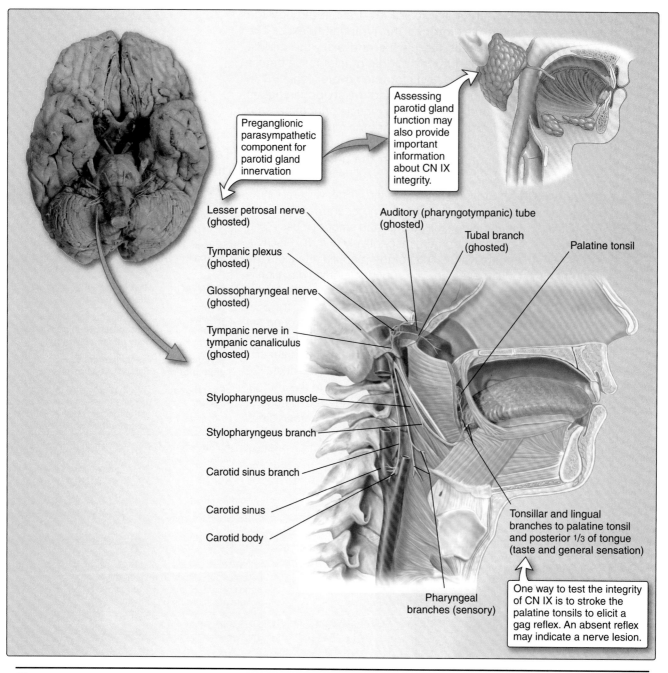

Figure 8.69
Glossopharyngeal nerve.

larynx, whereas the external laryngeal nerve courses inferiorly to the cricothyroid muscle. Left and right recurrent laryngeal nerves actually originate in the thorax, but travel superiorly, running between the trachea and esophagus, to reach target structures in the larynx. The main GVE portion of the vagus nerve continues into the mediastinum, posterior to the root of the lung, and distributes to the walls of thoracic and abdominal visceral to the approximate level of the distal third of the transverse colon.

11. **Spinal accessory nerve (CN XI):** CN XI provides branchio-motor innervation to the sternocleidomastoid (SCM) and trapezius muscles (see Figs. 9.10B and 9.12). Nerve rootlets arise from cervical spinal levels (C_1–C_5), travel superiorly through the foramen magnum, and then exit the skill through the jugular foramen. CN X descends posterolaterally toward the SCM muscle, giving off motor fibers as it continues into the posterior triangle of the neck to the trapezius. Sensory (GSA) fibers from the cervical plexus join the motor branches of the spinal accessory nerve to mediate proprioception from its respective muscles.

12. **Hypoglossal nerve (CN XII):** CN XII provides motor (GSE) innervation to all of the muscles of the tongue, except for the palatoglossus (CN X). CN XII arises from the preolivary sulcus of the medulla and exits through the hypoglossal canal (Fig. 8.71). It travels inferomedially into the carotid triangle of the neck before passing medial to the stylohyoid and posterior belly of the digastric muscle to enter the submandibular triangle. A small C_1 branch rides with the hypoglossal nerve to reach the thyrohyoid and geniohyoid muscles, although it is not considered part of the nerve. In the submandibular triangle of the neck, the hypoglossal nerve courses medial to the mylohyoid to enter the oral cavity.

C. Clinical implications: Neurologic examination

Damage to CNs is typically unilateral and may often involve more than one nerve, depending on the collective course. For example, cavernous sinus pathology may ultimately affect CNs III, IV, V_1, V_2 and VI, just as a fracture at the jugular foramen would likely damage CNs IX X, and XI. Understanding the functional components, receptors, and targets of each nerve is clinically important, especially when attempting to differentiate an upper motor neuron lesion from a lower motor neuron lesion. A typical neurologic examination incorporates the assessment of CN integrity. Table 8.15 provides detailed testing of each CN, clinical observations, and common causes.

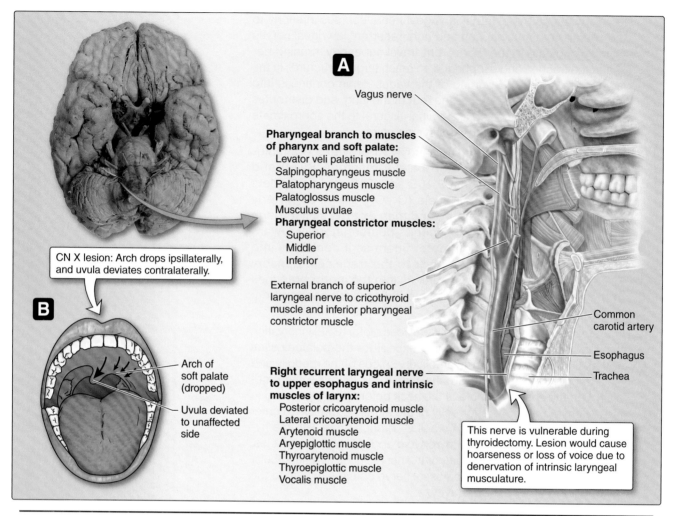

Figure 8.70
Vagus nerve. A, Pathway and distribution. B, Lesion presentation.

Table 8.14: Summary of CN X Distribution

Nerve	Structure
Recurrent meningeal	GSA to dura mater
Auricular	GSA from auricle, external auditory meatus, external surface of tympanic membrane
Carotid sinus nerve	GVA from carotid body (chemoreceptors)
Superior laryngeal	GVA from laryngeal mucosa superior to vocal folds (internal); branchiomotor to cricothyroid muscle (external)
Pharyngeal plexus	GVA to pharyngeal mucosa; branchiomotor to pharyngeal (constrictors and longitudinal muscles) and soft palate muscles (levator veil palatini, musculus uvulae, palatopharyngeus and palatoglossus muscles); small SS taste component to root of tongue, epiglottis, and laryngopharynx
Recurrent laryngeal	GVA from laryngeal mucosa inferior to vocal folds (inferior); branchiomotor to intrinsic laryngeal muscles except cricothyroid
Thoracic and abdominal nerves	GVA from thoracic and abdominal viscera; preganglionic parasympathetic to various postganglionic ganglia in walls of or close to thoracic and abdominal viscera

Abbreviations: GSA = general sensory afferent; GVA = general visceral afferent; SS = special sensory.

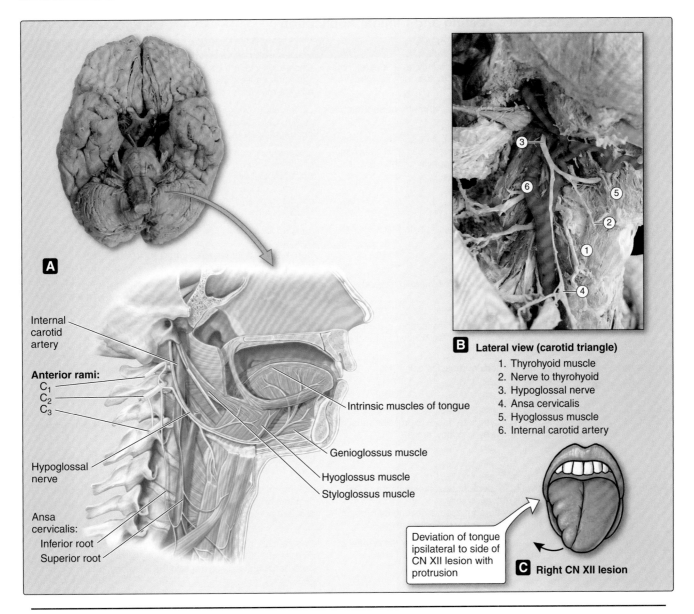

A

Internal carotid artery

Anterior rami:
C₁
C₂
C₃

Hypoglossal nerve

Ansa cervicalis:
Inferior root
Superior root

Intrinsic muscles of tongue

Genioglossus muscle
Hyoglossus muscle
Styloglossus muscle

B Lateral view (carotid triangle)
1. Thyrohyoid muscle
2. Nerve to thyrohyoid
3. Hypoglossal nerve
4. Ansa cervicalis
5. Hyoglossus muscle
6. Internal carotid artery

Deviation of tongue ipsilateral to side of CN XII lesion with protrusion

C Right CN XII lesion

Figure 8.71
Hypoglossal nerve. A, Pathway and distribution. B, Cadaveric specimen. C, Lesion presentation.

Table 8.15: Cranial Nerve Testing and Clinical Application

Cranial Nerve	Test	Clinical Application
Olfactory, I	Test nostrils independently, eyes closed, present common smells (coffee, cloves, citrus)	Observation: anosmia (loss of smell) typically unilateral Common causes: skull fractures, frontal lobe masses, temporal lobe masses/seizures
Optic, II	Visual field testing; asymmetry of pupils, check pupillary light reflex	Observation: changes in visual fields Common causes: stroke, CNS diseases, vascular insufficiency (diabetes), developmental defects, trauma
Oculomotor, III	Test extraocular muscles using "H"; asymmetry of pupils, check pupillary light reflex	Observation: oculomotor ophthalmoplegia-dilated pupil, ptosis, strabismus, downward, abducted eye, loss of accommodation Common causes: aneurysms of surrounding vessels (posterior cerebral, superior cerebrally), cavernous sinus pathology, temporal lobe herniation
Trochlear, IV	Test extraocular muscles using "H"	Looking for extortion of affected eye (unopposed inferior oblique) Common causes: vascular compression, cavernous sinus pathology, surgical injury (at midbrain)
Trigeminal, V V_1: Ophthalmic V_2: Maxillary V_3: Mandibular	All divisions: sensory testing in division distribution	Observation: trigeminal neuralgia–altered sensation throughout division distribution; asymmetry in jaw movement or difficulty coordinating mastication
	V_3: test muscles of mastication (clench teeth, palpate masseter to feel for symmetrical contraction bilaterally)	Common causes: facial/cranial fractures; aberrant vascular compression
Abducens, VI	Test extraocular muscles using "H"	Observation: loss of abduction passed midline gaze Common causes: aneurysms of neighboring vessels, cavernous sinus pathology, tumor in fourth ventricle, cranial base fractures
Facial, VII	Observe symmetry facial expression muscles (e.g., close eyes tightly, smile)	Observation: asymmetry facial expression; must differentiate upper motor neuron lesion (lower face affected = stroke) from lower motor neuron lesion (entire side of face = Bell palsy) Common causes: viral neuritis; lesion along course in facial canal
Vestibulocochlear, VIII	Vestibular portion: observe nystagmus, ask about dizziness/vertigo Auditory portion: assess hearing by rubbing fingers together by patient's ear	Common causes: vestibular division, vestibular apparatus dysfunction (benign paroxysmal positional vertigo); cochlear division, acoustic neuroma
Glossopharyngeal, IX	Assess gag reflex over tonsilar fossa (afferent limb)	Observation: absence of gag reflex; altered taste sensation on posterior third of the tongue Common causes: skull fracture (base), glossopharyngeal neuralgia
Vagus, X	Assess gag reflex over tonsilar fossa (efferent limb); assess hoarseness; observe palatal arch symmetry	Observation: asymmetry palatal muscles, hoarseness and vocal fatigue, difficulty swallowing, deviated uvula away from lesion Common cause: surgical injury during thyroidectomy or carotid endarterectomy, enlarged tumor, aortic aneurysm (left recurrent)
Spinal accessory, XI	Assess trapezius (shoulder shrug) and sternocleidomastoid (unilateral lateral bend, contralateral rotation) function	Observation: drooping shoulder Common cause: injury in posterior triangle of neck, surgical injury (removal of tumors, cervical fusions)
Hypoglossal, XII	Assess tongue movement	Observation: protruded tongue deviates toward side of lesion for lower motor neuron lesion, away from side of lesion for upper motor neuron lesion

Abbreviation: CNS = central nervous system.

Chapter Summary

Cranium

- The neurocranium consists of the flat bones of the skull (cranial vault) and the base of the skull.
- The viscerocranium consists of bones of the face involving the pharyngeal arches.
- Most of the neurocranium and viscerocranium form from cranial neural crest cells.
- Five sutures separate the flat bones of the skull: frontal, sagittal, lambdoid, coronal, and squamous.
- Six fontanelles occur where the sutures meet: anterior, posterior, two sphenoid, and two mastoid.
- Important neurovascular structures, including cranial nerves (CNs) and internal carotid and vertebral arteries, enter or exit the skull through foramina or fissures in the anterior, middle, and posterior fossae. Skull fractures may injure these structures, in addition to causing damage to cortical and brainstem structures.
- Layers of the SCALP can be remembered using the acronym: **S**kin, **C**onnective tissue, **A**poneurosis, **L**oose connective tissue, and **P**ericranium.

Brain and Meninges

- The three primary brain vesicles are the prosencephalon, mesencephalon, and rhombencephalon.
- The five secondary brain vesicles are the telencephalon, diencephalon, mesencephalon, metencephalon, and myelencephalon.
- The neural tube in the future brain region folds at the cephalic, cervical, and pontine flexures.
- The astrocytes and oligodendrocytes of the central nervous system (CNS) are derived from neuroectoderm.
- Astrocytes contributes to the blood–brain barrier along with the tight junctions between the endothelial cells of CNS capillaries.
- Oligodendrocytes myelinate axons in the CNS.
- Microglia are macrophages derived from colony-forming unit-granulocyte monocyte cells in the bone marrow (i.e., microglia are derived from mesoderm).

Face

- The face and the palate form via five swellings: one frontonasal prominence, two maxillary prominences (from pharyngeal arch 1), and two mandibular prominences (from pharyngeal arch 1).
- The formation of the adult palate occurs as a result of the embryologic development and fusion of the primary palate and secondary palate.
- The intermaxillary segment forms the philtrum of the lip, four incisor teeth, and primary palate.
- The secondary palate forms from the palatine shelves, horizontal outgrowths of the maxillary prominences of pharyngeal arch 1.
- Muscles of facial expression are paired and innervated by terminal branches of the facial nerve. Sensory innervation from the face is mediated by terminal branches of the trigeminal nerve.
- The facial artery—a branch of the external carotid artery—supplies structures of the face. Valveless tributaries of the facial vein drain the face. Connections between these valveless tributaries and dural sinuses may promote the spread of infection from the face into the cranial vault.

Orbit

- The bony orbit is formed of multiple bones from both the neurocranium and viscerocranium. It houses and protects the eyeball; lacrimal apparatus; and associated nervous, vascular, and muscular structures.
- The lacrimal gland functions to produce lacrimal fluid to keep the anterior surface of the eyeball hydrated. Blinking allows for lacrimal fluid to move medially across the cornea to drain into the lacrimal sac.
- The double-layered optic cup consists of an outer pigment layer and an inner neural layer.
- The optic cup gives rise to the retina, the epithelium of the ciliary body, and the epithelium of the iris.
- The adult eye consists of three concentric tunics:
  - The innermost tunic (retinal tunic) is derived from the neuroectoderm of the optic cup.
  - The middle tunic (uveal tunic) is derived from the mesenchyme of the choroid.
  - The outermost tunic (corneoscleral tunic) is derived from the mesenchyme of the sclera.
- The ciliary muscle is derived from mesenchyme continuous with the choroid.

Chapter Summary (continued)

- The dilator pupillae muscle and the sphincter pupillae muscles are formed from the epithelium of the outer pigment layer. These smooth muscles are under sympathetic and parasympathetic control, respectively. A fixed, dilated pupil is indicative of an oculomotor nerve lesion.

- The optic fissure on the ventral portion of the optic stalk seals and entraps the hyaloid artery and vein, which later become the central artery and vein of the retina.

- The cornea develops from both surface ectoderm and mesenchyme.

- The lens develops from the surface ectoderm of the lens placode.

- The wall of the eye consists of three concentric tunics: corneoscleral tunic (outermost tunic), uveal tunic (middle tunic), and the retinal tunic (innermost tunic).

- The cornea is composed of five layers: corneal epithelium, Bowman layer, stroma, Descemet membrane, and the corneal endothelium.

- The ciliary body and ciliary processes consist of an epithelium and a stroma.

- The iris consists of an epithelium and a stroma.

- The lens consists of a lens capsule, a subcapsular epithelium, and lens fibers.

- The light-sensitive pars optica of the retina consists of 10 layers: pigment epithelium, photoreceptor layer, outer limiting membrane, outer nuclear layer, outer plexiform layer, inner nuclear layer, inner plexiform layer, ganglion cell layer, optic nerve axon layer, and inner limiting membrane.

- Extraocular muscles are innervated by the oculomotor, trochlear, and abducens nerves. These muscles function to produce eye movement around anterior/posterior, horizontal, and vertical axes.

- The optic nerve carries visual input from the retina to the visual cortex in the occipital lobe of the brain. It travels through the optic canal and is an anterior extension of the forebrain.

Ear

- The ear is divided into external, middle, and internal components:
  - The external ear is characterized by the auricle, which funnels sound toward the middle ear cavity.
  - The middle ear cavity houses the ear ossicles—malleus, incus, and stapes—which propagate vibrations from the external environment to the internal ear for processing.
  - The internal ear develops from a thickening of the surface ectoderm called the otic placode.

- The otic placode invaginates into the underlying mesenchyme adjacent to the rhombencephalon and becomes the otic vesicle.

- The otic vesicle divides into the upper utricular portion and the lower saccular portion.

- The malleus and incus develop from pharyngeal arch 1.

- The stapes develops from pharyngeal arch 2.

- The epithelial lining of the auditory tube and middle ear cavity develop from pharyngeal pouch 1.

- The tympanic membrane develops from pharyngeal membrane 1. The internal surface of the membrane receives general visceral afferent (GVA) innervation from the glossopharyngeal nerve. The outer surface of the membrane receives general sensory afferent innervation (GSA) from glossopharyngeal, vagus, and facial nerve branches.

- The epithelial lining of the external auditory meatus develops from pharyngeal groove 1.

- The auricle develops from six auricular hillocks associated with pharyngeal arch 1 and pharyngeal arch 2.

- Within the ampulla of the semicircular ducts, an elevated ridge of connective tissue is covered by a specialized epithelium and the cupula called the ampullary crest.

- Types I and II hair cells within the ampullary crest possess a single kinocilium and 40–100 stereocilia of varying lengths embedded in the cupula.

- The semicircular ducts respond to rotational (angular) acceleration or deceleration of the head.

- On the floor of both the utricle and saccule, a region of connective tissue is covered by a specialized epithelium, the otolithic membrane, and otoconia called the macula.

- Types I and II hair cells within the macula possess a single kinocilium and 40–100 stereocilia of varying lengths embedded in the otolithic membrane.

- The macula responds to linear and vertical acceleration or deceleration of the head.

- The cochlear duct is a triangle-shaped, coiled duct suspended across the bony labyrinth.

Chapter Summary (continued)

- The cochlear duct is filled with endolymph, whereas the space above (scala vestibuli) and the space below the cochlear duct (scala tympani) are filled with perilymph.
- On the floor of the cochlear duct, a band of connective tissue is covered by a specialized epithelium and the tectorial membrane called the organ of Corti.
- The inner hair cells within the organ of Corti possess only 40–100 stereocilia of varying lengths arranged in a straight line and embedded in the tectorial membrane.
- The organ of Corti responds to sound.

Temporal Region

- The temporal region includes muscle of mastication, the mandibular division of the trigeminal nerve (CN V_3), and branches of the external carotid artery.
- The infratemporal fossa is a space bound laterally by the ramus of the mandible, medially by the lateral pterygoid plate, anteriorly by the posterior maxilla, and posteriorly by the condylar process of the mandible. It contains all or portions of the four muscles of mastication, as well as branches of V_3 and the maxillary artery.
- Branches of V_3 provide GSA to lower jaw structures, cheek mucosa and gingiva, the temporal region over the parotid gland, and the anterior two-thirds of tongue and branchiomotor innervation to the muscle of mastication.
- Branches of V_3 carry parasympathetic fibers from CN VII (chorda tympani) and CN IX (lesser petrosal) as well as taste fibers from CN VII (chorda tympani) from the anterior two-thirds of the tongue.
- Muscles of mastication include temporalis, masseter, and medial and lateral pterygoids. Collectively, they function to assist with chewing food.

Oral Region

- The oral cavity is made up of the oral vestibule and the oral cavity proper.
- The oral part of the tongue forms from the median tongue bud and two distal tongue buds associated with pharyngeal arch 1.
- General sensation from the mucosa of the oral part of the tongue is carried by the lingual branch of the trigeminal nerve (CN V).
- Taste sensation from the mucosa of the oral part of the tongue is carried by the chorda tympani branch of the facial nerve (CN VII).
- The pharyngeal part of the tongue forms from the copula associated with pharyngeal arch 2 and the hypopharyngeal eminence associated with pharyngeal arches 3 and 4.
- General sensation from the mucosa of the pharyngeal part of the tongue is carried primarily by the glossopharyngeal nerve (CN IX).
- Taste sensation from the mucosa of the pharyngeal part of the tongue is carried predominantly by the glossopharyngeal nerve (CN IX).
- The intrinsic muscles and most of the extrinsic muscles of the tongue (styloglossus, hyoglossus, and genioglossus) are derived from myoblasts that migrate into the tongue region from occipital myotomes.
- Motor innervation to the muscles of the tongue is supplied by the hypoglossal nerve (CN XII).
- The ventral mucosa of the tongue consists of nonkeratinized stratified squamous epithelium and connective tissue similar to the lining of the oral cavity.
- The dorsal mucosa is highly specialized consisting of filiform, fungiform, foliate, and circumvallate papillae.
- The intrinsic skeletal muscle bundles are arranged in three separate planes (longitudinal, transverse, and vertical) at right angles to one another.
- The taste buds are oval, light-staining structures found within the nonkeratinized stratified squamous epithelium that sense the contents of the oral cavity through the taste pore.
- The taste buds consist of neuroepithelial cells, supporting cells, and basal cells.
- The parotid gland is a serous gland arranged as a compound tubuloacinar gland that contains serous cells that are protein-secreting cell (they also secrete H_2O and ions).
- The duct system of the parotid gland consists of intercalated, intralobular (striated), and interlobular ducts and the main excretory duct.
- The submandibular gland is a mixed serous (mainly) gland and mucous gland arranged as a compound tubuloacinar gland that contains both serous cells that are protein-secreting cells (they also secrete H_2O and ions) and mucous

Chapter Summary (continued)

cells that are glycoprotein-secreting cells. The serous cells are located at the periphery of mixed acini and are called serous demilunes because they appear as a half-moon shape.

- The duct system of the submandibular gland consists of intercalated, intralobular (striated), and interlobular ducts and the main excretory duct.

- The sublingual gland is a mixed serous gland and mucous (mainly) gland arranged as a compound tubuloacinar gland that contains both serous cells that are protein-secreting cell (they also secrete H_2O and ions) and mucous cells that are glycoprotein-secreting cells.

- The duct system of the sublingual gland consists of intercalated, intralobular, and interlobular ducts and the main excretory duct.

- The parotid gland receives parasympathetic motor innervation (general visceral efferent [GVE]) by way of the lesser petrosal nerve (CN IX), which synapses in the otic ganglion, and postganglionic fibers travel to the parotid gland with the auriculotemporal nerve (CN III)

- The submandibular and sublingual glands receive parasympathetic motor innervation (GVE) by way of the chorda tympani nerve (CN VII), which synapses in the submandibular ganglion, and postganglionic fibers distribute to the glands.

Pterygopalatine Fossa

- The pterygopalatine fossa contains branches of the maxillary division of the trigeminal nerve (CN V_2) as well as terminal branches of the maxillary artery.

- Neurovascular structures associated with the pterygopalatine fossa supply the nasal and oral cavities, as well as portions of the face (GSA).

- The greater petrosal nerve (preganglionic parasympathetic fibers from CN VII) and the deep petrosal nerve (postganglionic sympathetic fibers from superior cervical ganglia) unite to form the nerve to the pterygoid canal, which distributes autonomic innervation to palatal and nasal mucosal glands and the lacrimal gland.

Nasal Region

- The nose is made up of both cartilaginous and bony structures.

- The medial nasal cavity is characterized by a vertical septum, whereas the lateral walls are characterized by shelf-like projections, the conchae (turbinates).

- The nasal cavity is divided into a lower respiratory region and an upper olfactory region. Innervation of the respiratory mucosa is mediated by branches of CN V (V_1 and V_2), whereas the olfactory area receives special sensory (SS) innervation (smell) from CN I, the olfactory nerve.

- The nasal cavity has a rich blood supply, with contributing terminal branches from branches of the ophthalmic, maxillary, and facial arteries.

Cranial Nerves

- Twelve pairs of CNs exit the ventral surface of the brain/brainstem to primarily serve structures of the head and neck.

- CNs carry GVE (parasympathetic), GVA, GSA, GSE, branchiomotor, and/or SS fibers.

- The olfactory and optic nerves mediate the SS input of smell and vision, respectively. They are the only two pairs of nerves that exit directly from the ventral surface of the cerebrum.

- The oculomotor, trochlear, and abducens nerves collectively provide motor innervation to the extraocular muscles.

- Four CNs contain parasympathetic components, three of which provide GVE innervation to structures in the head and neck—oculomotor, facial, and glossopharyngeal. Vagus nerve fibers travel into the thorax and abdomen to provide GVE innervation.

- Four autonomic ganglia are functionally associated with oculomotor, facial, and glossopharyngeal preganglionic parasympathetic fibers—ciliary (oculomotor), pterygopalatine (facial), submandibular (facial), and otic (glossopharyngeal). These ganglia are structurally associated with branches of the trigeminal nerve.

- Postganglionic sympathetic fibers "ride" vasculature to reach glands and smooth muscle in the head.

- The trigeminal nerve is the primary sensory nerve of the head/face. It is separated into three divisions—ophthalmic (V_1), maxillary (V_2), and mandibular (V_3). The mandibular division also sends branchiomotor fibers to muscles of mastication.

- Pupillary constriction is mediated by GVE fibers from the oculomotor nerve.

- The facial nerve contains all functional components. Importantly, it innervates muscles of facial expression and submandibular/sublingual glands. The chorda tympani branch mediates taste from the anterior two-thirds of the tongue. Inflammation may present with ipsilateral facial paralysis, known as Bell palsy.

Chapter Summary (continued)

- The vestibulocochlear nerve mediates hearing and balance. Disruption can result in hearing loss and vertigo.
- The glossopharyngeal nerve is the main sensory nerve for the pharyngeal mucosa and posterior third of the tongue. It also mediates taste from the posterior third of the tongue. An absent gag reflex may indicate damage.
- In the head and neck, the vagus nerve provides branchiomotor innervation to most of the pharyngeal, palatal, and laryngeal muscles. A lesion may present with gag reflex dysfunction, hoarseness of voice, and difficulty swallowing.
- Because the trigeminal, facial, glossopharyngeal, and vagus nerves are associated with pharyngeal arch development, they contain branchiomotor fibers.
- The spinal accessory nerve innervates the trapezius and sternocleidomastoid muscles. Muscle testing can reveal damage (shrug shoulders to test trapezius bilaterally).
- The hypoglossal nerve innervates all but one extrinsic and intrinsic tongue muscles. If the nerve is damaged, a protruded tongue will deviate toward the side of the lesion.

Study Questions:

Choose the ONE correct answer.

8.1 A 21-year-old male patient suffered a fracture to the base of the skull after falling backward off a ladder. He now presents with asymmetry in tongue motor function and loss of taste and sensation from the posterior third of the tongue. Which of the following foramina were likely affected by his injuries?

A. Facial hiatus and jugular foramen
B. Foramen ovale and hypoglossal canal
C. Internal acoustic meatus and foramen ovale
D. Hypoglossal canal and jugular foramen
E. Facial hiatus and foramen ovale

Correct answer = D. Impaired motor function of the tongue is a result from a lesion of the hypoglossal nerve, which travels through the hypoglossal canal. Loss of taste and sensation from the posterior third of the tongue is due to a lesion of the glossopharyngeal nerve, which travels through the jugular foramen. Both of these foramina are located in the occipital bone at the base of the skull.

8.2 An 18-year-old male sustained a moderate traumatic brain injury (TBI) during his final high school football game. Once stable, he was transferred to an inpatient rehabilitation facility. During the recovery process following a TBI, which of the following cells are responsible for forming a glial scar within the central nervous system (CNS)?

A. Oligodendrocyte
B. Microglia
C. Neuroblast
D. Neuron
E. Astrocyte

Correct answer = E. In astrogliosis, astrocytes form a glial scar in and around damaged areas of the CNS. Oligodendrocytes are involved primarily in myelination, whereas microglia have a more phagocytic role in the recovery process.

8.3 A 38-year-old woman is in a car accident and hits her head on the steering wheel. Her computed tomography (CT) scan shows a subdural hemorrhage. Which of the following vessels could be a cause of the hemorrhage?

A. Vertebral artery
B. External jugular vein
C. Bridging veins
D. Anterior inferior cerebellar artery
E. Internal jugular vein

Correct answer = C. Bridging veins connect the cerebral veins to the superior sagittal sinus. Injury to these veins—typically due to shearing forces sustained during head injury—causes blood to collect between the meningeal dura and the arachnoid, thus within the subdural space.

8.4 Your patient presents with signs of a stroke. Based on the angiograph and the patient's balance impairments, you suspect that the right posterior inferior cerebellar artery was occluded. The posterior inferior cerebellar artery is a direct branch of which of the following arteries?

A. Basilar
B. Vertebral
C. Internal carotid
D. Posterior cerebral
E. Superior cerebellar

Correct answer = B. The normal branching location for the posterior inferior cerebellar artery is off of the vertebral arteries prior to uniting into the basilar artery.

8.5 A 53-year-old female patient presents with painful sensory changes along the skin of her superior lip, lateral nose, and cheekbones following a herpes zoster viral infection. Which of the following nerves is mediating pain from the affected structures?

A. Supratrochlear
B. Auriculotemporal
C. Infratrochlear
D. External nasal
E. Infraorbital

Correct answer = E. The infraorbital nerve is a branch of the maxillary division of the trigeminal nerve. It, along with the zygomaticofacial and zygomaticotemporal nerves, supplies the skin over the lateral nose, superior lip, inferior eye lid, cheekbone, and anterior temporal fossa. The clinical scenario described is consistent with trigeminal neuralgia.

8.6 During a neurologic examination, you test your patient's visual tracking ability by asking her to follow your finger with her eyes. You notice that she is unable to produce pure elevation of her eyes. Which of the following muscle pairs is likely involved?

A. Inferior rectus and inferior oblique
B. Superior rectus and inferior oblique
C. Superior and inferior oblique
D. Inferior rectus and superior oblique
E. Lateral rectus and inferior oblique

Correct answer = B. Superior rectus and inferior oblique muscles produce pure elevation when functioning together. The muscles also produce secondary and tertiary movements that are cancelled out (abduction/adduction; medial/lateral rotation).

8.7 A 35-year-old female patient is admitted into the emergency department following a motor vehicle accident. She presents with a normal pupil on the right but a fixed, dilated pupil on the left. This presentation indicates injury to which of the following nerves?

A. Trochlear nerve
B. Abducens nerve
C. Optic nerve
D. Oculomotor nerve
E. Ophthalmic nerve

Correct answer = D. The oculomotor nerve contains autonomic parasympathetic fibers that are associated with innervation of the sphincter pupillae muscle. Damage to these preganglionic fibers would interrupt the parasympathetic control of the sphincter pupillae, thus allowing sympathetic control to take over. This results in a fixed, dilated pupil because the sympathetic fibers innervate the dilator pupillae muscle.

8.8 A 65-year-old female patient present with vestibular dysfunction, including nystagmus. Based on the patient's presentation, you suspect dysfunction in the semicircular ducts. Which of the following structures would likely be involved in this patient's vestibular dysfunction and is also associated with the semicircular ducts?

A. Organ of Corti
B. Macula
C. Otolithic membrane
D. Ampullary crest
E. Tectorial membrane

Correct answer = D. The ampullary crest is the elevated ridge of connective tissue covered by a specialized epithelium and the cupula. Dysfunction of this complex may present with vestibular signs, such as nystagmus.

8.9 A 4-year-old male patient with history of multiple middle ear infections now presents with reoccurring pain in his ear. Which of the following nerves mediates this sensation within the middle ear cavity?

A. CN X (vagus)
B. CN VII (facial)
C. Chorda tympani nerve
D. CN V_3 (mandibular division of the trigeminal nerve)
E. CN IX (glossopharyngeal)

Correct answer = E. The tympanic plexus of the glossopharyngeal nerve provides general visceral afferent innervation to the middle ear cavity before exiting at the lesser petrosal nerve. Pain is caused by inflammation and swelling of the middle ear mucosa.

8.10 During a fistfight, Jinal gets hit in the lower jaw and loses a tooth. She immediately feels pain in her jaw. Which of the following nerves mediates pain from her lost tooth?

A. Buccal
B. Lingual
C. Inferior alveolar
D. Auriculotemporal
E. Posterior superior alveolar

Correct answer = C. The inferior alveolar nerve courses through the mandible to provide general sensory afferent innervation to the lower teeth.

8.11 A 24-year-old male patient presents in the emergency department with several face lacerations following a motor vehicle accident. Over the course of 2 days in the hospital, the lacerations become infected with methicillin-resistant *Staphylococcus aureus*, and the clinical team begins to worry about spread of infection into the cranial vault. Which of the following is the most likely potential route of infection based on your knowledge of the connection in this area?

A. From the pterygoid plexus
B. From the facial artery
C. From the external carotid artery
D. From the nasal cavity
E. From the oral cavity

Correct answer = A. Deep face infections can travel into the cavernous sinus through valveless veins of the face and temporal region. The pterygoid plexus is located in the infratemporal fossa, and it communicates directly with the cavernous sinus. Thrombosis in the cavernous sinus can affect several cranial nerves associated with that space.

8.12 A 78-year-old female patient is admitted to the emergency department with a penetrating wound just deep to the ramus of her mandible on the right side. Which of the following deficits would you expect with the location of this injury?

A. Inability to close the mouth
B. Loss of taste from posterior third of the tongue
C. Decreased sensation over the upper lip
D. Inability to abduct the eye
E. Decreased salivation

Correct answer = E. Injury to the structures deep to the mandible would involve branches of V_3 in addition to the autonomic and special sensory branches that "ride" along with them. Therefore, damage to the lesser petrosal nerve, auriculotemporal nerve, and the chorda tympani may result in decreased salivation due to the denervation of the parotid, sublingual, and submandibular glands.

8.13 Your patient is found in her hospital bed crying. As you attempt to assess the situation, you notice that clear fluid is running out of her nose. Through which of the following associated spaces are the tears traveling to exit through the nasal cavity?

A. Middle meatus
B. Inferior meatus
C. Maxillary sinus
D. Superior meatus
E. Cribriform plate

Correct answer = B. The inferior meatus communicates directly with the nasolacrimal duct, which explains how tears can flow through the nasal cavity.

8.14 A 52-year-old man is diagnosed with a berry aneurysm of his superior cerebellar artery after he finds drooping of his eyelid and double vision. What nerve was affected from this aneurysm?

A. Ophthalmic
B. Oculomotor
C. Trochlear
D. Optic
E. Abducens

Correct answer = B. The oculomotor nerve exits the brainstem between the superior cerebellar and posterior cerebral arteries. This area is often prone to berry aneurysms, which can put pressure on the oculomotor nerve, resulting in downstream effects including drooping eyelid (ptosis), blurred or double vision due to impaired extraocular muscle function, dilated pupil, and loss of accommodation.

8.15 Damage to the chorda tympani nerve results in which of the following conditions?

A. Loss of taste in the nasopharynx and oropharynx
B. Loss of taste in the posterior third of the tongue
C. Loss of mucous gland secretion in sublingual and submandibular salivary glands
D. Loss of mucous gland secretion in the nose and palate
E. Loss of lacrimal gland secretion

Correct answer = C. The chorda tympani enters the infratemporal fossa and "rides" along with the lingual nerve into the oral cavity. It is carrying both taste and preganglionic parasympathetic genera; visceral efferent (GVE) fibers. GVE neurons synapse in the submandibular ganglion. Postganglionic fibers then distribute to the sublingual and submandibular glands.

8.16 Dr. Smith goes to his physician and is diagnosed with a shingles rash, which attacks sensory nerves. The rash has reached the tip of his nose. What nerve branch is affected by shingles?

A. Maxillary
B. Mandibular
C. Zygomatic
D. Alveolar
E. Ophthalmic

Correct answer = E. The ophthalmic division of the trigeminal nerve mediates sensory information from the tip of the nose.

8.17 A man with a history of cardiomegaly (an enlarged heart) comes into your office with a hoarse voice. Impingement of which of the following nerves could cause this?

A. Glossopharyngeal nerve
B. Chorda tympani
C. Pharyngeal branches of the vagus nerve
D. Left recurrent laryngeal nerve
E. Superior laryngeal nerve

Correct answer = D. The left recurrent laryngeal nerve travels around the arch of the aorta to ascend into the neck to innervate intrinsic laryngeal musculature. Damage to this nerve would present initially as hoarseness of the voice due to denervation of these muscles.

8.18 Infection in the cavernous sinus may cause which of the following impairments?

A. Loss of taste from the posterior third of the tongue
B. Inability to close the eyelid
C. Loss of abduction of the eye
D. Decreased parotid gland secretion
E. Loss of smell

Correct answer = C. The oculomotor, trochlear, abducens, ophthalmic (V_1), and maxillary (V_2) nerves travel through the cavernous sinus. Loss of abduction of the eye would indicate an abducens nerve lesion, which travels most medially in the sinus, closest to the internal carotid artery.

Neck

I. OVERVIEW

The neck represents the region that connects the head to the thorax and upper limbs, thus serving as a passageway for important neurovascular, lymphatic, and visceral structures. The contents of the neck are commonly organized into triangles and further compartmentalized by thick fascial layers.

II. OSTEOLOGY

Neck stability is provided by the cervical vertebrae (C1–C7). As described in Chapter 2, cervical vertebrae 1–7 are separated by fibrocartilaginous intervertebral discs (absent between C1 and C2) and united through a series of joints, ligaments, and capsules. The hyoid bone is located anteriorly in the neck, suspended between muscle and connective tissue at the C3 vertebral level. The sternum and clavicles serve as attachment sites for neck musculature and fascia (Fig. 9.1). For a more detailed description of cervical vertebrae anatomy and clinical considerations, refer to Chapter 2.

III. FASCIA

The neck is surrounded by a protective layer of subcutaneous adipose that makes up the **superficial cervical fascia**. It is further divided into multiple compartments by layers of deep cervical fascia.

A. Superficial cervical fascia

Cutaneous nerves, blood vessels, and lymphatic vessels and nodes can be found within the fatty substance of the superficial cervical fascia. The **platysma muscle**—a muscle of facial expression running from the inferior mandible to infraclavicular fascia—is also located in this layer.

B. Deep cervical fascia

The **deep cervical fascia** is a series of connective tissue cylinders arranged into four main layers—the **investing**, **visceral** (**pretracheal**

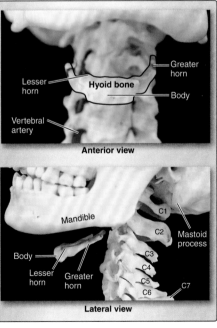

Figure 9.1
Neck osteology.

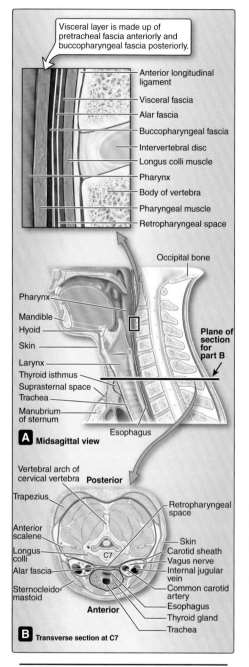

Figure 9.2
Fascial layers and spaces in
the neck. A, Note structures
forming retropharyngeal space. B,
Compartments and fascial arrangement.
Superficial cervical fascia: yellow =
subcutaneous tissue of neck. Layers of
deep cervical fascia: Green = investing
layer, Violet = visceral layer,
Blue = prevertebral layer, Red = alar
fascia and carotid sheath.

and **buccopharyngeal**), **prevertebral**, and **carotid sheath/alar** fascia layers (Fig. 9.2).

1. **Investing layer:** The tough investing layer encompasses the structures of the neck in a single connective tissue sheet. It splits to completely enclose the trapezius and **sternocleidomastoid (SCM)** muscles and forms sheaths around the parotid and submandibular glands.

2. **Visceral layer:** This layer is subdivided into anterior pretracheal and posterior buccopharyngeal layers. It encompasses neck viscera, including the thyroid gland, trachea, esophagus (pretracheal), and the pharyngeal constrictor and buccinators muscles (buccopharyngeal).

3. **Prevertebral layer:** This layer encloses the vertebrae and associated neck musculature.

4. **Carotid sheath and alar fascia:** The carotid sheath is a tubal structure that extends from the base of the skull to the root of the neck and contains the common and internal carotid arteries, internal jugular vein, vagus nerve, lymph nodes, sympathetic fibers, and the nerve to the carotid sinus. The alar fascia extends between right and left carotid sheaths within the retropharyngeal space.

C. Retropharyngeal space

The **retropharyngeal space** is the largest space between fascial layers in the neck. It is found anterior to the prevertebral fascia and posterior to the buccopharyngeal fascia. The space functions to allow movement of the neck viscera on the vertebral column during swallowing but can also be a conduit for the spread of infection, inflammation, and air into the thorax (see Fig. 9.2A).

Clinical Application 9.1: Retropharyngeal Space

The deep cervical fascia functions not only to compartmentalize structures but also to prevent the spread of infection. However, the retropharyngeal space—situated between the prevertebral and buccopharyngeal fascial layers—is a passageway between the head, neck, and thorax that can transmit infection. Inflammation and infection of the prevertebral fascia can create a retropharyngeal abscess that may extend into the thorax, resulting in a mediastinitis. Additionally, air can travel from the retropharyngeal space to the thorax, resulting in a pneumomediastinum.

IV. ORGANIZATION AND CONTENTS

The organization of the neck is such that the **SCM muscle** divides the region into anterior and posterior triangles, bilaterally. The **posterior triangle** is bound anteriorly by the posterior border of the SCM, posteriorly by the anterior border of the upper trapezius, and inferiorly by the middle third of the clavicle. The **anterior triangle** is bound posteriorly by the anterior border of the SCM, superiorly by the inferior border of the mandible, anteriorly by the midline of the neck, and inferiorly by the jugular notch of the manubrium. The anterior triangle is further divided by muscular and osseous boundaries to create smaller **carotid, submandibular, muscular**, and **submental triangles** (Fig. 9.3). Contents include the following:

A. Cervical plexus

The **cervical plexus** is a collection of cervical anterior primary rami (C_1–C_5) that mediate sensory and motor function in the neck region. Cutaneous branches of the cervical plexus emerge at the nerve point of the neck along the posterior border of the SCM. These branches include the **lesser occipital** (C_2), **great auricular** (C_2–C_3), **transverse cervical** (C_2–C_3), and **supraclavicular nerves** (C_3–C_4). They distribute in the superficial cervical fascia to the scalp, parotid region, anterior neck, and clavicle and superior shoulder region, respectively. Sensory branches that mediate proprioception also distribute to the SCM (C_2–C_3) and trapezius (C_3–C_4). Although these muscles receive sensory innervation from branches of the cervical plexus, motor input is provided by the **accessory nerve (cranial nerve [CN] IX)**.

1. **Ansa cervicalis:** The **ansa cervicalis** ("loop of the neck"; C_1–C_3) represents the purely motor component of the cervical plexus. It is partitioned into **superior** and **inferior roots**. The C_1 superior root component travels a short distance with the **hypoglossal nerve (CN XII)** before exiting to descend in the carotid triangle of the neck to innervate the infrahyoid muscles in the muscular triangle. The inferior root (C_2–C_3) loops posteriorly around the internal jugular vein, giving branches to the infrahyoid muscles along its course.

2. **Nerves to thyrohyoid** and **geniohyoid (C_1):** These nerves also travel with the hypoglossal nerve before exiting to provide motor innervation to these muscles, respectively.

3. **Phrenic nerve (C_3–C_5):** This nerve travels inferiorly in the posterior triangle into the thorax to provide motor innervation to the diaphragm and sensory innervation to associated parietal pleura (Fig. 9.4).

B. Musculature

Muscles of the neck can be subdivided into superficial, prevertebral, anterior cervical (suprahyoid and infrahyoid), and visceral (laryngeal and pharyngeal). Many of these muscles serve as boundaries of the triangles of the neck and act on the cervical vertebrae, mandible,

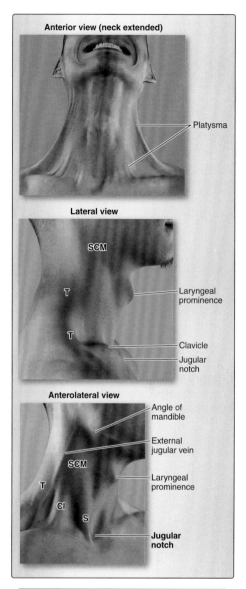

Figure 9.3
Surface anatomy of neck.
Cl = clavicular head, S = sternal head, SCM = sternocleidomastoid, T = trapezius (anterior border).

Clinical Application 9.2: Nerve Blocks

Anesthesia administered within the neck region targets specific nerve structures (see Fig. 9.11).

Stellate (inferior cervical) ganglion: Administered between the trachea and sternocleidomastoid (SCM) muscle and common carotid artery, anesthesia bathes cervical ganglia and is used to decrease sympathetic vasomotor outflow, thereby causing vasodilation. This technique may be used to treat excess vasoconstriction that occurs in diagnoses, such as Raynaud disease.

Cervical plexus: Administered around the nerve point of the neck along the posterior border of the SCM, this technique targets cutaneous nerve branches and is commonly used during neck surgery and for pain management in the cervical plexus distribution.

Brachial plexus: Administered between the anterior and middle scalene muscles at the C6 vertebral level, this targets the brachial plexus rami and trunks. The cricoid cartilage is commonly used as a landmark, along with the posterior border of the SCM muscle.

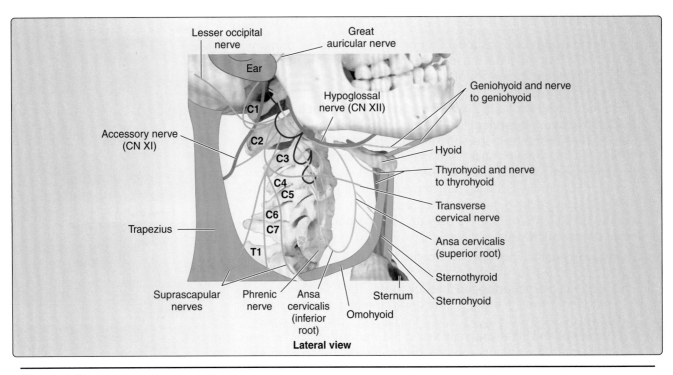

Figure 9.4
Cervical plexus. Arrangement and distribution. Orange: somatic motor; light blue: somatic sensory; green: cranial nerve; dark blue: connecting fibers of cervical plexus.

hyoid, mouth, larynx, and pharynx. Muscle attachments, action(s), and innervation are detailed in subsequent sections.

1. **Superficial:** These muscles include the **platysma**, **SCM**, and **trapezius** (see Fig. 9.3).

2. **Prevertebral:** These muscles include the **longus colli**; **longus capitis** and **rectus capitis** (suboccipital triangle musculature); **anterior, middle,** and **posterior scalenes**; **oblique capitis** (suboccipital triangle musculature) and **splenius capitis**; and **levator scapulae**.

3. **Anterior cervical: Suprahyoid muscles** include the **digastric (posterior** and **anterior bellies), mylohyoid, hyoglossus, stylohyoid,** and **geniohyoid muscles. Infrahyoid muscles** include the **sternohyoid, sternothyroid, omohyoid (superior** and **inferior bellies),** and **thyrohyoid**.

4. **Visceral: Laryngeal muscles** include the **cricothyroid, thyroarytenoid, posterior** and **lateral cricoarytenoid, vocalis,** and **transverse** and **oblique arytenoid muscles. Pharyngeal muscles** include the **constrictors (superior, middle,** and **inferior), palatopharyngeus, stylopharyngeus,** and **salpingopharyngeus**.

C. Vasculature and lymphatics

The neck receives a rich blood supply from the carotid system, which also contributes to blood supply of the head. Venous drainage occurs through tributaries of the jugular system. Lymphatic channels follow the veins and drain through a subset of cervical and visceral nodes.

1. **Arterial supply:** Arterial supply to the neck is supplied by branches of the **external carotid** and **subclavian arteries**. In the neck, the right and left **common carotid arteries** travel in the **carotid sheath**

Clinical Application 9.3: Torticollis

Torticollis involves contraction of cervical musculature, which produces rotation and side-bending of the neck, as well as suboccipital dysfunction. Congenital torticollis is the most common type, typically involving the fibrotic tumor growth in the sternocleidomastoid (SCM) muscle. Muscular torticollis results from damage to the SCM muscle during childbirth. Fibrotic scaring of the SCM may require surgical excision to improve range of motion of the neck. Spasmodic torticollis results from dystonia of the cervical muscles and commonly develops in adulthood. Although the SCM muscle is most commonly involved, other cervical musculature can also contribute to dysfunctional and painful positioning.

and bifurcate at the superior boundary of the thyroid cartilage into **external** and **internal carotid arteries**. The **carotid body** and **carotid sinus** are located at the level of bifurcation. The internal carotid artery continues unbranched toward the head, whereas the external gives off a series of branches in the neck. The subclavian artery, a branch of the **brachiocephalic trunk** on the right and a direct branch of the aortic arch on the left, travels through the posterior triangle of the neck on way to the upper limb, giving off important branches along its course. It is divided into three parts by the anterior scalene muscle (Fig. 9.5).

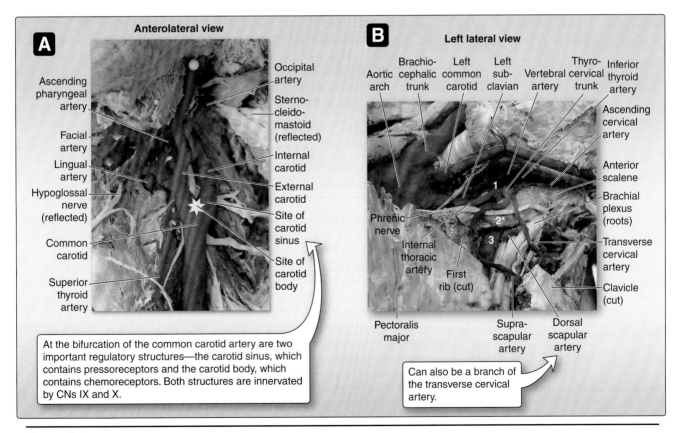

A Anterolateral view

Ascending pharyngeal artery
Facial artery
Lingual artery
Hypoglossal nerve (reflected)
Common carotid
Superior thyroid artery

Occipital artery
Sterno-cleido-mastoid (reflected)
Internal carotid
External carotid
Site of carotid sinus
Site of carotid body

At the bifurcation of the common carotid artery are two important regulatory structures—the carotid sinus, which contains pressoreceptors and the carotid body, which contains chemoreceptors. Both structures are innervated by CNs IX and X.

B Left lateral view

Aortic arch
Brachio-cephalic trunk
Left common carotid
Left sub-clavian
Vertebral artery
Thyro-cervical trunk
Inferior thyroid artery
Ascending cervical artery
Anterior scalene
Brachial plexus (roots)
Transverse cervical artery
Clavicle (cut)

Phrenic nerve
Internal thoracic artery
First rib (cut)
1
2*
3
Pectoralis major
Supra-scapular artery
Dorsal scapular artery

Can also be a branch of the transverse cervical artery.

Figure 9.5

Vasculature of the neck. A, Carotid system in the neck (image rotated to illustrate anatomy in the standing position). B, Subclavian artery and branches (supine). *costocervical trunk branches from second part of subclavian artery Note that the internal jugular vein has been removed. CN = cranial nerve.

Clinical Application 9.4: Carotid Obstruction and Endarterectomy

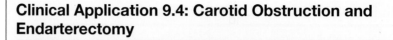

The internal carotid artery can become partially or completely obstructed (occluded) by the presence of fatty cholesterol deposits or plaques. The severity of obstruction often dictates the subsequent insult. For instance, partial occlusion may lead to transient ischemic attacks, in which neurologic deficits typically resolve quickly. Full occlusion can lead to stroke and death. Treatment of carotid obstruction includes endarterectomy, a surgical procedure to remove the plaque and vessel intimal layer. Surrounding structures, such as the vagus and hypoglossal nerves, may be at risk during this procedure. Stenting the narrowed artery may also be a treatment option.

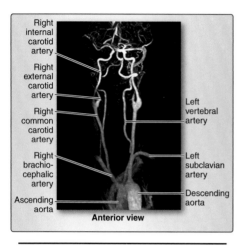

Figure 9.6
Angiograph of neck arteries.

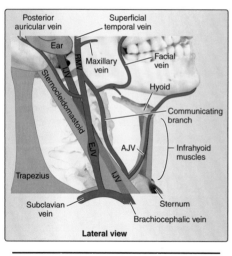

Figure 9.7
Venous network in the neck.
AJV = anterior jugular vein,
EJV = external jugular vein,
IJV = internal jugular vein,
RMV = retromandibular vein.

a. **External carotid:** The external carotid artery gives off branches originating in the carotid triangle of the neck, including the **superior thyroid** (which, in turn, gives off the **superior laryngeal branch**), **lingual**, **facial**, **ascending pharyngeal**, and **occipital branches**, as well as **posterior auricular**, **maxillary**, and **superficial temporal branches** (Fig. 9.6).

b. **Subclavian:** Part one gives off **vertebral**, **internal thoracic**, **thyrocervical trunk** (which, in turn, gives off **inferior thyroid, transverse cervical**, and **suprascapular branches**). Part two gives off the **costocervical trunk** (which, in turn, gives off the **deep cervical branch**). Part three gives off the **dorsal scapular branch** (which can also arise from the transverse cervical artery).

2. **Venous drainage:** Venous drainage occurs primarily by way of **internal jugular** and **subclavian vein tributaries**. A series of superficial venous structures, including the **external jugular**, **anterior jugular**, and **communicating branch veins**, also contribute to drainage of neck structures (Fig. 9.7).

Clinical Application 9.5: Venous Puncture and Catheterization

In the neck, large veins are commonly accessed to administer fluids and medications, enable blood samples, and measure venous pressure. Common puncture sites include the following:

Subclavian vein: The supraclavicular approach is typically used to place a central line adjacent to the junction between the subclavian and internal jugular veins. Identification of the lateral head of the sternocleidomastoid (SCM) muscle is important for proper placement of the needle, which should be inserted 1 cm lateral to the lateral head. Surrounding structures at risk include the cervical pleura, subclavian artery, and phrenic nerve.

Internal jugular vein: The internal jugular vein is typically accessed on the right side. The anterior approach occurs within the carotid triangle on the right side along the medial border of the SCM, two to three fingerbreadths superior to clavicle with needle entry angle 30°–45° toward the ipsilateral nipple. The central approach occurs at the apex of the triangle formed by the two heads of the SCM with the needle angled 30° toward the ipsilateral nipple. The carotid pulse can be palpated to assist with proper needle placement.

a. Internal jugular: This vein is continuous with the sigmoid sinus (dural) in the skull and joins the subclavian vein to form the brachiocephalic vein.

b. External jugular: This vein lies anterior to the SCM and is formed by converging **retromandibular** and **posterior auricular veins**.

3. **Lymphatics:** Lymphatic vessels in the neck generally follow the veins. **Superficial cervical lymph nodes** are located along the course of the external jugular vein and drain lymph from superficial neck structures into **deep cervical nodes**. The primary chain of deep cervical nodes is associated with the internal jugular vein, deep to the SCM muscle. Deep cervical node efferent vessels converge to form the right and left jugular lymphatic trunks, which drain into the right venous angle and thoracic duct, respectively. Several subgroups of lymph nodes are associated with specific neck structures (Fig. 9.8).

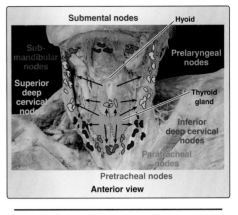

Figure 9.8
Lymphatic system in the neck. Black arrows indicate direciton of lymph flow.

D. Triangles

As previously described, the right and left sides of the neck are divided into posterior and anterior triangles by the SCM muscle (Fig. 9.9). The SCM originates from the mastoid process and superior nuchal line laterally and inserts onto the manubrium and medial clavicle. Acting unilaterally, it side-bends the neck to the same side and rotates opposite. Acting bilaterally, it flexes the neck and extends the atlanto-occipital joints. It receives motor innervation by the accessory nerve (CN XI) and proprioceptive and pain innervation by C_2–C_3 anterior primary rami.

1. **Posterior triangle:** The posterior triangle contains important muscular and neurovascular structures that function within the neck as well as travel to the upper limb and thorax (Figs. 9.10 and 9.11; Table 9.1). Muscles contribute to the floor of the posterior triangle in addition to acting on the head and neck.

   a. Scalenes: Common actions of these muscles include neck flexion and associated rib elevation during forced inspiration. Innervation is from cervical anterior primary rami.

   [1] Anterior: The anterior scalene originates on C3–C6 transverse processes (anterior tubercles) and inserts onto the first rib. The anterior scalene muscle serves as an important landmark in the posterior triangle. The subclavian vein, phrenic nerve, and transverse cervical and suprascapular vessels lie anterior to the anterior scalene. The subclavian artery, costocervical trunk, and brachial plexus roots/trunks lie posterior to the anterior scalene (see Fig. 9.11).

   [2] Middle: The middle scalene originates on C4–C7 transverse processes (posterior tubercles) and inserts onto the first rib.

   [3] Posterior: The posterior scalene originates on C4–C6 transverse processes (posterior tubercles) and inserts onto the second rib.

   b. Splenius capitis: This muscle originates from the inferior portion of the nuchal ligament and T1–T6 spinous processes and inserts onto the mastoid process and superior nuchal line.

   [1] Actions: Unilaterally, it side-bends and rotates the head to the same side. Bilaterally, it extends the head and neck.

   [2] Innervation: It is innervated by segmental posterior primary cervical rami.

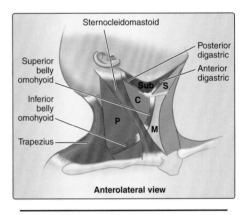

Figure 9.9
Triangles of the neck. Schematic representation of the muscular boundaries. P = posterior triangle, anterior triangle, C = carotid, M = muscular, S = submental, Sub = submandibular.

Table 9.1: Contents of the Posterior Triangle

Triangle	Contents
Posterior	Subclavian artery and branches, subclavian vein and tributaries, brachial plexus roots and trunks, phrenic nerve, accessory nerve (CN XI), external jugular vein, cervical plexus branches, and prevertebral musculature

Abbreviation: CN = cranial nerve.

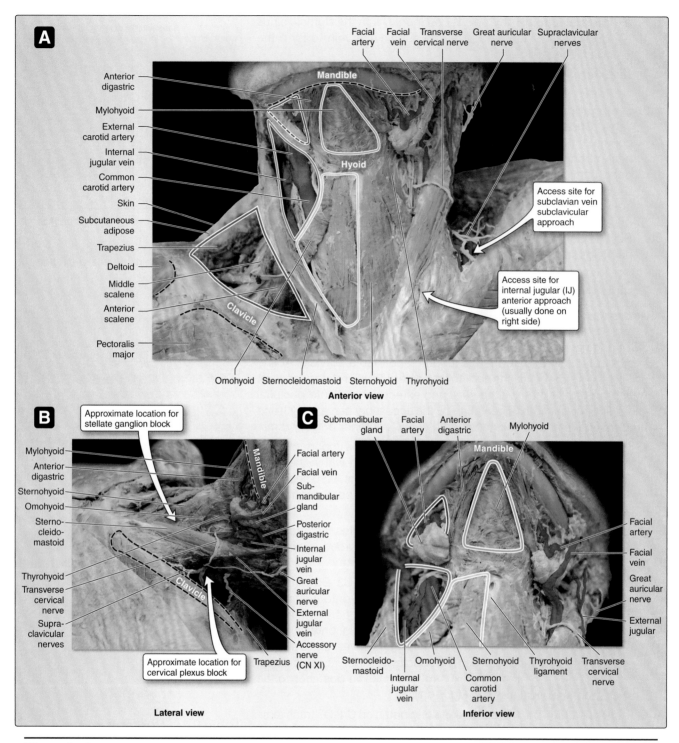

Figure 9.10

Dissection showing anterior and posterior triangles and associated structures. A, Paired (right side only) and unpaired triangles are outlined. B, Cervical plexus (supine). C, Relationship of anterior neck triangles. Blue = posterior triangle. Anterior triangle: Green = carotid, Yellow = muscular, Violet = submandibular, Aqua = submental.

    c. Longus colli: This muscle originates from the C1 anterior tubercle, C2–C3 vertebral bodies, and C3–C6 transverse processes and inserts onto C5–T3 vertebral bodies and C3–C5 transverse processes.

        [1] Actions: Longus colli flexes and side-bends the neck.

        [2] Innervation: It is innervated by C_2–C_6 anterior primary rami.

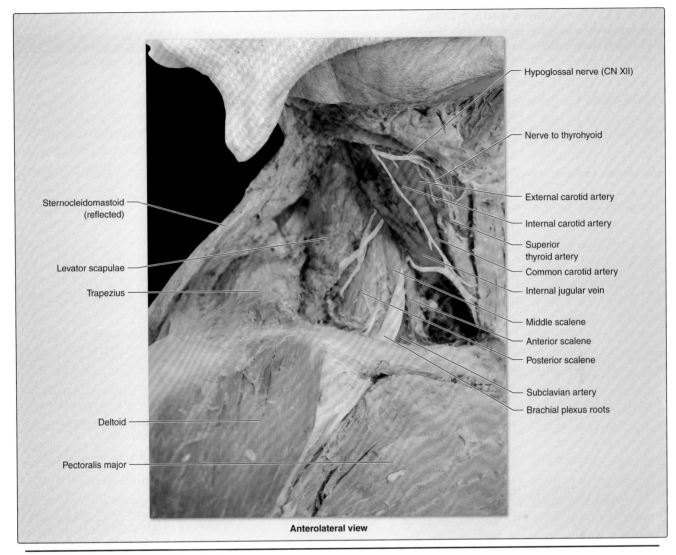

Sternocleidomastoid (reflected)

Levator scapulae

Trapezius

Deltoid

Pectoralis major

Hypoglossal nerve (CN XII)

Nerve to thyrohyoid

External carotid artery

Internal carotid artery

Superior thyroid artery

Common carotid artery

Internal jugular vein

Middle scalene

Anterior scalene

Posterior scalene

Subclavian artery

Brachial plexus roots

Anterolateral view

Figure 9.11
Posterior triangle: root of neck.

      d. Longus capitis: This muscle originates from the basilar occipital bone and inserts onto C3–C6 transverse processes (anterior tubercle).

          [1] Actions: Longus capitis flexes the head on the neck at atlanto-occipital joints.

          [2] Innervation: It is innervated by C_1–C_3 anterior primary rami.

  2. Anterior triangle: The anterior triangle is further divided by muscular and osseous boundaries (Table 9.2; also see Fig. 9.10A). Subdivisions include carotid, submandibular, muscular, and submental triangles.

      a. Carotid triangle: The carotid triangle serves as a passageway for the following important neurovascular structures.

          [1] External carotid artery: Five of the eight branches of the external carotid artery branch within the carotid triangle to reach the following structures in the head and neck (Fig. 9.12; also see Fig. 9.5A).

              (a) Superior thyroid: This branch serves the thyroid gland. It gives off the superior laryngeal artery that pierces the thyrohyoid membrane to enter the larynx.

Table 9.2: Boundaries and Contents of the Anterior Triangle

Anterior Triangle	Boundaries	Contents
Carotid	Posterior belly of digastric, superior belly of omohyoid, and anterior superior border of SCM	Common, internal, and external carotid (and five branches) arteries; internal jugular vein; CNs X, XI, and XII; superior root of ansa cervicalis; deep cervical lymph nodes; pharynx; larynx
Submandibular	Anterior and posterior bellies of digastric, inferior border of mandible	Submandibular gland, facial artery and vein, CN XII, mylohyoid nerve and artery, stylohyoid muscle, lymph nodes
Muscular	Superior belly of omohyoid, anterior inferior border of SCM, midline of neck	Infrahyoid muscles (sternohyoid, sternothyroid, thyrohyoid, superior belly of omohyoid), thyroid gland, parathyroid glands, recurrent laryngeal branch of CN X, lymph nodes
Submental (unpaired)	Anterior bellies of digastrics and hyoid bone	Mylohyoid muscles and lymph nodes

Abbreviations: CN = cranial nerve, SCM = sternocleidomastoid.

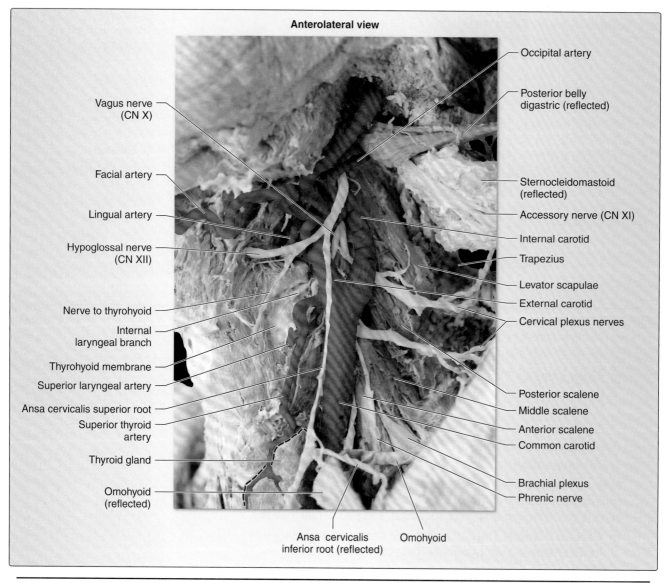

Anterolateral view

Occipital artery

Posterior belly digastric (reflected)

Vagus nerve (CN X)

Facial artery

Lingual artery

Sternocleidomastoid (reflected)

Accessory nerve (CN XI)

Internal carotid

Hypoglossal nerve (CN XII)

Trapezius

Levator scapulae

External carotid

Nerve to thyrohyoid

Cervical plexus nerves

Internal laryngeal branch

Thyrohyoid membrane

Superior laryngeal artery

Ansa cervicalis superior root

Posterior scalene

Middle scalene

Superior thyroid artery

Anterior scalene

Common carotid

Thyroid gland

Omohyoid (reflected)

Brachial plexus

Phrenic nerve

Ansa cervicalis inferior root (reflected)

Omohyoid

Figure 9.12

Branches of the external carotid artery and surrounding structures in the carotid triangle. Note that the submandibular gland and internal jugular vein have been removed.

(b) Lingual: This branch serves the oral cavity.

(c) Facial: Tortuous in nature, this branch serves the face. It is associated with the submandibular gland and branches in the face.

(d) Ascending pharyngeal: This small vessel branches just superior to the carotid bifurcation and travels supero-medially to serve the pharynx.

(e) Occipital: This branch serves the scalp in the occipital region.

[2] Internal jugular: This vein is located lateral to the carotid vessels. The ansa cervicalis typically loops around the internal jugular vein.

[3] Vagus nerve: CN X descends in the neck posterior to and between the internal jugular and carotid vessels within the carotid sheath. Along its course, the vagus nerve gives off a **superior laryngeal branch**, which splits into **internal laryngeal** and **external laryngeal nerves**. These branches either pierce the **thyrohyoid membrane** to mediate sensation to the laryngeal mucosa above the vocal folds or travel to the **cricothyroid muscle** to provide branchiomotor innervation, respectively.

[4] Cervical sympathetic trunk: Located at the same depth as the vagus nerve, the cervical sympathetic trunk lies medial to the contents of the carotid sheath (Fig. 9.13).

[5] Accessory nerve: CN XI exits the skull and passes through the carotid triangle on its way to the SCM and trapezius muscles.

[6] Hypoglossal nerve: CN XII travels through the carotid triangle on its way to the oral cavity. Branches of the cervical plexus run with the hypoglossal nerve and exit within the triangle as the superior root of the ansa cervicalis and the nerves to thyrohyoid and geniohyoid (C$_1$).

b. Submandibular triangle: Bound by the digastric muscle bellies and inferior mandible, the submandibular triangle is primarily occupied by the superficial portion of the **submandibular gland**. Facial vessels travel adjacent to the gland to reach the face (see Fig. 9.10B).

[1] Digastric muscle: The digastric muscle is made up of two bellies—anterior and posterior—which originate from the digastric fossa of the mandible and mastoid process, respectively. An intermediate tendon serves as a common insertion site, which is attached to the body and greater horn of the hyoid bone. The anterior belly receives branchiomotor innervation from the **trigeminal nerve** (CN V$_3$; nerve to mylohyoid), whereas the posterior belly receives branchiomotor innervation from the **facial nerve** (CN VII). Collectively, the digastric muscle assists in steadying the hyoid bone during swallowing and speech and also depresses the mandible against resistance.

[2] Hypoglossal nerve: CN XII passes posterior to the posterior belly of the digastric muscle to enter the triangle and continue to the oral cavity.

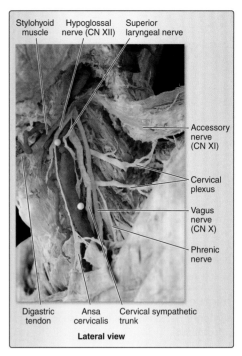

Stylohyoid muscle · Hypoglossal nerve (CN XII) · Superior laryngeal nerve · Accessory nerve (CN XI) · Cervical plexus · Vagus nerve (CN X) · Phrenic nerve · Digastric tendon · Ansa cervicalis · Cervical sympathetic trunk

Lateral view

Figure 9.13
Orientation of cervical sympathetic trunk and vagus nerve. Note that the cranial nerves are shown in orange color and internal jugular vein has been removed.

Clinical Application 9.6: Cervical Sympathetic Trunk Lesion

The sympathetic trunk in the cervical region is located deep to the carotid sheath contents and anterior to the longus capitis muscle. A lesion would result in Horner syndrome, which is characterized by pupillary constriction (miosis), eyelid drooping (ptosis), and flushing and drying of the face on the affected side. These signs and symptoms are similar for the stellate ganglion nerve block as well (see Clinical Application 9.2).

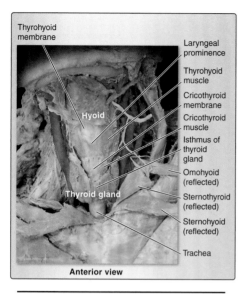

Figure 9.14
Anterior neck, muscular triangle (deep structures).

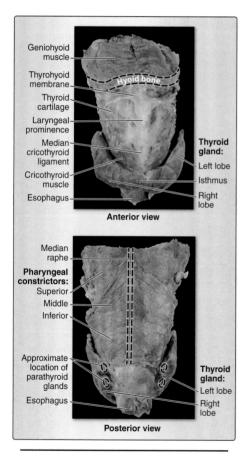

Figure 9.15
Viscera of the neck: larynx, pharynx, thyroid gland, and proximal esophagus.

[3] Stylohyoid muscle: Also associated with the posterior belly of the digastric muscle is the **stylohyoid**, which arises from the styloid process and sends muscle fibers on either side of the common digastric tendon to insert onto the hyoid bone. The stylohyoid is innervated by the **facial nerve** (CN VII) and assists the digastric muscles in elevating the hyoid bone during swallowing.

[4] Nerve and artery to mylohyoid: Finally, these emerge deep to the mandible to reach the **mylohyoid muscle** through the submandibular triangle.

c. **Muscular triangle:** The muscular triangle contains the **infrahyoid muscles** and underlying neck viscera (Fig. 9.14; see also Fig. 9.10).

[1] Infrahyoid muscles: The infrahyoid muscles receive motor innervation from the ansa cervicalis primarily. The exception to this is the thyrohyoid, which receives the nerve to thyrohyoid (C_1) directly. Collectively, the infrahyoid muscles— **sternohyoid**, **sternothyroid**, **thyrohyoid**, and **omohyoid** (*omo* = scapula)—attach to the structures in their names. The **omohyoid** has superior and inferior bellies, which serve as muscular borders in the neck. Infrahyoid muscles play an important role in swallowing and phonation. Specific functions include:

(a) **Sternohyoid:** This muscle depresses the hyoid bone from an elevated position during swallowing.

(b) **Sternothyroid:** This muscle depresses the hyoid bone and larynx.

(c) **Thyrohyoid:** This muscle depresses the hyoid bone and elevates the larynx.

(d) **Omohyoid:** This muscle depresses, steadies, and retracts the hyoid bone.

[2] Thyroid gland: The butterfly-shaped bilobar **thyroid gland** is found in the muscular triangle just inferior to the **thyroid cartilage**. The right and left lobes of the thyroid are connected anteriorly by an **isthmus** at approximately the second or third tracheal ring level.

[3] Parathyroid glands: These are typically located bilaterally on the posterior surface of the thyroid gland.

[4] Recurrent laryngeal nerve: This branch of the vagus nerve (CN X) courses in the muscular triangle in a groove between the trachea and esophagus, deep and lateral to the thyroid gland. It eventually courses into the larynx to mediate sensation to the mucosa below the vocal folds as well as to provide branchiomotor innervation to the remaining intrinsic laryngeal muscles. The recurrent laryngeal nerve is also referred to as the **inferior laryngeal nerve** once it enters the larynx.

d. **Submental triangle:** This unpaired triangle is bound by the anterior bellies of the digastric muscles laterally and the hyoid bone inferiorly (see Fig. 9.10A and C). The mylohyoid muscle, which originates from the mylohyoid line of the mandible and inserts along a midline raphe and hyoid bone, forms the floor of the triangle. The mylohyoid receives branchiomotor innervation from the trigeminal nerve (CN V$_3$) and assists in swallowing and phonation by elevating the hyoid bone, tongue, and floor of the oral cavity. Submental lymph nodes lie superficial to the mylohyoid muscle within the boundaries of the triangle.

V. VISCERA

From anterior to posterior, viscera of the neck includes the **thyroid** and **parathyroid glands**, the **larynx, upper trachea, pharynx**, and **proximal esophagus** (Fig. 9.15). These structures are contained within the visceral layer of the deep cervical fascia and have endocrine, respiratory, and digestive functions, respectively.

A. Thyroid gland

The thyroid gland is a bilobar endocrine organ responsible for production of thyroid hormone and calcitonin. These products regulate rate of metabolism and calcium metabolism, respectively. The thyroid gland is located anteriorly in the muscular triangle just inferior to the thyroid cartilage. Its midline connection—isthmus—is located at approximately the second or third tracheal ring level. Deep to the visceral fascia, the thyroid has a separate fibrous capsule that further divides the gland with intraglandular septa (Fig. 9.16; also see Figs. 9.14 and 9.15).

1. **Vasculature:** The thyroid gland receives blood supply from the **superior** and **inferior thyroid arteries**, which arise from the external carotid and thyrocervical trunk, respectively. Bilaterally, these vessels pierce the visceral fascia (pretracheal) and anastomose within the gland to ensure adequate collateral circulation. **Superior, middle**, and **inferior thyroid veins** drain the thyroid gland. Superior and middle thyroid veins are tributaries of the internal jugular vein, whereas the inferior thyroid vein drains directly into the brachiocephalic veins.

> The thyroid ima artery is present in ~10% of the population. It is located in the region of the thyroid isthmus. Care should be taken with any surgical procedure in the anterior thyroid region because damage to this artery can cause bleeding.

2. **Lymphatics:** Lymphatic drainage of the thyroid gland starts at associated lymph nodes, which include **pretracheal, paratracheal**, and **prelaryngeal groups**. Lymph then drains into deep cervical nodes.

3. **Innervation:** The thyroid gland receives autonomic innervation via postganglionic sympathetic fibers from the **cervical sympathetic ganglia** (see Fig. 9.13). These fibers distribute along the vasculature and function only to regulate vasoconstriction. Glandular function is regulated strictly by the pituitary gland.

Clinical Application 9.7: Thyroidectomy

Thyroidectomy is partial or complete surgical removal of the thyroid gland to treat thyroid disorders—both neoplastic (cancer and goiter) or non-neoplastic (hyperthyroidism). Identification and ligation of thyroid gland blood supply is important. Additionally, care must be taken to avoid damaging the recurrent laryngeal nerves and parathyroid glands during this procedure. Following full removal of the thyroid gland, supplemental thyroid hormone must be administered daily. Additional postoperative complications can include thyroid storm or hypothyroidism, which makes medical management of these patients even more important.

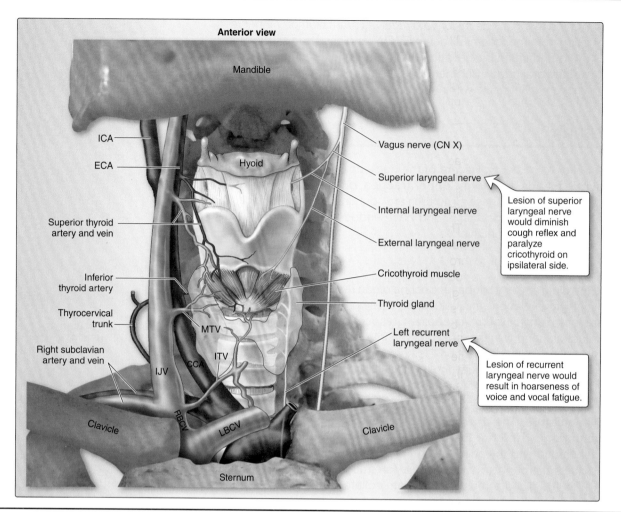

Anterior view

Figure 9.16

Viscera of the neck and associated structures. CCA = common carotid artery, CN = cranial nerve, ECA = external carotid artery, ICA = internal carotid artery, IJV = internal jugular vein, ITV = inferior thyroid vein, LBCV = left brachiocephalic vein, MTV = middle thyroid vein, RBCV = left brachiocephalic vein.

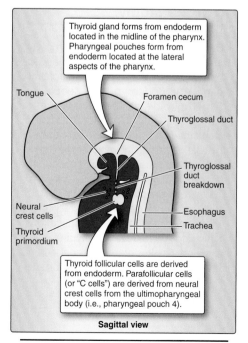

Sagittal view

Figure 9.17

Embryology of the thyroid.

4. **Embryology:** At week 4, the **thyroid primordium**, a small mass of endoderm, forms in the midline of the floor of the pharynx near the foramen cecum of the developing tongue. The thyroid primordium migrates caudally down the midline, passing ventral to the hyoid bone and the laryngeal cartilages to its adult location. During this migration, the thyroid primordium remains connected to the tongue by the **thyroglossal duct**. By week 5, the thyroglossal duct is obliterated, leaving only a remnant called the **foramen cecum** (Fig. 9.17). The endoderm of the thyroid primordium eventually differentiates into the **thyroid follicular cells**. In addition, the neural crest cells within the **ultimopharyngeal body** (i.e., pharyngeal pouch 4) disperse throughout the thyroid gland and differentiate into the **parafollicular cells** (or **C cells**).

A fragment of the thyroid gland may become detached during its descent and form ectopic thyroid tissue anywhere along its midline descent in the neck. Most commonly, additional thyroid tissue called the "pyramidal lobe" may be found near the superior surface of the thyroid gland.

5. **Histology:** The normal adult thyroid gland is red brown in color and butterfly shaped with two bulky lateral lobes connected by a thin isthmus. Each lateral lobe is about 2 cm wide by 6 cm long by 2 cm thick. The normal adult thyroid gland weighs about 15–25 g.

   [1] **Thyroid follicle:** The thyroid gland is surrounded by a connective tissue **capsule** that sends **trabeculae** into the interior of the gland to provide a delicate loose connective tissue **stroma** that surrounds the thyroid follicles. The functional unit of the thyroid gland is the **thyroid follicle** (Fig. 9.18). The thyroid follicle is a spherical structure that contains a gel-like substance called **colloid** that is composed mainly of iodinated **thyroglobulin (660 kDa)**. Thyroglobulin is the inactive storage form of the thyroid hormones (**triiodothyronine [T$_3$]** and **thyroxin [T$_4$]**). The wall of the thyroid follicle is formed by **follicular cells** and **parafollicular cells**.

   [2] **Follicular cells:** The follicular cell is a cuboidal-shaped cell in an inactive thyroid gland and columnar-shaped cell in an active thyroid gland. It has a round, basally located nucleus with one or more nucleoli. Follicular cells contain rough endoplasmic reticulum, polyribosomes, a Golgi complex, mitochondria, endocytotic vesicles, juxtaluminal zonula occludens (tight junctions), apical microvilli, lysosomes, and lipid droplets. They synthesize iodinated thyroglobulin and secrete **T$_3$** and **T$_4$**, both of which are lysosomal degradation products of iodinated thyroglobulin.

The thyroid gland begins to secrete hormone as early as weeks 10–12. Thyroid function is necessary for proper brain development. Hypothyroidism during embryologic development is characterized by intellectual disability, deafness, muscle hypertonia, and dwarfism.

   [3] **Parafollicular cell:** The parafollicular cell is a spherical cell with a round, centrally located nucleus. It contains rough endoplasmic reticulum, polyribosomes, a Golgi complex, mitochondria, and numerous secretory granules. Parafollicular cells may lie within the basal lamina that surrounds the thyroid follicle or as a cluster of cells in the loose connective tissue between follicles. They synthesize and secrete **calcitonin**. Calcitonin lowers blood Ca^{2+} levels by acting directly on osteoclasts to decrease their bone resorption activity.

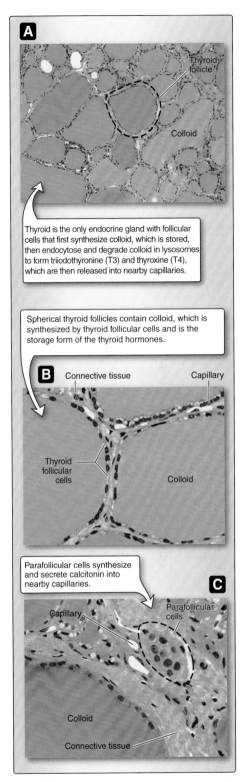

Thyroid is the only endocrine gland with follicular cells that first synthesize colloid, which is stored, then endocytose and degrade colloid in lysosomes to form triiodothyronine (T3) and thyroxine (T4), which are then released into nearby capillaries.

Spherical thyroid follicles contain colloid, which is synthesized by thyroid follicular cells and is the storage form of the thyroid hormones.

Parafollicular cells synthesize and secrete calcitonin into nearby capillaries.

Figure 9.18
Thyroid histology. Thyroid follicles at a low (A) and higher (B) magnification. C, Parafollicular cells.

B. Parathyroid glands

Superior and inferior **parathyroid glands** are typically located bilaterally on the posterior surface of the thyroid gland (see Fig. 9.16 posterior view). Multiple in number, these small, oval glands produce **parathyroid hormone** (PTH), which regulates phosphorus and calcium metabolism in the bloodstream.

1. **Vasculature and lymphatics:** The main blood supply to the parathyroid glands is by way of the **inferior thyroid artery**, although surrounding arterial supply can also contribute depending on the exact location. **Parathyroid veins** drain the glands, and lymphatic drainage communicates with that of the thyroid gland. Also, like the thyroid gland, the parathyroid glands are regulated hormonally. Nerves arising from the cervical sympathetic ganglia carry a vasomotor function, but do not control gland function.

2. **Histology:** The parathyroid glands are yellow to orange tan in color (depending on the amount of stromal fat). Most individuals have four parathyroid glands, but the number may vary from 1 to 12. They measure about 4 mm wide by 6 mm long by 4 mm thick. The shape of the parathyroid glands varies because the glands are molded by adjacent anatomical structures. Each parathyroid gland is surrounded by a connective tissue capsule that sends connective tissue septae into the parathyroid gland for support. The parathyroid glands contain two types of cells: **chief cells** and **oxyphil cells**.

   a. **Chief cell:** Chief cells are polygon-shaped cells with a round, centrally located nucleus (Fig. 9.19). They contain rough endoplasmic reticulum, polyribosomes, a Golgi complex, mitochondria, secretory granules, lipid, and glycogen. The chief cell secretes **PTH** that binds to the **PTH receptor** (a G protein–linked receptor). PTH is involved in **calcium homeostasis** (i.e., raises blood calcium levels).

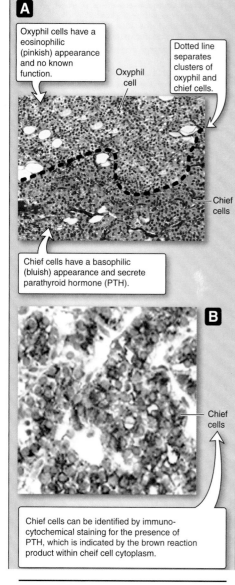

A Oxyphil cells have a eosinophilic (pinkish) appearance and no known function.

Oxyphil cell

Dotted line separates clusters of oxyphil and chief cells.

Chief cells

Chief cells have a basophilic (bluish) appearance and secrete parathyroid hormone (PTH).

B Chief cells

Chief cells can be identified by immunocytochemical staining for the presence of PTH, which is indicated by the brown reaction product within chief cell cytoplasm.

Figure 9.19
Parathyroid histology. A, Mallory trichrome stain. B, Anti–parathyroid hormone/diaminobenzidene stain.

Clinical Application 9.11: Primary Hyperthyroidism

Primary hyperthyroidism is characterized by excessive secretion of parathyroid hormone (PTH), leading to hypercalcemia. It may be caused by the presence of an adenoma, hyperplasia, or in association with multiple endocrine neoplasia syndromes. Clinical features include osteitis fibrosa cystica (bone softening and painful fractures), urinary calculi, abdominal pain (due to constipation, pancreatitis, or biliary stones), depression/lethargy, and cardiac arrhythmias. Think "painful bones, kidney stones, belly groans, and mental moans."

b. **Oxyphil cell:** Oxyphil cells appear after puberty and have a distinct eosinophilic cytoplasm because of numerous mitochondria. The cell has no known function.

c. **Weight:** The weight of the parathyroid glands is an important parameter in histopathologic assessment. All parathyroid glands (or parts of parathyroid glands) must be carefully weighed. Each parathyroid gland weighs about **35–40 mg**. The total parathyroid weight ranges from **120 to 140 mg**.

C. Larynx

Multifunctional by design, the **larynx** plays an important role in both respiration and phonation. It is located in the midline of the muscular triangle of the neck between the fourth and sixth cervical vertebrae. It is attached superiorly to the hyoid bone by the **thyrohyoid membrane** and is continuous inferiorly with the trachea (see Figs. 9.15 and 9.16).

1. **Anatomy:** Structurally, the larynx is made up of a cartilaginous scaffold, onto which thick connective tissue membranes and intrinsic laryngeal, infrahyoid, and pharyngeal muscles attach (Fig. 9.20).

Clinical Application 9.10: Primary Hypothyroidism

Primary hypoparathyroidism is characterized by the absence of parathyroid hormone (PTH), leading to hypocalcemia. It may be caused by accidental surgical removal, DiGeorge syndrome, or autoimmune destruction. Chronic renal failure and vitamin D deficiency also may lead to hypocalcemia. Clinical features include carpopedal spasm, laryngospasm, Chvostek sign (tapping facial nerve elicits spasm of facial muscles), Trousseau phenomenon (elated blood pressure cuff on arm elicits carpel tunnel spasm), calcification of basal ganglia, cataracts, and tetany. Seizures and cardiac arrest may occur in severe cases.

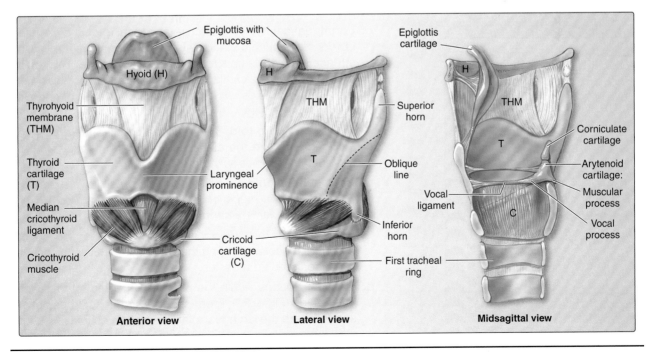

Figure 9.20
Cartilaginous skeleton of the larynx and associated ligamentous structures.

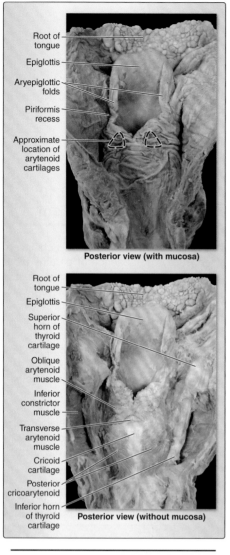

Root of tongue
Epiglottis
Aryepiglottic folds
Piriformis recess
Approximate location of arytenoid cartilages

Posterior view (with mucosa)

Root of tongue
Epiglottis
Superior horn of thyroid cartilage
Oblique arytenoid muscle
Inferior constrictor muscle
Transverse arytenoid muscle
Cricoid cartilage
Posterior cricoarytenoid
Inferior horn of thyroid cartilage

Posterior view (without mucosa)

Figure 9.21
Larynx and laryngopharynx (opened).

a. **Cartilage:** The cartilaginous framework consists of the **thyroid, cricoid, arytenoid** (2), **epiglottic, corniculate** (2), and **cuneiform** (2) **cartilages**.

[1] **Thyroid cartilage:** This shield-link cartilage is the largest of the laryngeal cartilages. Right and left lamina fuse anteriorly to form the **laryngeal prominence**. It is incomplete posteriorly and articulates with the cricoid cartilage inferiorly (Fig. 9.21).

[2] **Cricoid cartilage:** This cartilage is ring shaped and is the most inferior of the thyroid cartilages, located at the C6 vertebral level.

[3] **Arytenoids:** These paired structures have **vocal** and **muscular processes** and articulate on the posterior superior cricoid cartilage. They can abduct, adduct, tilt, and rotate to aid in respiration and phonation.

[4] **Epiglottis:** This is a singular, leaf-shaped cartilage that borders the laryngeal inlet anteriorly and superiorly and articulates with anterior superior thyroid cartilage. It has a soft tissue muscular fold attached laterally and functions to cover the laryngeal inlet during swallowing. A **quadrangular membrane** connects the arytenoid cartilages.

b. **Ligamentous capsules:** The abovementioned cartilaginous articulations possess ligamentous capsules. Additional connections include the **cricothyroid ligament**, which connects the thyroid and cricoid cartilages anteriorly. The thickened middle portion of the ligament—**median cricothyroid ligament**—can be palpated easily and is clinically important for securing the airway in an emergency. **Vocal ligaments** span between the inner surface of the thyroid cartilage and arytenoid vocal process. Superior to the vocal ligaments is the inferior free margin of the quadrangular membrane, which constitutes the **vestibular ligaments**. The superior free margin constitutes the **aryepiglottic ligament**.

c. **Laryngeal cavity:** Between the **laryngeal inlet** and the inferior border of the cricoid cartilage is the **laryngeal cavity**. The inner surface of cavity is covered with a thick mucosa. This mucous membrane overlies cartilage, muscles, and ligaments to produce a collection of folds, which serve as boundaries of and within the laryngeal cavity.

[1] **Aryepiglottic fold:** This mucosa overlies the aryepiglottic ligaments and the distal portion of the oblique arytenoid muscles. It serves as the lateral boundary of the laryngeal inlet.

[2] **Vestibular fold:** The "false vocal cords" have a protective function. Lying superior to the vocal fold, this mucosa overlies the vestibular ligaments.

[3] **Vocal fold:** The "true vocal cords" have a phonation function and is mucosa overlying the vocal ligaments and vocalis and thyroarytenoid muscles.

d. **Spaces:** Spaces within the cavity are named in reference to these folds (Fig. 9.22). From superior to inferior, these spaces and folds are the laryngeal inlet, laryngeal vestibule, vestibular fold, laryngeal ventricle, vocal fold, and the infraglottic cavity. The spaces located medially between the vestibular and vocal

Clinical Application 9.12: Laryngoscopy

Visualization of internal laryngeal and pharyngeal spaces and folds can be easily accessed with the use of a laryngeal mirror—similar to that found in a dentist's office. An indirect laryngoscope can be performed quickly with this tool to assess these spaces and structures. A more in-depth exploration of the larynx and pharynx can be achieved using an endoscopic tool called a laryngoscope.

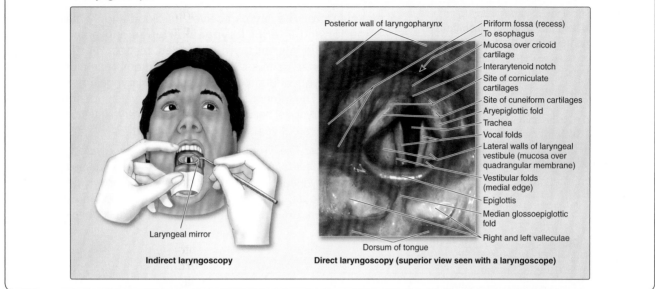

Indirect laryngoscopy

Laryngeal mirror

Direct laryngoscopy (superior view seen with a laryngoscope)

Posterior wall of laryngopharynx

Piriform fossa (recess)
To esophagus
Mucosa over cricoid cartilage
Interarytenoid notch
Site of corniculate cartilages
Site of cuneiform cartilages
Aryepiglottic fold
Trachea
Vocal folds
Lateral walls of laryngeal vestibule (mucosa over quadrangular membrane)
Vestibular folds (medial edge)
Epiglottis
Median glossoepiglottic fold
Right and left valleculae

Dorsum of tongue

folds are the **rima vestibule** and **rima glottidis**, respectively. Collectively, the rima glottidis and vocal folds make up the **glottis**, which constitutes the vocal apparatus.

2. **Innervation:** General visceral afferent sensation to the laryngeal mucosa is mediated by branches of the **vagus nerve** (**CN X**) and divided by at the level of the vocal folds. The **internal branch of the superior laryngeal nerve** supplies the mucosa above the vocal folds, whereas the **inferior laryngeal nerve** (continuation of the recurrent laryngeal nerve) supplies the mucosa below the vocal folds.

3. **Musculature:** Intrinsic muscles of the larynx function to open (abduct) and close (adduct) the airway and alter vocal pitch and tone. All intrinsic laryngeal muscles receive branchiomotor innervation by way of the vagus nerve (CN X).

   a. **Cricothyroid muscle:** Specifically, the **cricothyroid muscle** is innervated by the external laryngeal branch, and the remaining muscles are innervated by the recurrent laryngeal branch (also referred to as the inferior laryngeal nerve once inside the larynx). Muscle nomenclature describes attachment sites (Table 9.3; also see Figs. 9.20–9.22).

   b. **Vocalis:** The **vocalis** muscle constitutes the medial most fibers of the **thyroarytenoid muscle**. The vocalis muscle functions to make minute adjustments along the course of the vocal ligament, thus allowing for relaxation of the ligament in one region, while maintaining tension in another (Figs. 9.23 and 9.24).

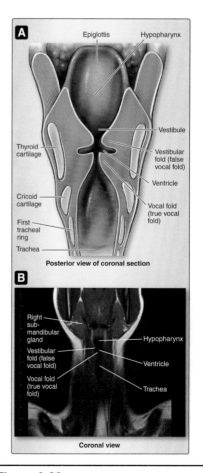

A

Epiglottis   Hypopharynx

Vestibule
Vestibular fold (false vocal fold)
Ventricle
Vocal fold (true vocal fold)

Thyroid cartilage

Cricoid cartilage

First tracheal ring

Trachea

Posterior view of coronal section

B

Right submandibular gland

Hypopharynx

Vestibular fold (false vocal fold)

Ventricle

Vocal fold (true vocal fold)

Trachea

Coronal view

Figure 9.22
Laryngeal folds and spaces. A, Schematic view. B, Computed tomography scan.

Clinical Application 9.13: Laryngeal Nerve Lesion

Superior laryngeal: A lesion will diminish the cough reflex (via loss of general visceral afferent sensation to the mucosa above the vocal folds; internal laryngeal branch) and limit the ability to tense the vocal ligaments on the damaged side (cricothyroid muscle paralysis; external laryngeal branch).

Recurrent laryngeal: Unilateral damage results in hoarseness of voice, vocal fatigue, and midline shift of the affected vocal fold. Bilateral damage results in adduction of vocal folds and subsequent dyspnea (shortness of breath).

Table 9.3:   Muscle Function(s) on the Vocal Ligaments

Abduction	Adduction	Tenses	Relaxes
Posterior cricoarytenoid	Lateral cricoarytenoid *Arytenoids (transverse and oblique fibers)*	Cricothyroid	Thyroarytenoid

4. **Vasculature:** The larynx receives its blood supply mainly by the **superior** and **inferior laryngeal arteries** and branches of the **superior** and **inferior thyroid arteries**, respectively. The superior laryngeal artery pierces the thyrohyoid membrane along with the internal laryngeal branch of the superior laryngeal nerve to enter the organ. The inferior laryngeal artery travels superiorly with the recurrent laryngeal nerve on the side of the larynx. Venous drainage occurs by way of veins of the same names.

5. **Lymphatics:** The lymphatics of the larynx are divided at the level of the vocal folds. Above the vocal folds, lymph vessels follow the superior laryngeal artery to the superior deep cervical nodes. Below the vocal folds, lymph drains into paratracheal and pretracheal nodes before draining into the inferior deep cervical nodes.

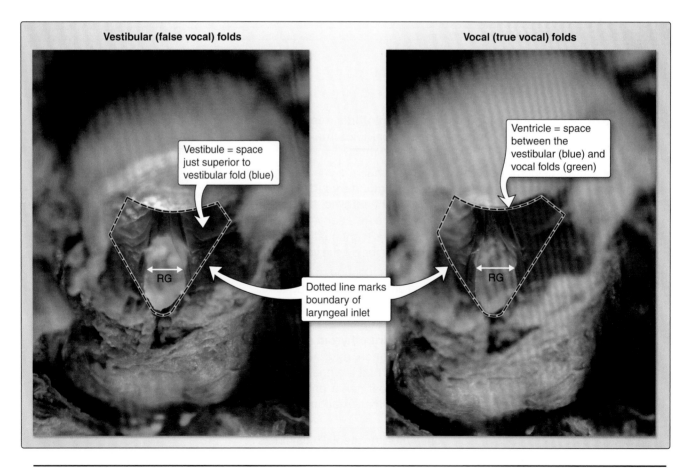

Figure 9.23
Vocal cords. RG = Rima glottidis

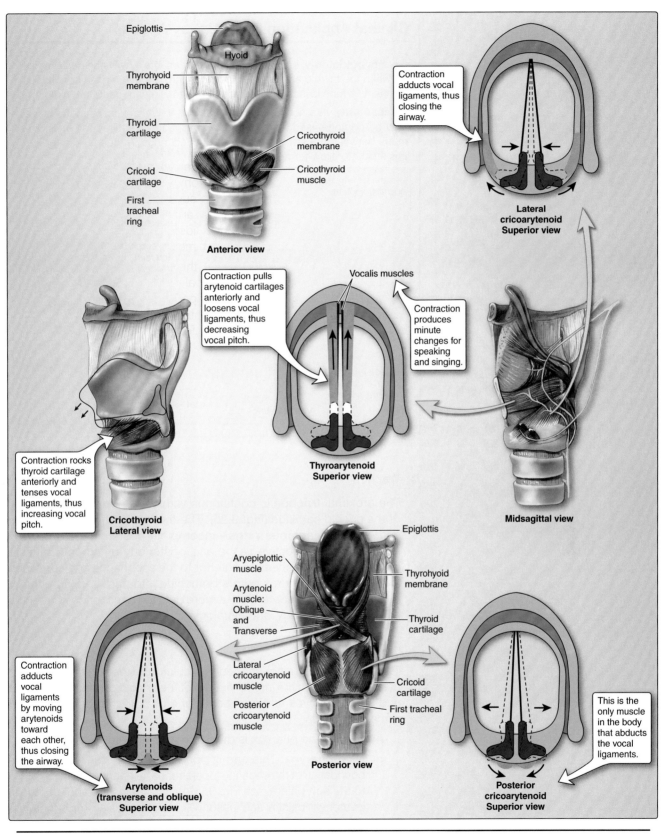

Figure 9.24

Intrinsic laryngeal structures and muscular actions on vocal ligaments.

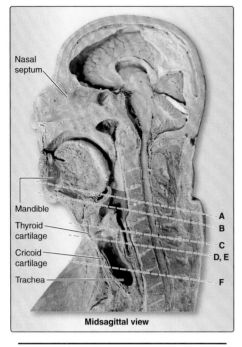

Nasal
septum

Mandible

Thyroid
cartilage

Cricoid
cartilage

Trachea

A
B
C
D, E
F

Midsagittal view

Figure 9.25
Midsagittal view of neck. Dashed
lines indicate level of radiographs (see
Clinical Application 9.15).

Clinical Application 9.14: Airway Access

Cricothyroidotomy: In an emergency situation, the airway can be accessed between the thyroid and cricoid cartilages through the median cricothyroid ligament. A tube is inserted into this space to allow for adequate airflow.

Tracheotomy: In a nonemergency situation, in which access to the airway may be compromised long term and ventilation is required, an incision is made between the second and third tracheal rings. A tube is inserted into this space to allow for adequate airflow.

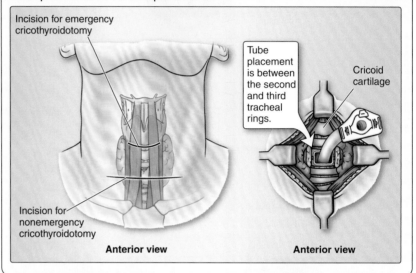

Incision for emergency
cricothyroidotomy

Tube placement is between the second and third tracheal rings.

Cricoid cartilage

Incision for nonemergency cricothyroidotomy

Anterior view   **Anterior view**

D. Trachea

The proximal **trachea** is continuous with the larynx below the level of the cricoid cartilage (Fig. 9.25). The trachea is characterized by a series of **cartilaginous rings**—incomplete posteriorly—connected anteriorly by connective tissue and posteriorly by smooth muscle (trachealis). The trachea lies anterior to the esophagus and continues inferiorly into the thorax before branching into right and left primary bronchi. Refer to Chapter 3 for a more detailed description of tracheal anatomy, embryology, and histology.

E. Pharynx

The **pharynx** is a funnel-shaped muscular tube that extends from the base of the skull to the inferior margin of the cricoid cartilage (Figs. 9.26 and 9.27). It serves as the superior end of both the respiratory and alimentary tracts.

1. **Anatomy:** The pharynx is divided regionally into three parts.

   a. **Nasopharynx:** This part is posterior to the nasal cavity at the boundaries of the choanae (posterior nasal apertures) and superior to the soft palate (see Fig. 9.26A). It contains the auditory tube, levator veli palatini and tensor veli palatini muscles, torus tubarius, salpingopharyngeal fold (mucosa overlying salpingopharyngeus muscle), and tubular and pharyngeal tonsils.

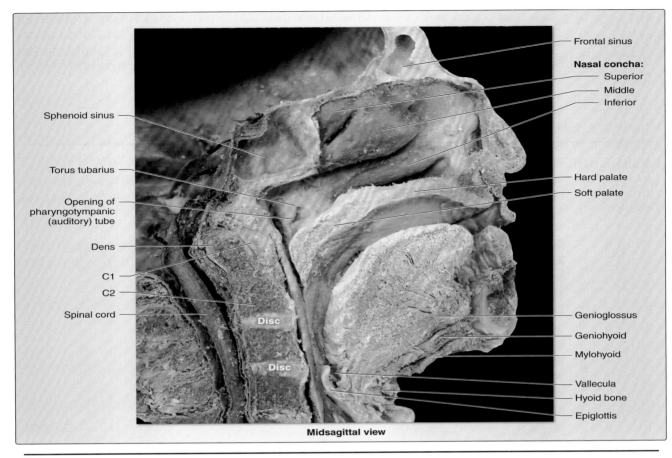

Frontal sinus

Nasal concha:
Superior
Middle
Inferior

Sphenoid sinus

Torus tubarius

Opening of
pharyngotympanic
(auditory) tube

Dens

C1

C2

Spinal cord

Disc

Disc

Hard palate
Soft palate

Genioglossus

Geniohyoid

Mylohyoid

Vallecula
Hyoid bone
Epiglottis

Midsagittal view

Figure 9.26
Pharynx and associated structures. Green = nasopharynx, Yellow = oropharynx, Blue = laryngopharynx.

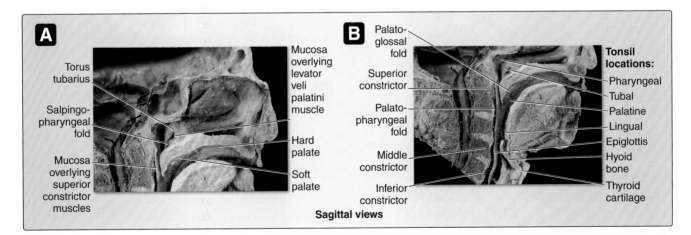

A

Torus
tubarius

Salpingo-
pharyngeal
fold

Mucosa
overlying
superior
constrictor
muscles

Mucosa
overlying
levator
veli
palatini
muscle

Hard
palate

Soft
palate

B

Palato-
glossal
fold

Superior
constrictor

Palato-
pharyngeal
fold

Middle
constrictor

Inferior
constrictor

**Tonsil
locations:**
Pharyngeal
Tubal
Palatine
Lingual
Epiglottis
Hyoid
bone
Thyroid
cartilage

Sagittal views

Figure 9.27
Pharynx. A, Nasopharynx and nasal cavity. B, Oropharynx, oral cavity, laryngopharynx, and upper pharynx.

b. Oropharynx: This part is posterior to the oral cavity at the boundaries of the palatoglossal folds, inferior to the soft palate, and superior to the root of the tongue and epiglottis (see Fig. 9.26B). It contains the palatoglossal and palatopharyngeal

Clinical Application 9.15: Radiologic Approach to the Neck

Visualizing neck structures through radiologic images requires a sound understanding of the regional organizations. Radiologists commonly use a spaces approach when diagnosing neck pathology. Bony, cartilaginous, and soft tissue landmarks, such as the hyoid bone, laryngeal cartilages, sternocleidomastoid (SCM) muscle, and thyroid gland can aid in structure identification. A progression of structures from superior to inferior in the sagittal and axial planes is shown.

A

Right submandibular gland
Right common carotid
Right internal jugular vein
Left vallecula
Epiglottis
Left piriform recess

Axial MRI at level of valeculae

B

Right sternocleidomastoid muscle
Right piriform recess
Right aryepiglottic fold
Hyoid bone
Longus capitus muscle

Axial CT at level of piriform recess and hyoid bone

C

Right vocal cord
Right external jugular vein
Right arytenoid cartilage
Thyroid cartilage
Left internal jugular vein
Left common carotid artery

Axial CT image at level of arytenoid cartilages

D

Thyroid cartilage
Right thyro-arytenoid muslce
Right vocal ligament
Right facet joint
Left vertebral artery

Axial MRI at level of true vocal cords

E

True vocal cord
Thyroid cartilage
Right internal jugular
Right common carotid artery
Cricoid cartilage

Axial MRI at level of the vocal cords and cricoid cartilage

F

Thyroid gland
Right internal jugular vein
Right external jugular vein
Trachea
Esophagus
Left common carotid artery
Vertebral body
Left cervical nerve root

Axial MRI at level of trachea

folds, palatine tonsils, root of the tongue, lingual tonsils, glossoepiglottic folds (median and lateral), and valleculae. The glossopharyngeal nerve enters this region to reach the tonsillar bed and posterior tongue.

   c. **Laryngopharynx:** This part is posterior to the larynx between the laryngeal inlet and the inferior margin of the cricoid cartilage (see Fig. 9.26B). It contains the piriform recess (where bits of food sometimes get stuck).

2. **Musculature:** The muscular tube is formed by an outer circular layer and an inner longitudinal layer (Fig. 9.28; also see Fig. 9.16). Posteriorly, the pharyngeal musculature is covered by buccopharyngeal fascia and internally lined by a thick mucosa.

   a. **Pharyngeal constrictor muscles:** Constrictor muscles function is such that they contract in sequence from superior to inferior in order to propel the bolus of food inferiorly toward the esophagus.

      [1] **Superior constrictor:** This muscle originates on the pterygoid hamulus, pterygomandibular raphe, mylohyoid line, and lateral side of the tongue and inserts posteriorly onto the pharyngeal tubercle (occipital bone). It is positioned mainly in the nasopharynx region.

      [2] **Middle constrictor:** This muscle originates on the stylohyoid ligament and hyoid bone and inserts onto the median pharyngeal raphe. It is positioned mainly in the oropharynx region.

      [3] **Inferior constrictor:** This muscle originates on the oblique line of the thyroid cartilage and lateral side of cricoid cartilage and inserts at the junction of the esophagus. It is positioned mainly in the laryngopharynx region.

      [4] **Motor Innervation:** Pharyngeal branches of the vagus nerve (CN X) provide branchiomotor innervation to the constrictor muscles. The inferior constrictor may also receive branches of the external branch of the superior laryngeal nerve or the recurrent laryngeal nerve.

   b. **Longitudinal muscles:** Although the constrictor muscles form a complete tube posteriorly, their arrangement creates gaps laterally that permit structures to enter the pharyngeal space.

      [1] **Salpingopharyngeus:** This muscle originates from the cartilaginous extension of the pharyngotympanic tube (auditory tube) and blends with the palatopharyngeus.

      [2] **Palatopharyngeus:** This muscle originates from the hard palate and palatine aponeurosis and inserts onto the thyroid cartilage, pharynx, and esophagus.

      [3] **Stylopharyngeus:** This muscle originates on the styloid process and inserts onto the thyroid cartilage with the palatopharyngeus. It enters the pharynx between the superior and middle constrictors along with the glossopharyngeal nerve (CN IX).

      [4] **Motor Innervation:** The salpingopharyngeus and palatopharyngeus muscles receive branchiomotor innervation from the pharyngeal branches of vagus nerve (CN X).

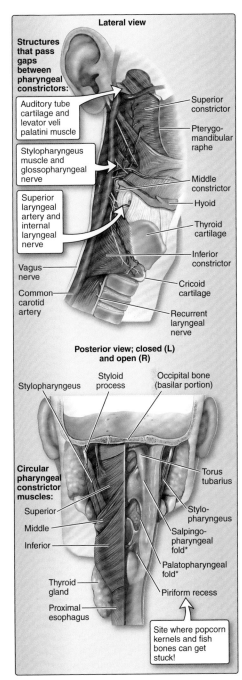

Figure 9.28

Pharynx musculature and associated structures.
Green = nasopharynx, Pink = oropharynx, Yellow = laryngopharynx. Muscles underlying these folds contribute to pharyngeal longitudinal layer (*). THM = thyrohyoid membrane.

The stylopharyngeus is unique in that it is the only pharyngeal muscle that received branchiomotor innervation from the glossopharyngeal nerve (CN IX).

3. **Sensory Innervation:** The primary sensory nerve of the pharynx is the glossopharyngeal nerve (CN IX), although pharyngeal branches from the vagus nerve (CN X) also contribute. A small portion of the nasopharynx receives sensory innervation by the maxillary division of the trigeminal nerve (CN V).

4. **Vasculature:** The pharynx receives blood primarily from the **tonsillar artery**, which branches from the facial artery and enters the pharynx by piercing the superior constrictor muscle. Contributions from the ascending palatine and pharyngeal, lingual, and descending palatine arteries complete the pharyngeal blood supply. Venous drainage occurs by way of the **pharyngeal venous plexus**.

5. **Lymphatics:** The pharynx has abundant lymphoid tissue, including **palatine**, **lingual**, **tubal**, and **pharyngeal tonsils**. Collectively, these tonsils make up the tonsillar ring (ring of Waldeyer). The jugulodiagnostic node, or tonsillar node, is also associated with the pharynx and commonly becomes enlarged in the case of tonsillitis.

> Location of lymphoid tissue in the pharynx includes (see Fig. 9.26):
> **Tubular:** adjacent to the opening of the auditory tube (nasopharynx region)
> **Pharyngeal:** in the midline of the posterior nasopharynx mucosa (called "adenoids" when enlarged)
> **Palatine:** between the palatoglossal and palatopharyngeus arches, formed by mucosa and underlying muscles of the same names, respectively (oropharynx region)
> **Lingual:** located at the root of the tongue (laryngopharynx region)

Clinical Application 9.16: Tonsillectomy and Adenoids

A tonsillectomy is the surgical removal of the palatine tonsils from the tonsillar bed between the palatoglossus and palatopharyngeus arches. Excessive bleeding may occur during the procedure, so care must be taken to identify both the arterial and venous supply. Care must also be taken to identify the glossopharyngeal nerve (CN IX), which enters this area to mediate sensation over the palatine tonsils.

Enlarged pharyngeal tonsils are called "adenoids." They lie in the posterior midline mucosa of the nasopharynx. Adenoids can grow large enough to block the inlet between the nasopharynx and oropharynx, making nose breathing impossible. Surgical removal may alleviate this issue.

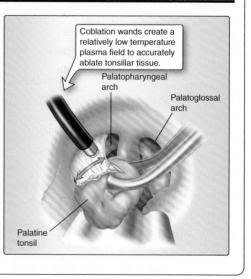

Coblation wands create a relatively low temperature plasma field to accurately ablate tonsillar tissue.

Palatopharyngeal arch

Palatoglossal arch

Palatine tonsil

F. Esophagus

The **proximal esophagus** is continuous with the laryngopharynx superiorly and the distal esophagus inferiorly. Inferior thyroid arteries and veins constitute the blood supply to the cervical esophagus. Somatic motor and sensory nerves supply the upper third of the esophagus before the autonomic plexus takes over distally. The esophagus is further detailed in Chapter 3.

Chapter Summary

- The neck is supported by cervical vertebrae and fascial layers and contains important neurovascular, visceral, and muscular structures that extend between the head and thorax.
- The neck is organized into triangles, where the sternocleidomastoid (SCM) serves as the major boundary between anterior and posterior triangles. The anterior triangle is subdivided into submental, submandibular, carotid, and muscular triangles.
- Vasculature of the neck includes branches of the subclavian and external carotid arteries. The internal carotid artery travels unbranched to the head.
- Motor and sensory innervation to structures of the neck include branches of the cervical plexus, ansa cervicalis, cervical sympathetic trunk and cranial nerves IX, X, and XI.
- Viscera of the neck include the pharynx, larynx, thyroid gland, submandibular gland, parathyroid glands, and proximal trachea and esophagus. All of these structures, aside from the submandibular gland, are encapsulated by visceral fascia.
- The thyroid gland is a butterfly-shaped gland that sits inferior to the cricoid cartilage. The recurrent laryngeal nerve runs deep to the gland, between the esophagus and trachea.
- The thyroid primordium forms in the midline of the floor of the pharynx near the foramen cecum of the developing tongue.
- As the thyroid primordium migrates caudally down the midline, it remains connected to the tongue by the thyroglossal duct.
- The endoderm of the thyroid primordium differentiates into the thyroid follicular cells
- The neural crest cells within the ultimopharyngeal body (i.e., pharyngeal pouch #4) disperse throughout the thyroid gland and differentiate into the parafollicular cells (or C cells).
- The functional unit of the thyroid gland is the thyroid follicle.
- The thyroid follicle is a spherical structure that contains a gel-like substance called colloid whose main component is iodinated thyroglobulin (660 kDa).
- The wall of the thyroid follicle is formed by follicular cells and parafollicular cells.
- The follicular cell secretes triiodothyronine (T_3) and thyroxin (T_4).
- The parafollicular cell secretes calcitonin.
  - Most individuals have four parathyroid glands, but the number may vary from 1-12 parathyroid glands.
  - The parathyroid glands contain two types of cells: chief cells and oxyphil cells.
  - The chief cell secretes parathyroid hormone (PTH) that binds to the PTH receptor (a G protein–linked receptor).
  - PTH is involved in calcium homeostasis (i.e., raises blood calcium levels).
  - The pharynx is a muscular tube divided into nasopharynx, oropharynx, and laryngopharynx regions associated with the nasal cavity, oral cavity, and larynx, respectively.
  - The vagus nerve (CN X) is the main sensory nerve of the larynx, while the glossopharyngeal nerve (CN IX) is the main sensory nerve of the pharynx.
  - Damage to branches of the vagus nerve in the neck can result in alterations in phonation, diminished cough reflex, and vocal fatigue.
  - The posterior cricoarytenoid is the only muscle in the body that abducts (opens) the vocal ligaments.
  - Radiological assessment in the neck follows a spaces approach, where neck fascia compartmentalizes structures and allows for a systematic evaluation.

Study Questions:

Choose the ONE correct answer.

9.1 A man is stabbed in the back of the neck severing a structure in the right posterior triangle. He is now unable to shrug (elevate) his right shoulder. Which of the following nerves is most likely injured?

A. Great auricular
B. Recurrent laryngeal
C. Accessory
D. Supraclavicular
E. Phrenic

Correct answer = C. The accessory nerve travels in the posterior triangle to reach the trapezius muscle, which is the primary elevator of the scapula. If you suspect an accessory nerve lesion, a simple test would be to ask your patient to shrug his/her shoulders. Attention should be given to any asymmetry in this movement.

9.2 You reluctantly discover that your new significant other is a mouth breather. With your thorough understanding of neck anatomy you believe that which of the following structure(s) is enlarged, resulting in mouth breathing?

A. Tubular tonsil
B. Pharyngeal tonsils
C. Lingual tonsils
D. Palatine tonsils
E. Epiglottis

Correct answer = B. The pharyngeal tonsils sit in the posterior midline of the nasopharynx. When they become enlarged they are called adenoids. Adenoids can become so large that they occlude the inlet between the nasopharynx and the oropharynx. This makes the person a mouth breather.

9.3 You are eating a delicious dish of fried catfish and hushpuppies, but accidentally choke on a fish bone. In which space is this fish bone most likely stuck?

A. Piriform recess
B. Epiglottic valleculae
C. Ventricle
D. Retropharyngeal space
E. Vestibule

Correct answer = A. The piriform recess is located in the laryngopharynx and is bound medially by the aryepiglottic membrane and laterally by the thyrohyoid membrane. This space often is a site for food—like fish bones and popcorn kernels—to get stuck.

The following clinical vignette should be used to answer questions 9.4 and 9.5:

A 46-year-old female patient underwent a subtotal thyroidectomy to remove thyroid nodules. Preparation prior to surgery includes marking key anatomical landmarks, including the thyroid notch, cricoid cartilage, sternal notch, and superior edges of the clavicles. During the procedure, blood supply to/from the thyroid is identified and ligated. Adjacent nerve branches are also identified and monitored to decrease the risk of surgical lesion.

9.4 Which of the following nerves is most susceptible to lesion during this surgical procedure?

A. Vagus
B. Recurrent laryngeal
C. Internal laryngeal
D. Glossopharyngeal
E. Hypoglossal

Correct answer = B. The recurrent laryngeal nerve travels deep to the thyroid gland, in a groove between the trachea and esophagus. This location makes it the most susceptible to injury with a thyroidectomy.

9.5 What adult structure marks the origin of the thyroid primordium?

A. Hyoid bone
B. Foramen cecum
C. Parathyroid glands
D. Neural crest cells
E. Mesenchyme

Correct answer = B. At week 4, the thyroid primordium, a small mass of endoderm, forms in the midline of the floor of the pharynx near the foramen cecum of the developing tongue. By week 5, the thyroglossal duct is obliterated, leaving only a remnant called the foramen cecum.

9.6 You are working at a community clinic when you notice a female patient who has bulging, inflamed eyes with puffy eyelids. She comes to your station and you begin your history and physical. She appears a bit anxious and has tachycardia. She reports fatigue, muscles weakness and visual problems. You suspect Graves disease and take a blood sample to confirm. Which of the following autoantibodies specifically characterizes Graves disease and would most likely be present in this patient's blood?

A. TSH receptor–stimulating autoantibodies
B. Thyroid peroxidase autoantibodies
C. Thyroglobulin autoantibodies
D. Calcitonin autoantibodies
E. Thyroxin (T_4) autoantibodies

Correct answer = A. Graves disease (GD) is an autoimmune disease that produces thyroid-stimulating hormone (TSH) receptor–stimulating autoantibodies. These autoantibodies mimic TSH and cause increased secretion of triiodothyronine (T_3) and T_4. GD is hyperthyroidism caused by a diffuse, hyperplastic (toxic) goiter. GD is the most common form of hyperthyroidism.

9.7 A 70-year-old male patient is being seen for his annual check-up, which includes a comprehensive metabolic panel blood test. His results reveal high blood calcium levels. Additional blood tests reveal high parathyroid hormone (PTH). Which of the following cells is over secreting PTH, causing the increased blood calcium?

A. Oxyphil cell
B. Chief cell
C. Parafollicular cell (or C cell)
D. Basophil
E. Acidophil

Correct answer = B. The chief cell found in the parathyroid gland secretes PTH, which is involved in calcium homeostasis (i.e., raises blood calcium levels). Increased production and secretion of PTH would result in an increase in blood calcium levels, which should always be considered abnormal.

9.8 Which of the following cells secretes thyroxine (T_4)?

A. Parafollicular cell
B. Follicular cell
C. Oxyphil cell
D. Chief cell
E. Basophil

Correct answer = B. The follicular cell that lines the thyroid follicle secretes T_3 and T_4.

9.9 A nursing student is practicing venous puncture techniques on a simulation model and recalls that access to the internal jugular vein is most often performed on the right side. However, he cannot recall if the anterior approach is performed along the medial or lateral border of the sternocleidomastoid. If he places the needle along the lateral border of the sternocleidomastoid, which of the following structures is most likely to be at risk of injury?

A. Superior thyroid artery
B. Supraclavicular nerves
C. Ansa cervicalis, superior root
D. Cervical sympathetic trunk
E. External laryngeal nerve

Correct answer = B. Of the answer choices, supraclavicular nerves are the only structures located in the posterior triangle, which is bound anteriorly by the lateral border of the sternocleidomastoid. All other structures listed are located in anterior triangles.

Figure, Table, and Box Credits

Figure 1.1. Modified from McConnell TH, Hull KL. *Human Form, Human Function: Essentials of Anatomy & Physiology*. Baltimore, MD: Wolters Kluwer; 2011. Figure 1.11.

Figure 1.2. Modified from Archer P, Nelson LA. *Applied Anatomy & Physiology for Manual Therapists*. Baltimore, MD: Wolters Kluwer; 2012. Figures 2.4, 2.6, 5.26, and Table 5.4.

Figure 1.5. Modified from Chandler TJ, Brown LE. *Conditioning for Strength and Human Performance*. 2nd ed. Philadelphia, PA: Wolters Kluwer; 2013. Figure 4.1A.

Figure 1.10A, B, C. From Wingerd B. *Human Body*. 3rd ed. Baltimore, MD: Wolters Kluwer; 2014. Figure 4.17.

Figure 1.11. Modified from Anatomical Chart Company.

Figure 1.12. From Preston RR, Wilson TE. *Lippincott's Illustrated Reviews: Physiology*. Baltimore, MD: Wolters Kluwer; 2013. Figure 12.6.

Figure 1.16. Modified from Anatomical Chart Company.

Figure 1.17. Modified from Carter PJ. *Lippincott's Textbook for Long-Term Care Nursing Assistants*. 4th ed. Philadelphia, PA: Wolters Kluwer; 2016. Figure 34.8.

Figure 1.18. From Preston RR, Wilson TE. *Lippincott's Illustrated Reviews: Physiology*. Baltimore, MD: Wolters Kluwer; 2013. Figure 19.2.

Figure 1.19. From Preston RR, Wilson TE. *Lippincott's Illustrated Reviews: Physiology*. Baltimore, MD: Wolters Kluwer; 2013. Figure 19.4.

Figure 1.20. From Preston RR, Wilson TE. *Lippincott's Illustrated Reviews: Physiology*. Baltimore, MD: Wolters Kluwer; 2013. Figure 19.7.

Figure 1.21. Modified from Anatomical Chart Company.

Figure 1.22. From Doan T, Melvold R, Viselli S, Waltenbaugh C. *Lippincott Illustrated Reviews: Immunology*. 2nd ed. Philadelphia, PA: Wolters Kluwer; 2013. Figure 7.9.

Figure 1.23. From Doan T, Melvold R, Viselli S, Waltenbaugh C. *Lippincott Illustrated Reviews: Immunology*. 2nd ed. Philadelphia, PA: Wolters Kluwer; 2013. Figure 7.8.

Figure 1.26A, B, C. Modified from Krebs C, Weinberg J, Akesson E, Dilli E. *Lippincott Illustrated Review: Neuroscience*. 2nd ed. Baltimore, MD: Wolters Kluwer; 2018. Figure 1.5.

Figure 1.29. Modified from Krebs C, Weinberg J, Akesson E, Dilli E. *Lippincott Illustrated Review: Neuroscience*. 2nd ed. Baltimore, MD: Wolters Kluwer; 2018. Figure 2.6.

Figure 1.30A, B, C. Modified from Krebs C, Weinberg J, Akesson E, Dilli E. *Lippincott Illustrated Review: Neuroscience*. 2nd ed. Baltimore, MD: Wolters Kluwer; 2018. Figure 1.6.

Figure 1.31. From Preston RR, Wilson TE. *Lippincott's Illustrated Reviews: Physiology*. Baltimore, MD: Wolters Kluwer; 2013. Figure 5.13.

Figure 1.36. Modified from Surface Anatomy Photography Collection.

Table 1.2. Modified from Anderson MK. *Foundations of Athletic Training*. 5th ed. Baltimore, MD: Wolters Kluwer; 2012. Figure 19-8.

Table 1.3. Modified from Archer P, Nelson LA. *Applied Anatomy & Physiology for Manual Therapists*. Baltimore, MD: Wolters Kluwer; 2013. Figure 6.13.

Figure 2.1. Modified from Anatomical Chart Company.

Figures 2.4A, B, C, 2.6A, B, and 2.8A, B, C. Images courtesy of Dr. Michael Berry, Eastern Radiology, Greenville, NC.

Figure 2.11. Modified from Moore KL, Dalley AF II, Augur AM. *Clinically Oriented Anatomy*. 8th ed. Baltimore, MD: Wolters Kluwer; 2018. Figure 2.23.

Figure 2.12A, B, C. Modified from Surface Anatomy Photography Collection.

Figure 2.13. Modified from Krebs C, Weinberg J, Akesson E, Dilli E. *Lippincott Illustrated Review: Neuroscience*. 2nd ed. Baltimore, MD: Wolters Kluwer; 2018. Figure 5.2, left.

Figure 2.15. (Image courtesy of Dr. Michael Berry, Eastern Radiology, Greenville, NC.)

Figure 2.16. Modified from Krebs C, Weinberg J, Akesson E, Dilli E. *Lippincott Illustrated Review: Neuroscience*. 2nd ed. Baltimore, MD: Wolters Kluwer; 2018, Figure 5.3.

Figure 2.17. Image courtesy of Dr. Michael Berry, Eastern Radiology, Greenville, NC.

Figure 2.19. Modified from Krebs, C.; Weinberg, J.; Akesson, E.;

Dilli, E. *Lippincott Illustrated Review: Neuroscience*, 2 ed. Baltimore, MD: Wolters Kluwer, 2018. Figure 5.6.

Figure 2.20. Modified from Krebs C, Weinberg J, Akesson E, Dilli E. *Lippincott Illustrated Review: Neuroscience*. 2nd ed. Baltimore, MD: Wolters Kluwer; 2018, Figure 5.14, upper right.

Figure 2.21. Modified from Krebs C, Weinberg J, Akesson E, Dilli E. *Lippincott Illustrated Review: Neuroscience*. 2nd ed. Baltimore, MD: Wolters Kluwer; 2018, Figure 5.2, right.

Figure 2.22A, B. Adapted from Johnson KE. *NMS Human Developmental Anatomy*. Baltimore, MD: Williams & Wilkins; 1988:211, A, top; B, bottom: Figure 7.1 B, F; Modifed from Carpenter MB, Sutin J. *Human Neuroanatomy*. 8th Ed. Baltimore, MD: Lippincott Williams & Wilkins; 1983:63.

Figure 2.23A, B, C. Adapted from Larsen WJ. *Human Embryology*. 2nd ed. New York, NY: Churchill Livingston; 1997:69. A, Figure 7.1B, F; Modified from Carpenter MB, Sutin J. *Human Neuroanatomy*. 8th ed. Baltimore, MD: Lippincott Williams & Wilkins; 1983:63; B, Figure 17.9A; C, Figure 17.9B. Redrawn from Larsen WJ. *Human Embryology*. 2nd ed. New York, NY: Churchill Livingston; 1997:77.

Figures 2.24, 2.25, and 2.26A, B, C. Modified from Dudek RW. *BRS Embryology*. 6th ed. Baltimore, MD: Wolters Kluwer; 2015. A, Figure 17.9C; B, Figure 18.1; A and B, Figures 7.11, 7.12.

Figure 2.27. Modified from Dudek RW. *High-Yield Embryology*. 5th ed. Baltimore, MD: Wolters Kluwer; 2015. Figure 13.3.

Figure 2.30B. Image courtesy of Dr. Michael Berry, Eastern Radiology, Greenville, NC.

Figure 2.31B. Modified from Moore KL, Dalley AF II, Augur AM. *Clinically Oriented Anatomy*. 8th ed. Baltimore, MD: Wolters Kluwer; 2018. B, Figure 2.20A bottom.

Clinical Application 2.1. Image courtesy of Dr. Michael Berry, Eastern Radiology, Greenville, NC.

Clinical Applications 2.3 and 2.4A, C. Images courtesy of Michael Meuse, MD, Charlotte Radiology.

Clinical Application 2.5. Modified from Neil O. Hardy, Westpoint, CT.

Clinical Application 2.6: Modified from Krebs, C.; Weinberg, J.; Akesson, E.;

Dilli, E. *Lippincott Illustrated Review: Neuroscience*, 2 ed. Baltimore, MD: Wolters Kluwer, 2018. Unfig 5-1.

Figure 3.5A, B. Modified from Oatis CA. *Kinesiology: The Mechanics and Pathomechanics of Human Movement*. 3rd ed. Baltimore, MD: Wolters Kluwer; 2017. Figure 29-21.

Figure 3.7. Bottom: Modified from Fischer JE. *Fischer's Mastery of Surgery*. 7th ed. Baltimore, MD: Wolters Kluwer; 2019. Figure 46-5.

Figure 3.8A, B. Modified from Moore KL, Agur AMR, Dalley AF. *Clinically Oriented Anatomy*. 8th ed. Baltimore, MD: Wolters Kluwer; 2018. Figures 1-19 and 1-20.

Figure 3.9A, B, C, D. Modified from Dudek RW. *BRS Embryology*. 6th ed. Baltimore, MD: Wolters Kluwer; 2014. Figure 16.14. Adapted from Grumback MM, Styne DM. Puberty: ontogeny, neuroendocrinology, physiology, and disorders. In: Wilson JD, Foster DW, eds. *Williams Textbook of Endocrinology*. 8th ed. Philadelphia, PA: WB Saunders; 1992; Marshall WA, Tanner JM. Variations in pattern of pubertal changes in girls. *Arch Dis Child*. 1969;44:291.

Figure 3.10A, B. Modified from Surface Anatomy Photography Collection. *A, Grant's Atlas*, 14th ed.

Figure 3.11. Modified from Porth C. *Essentials of Pathophysiology: Concepts of Altered Health States*. 4th ed. Philadelphia, PA: Wolters Kluwer; 2016. Figure 40-18.

Figure 3.14. Modified from Jones RM. *Patient Assessment in Pharmacy Practice*. 3rd ed. Philadelphia, PA: Wolters Kluwer; 2016. Figure 22-5.

Figure 3.15. Modified from Surface Anatomy Collection. Top to *Grant's Atlas*, 14th ed., middle to Moore COA, 8th ed.

Figure 3.16. Modified from Moore KL, Agur AMR, Dalley AF. *Clinically Oriented Anatomy*. 8th ed. Baltimore, MD: Wolters Kluwer; 2018. Chapter 4 Box image 5.

Figure 3.17A, B, C. Modified from Dudek RW. *BRS Embryology*. 6th ed. Baltimore, MD: Wolters Kluwer; 2014. Figure 21-1.

Figure 3.18. Modified from Preston RP, Wilson TE. *LIR Physiology*. Baltimore, MD: Wolters Kluwer; 2013 and Moore KL, Agur AMR, Dalley AF. *Clinically Oriented Anatomy*. 8th ed. Baltimore, MD: Wolters Kluwer; 2018. Figure 22-9.

Figure 3.19A, B, C, D, E, F, G. Modified from Dudek RW. *BRS Embryology*. 6th ed. Baltimore, MD: Wolters Kluwer; 2014. A–C, Figure 11-1 (BRS) from *Dudek High-Yield Embryology*, 5th ed., 2014; modified from Dudek and *Fix BRS Embryo*, 3rd edition. In *BRS Embryo*, 6th ed., these are credited back to *HY Embryo*, 2nd ed. D–E, Figures

11-11 through 11-13. In each, the left is modified from Rohen JW, Yokochi C, Lütjen-Drecoll E. *Color Atlas of Anatomy*. 4th ed. Philadelphia, PA: Lippincott Williams & Wilkins; 1998:235: and the right to redrawn from Sweeney LJ. *Basic Concepts in Embryology*. New York, NY: McGraw-Hill; 1998:321. Except the right in 11.13, from Gartner LP, Hiatt JL. *Color Atlas of Histology*. 4th ed. Philadelphia, PA: Lippincott Williams & Wilkins; 2006:253; from Gartner LP. *Color Atlas and Text of Histology*. 7th ed. Baltimore, MD: Wolters Kluwer, 2018:341.

Figure 3.22A. Modified from Archer P, Nelson LA. *Applied Anatomy and Physiology for Manual Therapists*. Baltimore, MD: Wolters Kluwer; 2013. Figure 13-7.

Figure 3.23A. Modified from Anatomical Chart Company.

Figure 3.24. Modified from Tank PW, Gest TR. *Lippincott Williams & Wilkins Atlas of Anatomy*. Baltimore, MD: Wolters Kluwer; 2009. Figure 4-34.

Figure 3.26. Modified from Tank PW, Gest TR. *Lippincott Williams & Wilkins Atlas of Anatomy*. Baltimore, MD: Wolters Kluwer; 2009. Figure 4-32.

Figure 3.27E. Modified from Dudek, R. W. and Louis, T. M. *High-Yield Gross Anatomy*, 5 ed. Baltimore, MD: Wolters Kluwer, 2015.

Figure 6-9 in Dudek: From Freundlich IM, Bragg DG. *A Radiologic Approach to Diseases of the Chest*. 2nd ed. Baltimore, MD: Lippincott Williams & Wilkins; 1997:309.

Figure 3.33. Modified from Detton AJ. *Grant's Dissector*. 16th ed. Baltimore, MD: Wolters Kluwer; 2017. Figure 3-24.

Figure 3.34. Modified from Hull K, Cohen BJ. *Memmler's The Human Body in Health and Disease*. 13th ed. Baltimore, MD: Wolters Kluwer; 2015. Figure 13-2.

Figure 3.35A. Modified from Detton AJ. *Grant's Dissector*. 16th ed. Baltimore, MD: Wolters Kluwer; 2017. Figure 3-27.

Figure 3.37D, E, F, G. Modified from Dudek RW. *BRS Embryology*. 6th ed. Baltimore, MD: Wolters Kluwer; 2014. Figure 5-1.

Figure 3.38A, B, C, D. Modified from Dudek RW. *BRS Embryology*. 6th ed. Baltimore, MD: Wolters Kluwer; 2014. Figure 5-2 in Dudek (BRS) A and B, modified substantially from Dudek RW. *High-Yield Embryology*. 2nd ed. Philadelphia, PA: Lippincott Williams & Wilkins; 2001:27. C and D, from Johnson KE. *NMS Human Developmental Anatomy*. Baltimore, MD: Williams & Wilkins; 1988:147.

Figure 3.39. Modified from Dudek RW. *BRS Embryology*. 6th ed. Baltimore, MD: Wolters Kluwer; 2014. Figure 5-11.

Figure 3.40. Modified from Dudek RW. *BRS Embryology*. 6th ed. Baltimore, MD: Wolters Kluwer; 2014. Figure 5.8 in Dudek. Modified from Johnson KE. *NMS Human Developmental Anatomy*. Baltimore, MD: Williams & Wilkins; 1988:149.

Figure 3.41. Modified from Dudek RW. *BRS Embryology*. 6th ed. Baltimore, MD: Wolters Kluwer; 2014. Figure 5-16.

Figure 3.42. Modified from Dudek RW. *BRS Embryology*. 6th ed. Baltimore, MD: Wolters Kluwer; 2014. Figure 5-3.

Figure 3.43A, B. Modified from Cohen BJ, Hull K. *Memmler's The Human Body in Health and Disease*. 13th ed. Baltimore, MD: Wolters Kluwer; 2015. Figure 24-2.

Figure 3.44. Modified from Moscucci M. *Grossman & Baim's Cardiac Catheterization, Angiography, and Intervention*. 8th ed. Baltimore, MD: Wolters Kluwer; 2014. Figure 38-1.

Figure 3.45A. Modified from Tank PW, Gest TR. *Lippincott Williams & Wilkins Atlas of Anatomy*. Baltimore, MD: Wolters Kluwer; 2009. Figure 4-21A.

Figure 3.46A. Modified from Tank PW, Gest TR. *Lippincott Williams & Wilkins Atlas of Anatomy*. Baltimore, MD: Wolters Kluwer; 2009. Figure 4-21B.

Figure 3.47A, B. Modified from Preston RP, Wilson TE. *LIR Physiology*. Baltimore, MD: Wolters Kluwer; 2013. Figure 17-2.

Figure 3.50. Modified from Craven RF, Hirnle CJ, Henshaw CM. *Fundamentals of Nursing: Human Health and Function*. 8th ed. Philadelphia, PA: Wolters Kluwer; 2017. Figure 17-16.

Figure 3.51. Modified from Preston RP, Wilson TE. *LIR Physiology*. Baltimore, MD: Wolters Kluwer; 2013. Figures 17-4 and 17-5.

Figure 3.55. Modified from Tank PW, Gest TR. *Lippincott Williams & Wilkins Atlas of Anatomy*. Baltimore, MD: Wolters Kluwer; 2009. Figure 4-39.

Clinical Application 3.1. Courtesy of Dr. Michael Berry, Eastern Radiology, Greenville, NC.

Clinical Application 3.2A. Modified from Talreja D, Talreja RR, Talreja RS. *The Internal Medicine Peripheral Brain*. Philadelphia, PA: Wolters Kluwer; 2005. Figure 164-1.

Clinical Application 3.2B. Modified from Rathmell, J. P. *Atlas of Image-Guided Intervention in Regional Anesthesia and Pain Medicine*, 2 ed. Philadelphia, PA: Wolters Kluwer, 2012. Figure 14-2.

Clinical Application 3.3. From Harris JR, Harris JR, Lippman ME, Morrow M, Osborne CK. *Diseases of the Breast*. 5th ed. Philadelphia, PA: Wolters Kluwer; 2015. Figure 59-1B.

Clinical Application 3.4. From Kline-Tilford AM. *Lippincott Certification Review: Pediatric Acute Care Nurse Practitioner*. Philadelphia, PA: Wolters Kluwer; 2015. Figure 3-7.

Clinical Application 3.5. Modified from Dudek RW. *BRS Embryology*. 6th ed. Baltimore, MD: Wolters Kluwer; 2014. Figure 11-2 . Inset: From Yamada T, Alpers DH, Kaplowitz N, Laine L, Owyang C, Powell DW, eds. *Textbook of Gastroenterology*. Vol 1. Philadelphia, PA: Lippincott Williams & Wilkins; 1999:1186. Radiograph: From Kirks DR. *Practical Pediatric Imaging*. 3rd ed. Philadelphia, PA: Lippincott Williams & Wilkins; 1998:845.

Clinical Application 3.7. Courtesy of Dr. Michael Berry, Eastern Radiology, Greenville, NC.

Clinical Application 3.8. From Hull K, Cohen BJ. *Memmler's The Human Body in Health and Disease*. 13th ed. Baltimore, MD: Wolters Kluwer; 2015. Figure 18-19.

Clinical Application 3.9A, B. Modified from Dudek RW, Louis TM. *High-Yield Gross Anatomy*. 5th ed. Baltimore, MD: Wolters Kluwer; 2015. Figure 6-7. From Daffner RH. *Clinical Radiology: The Essentials*. 2nd ed. Philadelphia, PA: Lippincott Williams & Wilkins; 1999:146. Figure 6-8. From Daffner RH. *Clinical Radiology: The Essentials*. 2nd ed. Philadelphia, PA: Lippincott Williams & Wilkins; 1999:152.

Clinical Application 3.9C. Courtesy of Dr. Michael Berry, Eastern Radiology, Greenville, NC.

Clinical Application 3.10. Modified from Dudek RW, Louis TM. *High-Yield Gross Anatomy*. 5th ed. Baltimore, MD: Wolters Kluwer; 2015. Figure 6-5 in Dudek: From Daffner RH. *Clinical Radiology: The Essentials*. 2nd ed. Philadelphia, PA: Lippincott Williams & Wilkins; 1999:158.

Clinical Application 3.11. A. Modified from Dudek, R. W. and Louis, T. M. *High-Yield Gross Anatomy*, 5 ed. Baltimore, MD: Wolters Kluwer, 2015. Figure 6.10. B. Courtesy of Dr. Michael Berry, Eastern Radiology, Greenville, NC.

Clinical Application 3.12. A. From Dudek, R. W. and Louis, T. M. *High-Yield Embryology*, 5 ed. Baltimore, MD: Wolters Kluwer, 2015. B., C. Courtesy of Robert J Hartman, MD, Clinical Assistant Professor of Pediatrics Section of Pediatric Cardiology Brody School of Medicine, East Carolina University.

Clinical Application 3.14A. From Dudek RW, Louis TM. *High-Yield Embryology*. 5th

ed. Baltimore, MD: Wolters Kluwer; 2015. Figure 6-4B; BRS, Embryo 3rd edition.

Clinical Application 3.14B, C. Courtesy of Robert J Hartman, MD, Clinical Assistant Professor of Pediatrics Section of Pediatric Cardiology, Brody School of Medicine, East Carolina University.

Clinical Application 3.15A, B. From Dudek RW, Louis TM. *High Yield Gross Anatomy*. 5th ed. Baltimore, MD: Wolters Kluwer; 2015. Figure 6-3B,C; BRS, Embryo 3rd edition.

Clinical Application 3.15C. Courtesy of Robert J Hartman, MD, Clinical Assistant Professor of Pediatrics Section of Pediatric Cardiology, Brody School of Medicine, East Carolina University.

Clinical Application 3.16A. From Kline-Tilford, A. M. *Lippincott Certification Review: Pediatric Acute Care Nurse Practitioner*. Philadelphia, PA: Wolters Kluwer, 2015. Figure 5-2.

Clinical Application 3.17A. Modified from Moscucci M. *Grossman & Baim's Cardiac Catheterization, Angiography, and Intervention*, 8 ed. Baltimore, MD: Wolters Kluwer, 2014. Figure 22-19A.

Clinical Application 3.18A, B. Radiology images provided by Dr. Michael Berry, Eastern Radiology, Greenville, NC.

Clinical Application 3.19A, B, C. Radiology images provided by Dr. Michael Berry, Eastern Radiology, Greenville, NC.

Figure 3.56, 3.57A, B, C, D, E. Courtesy of Dr. Michael Berry, Eastern Radiology. Greenville, NC.

Figure 4.1. Modified from Detton AJ. *Grant's Dissector*. 16th ed. Baltimore, MD: Wolters Kluwer; 2017. Figure 4-20.

Figure 4.2A, B. Modified from Surface Anatomy Photography Collection; Modified from Base photograph previously used in: Agur AMR, Dalley AF. *Grant's Atlas of Anatomy*. 14th ed., Figure 4.2, page 290. Also used in Moore. COA 8th ed., Figure 5.10, p. 416; Figure 5.11, p. 417; Moore. ECA5, Figure 2.8, p. 121. Credit Grant's.

Figure 4.5A, B. Modified from Surface Anatomy Photography Collection. This is the same base photograph as in 4.2.

Figure 4.8. From Dudek RW, Louis T. *High-Yield Gross Anatomy*. 5th ed. Baltimore, MD: Wolters Kluwer; 2015. Figure 8.4.

Figure 4.9. Modified from Detton AJ. *Grant's Dissector*. 16th ed. Baltimore, MD: Wolters Kluwer; 2017. Figure 4.20.

Figure 4.12. Modified from Anatomical Chart Company.

Figure 4.17. Modified from Neil O. Hardy Art Collection.

Figure 4.19. Modified from McConnell TH. *The Nature of Disease: Pathology for the Health Professions*. 2nd ed. Philadelphia, PA: Wolters Kluwer; 2017. Figure 12-8.

Figure 4.22. Modified from Dudek RW. *BRS Embryology*. 6th ed. Baltimore, MD: Wolters Kluwer; 2015. Figure 10.1D.

Figure 4.23. Modified from Brant WE, Helms CA. *Brant and Helms' Solution: Fundamentals of Diagnostic Radiology*. 4th ed. Baltimore, MD: Wolters Kluwer; 2013. Figure 29-2.

Figures 4.25. Modified from Dudek RW. *BRS Embryology*. 6th ed. Baltimore, MD: Wolters Kluwer; 2015. Figure 10.7. Modified from Johnson KE. *NMS Human Developmental Anatomy*. Baltimore, MD: Williams & Wilkins; 1988:211.

Figure 4.28. Modified from Dudek RW. *BRS Embryology*. 6th ed. Baltimore, MD: Wolters Kluwer; 2015. Figure 10.9. Modified from Johnson KE. *NMS Human Developmental Anatomy*. Baltimore, MD: Williams & Wilkins; 1988:211.

Figure 4.34B. Modified from Preston RP, Wilson TE. *LIR Physiology*. Baltimore, MD: Wolters Kluwer; 2013. Figure 32.6.

Figure 4.41. Modified from Dudek RW. *High-Yield Histopathology*. 2nd ed. Baltimore, MD: Wolters Kluwer; 2011. Figure 14-1A. Redrawn from Ross MH, Romrell LJ, Kaye GI. *Histology: A Text and Atlas*. 3rd ed. Philadelphia, PA: Lippincott Williams & Wilkins; 1995:350, Figure 13-14. Based on Weiss L, Tavossoli M. Anatomical hazards to the passage of erythrocyte through the spleen. *SEM Hematol*. 1970;7:372.

Figure 4.49A. Modified from Preston RP, Wilson TE. *LIR Physiology*. Baltimore, MD: Wolters Kluwer; 2013. Figure 31.11.

Figures 4.50A, 4.55, and 4.56A, B, C, D. Courtesy of Dr. Doug Shusterman, Eastern Radiology, Greenville, NC.

Clinical Application 4.1. From MacDonald MG, Seshia MMK. *Avery's Neonatology: Pathophysiology and Management of the Newborn*. 7th ed. Philadelphia, PA: Wolters Kluwer; 2016. Figure 41-22.

Clinical Application 4.2. From Dudek RW, Louis T. *High-Yield Gross Anatomy*. 5th ed. Baltimore, MD: Wolters Kluwer; 2015. Moore, Figure B5.2.

Clinical Application 4.3A, B. Modified from Wineski L. *Snell's Clinical Anatomy by Regions*. 10th ed. Baltimore, MD: Wolters Kluwer; 2019. Figure 6.40.

Clinical Application 4.5A, B. Modified from Daffner RH, Hartman M. *Clinical Radiology: The Essentials*. 4th ed. Baltimore, MD: Wolters Kluwer; 2014. Figure 7-3A.

Clinical Application 4.7 Modified from Morton PG, Dorrie K, Fontaine DK. *Critical Care Nursing: A Holistic Approach*. Philadelphia, PA: Wolters Kluwer; 2018. Figure 41-5.

Clinical Application 4.8A. Modified from Nath JL. *Stedman's Medical Terminology*. 2nd ed. Philadelphia, PA: Wolters Kluwer; 2017. Figure 12-24.

Clinical Application 4.8B. From Noffsinger AE. *Fenoglio-Preiser's Gastrointestinal Pathology*. 4th ed. Philadelphia, PA: Wolters Kluwer; 2018. Figure 2-53.

Clinical Application 4.9A, B. Modified from Porth C. *Essentials of Pathophysiology: Concepts of Altered Health States*. 4th ed. Philadelphia, PA: Wolters Kluwer; 2016. Figure 29-1.

Clinical Application 4.11A, B, C. From Makary M, Cooper M. *Surgery Review*. 3rd ed. Philadelphia, PA: Wolters Kluwer; 2014. Figure 15-4.

Clinical Application 4.12. From Daffner RH, Hartman M. *Clinical Radiology: The Essentials*. 4th ed. Baltimore, MD: Wolters Kluwer; 2014. Figure 8-57A.

Clinical Application 4.14. From Lee E. *Pediatric Radiology: Practical Imaging Evaluation of Infants and Children*. Baltimore, MD: Wolters Kluwer; 2018. Figure 15-18B.

Clinical Application 4.15. From Chapman T, Iyer R. *Pediatric Imaging: The Essentials*. Baltimore, MD: Wolters Kluwer; 2016. Figure 14-3.

Clinical Application 4.16. From Lee E. *Pediatric Radiology: Practical Imaging Evaluation of Infants and Children*. Baltimore, MD: Wolters Kluwer; 2018. Figure 16-22.

Clinical Application 4.17. From Noffsinger AE. *Fenoglio-Preiser's Gastrointestinal Pathology*. 4th ed. Philadelphia, PA: Wolters Kluwer; 2018. Figure 11-6.

Clinical Application 4.18. From Shirkhoda A. *Variants and Pitfalls in Body Imaging*. 2nd ed. Philadelphia, PA: Wolters Kluwer; 2011. Figure 13-35B.

Clinical Application 4.19A, B, C, D, E. From Corman M, Nichols RJ, Fazio VW, Bergamaschl R. *Corman's Colon and Rectal Surgery*. 6th ed. Philadelphia, PA: Wolters Kluwer; 2013. Figure 29-1.

Clinical Application 4.20. From Riddell R, Jain D. *Lewin, Weinstein and Riddell's Gastrointestinal Pathology and Its Clinical Implications*. 2nd ed. Philadelphia, PA: Wolters Kluwer; 2015. Figure 6-52.

Figure 5.5A, B. Modified from Oatis CA. *Kinesiology: The Mechanics and Pathomechanics of Human Movement*. 3rd ed. Baltimore, MD: Wolters Kluwer; 2017. Figure 36.1A, B.

Figure 5.6. Modified from Berek JS. *Berek and Novack's Gynecology*. 15th ed. Philadelphia, PA: Wolters Kluwer; 2012. Figure 27.7.

Figure 5.7. Modified from Oatis CA. Kinesiology: *The Mechanics and Pathomechanics of Human Movement*. 3rd ed. Baltimore, MD: Wolters Kluwer, 2017. Figure 36.6.

Figure 5.7. Modified from Dudek RW. *BRS Embryology*. 6th ed. Baltimore, MD: Wolters Kluwer; 2015.

Figure 5.9. Modified from Dudek RW. *BRS Embryology*. 6th ed. Baltimore, MD: Wolters Kluwer; 2015. Figure 15.3A, B.

Figure 5.10A, B. Modified from Surface Anatomy Photography Collection. See column U.

Figure 5.11. Right: Modified from Oatis CA. *Kinesiology: The Mechanics and Pathomechanics of Human Movement*. 3rd ed. Baltimore, MD: Wolters Kluwer; 2017. Figure 36.4.

Figure 5.12A. Modified from Surface Anatomy Photography Collection. See column U.

Figure 5.13. Right: Modified from Oatis CA. *Kinesiology: The Mechanics and Pathomechanics of Human Movement*. 3rd ed. Baltimore, MD: Wolters Kluwer; 2017. Figure 36.4.

Figure 5.14A, B. Modified from Detton AJ. *Grant's Dissector*. 16th ed. Baltimore, MD: Wolters Kluwer; 2017, bottom half of both A and B = Figures 5-12 and 5-30.

Figure 5.15. From Sadler TW. *Langman's Medical Embryology*. 8th ed. Philadelphia, PA: Lippincott Williams & Wilkins; 2000:299 (line drawings); From Sternberg SS. *Histology for Pathologists*. 2nd ed. Philadelphia, PA: Lippincott-Raven; 1997:554 (Photo). Figure 10.26.

Figure 5.16. Modified from Dudek RW, Louis T. *High-Yield Gross Anatomy*. 5th ed. Baltimore, MD: Wolters Kluwer; 2015. Figure 12.4.

Figure 5.17. Modified from Mulholland MW. *Greenfield's Surgery*. 6th ed. Philadelphia, PA: Wolters Kluwer; 2017. Figure 70.8.

Figure 5.19A Modified from Oatis CA. *Kinesiology: The Mechanics and Pathomechanics of Human Movement*. 3rd ed. Baltimore, MD: Wolters Kluwer; 2017. Figure 36-09.

Figure 5.22. Modified from Pansky B, Gest TR. *Lippincott Concise Illustrated Anatomy: Thorax, Abdomen, and Pelvis*. Baltimore, MD: Wolters Kluwer; 2013. Figure 3-19a.

Figure 5.23. Modified from Pansky B, Gest TR. *Lippincott Concise Illustrated Anatomy: Thorax, Abdomen, and Pelvis*. Baltimore, MD: Wolters Kluwer; 2013. Figure 3-19b.

Figure 5.24A, B. Modified from Pansky B, Gest TR. *Lippincott Concise Illustrated Anatomy: Thorax, Abdomen, and Pelvis*. Baltimore, MD: Wolters Kluwer; 2013. Figures 6-34 and 6-33.

Figure 5.28B. Modified from Dudek RW. *BRS Embryology*. 6th ed. Baltimore, MD: Wolters Kluwer; 2015. Figures 13-1 and 13-2.

Figure 5.29. Modified from Porth C. *Essentials of Pathophysiology: Concepts of Altered Health States*. 4th ed. Philadelphia, PA: Wolters Kluwer; 2016. Figure 24-1.

Figure 5.30. Modified from Anatomical Chart Company.

Figure 5.31A. Modified from Dudek RW. *High-Yield Kidney*. Baltimore, MD: Wolters Kluwer; 2008. Figure 4-4.

Figure 5.36A, B, C. Modified from Chung KW, Chung HM, Halliday NL. *BRS Gross Anatomy*. 8th ed. Baltimore, MD: Wolters Kluwer; 2016. Figure 5-21.

Figure 5.37. Modified from Stepherson SR. *Obstetrics and Gynecology*. Philadelphia, PA: Wolters Kluwer; 2013. Figure 5-19.

Figure 5.38. Modified from Anatomical Chart Company.

Figure 5.40C, D, E, F. Modified from Dudek RW. *BRS Embryology*. 6th ed. Baltimore, MD: Wolters Kluwer; 2015. Figure 13.12.

Figure 5.41. Modified from Mulholland MW. *Greenfield's Surgery*. 6th ed. Philadelphia, PA: Wolters Kluwer; 2017. Figure 77-1.

Figure 5.43. Modified from Dudek RW. *BRS Embryology*. 6th ed. Baltimore, MD: Wolters Kluwer; 2015. Figure 14-1. Courtesy of Dr. R.W. Dudek.

Figure 5.44A, B, C. Modified from Dudek RW. *BRS Embryology*. 6th ed. Baltimore, MD: Wolters Kluwer; 2015, Figures 14.1B, 14.2 D&E, and 14.4 A&B.

Figure 5.45A. Modified from Smeltzer SC, Bare BG. *Brunner & Suddarth's Textbook of Medical-Surgical Nursing*. 9th ed. Philadelphia, PA: Lippincott Williams & Wilkins; 2000. Figure 42-2.

Figure 5.45B. Modified from Dudek RW, Louis TM. *High-Yield Gross Anatomy*.

5th ed. Baltimore, MD: Wolters Kluwer; 2015. Figure 16.1B.

Figure 5.46. Modified from Casanova R. *Beckmann and Ling's Obstetrics and Gynecology*. 8th ed. Baltimore, MD: Wolters Kluwer; 2019. Figure 47.1.

Figure 5.47. Modified from Anatomical Chart Company.

Figure 5.48. Modified from Menihan CA, Kopel E. *Point-of-Care Assessment in Pregnancy and Women's Health*. Philadelphia, PA: Wolters Kluwer; 2015. Figure 10-9a.

Figure 5.49. Modified from Menihan CA, Kopel E. *Point-of-Care Assessment in Pregnancy and Women's Health*. Philadelphia, PA: Wolters Kluwer; 2015. Figure 10-9b.

Figure 5.54A, B. Modified from Dudek RW. *BRS Embryology*. 6th ed. Baltimore, MD: Wolters Kluwer; 2015. Figures 15.1B, 15.2 D&E, and 15.3 A&B.

Figure 5.55. Modified from Hull K, Cohen BJ. *Memmler's The Human Body in Health and Disease*. 13th ed. Baltimore, MD: Wolters Kluwer; 2015. Figure 20-2.

Figure 5.56. Modified from Carter PJ. *Lippincott's Textbook for Long-Term Care Nursing Assistants*. 4th ed. Philadelphia, PA: Wolters Kluwer; 2016. Figure 40-6.

Figure 5.57. Modified from Detton AJ. *Grant's Dissector*. 16th ed. Baltimore, MD: Wolters Kluwer; 2017. Figure 5-9.

Figures 5.58 and 5.59. Modified from Anatomical Chart Company.

Clinical Application 5.1. Image courtesy of Michael Meuse, MD.

Clinical Application 5.2A,B, C, D. Modified from Smith NE, Timby BK. *Introductory Medical-Surgical Nursing*. 12th ed. Philadelphia, PA: Wolters Kluwer; 2018. Figure 53-6.

Clinical Application 5.3. From Albo D. *Operative Techniques in Colon and Rectal Surgery*. Philadelphia, PA: Wolters Kluwer; 2016. Figure 45-1.

Clinical Application 5.4. Modified from Lambert HW, Wineski LE. *Lippincott's Illustrated Q&A Review of Anatomy and Embryology*. Baltimore, MD: Wolters Kluwer; 2011. Unnumbered figure 5.20.

Clinical Application 5.8. From Bickley LS. *Bates' Guide to Physical Examination and History Taking*. 12th ed. Baltimore, MD: Wolters Kluwer; 2017. Figure 17-18 in Bickley from McMillan J, DeAngelis C, Feigin R, Warshaw J. *Oski's Pediatrics*. 3rd ed. Philadelphia, PA: Lippincott Williams & Wilkins; 1999.

Clinical Application 5.9. From Rubin E, Farber JL. *Pathology*. 3rd ed. Philadelphia, PA: Lippincott Williams & Wilkins; 1999. Figure 21-37.

Clinical Application 5.10A, B. Modified from Dudek RW. *BRS Embryology*. 6th ed. Baltimore, MD: Wolters Kluwer; 2015, Figures 15-8 and 15-9 in Dudek credited to Courtesy of Dr. J. Kitchin, Department of Obstetrics and Gynecology, University of Virginia, Charlottesville, VA and from Warkany J. *Congenital Malformations: Notes and Comments*. Chicago, IL: Year Book Medical Publishers; 1971:337. Copyright © Elsevier.

Clinical Application 5.11. From Labus D, Cohen A. *Lippincott Advisor*. Baltimore, MD: Wolters Kluwer; 2017.

Clinical Application 5.12. Image courtesy of Carolyn Chiantera.

Clinical Application 5.13. From Kini SR. *Cytopathology of Neuroendocrine Neoplasia*. Philadelphia, PA: Wolters Kluwer; 2014. Figure 2-9.

Clinical Application 5.14. Modified from Nath JL. *Stedman's Medical Terminology*. 2nd ed. Philadelphia, PA: Wolters Kluwer; 2017. Figure 11-23.

Clinical Application 5.15. Modified from Hatfield NT, Kinchelow CA. *Introductory Maternity and Pediatric Nursing*. 4th ed. Philadelphia, PA: Wolters Kluwer; 2018. Figure 9-5.

Clinical Application 5.16. Modified from Stepherson SR. *Obstetrics and Gynecology*. Philadelphia, PA: Wolters Kluwer; 2013. Figure 8-40.

Figure 6.6. Modified from Surface Anatomy Photography Collection.

Figure 6.7. Modified from Pansky B, Gest TR. *Lippincott's Concise Illustrated Anatomy*. Baltimore, MD: Wolters Kluwer; 2012. Figure 3-3A, B.

Figure 6.9. Modified from Wineski L. *Snell's Clinical Anatomy by Regions*. 10th ed. Baltimore, MD: Wolters Kluwer; 2019. Figure 11.15.

Figure 6.10. Modified from Chung KW, Chung HM, Halliday NL. *BRS Gross Anatomy*. 8th ed. Baltimore, MD: Wolters Kluwer; 2016. Figure 6.14.

Figure 6.11. Modified from Barash PG, Cahalan MK, Cullen BF, et al. *Clinical Anesthesia*. 8th ed. Philadelphia, PA: Wolters Kluwer; 2018. Figure 36-13.

Figure 6.12. Modified from Chung KW, Chung HM, Halliday NL. *BRS Gross Anatomy*. 8th ed. Baltimore, MD: Wolters Kluwer; 2016. Figure 6.12.

Figure 6.16. Modified from Surface Anatomy Photography Collection.

Figure 6.19. Modified from Krebs C, Weinberg J, Akesson E, Dilli E. *Lippincott Illustrated Review: Neuroscience*. 2nd ed. Baltimore, MD: Wolters Kluwer; 2018. Figure 5.8.

Figure 6.34 and 6.36, 6.40, 6.42. Images courtesy of Michael Meuse, MD, Charlotte Radiology.

Figure 6.35. Modified from Chung KW, Chung HM, Halliday NL. *BRS Gross Anatomy*. 8th ed. Baltimore, MD: Wolters Kluwer; 2016. Figure 6.9. From Freundlich IM, Bragg DG. *A Radiologic Approach to Diseases of the Chest*. 2nd ed. Baltimore,MD: Lippincott Williams & Wilkins; 1997:309.

Clinical Applications 6.1 and 6.2. Images courtesy of Michael Meuse, MD, Charlotte Radiology.

Clinical Application 6.5. Modified from Neil O. Hardy, Westpoint, CT. Wolters Kluwer.

Clinical Application 6.5A, B, C. Modified from Dudek RW, Louis TM. *High-Yield Gross Anatomy*. 5th ed. Baltimore, MD: Wolters Kluwer; 2016. Table 21-1 figures.

Clinical Application 6.7A, B, C. Modified from Chhabra A, Soldatos T. *Musculoskeletal MRI Structured Evaluation*. Philadelphia, PA: Wolters Kluwer; 2015. Figure 9.64.

Clinical Application 6.8. Modified from Shirkhoda A. *Variants and Pitfalls in Body Imaging*. 2nd ed. Philadelphia, PA: Wolters Kluwer; 2011. Figure 17-54.

Clinical Application 6.13. Modified from Chew FS. *Skeletal Radiology*. 3rd ed. Philadelphia, PA: Wolters Kluwer; 2011. Figure 4-17b.

Clinical Application 6.14. From Werner R. *Massage Therapist's Guide to Pathology*. 5th ed. Baltimore, MD: Wolters Kluwer; 2013. Figure 3-37.

Figures 7.3, 7.5, 7.6. These were all courtesy of Dr. Michael Meuse, MD, Charlotte Radiology.

Figure 7.7. From Surface Anatomy Photography Collection.

Figure 7.9A, B. From Dudek RW, Louis T. *High-Yield Gross Anatomy*. 5th ed. Baltimore, MD: Wolters Kluwer; 2015. Figure 20-21.

Figure 7.12A. Modified from Wineski L. *Snell's Clinical Anatomy by Regions*. 10th ed. Baltimore, MD: Wolters Kluwer; 2019. Figure 3.64.

Figure 7.13A. Courtesy of artist Alan Branigan.

Figure 7.13B. From Williams A. *Massage Mastery*. Baltimore, MD: Wolters Kluwer; 2012. Figure 5-8.

Figure 7.15. Modified from Chung KW, Chung HM, Halliday NL. *BRS Gross Anatomy*. 8th ed. Baltimore, MD: Wolters Kluwer; 2016. Figure 7-4.

Figure 7.19. From Surface Anatomy Photography Collection.

Figure 7.23. Modified from Moore KL, Dalley AF II, Augur AM. *Clinically Oriented Anatomy*. 8th ed. Baltimore, MD: Wolters Kluwer; 2018. Figure 3-37, top right.

Figure 7.35. Modified from Surface Anatomy Photography Collection

Figure 7.38. Modified from Surface Anatomy Photography Collection.

Figure 7.39. Modified from Oates CA. *Kinesiology: The Mechanics and Pathomechanics of Human Movement*. Baltimore, MD: Wolters Kluwer; 2017. Figure 8-25.

Figure 7.40. Modified from Anatomical Chart Company.

Clinical Applications 7.1, 7.2, 7.3, 7.4, 7.17, 7.18, 7.19. Images all courtesy of Michael Meuse, MD, Charlotte Radiology.

Clinical Application 7.8A. From Ianotti JP, Williams GR. *Disorders of the Shoulder: Reconstruction.* Philadelphia, PA: Wolters Kluwer; 2014. Figure 32-22.

Clinical Application 7.8B. From Maschke S, Graham TJ, Evans P. *Master Techniques in Orthopaedic Surgery: The Hand*. 3rd ed. Philadelphia, PA: Wolters Kluwer; 2016. Figure 3-31.

Clinical Application 7.11. Courtesy of Natalie McIver.

Clinical Application 7.14. From Werner R. *Massage Therapist's Guide to Pathology*. 6th ed. Baltimore, MD: Wolters Kluwer; 2016. Figure 3-31.

Clinical Application 7.15A. From Frassica FJ, Sponseller PD, Wilckens JH. *5-Minute Orthopaedic Consult*. Baltimore, MD: Lippincott Williams & Wilkins; 2002. Figure 27-1.

Clinical Application 7.20. From Dines JS, Altchek DW, Andrews J, ElAttrache NS, Wilk KE, Yocum LA. *Sports Medicine of Baseball*. Baltimore, MD: Lippincott Williams & Wilkins; 2013. Figure 8-16a.

Figure 8.1. Modified from Anatomical Chart Company.

Figure 8.2A, B, C. Modified from Dudek RW. *BRS Embryology*. 6th ed. Baltimore, MD: Wolters Kluwer; 2014. Figure 17-1.

Figures 8.3A, C and 8.5A, C, E. Modified from Anatomical Chart Company.

Figures 8.4, 8.15, 8.17A, 8.54B. Courtesy of Greg Lewis, MD, Eastern Radiology, Greenville, NC.

Figure 8.5A, C, E. Modified from Anatomical Chart Company.

Figure 8.6A. Modified from Chung KW, Chung HM, Halliday NL. *BRS Gross Anatomy*. 8th ed. Baltimore, MD: Wolters Kluwer; 2015. Figure 8.15.

Figure 8.6B. Modified from Surface Anatomy Collection.

Figure 8.7A, B. Modified from Dudek RW. *BRS Embryology*. 6th ed. Baltimore, MD: Wolters Kluwer; 2014. Figure 7.4.

Figure 8.11A, B, C, D. Modified from Krebs C, Weinberg J, Akesson E, Dilli E. *Lippincott Illustrated Review: Neuroscience*. 2nd ed. Baltimore, MD: Wolters Kluwer; 2018. Figure 2.8.

Figure 8.12A, B. Modified from Krebs C, Weinberg J, Akesson E, Dilli E. *Lippincott Illustrated Review: Neuroscience*. 2nd ed. Baltimore, MD: Wolters Kluwer; 2018. Figures 2.16 and 2.17.

Figure 8.13A, B. Modified from Wineski L. *Snell's Clinical Anatomy*. 10th ed. Baltimore, MD: Wolters Kluwer; 2019. Figure 8.18.

Figure 8.14. Modified from Detton AJ. *Grant's Dissector*. 16th ed. Baltimore, MD: Wolters Kluwer; 2017. Figure 7.40.

Figure 8.16B. Modified from Krebs C, Weinberg J, Akesson E, Dilli E. *Lippincott Illustrated Review: Neuroscience*. 2nd ed. Baltimore, MD: Wolters Kluwer; 2018. Figure 13-23, left half.

Figure 8.17A. Modified from Krebs C, Weinberg J, Akesson E, Dilli E. *Lippincott Illustrated Review: Neuroscience*. 2nd ed. Baltimore, MD: Wolters Kluwer; 2018. Figure 2.21.

Figure 8.18. Modified from Dudek RW. *BRS Embryology*. 6th ed. Baltimore, MD: Wolters Kluwer; 2014. Figure 12.1A,B.

Figure 8.19A, B. Modified from Dudek RW. *BRS Embryology*. 6th ed. Baltimore, MD: Wolters Kluwer; 2014. Figure 12-1C,D.

Figure 8.20A. Modified from Dudek, RW. *BRS Embryology*, 6e. Baltimore, MD: Wolters Kluwer, 2014. B, Modified from Thorne CH, Gurtner GC, Chung K, Gosain A, Mehrara B, Rubin P, Spear SL.

Grabb and Smith's Plastic Surgery, 7e. Philadelphia: Wolters Kluwer, 2014. Figure 19-2.

Figure 8.23B. Modified from Surface Anatomy Photography Collection.

Figure 8.24A, B. Modified from Chung KW, Chung HM, Halliday NL. *BRS Gross Anatomy*. 8th ed. Baltimore, MD: Wolters Kluwer; 2015. Figures 8.14 and 8.13.

Figure 8.25. Modified from Chung KW, Chung HM, Halliday NL. *BRS Gross Anatomy*. 8th ed. Baltimore, MD: Wolters Kluwer; 2015. Figure 8.14 (with lymph added digitally on top).

Figure 8.26. Modified from Chung KW, Chung HM, Halliday NL. *BRS Gross Anatomy*. 8th ed. Baltimore, MD: Wolters Kluwer; 2015. Figure 8.29.

Figure 8.27. Modified from Weber J, Kelley J. *Health Assessment in Nursing*. 2nd ed. Philadelphia, PA: Lippincott Williams & Wilkins; 2003. Figure 11-2 .

Figure 8.29. Modified from Dudek RW. *BRS Embryology*. 6th ed. Baltimore, MD: Wolters Kluwer; 2014. Figure 9.2A,B.

Figure 8.30. Modified from Dudek RW. *BRS Embryology*. 6th ed. Baltimore, MD: Wolters Kluwer; 2014. Figure 9.1B.

Figure 8.32. Modified from Dudek RW. *BRS Embryology*. 6th ed. Baltimore, MD: Wolters Kluwer; 2014. Figure 9.1A.

Figure 8.34. Modified from Krebs C, Weinberg J, Akesson E, Dilli E. *Lippincott Illustrated Review: Neuroscience*. 2nd ed. Baltimore, MD: Wolters Kluwer; 2018. Figures 9-6 and 9-3.

Figure 8.35. Modified from Krebs C, Weinberg J, Akesson E, Dilli E. *Lippincott Illustrated Review: Neuroscience*. 2nd ed. Baltimore, MD: Wolters Kluwer; 2018. Figure 9-1.

Figure 8.36A. Modified from Detton AJ. *Grant's Dissector*. 16th ed. Baltimore, MD: Wolters Kluwer; 2017. Figures 7.52 and 7.53.

Figure 8.37. Modified from Dudek RW. *BRS Embryology*. 6th ed. Baltimore, MD: Wolters Kluwer; 2014. Figure 8.1; Original credit line: Figure 8.1. C. Redrawn from Moore KL, Persaud TVN. *The Developing Human*. 6th ed. Philadelphia, PA: WB Saunders; 1998:505. E. From Rohen JW, Yokochi C, Lütjen-Drecoll E. *Color Atlas of Anatomy*. 4th ed. Philadelphia, PA: Lippincott Williams & Wilkins; 1998:124.

Figure 8.38B, C, E, F. Modified from Cui D, Haines DE, Lynch JC, et al. *Atlas of Histology with Functional and Clinical Correlations*. Baltimore, MD: Lippincott Williams & Wilkins; 2011. Figures 21-8B, 21-9B, 21-10B, and 21-11A.

Figure 8.40. Modified from Krebs C, Weinberg J, Akesson E, Dilli E. *Lippincott Illustrated Review: Neuroscience*. 2nd ed. Baltimore, MD: Wolters Kluwer; 2018. Figure 11-3.

Figure 8.41. Modified from Detton AJ. *Grant's Dissector*. 16th ed. Baltimore, MD: Wolters Kluwer; 2017; Krebs C, Weinberg J, Akesson E, Dilli E. *Lippincott Illustrated Review: Neuroscience*. 2nd ed. Baltimore, MD: Wolters Kluwer; 2018, Detton = Figure 7-90; Krebs = 11-19.

Figure 8.42. Modified from Surface Anatomy Photography Collection.

Figure 8.47. Modified from Detton AJ. *Grant's Dissector*. 16th ed. Baltimore, MD: Wolters Kluwer; 2017. Figure 7.34.

Figure 8.49B. Modified from Detton AJ. *Grant's Dissector*. 16th ed. Baltimore, MD: Wolters Kluwer; 2017. Figure 7.79.

Figure 8.50. Modified from Dudek RW. *BRS Embryology*. 6th ed. Baltimore, MD: Wolters Kluwer; 2014. Figure 12.2.

Figure 8.52B. Modified from Oatis CA. *Kinesiology: The Mechanics and Pathomechanics of Human Movement*. 3rd ed. Baltimore, MD: Wolters Kluwer; 2017. Figure 22-3.

Figure 8.53. Modified from Detton AJ. *Grant's Dissector*. 16th ed. Baltimore, MD: Wolters Kluwer; 2017. Figures 7.82 and 7.84.

Figure 8.54A. Modified from Anatomical Chart Company.

Figure 8.54B. Courtesy of Greg Lewis, Eastern Radiology, Greenville, NC.

Figure 8.56. Modified from LifeArt.

Figure 8.58. Image adapted by Dr. Kelly Harrell from original drawing by Dr. Alex Meredith, Medical College of Virginia, Richmond, VA.

Figure 8.59. Modified from Surface Anatomy Photography Collection.

Figure 8.60B. Modified from Detton AJ. *Grant's Dissector*. 16th ed. Baltimore, MD: Wolters Kluwer; 2017. Figure 7.72.

Figures 8.60C Modified from Detton AJ. *Grant's Dissector*. 16th ed. Baltimore, MD: Wolters Kluwer; 2017. Figure 7.71.

Figures 8.61 Modified from Detton AJ. *Grant's Dissector*. 16th ed. Baltimore, MD: Wolters Kluwer; 2017. Figures 7.71 and 7.69.

Figure 8.63A, B. Modified from Krebs C, Weinberg J, Akesson E, Dilli E. *Lippincott Illustrated Review: Neuroscience*. 2nd ed. Baltimore, MD: Wolters Kluwer; 2018. Figure 21.1.

Figure 8.64. Modified from Krebs C, Weinberg J, Akesson E, Dilli E. *Lippincott Illustrated Review: Neuroscience*. 2nd ed. Baltimore, MD: Wolters Kluwer; 2018. Figure 15.11.

Figure 8.65A. Modified from Detton AJ. *Grant's Dissector*. 16th ed. Baltimore, MD: Wolters Kluwer; 2017. Right half of A and B are Figure 7.53 and 7.52.

Figure 8.66A. Modified from Pansky B, Gest TR. *Lippincott Illustrated Anatomy: Head and Neck*. Baltimore, MD: Wolters Kluwer; 2014. Figure 3.35.

Figure 8.66B. Modified from Surface Anatomy Photography Collection.

Figure 8.67A, B. Modified from Pansky B, Gest TR. *Lippincott Illustrated Anatomy: Head and Neck*, Baltimore, MD: Wolters Kluwer, 2014. C, Moore KL, Agur AM. (2002). *Essential clinical anatomy* (2nd ed.). Baltimore: Lippincott Williams & Wilkins. Figure 8-3.

Figure 8.67C. Modified from Lippincott's Nursing Advisor.

Figure 8.68. Modified from Krebs C, Weinberg J, Akesson E, Dilli E. *Lippincott Illustrated Review: Neuroscience*. 2nd ed. Baltimore, MD: Wolters Kluwer; 2018. Figure 11.4.

Figure 8.69. Modified from Pansky B, Gest TR. *Lippincott Illustrated Anatomy: Head and Neck*. Baltimore, MD: Wolters Kluwer; 2014; from Anatomical Chart Company. Figure 3.46.

Figure 8.70A. Modified from Pansky B, Gest TR. *Lippincott Illustrated Anatomy: Head and Neck*. Baltimore, MD: Wolters Kluwer; 2014; from Anatomical Chart Company. Figure 3.47.

Figure 8.70B. Based on Figure X-3 from Wilson-Pauwels, L, Akesson, E, Stewart, PA. *Cranial Nerves: Anatomy and Clinical Comments*. Hamilton, Ontario: B C Decker, Inc., 1998.

Figure 8.71A. Modified from Pansky B, Gest TR. *Lippincott Illustrated Anatomy: Head and Neck*. Baltimore, MD: Wolters Kluwer, 2014 and from Anatomical Chart Company. Figure 3.50.

Figure 8.71C. Modified from Moore KL, Agur AMR, Dalley AF. *Clinically Oriented Anatomy*. 8th ed. Baltimore, MD: Wolters Kluwer; 2018. Chapter 10 box image 2.

Clinical Application 8.1. From Chung EK, Atkinson-McEvoy LR, Terry M, Lai NL. *Visual Diagnosis and Treatment in Pediatrics*. 3rd ed. Philadelphia, PA: Wolters Kluwer; 2015. Figure 4.10.

Clinical Application 8.2. From Anderson MK. *Foundations of Athletic Training*. Philadelphia, PA: Wolters Kluwer; 2017, Figure 20-13.

Clinical Application 8.4. From Farrell, M. and Dempsey, *J. Smeltzer & Bare's Textbook of Medical-Surgical Nursing*, 4th ed., Philadelphia, PA: Wolters Kluwer, 2017. Figure 58-3.

Clinical Application 8.5A, B, C. From Farrell M, Dempsey J. *Smeltzer & Bare's Textbook of Medical-Surgical Nursing*. 2nd ed. Philadelphia, PA: Wolters Kluwer; 2017. Figure 58-3.

Clinical Application 8.6A. Modified from Pansky B, Gest TR. *Lippincott Illustrated Anatomy: Head and Neck*. Baltimore, MD: Wolters Kluwer; 2014. Figure 3.7.

Clinical Application 8.6B. From Lee EY. *Pediatric Radiology: Practical Imaging Evaluation of Infants and Children*. Philadelphia, PA: Wolters Kluwer; 2018. Figure 3.66.

Clinical Application 8.8. Dudek RW. *High-Yield Embryology*. 5th ed. Baltimore, MD: Wolters Kluwer; 2015. Figure 12.5.

Clinical Application 8.16. Modified from Krebs C, Weinberg J, Akesson E, Dilli E. *Lippincott Illustrated Review: Neuroscience*. 2nd ed. Baltimore, MD: Wolters Kluwer; 2018. Unnumbered figure 15.1.

Figure 9.2A, B. Modified from Moore KL, Dalley AF II, Agur AMR. *Clinically Oriented Anatomy*, 8th ed. Baltimore: Wolters Kluwer, 2018. Figure 9-4.

Figure 9.3. From Surface Anatomy Collection.

Figure 9.24. Modified from Johnson J. *Bailey's Head and Neck Surgery*. 5th ed. Philadelphia, PA: Wolters Kluwer; 2014.

Figure 9.28. From Anatomical Chart Company.

Clinical Application 9.12. Modified from Moore KL, Dalley AF II, Agur AMR. *Clinically Oriented Anatomy*. 8th ed. Baltimore, MD: Wolters Kluwer; 2018. Chapter 9 Box image 11a,b.

Clinical Application 9.14. From Labus D, Cohen A. *Lippincott Advisor*. Baltimore, MD: Wolters Kluwer, 2018. PT Treatment_Tracheotomy_02.jpg.

Clinical Application 9.16. From Johnson J. *Bailey's Head and Neck Surgery*. 5th ed. Philadelphia, PA: Wolters Kluwer, 2014. Figure 139-3.

Index

Note: Page numbers followed by *f* and *t* indicates figures and tables respectively.